THE NEW NATURALIST

A SURVEY OF BRITISH NATURAL HISTORY

SNOWDONIA

In the National Park of North Wales

The aim of this series is to interest the general reader in the wild life of Britain by recapturing the inquiring spirit of the old naturalists. The Editors believe that the natural pride of the British public in the native fauna and flora, to which must be added concern for their conservation, is best fostered by maintaining a high standard of accuracy combined with clarity of exposition in presenting the results of modern scientific research. The plants and animals are described in relation to their homes and habitats and are portrayed in the full beauty of their natural colours, by the latest methods of colour photography and reproduction

THE NEW NATURALIST

SNOWDONIA

THE NATIONAL PARK OF
NORTH WALES

by

F. J. NORTH
D.Sc., F.G.S., F.S.A.
KEEPER OF THE DEPARTMENT OF GEOLOGY
NATIONAL MUSEUM OF WALES

BRUCE CAMPBELL
Ph D.
SECRETARY OF THE BRITISH TRUST FOR ORNITHOLOGY

RICHENDA SCOTT
Ph.D. (Econ.)

WITH 56 COLOUR PLATES BY JOHN MARKHAM AND OTHERS
48 BLACK AND WHITE PHOTOGRAPHS
6 MAPS AND 26 DIAGRAMS

COLLINS ST. JAMES'S PLACE LONDON

First published in 1949 *by*
Collins 14 *St. James's Place London*
Produced in conjunction with Adprint
and printed in Great Britain
by Richmond Hill Printing Works Ltd
Bournemouth
for Collins Clear-Type Press
London and Glasgow
All rights reserved

CONTENTS

CONTENTS *(continued)*

It should be noted that throughout this book Plate numbers in arabic figures refer to Colour Plates, while roman numerals are used for Black-and-White Plates

PLATES IN COLOUR

PLATES IN BLACK AND WHITE

Owing to difficulties which will be appreciated by bird photographers not all the photographs of birds in this book were actually taken in North Wales

DIAGRAMS

MAPS

EDITORS' PREFACE

SOME of the volumes of the NEW NATURALIST series deal with a major group of animals or plants; others with the life of a special type of habitat; still others with the natural history of one of the regions of the British Isles. The present volume belongs to the last category and is concerned with the natural history of that magnificent stretch of mountainous country in North Wales which culminates in the rugged heights of Snowdon—the loftiest mountain in Britain south of the Scottish border.

The region which has been for convenience called Snowdonia has a special claim to a book of its own. In 1947 after the Government of the day had already declared itself in favour of the setting up of National Parks in Britain, the Committee on National Parks appointed by the Minister of Town and Country Planning recommended that Snowdonia should not only be one of the Parks but also that it should be one of first priority. When the Committee delineated provisional boundaries, they included areas some distance beyond Snowdonia proper (see p. 160).

The Editors of the NEW NATURALIST series feel that there will be very great interest in the first of Britain's National Parks and that those who already know North Wales will visit with renewed enthusiasm an area to be thus guarded as a national possession for ever. Though many of the visitors to the National Park will be interested in the fascinating fauna and flora, there will be others who will seek first to see and understand the mountains and hills themselves, and all those features which make up the background of the scenery—and the setting for both plant and animal life. Other visitors will probably find their main interest in the evidences of the long story of man's occupation of the region—whether it be in the hill forts, or in the great man-raised stones of ancient times, or in the castles and churches of the surrounding mediæval villages and towns.

It is to meet this varied circle of readers that this book covers a wider field than others in the series. The first part is by Dr. F. J. North, who for many years has been in charge of the Department of Geology of the National Museum of Wales at Cardiff. In this book Dr. North has made the mountains of North Wales tell their own part of the story. His section deals with the geology and the physical background, and shows his great ability to make the complex seem simple.

The second part deals with the natural history and is by Bruce Campbell, already well known to young people in Wales who owe to his leadership in the field and classroom, or to his voice on the wireless, their first introduction to the natural history of their native soil. As an ornithologist he is responsible, too, for many original observations on bird life in Wales.

In the third part Dr. Richenda Scott has used her wide knowledge of ancient and mediæval history in a special study of the part played by man in shaping the face of North Wales as it is seen to-day. Her infectious enthusiasm, and the way in which she has managed to bring the past to life, and reveal its share of the present, will, in our opinion, attract many converts to the study of the natural history of man. Good history is good natural history; a good historian, like Dr. Scott, has an awareness of the web of animal and plant life in which man is entangled.

The composite picture thus presented by the three authors is not intended as an orthodox guide book to Snowdonia but rather to awaken interest in the many aspects of natural history, regarded in the broadest sense, to be encountered in that area.

THE EDITORS

NOTES ON WELSH PLACE-NAMES

by F. J. North

MOST Welsh place-names are descriptive of the physical characters or setting of the feature or spot concerned. *Twll Du,* for example, is the black hollow; *Cwm Brwynog,* the rushy cwm; *Crib Goch,* the red ridge or crest; *Mynydd Mawr,* the big mountain; and *Caernarvon* (in Welsh, Caernarfon) is *Caer yn Arfon,* the fort in Arfon [the land adjacent to Môn (Anglesey)]. Other names refer to historic or legendary persons, such as *Carnedd Llywelyn,* the cairn or heap of stones of Llywelyn [the Great, 1194-1240]; *Llyn Idwal,* Idwal's lake; *Betws Garmon,* the bedehouse of Garmon, i.e., [St.] Germanus; and *Llyn Padarn,* Padarn's lake.

Some names, especially those connected with historical events, with persons, or with legends, may be very old and the original associations difficult to determine; whilst, with the passage of time, names of all kinds may have been so altered that, in spite of the ingenuity and scholarship expended in efforts to explain them, the meaning of some of them is still obscure. In addition to this, many place-names have suffered severely at the hands of those who have tried to spell them phonetically without regard to their meaning.

Fortunately, the majority of the names we shall have occasion to use present little or no difficulty, and the list of words (given below) which frequently enter into the formation of Welsh place-names, together with the translations and comments that have been introduced here and there in the text, will, it is hoped, encourage those interested in Snowdonia to regard the names as friendly companions and not as unpronounceable concatenations of letters, and will lead them to sympathize with those who resist attempts further to "anglicize" the names under the pretence of making them simpler.

The writer gratefully acknowledges his indebtedness to his colleagues Dr. Iorwerth Peate and Mr. Ff. G. Payne, B.A., and to Mr. R. J. Thomas, M.A., of Aberystwyth, for advice in the matter of place-names, but he and not they must be held responsible for the course adopted in cases where there are no standard rules, as in the use of hyphens and capital letters in compound words, and for the occasional compromise between a desire to do justice to the Welsh language and the equally reasonable desire not to be pedantic. For example, Dolgelley is used instead of the Welsh Dolgellau, and Caernarvon instead of the Welsh Caernarfon, because to do so is to follow long established custom on the part of Welsh writers writing in English, but Carneddau is used as the plural of Carnedd, instead of the indefensible hybrid "Carnedds" which in recent years has been creeping into guide books and popular topographical works, and Arfon is used for the region between the mountains and the Menai Straits because the name has no tradition of English usage to justify Arvon.

English-speaking people who are anxious to do justice to Welsh place-names are handicapped by the dearth of reliable works upon the subject. They would be greatly helped by an English translation of Sir Ifor Williams' little book on place-names called *Enwau Lleoedd.*

A few descriptive names that do not truly record present conditions may have special interest by reason of the evidence they provide of conditions which obtained in the past. *Coed*, for example (meaning wood or trees), in the name of a locality where there are no trees is a relic of a time before the land was cleared for man's use or the trees had been felled for his fires or furnaces. In the modern sense of the word *glo*, Cwm-y-glo (at the lower end of Llyn Padarn) means the valley of coal, but there neither is nor ever was any coal in the rocks of any part of Snowdonia. *Glo* in Welsh, like *coal* in English, has changed its meaning; it originally signified wood fuel, sometimes charcoal, but began to be transferred to "pit coal" when that commodity came into general use about three centuries ago.

Welsh letters are, on the whole, pronounced like their English equivalents, but *f* has the sound of *v* (the English *f* is *ff* in Welsh); *ch* is not unlike the Scottish *ch* in loch, while *dd* has the sound of *th* in them (not as in thin); *ll*, which occurs so frequently in place-names, has no English equivalent although it is fairly well imitated by *thl* if the first letter is, as far as possible, suppressed; *w* is like the *oo* in cool, while *y* usually has the sound of *u* in cut, but sometimes resembles the *i* in is.

In certain circumstances the initial letters of some Welsh words are changed or mutated. The mutations of most frequent occurrence in Snowdonian place-names are *C* becoming *G*, *P* becoming *B*, *T* becoming *D*, *M* becoming *F*, *B* also becoming *F*, *D* becoming *Dd*, and *G* disappearing altogether. Moel, for example, has the same meaning as Foel, Mynydd as Fynydd, Craig as Graig, and bach as fach.

Words which, with their mutations, are of common occurrence in the place names of Snowdonia include the following :—

aber	where one river joins another or a river falls into the sea ; a stream	*dinas* (or din)	fortification, city
		dôl	meadow
		drws	door
		du	black
afon	river	*dwfr* (or *dwr*)	water
allt	a wooded cliff, hill	*dysgl*	dish
·ch	little, small	*ffynnon*	well, spring
	grave	*gallt*	wooded cliff
be s (old spel-ling, *bettws*)	bede-house, chapel	*glan*	a bank or shore
blaen	head or extremity,	*glas* (pl. *gleision*)	green, also blue
(pl. *blaenau*)	e.g. of a valley	*glo*	coal
braich	arm	*graeanog* (or *graianog*)	gravelly
bras	fat, great		
brwynog	rushy	*gwastad*	level, smooth
bwlch	defile, pass	*gwyn*	white
bryn	mount, hill	*hafod*	summer residence
cadair (popularly spelt *cader*)	chair, seat	*llan*	enclosed place, a church, village near a church
·e	field		
c· r	fort	*llech*	slate
capel	chapel	*llechog*	slaty
carn	cairn, heap of stones	*llyn* (pl. *llynnoedd* or *llynnau*)	lake
carnedd (pl. *carneddau*)	cairn, heap of stones	*maen* (pl. *meini*)	stone
		maes	field
carreg (pl. *cerrig*)	stone	*mawr*	great, big
cefn	ridge	*melyn*	yellow
celli	grove, bower	*moel*	bare rounded hill
ceunant	ravine	*mynydd*	mountain
clogwyn	cliff, precipice	*nant*	brook, valley, glen
coch	red	*ogof* (old form, *gogof*)	cave
coed	trees, a wood		
craig (pl. *creigiau*)	rock	*pen*	head, top
		pen-maen	rocky headland
crib (pl. *cribau*)	crest, ridge	*pennant*	upper reaches of a glen
croes	cross		
cwm	valley [but the Snowdonian Cwm is an amphitheatre-like hollow at the head of a valley]	*plas*	mansion, hall
		pont	bridge
		rhaeadr	waterfall
		rhos	moor
		rhyd	ford

sarn	causeway	*traeth*	strand, shore, beach
sych	dry		
tal	front, end	*twll*	hollow
tan	under, beneath	*tywarchen*	sod, turf

1
GEOLOGY AND
THE PHYSICAL BACKGROUND

By F. J. North

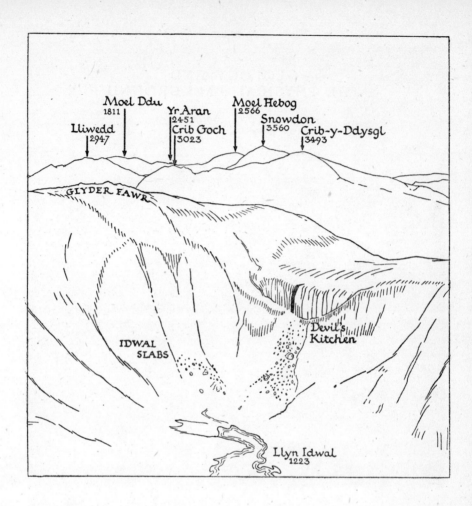

PLATE I

Aerofilms

SNOWDON: aerial view of the range from N.E.; at bottom of cwm is Llyn Idwal
For rest see diagram. July

PLATE II

VALLEY OF THE CONWAY from the Fairy Glen south of Betws-y-coed to Llanrwst. Oriented approximately north:top. The River Conway runs from south to north. As it widens out into an alluvial plain, on which the outlines of the fields can be seen, it is joined from the west, at Betws, by the Afon Llugwy. Llanrwst is at the middle of the north edge of the picture. October

CHAPTER I

THE MOUNTAINS AND
VALLEYS OF SNOWDONIA

---

1. INTRODUCTION

When we mean to build
We first survey the plot, then draw the model.

Shakespeare, in *Henry IV*.

"I MUST not pass over in silence the mountains called by the Welsh Eryri, but by the English Snowdon or Mountains of Snow, which, gradually increasing from the land of the sons of Conan and extending themselves northwards near Degannwy, seem to rear their lofty summits even to the clouds when viewed from the opposite coast of Anglesey."

Thus wrote Giraldus Cambrensis (Gerald the Welshman) in 1188. He had been with Baldwin, Archbishop of Canterbury, on a mission to preach the Third Crusade and had made an excursion into the island beyond the Menai Straits. Returning towards Bangor at the leisurely pace which characterized travel in those days he saw the Caernarvonshire mountains to advantage, and it is not surprising that he mentioned them in the account of his journey—*The Itinerary Through Wales*. He was not, as we shall be in these pages, concerned with the origin of the mountains, but no one could, in so few words, have conveyed a better impression of their form and distribution. It will be our business to try to understand the significance of what he wrote, but before doing so it will be convenient to amplify his reference to the names by which the mountains were, and still are, known.

Although it is so firmly fixed in the popular mind that it is unlikely ever to be displaced, *Snowdonia* as a general term for the mountains of Caernarvonshire is not really necessary, for the English name Snowdon was given to the whole region, not to a single mountain. This appears not only from written records like that of Giraldus, but also from early maps such as those of Britain prepared in the school of historical studies at St. Albans by or under the direction of Matthew Paris who died in A.D. 1259. On these, the name *Snaudun* is associated with a pictorial representation of mountains covering an area nearly as large as the neighbouring island of Anglesey and they are the only mountains on the map.

As we learned from Giraldus the Welsh name for the region is Eryri —popularly supposed, as George Borrow recorded, to have been given "because in the old time it abounded with eagles, Eryri in the ancient British language signifying an eyrie or breeding place of eagles." Sir Ifor Williams has, however, recently traced the Welsh name back to *eryr*, which, in the *Black Book of Carmarthen*, a Welsh manuscript of the beginning of the thirteenth century, signifies the bank of a river or the sea shore, i.e. a rise of the land—the root being *er* or *or* "to rise," as in the Latin *orior*, I rise, and the Greek *oros*, a mountain. This suggests that the name really means "the mountain land" or "the high land," and *eryr*, for the bird that flies higher than any other, the eagle, derives from the same root.

Thomas Pennant, the eighteenth-century naturalist, seems to have been responsible for "Snowdonia." He used the name in the account of his tour in Wales as if it were intended to include the mountains west of the river Conway, as far southwards as Pont Aberglaslyn and as far westwards as the Nantlle lakes. He was, however, not consistent, because he also wrote of "The vast mountains of Snowdon rising in a majestic range," and yet referred to Snowdon as if it were the single mountain tract south-westwards of the Pass of Llanberis : "Snowdon and all his sons, Crib Goch, Crib-y-Distill, Lliweddy yr Aran and many others."

Thomas Roscoe used Snowdonia as the title of a chapter in his *Wanderings and Excursions in North Wales*, 1836, but also wrote of Snowdon as embracing "within its limits a distinct region of subject hills, valleys, and lakes stretching across the country in one vast unbroken chain from sea to sea." Of those limits he wrote, "Snowdon, like a vast mountain fortress, boasted its defensive moat in the two rivers which, extending to Conway and Traeth Mawr, fall into the sea, giving to Anglesey that security on the land side which pointed it out as the natural seat of sovereignty."

A glance at a contoured map, Fig. 1, for example, shows how apt that description is; the valley of the river Conway in the east and the vale of Ffestiniog in the south have been so deeply cut that, for about two-thirds of its distance, a curved line connecting the mouth of the Conway with Traeth Bach stands at less than 100 feet above sea level. The 600-feet contour nearly closes the gap, leaving only about three miles between Blaenau Ffestiniog and the head of Cwm Machno, the pass between which is crossed at 1,500 feet. If we connect them by the

FIG. 1.—The high ground of Snowdonia and its relation to North Wales
·in general

The map shows the 100 foot and 600 foot land contours and the 5, 10 and 20 fathom
submarine contours (the two last-named only in the south-west). It also illustrates
the radial pattern of the Snowdonian rivers and its relation to the curved belt
of low ground that nearly isolates the region. A. Anglesey. S. Snowdonia.
H. Harlech Dome. L. Llŷn (Lleyn Peninsula).

road from Portmadoc by way of Llanllyfni to Caernarvon, this curved
line on the one side and the sea on the other roughly delimit the region
with which this book is concerned, although in order to appreciate its
geological structure and history we shall on occasion have to regard it
as part of a vaguely defined larger area.

The heart of this great mountain tract rises above three thousand
feet in a number of summits that stretch from Y Foel Fras (3,091 ft.)
in the north-east, by way of Carnedd Llywelyn (3,484) and Y Glyder
Fach (3,262), to Yr Wyddfa[1] (3,560). Although so little higher than
the rest, the mountain which culminates in the last-named peak, is so

[1]Wyddfa, mutation of Gwyddfa, a heap or cairn.

evidently the dominating feature of the area, and is so accessible and
easily climbed, as to make it understandable that, with "Snowdonia" available for the whole, there should have been a tendency to
restrict "Snowdon" to this single mass; and since no other name is
available for it, and "Yr Wyddfa" really relates to the summit, we
cannot very well do otherwise than follow prevalent practice and use
Snowdon to mean the mass that occupies most of the triangle between
Llanberis, Pen-y-gwryd and Beddgelert, and Snowdonia for the region
as a whole. It is not a case of choice but of necessity, since to do otherwise would often leave the reader in doubt as whether a particular
reference was to the whole of the area or only to a part.

A striking feature of the Snowdonian mountains, as they are viewed
from the Anglesey side of the straits, is the comparatively even skyline
to which they give rise (Pl. I, p. 2). It comes as a surprise to one
who has stood at the foot of Y Tryfan (i.e. high or pointed peak)
or looked down from the crest of Crib Goch. There are, to be sure,
some conspicuous depressions in the line where rivers have cut deep
valleys, and some isolated peaks that rise conspicuously above the rest,
but they do not destroy the impression of continued massiveness for
the elevated region as a whole.

A line connecting Yr Wyddfa with Y Foel Fras—a line which crosses
some of the highest mountains of the region, Y Glyder Fawr, Carnedd
Ddafydd, and Carnedd Llywelyn—falls only 469 feet in its nine and a
half miles of length: the average slope is 1 in 107. In the other direction the line south-westwards from Yr Wyddfa to Moel Hebog falls
just under 1,000 feet in five and a half miles with a slope of 1 in 29,
and although this is steeper than its counterslope it is hardly noticeable
to the unaided eye. From Y Foel Fras to sea level at the mouth of the
Conway the fall is 1 in 13, and from Moel Hebog to Criccieth it is 1 in
15. Together these lines appear like a section across a low and slightly
asymmetric dome, somewhat like an inverted saucer (Fig. 2, p. 7),
and it is one of our objects to try and discover how that dome came
into being and how and by what means Nature has been able to carve
from it one of the most attractive mountain regions in Britain.

MAP 1.—Topographical map of Snowdonia and the adjacent parts of North
Wales

Reproduced from the Ordnance Survey Map, scale : ¼ inch to 1 mile, with the
sanction of the Controller of H.M. Stationery Office

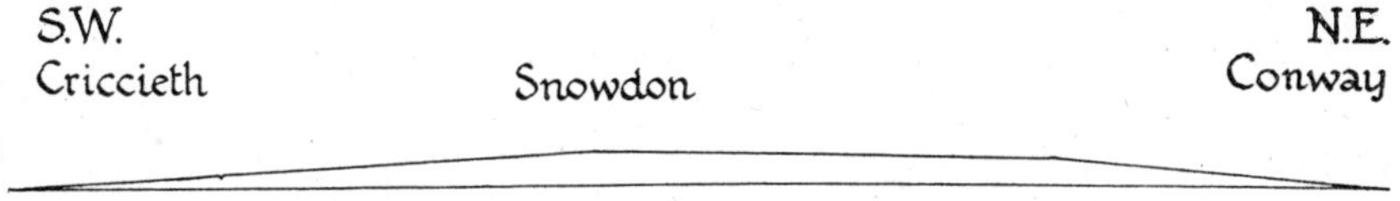

S.W. Criccieth Snowdon N.E. Conway

FIG. 2.—Section from Criccieth to Conway

A line connecting the highest summits, to illustrate the dome-shaped mass from which the mountains have been carved

Although the dome, with its gentle slopes, appears to be unpromisingly low, many of its mountains rise, as we have seen, to more than 3,000 feet above sea level. That may seem trifling in comparison with the mountainous regions of other countries, but the effective height of a mountain is determined by the general level of the region from which it rises, and since Caernarvonshire is a maritime county, deeply cut into by rivers, the slopes are necessarily steep. The rivers are rarely more than eight or ten miles long (omitting local curves and meanders) and yet they have cut their valleys so deeply that the 600-feet contour line sends long finger-like protrusions into the area from all sides: four of them approach to within three miles of one another around Moel Siabod.

In these circumstances, the peaks retain most of the magnificence that is associated with height. It is only four miles from the meadows around Beddgelert, about 100 feet above sea level, to the summit of Yr Wyddfa at 3,560 feet, and from the same peak to Nant Gwynant (really Nanhwynein, perhaps from Gwynein, a personal name) over 3,300 feet below, the distance is only about two miles and a half. It is not surprising to find Humphrey Llwyd, the sixteenth-century topographer, writing of "Snowdon hils, called Eryri, neither in height, fertilitie of the ground, wood, cattell, fish and foule, giving place to the famous Alpes"; what is surprising is the discovery that the really high ground is so limited in extent. Only seventy square miles of Caernarvonsiire lie above the 1,500-foot contour line; that is about 12 per cent. of the total area, and of the remainder about half lies above and half below the 500-foot line.

The best general views of the Caernarvonshire mountains as a series of separate peaks are, on the whole, those obtained from the east —from the moors beyond the Conway valley, from Capel Curig, from the summit of Moel Siabod, or from Bwlch-y-groes above Dolwyddelan (Pl. 2b, p. 19, Pl. 3, p. 26). These are better viewpoints than the summit of Snowdon itself for those who would see the sunrise on the mountains. From them it is possible to enjoy a prospect like that which must have inspired the Welsh bard Islwyn (Rev. Wm. Thomas) to write a poem that has lost little if anything by translation into English as *Dawn on the Mountains*:

> See how the light advancing
> From hill to hill moves on . . .
> From the chill mists emerging
> Slope after slope is won,
> And summit after summit
> Enkindles to the sun.

Other fine views of the mountains are obtained from the estuary of the river Glaslyn (Pl. 2a, p. 14), from the cliffs near Harlech Castle, and from Pen-y-groes and other places in the Nantlle[1] valley (Pl. 9, p. 126), but everyone familiar with the region has his or her own favourite "best view."

Valleys and passes divide our dissected "dome" into five areas of unequal size and character. The largest and northernmost is the roughly triangular tract between the valley of the Conway on the east and the valleys of the Ogwen and Llugwy on the south-west: it includes the largest stretches of ground above 2,500 feet and four named summits that rise above 3,000 feet. Being crossed by no good roads it is relatively little known either to geologists or to tourists, and its structure is such that although in parts it has a wild and rugged aspect its mountains do not present striking profiles like those of Snowdon, Moel Siabod, or even the much lower Cnicht (Pl. 4, p. 27)[2]. Its principal heights, Carnedd Llywelyn and Carnedd Ddafydd[3], are transitional in appearance between the more isolated peaks and the rather featureless moorlands on either side of the Conway valley. There are five large lakes and a considerable number of small ones.

Separated from this tract by Nant Ffrancon and the river Llugwy is one shaped something like a child's sock with the toe at Capel Curig. A considerable area lies above 2,500 feet and there are five named peaks above 3,000 feet, but the high ground is discontinuous. The north-eastern side is especially impressive on account of the tributary valleys.

---

[1]Nant-lleu, vale of Lleu : a reference to Lleu, a legendary character in one of the ancient Welsh stories or *Mabinogion*.

[2]Probably a borrowing from the English "knight": often spelt (incorrectly) Cynicht.

[3]The Cairns of Llywelyn and Dafydd respectively. The former may have been Llywelyn the Great, 1194-1240, and the latter Dafydd, brother of Llywelyn ap Gruffydd, the last of the Welsh princes.

This region, notably its southern portion which includes Y Glyder Fawr, Cwm Idwal, and Twll Du (the Black Hollow, called in English the Devil's Kitchen), is highly esteemed by climbers, and has, at its northern end, the two greatest slate quarries in the world.

The Pass of Llanberis separates the last-named area from one that in plan is not unlike a mirror image of it. This is the region which includes what Pennant called "Snowdon and his sons." It is the best known of the mountain tracts because it is the most accessible, but only a comparatively small part rises above 2,500 feet, and only Yr Wyddfa (Pl. IX, p. 98) and the narrow ridge by way of Crib-y-ddysgl to Crib Goch rise above 3,000 feet.

Its structure and comparative isolation give Snowdon a characteristic pyramidal outline recognizable from many near and distant viewpoints, from some of which it appears gracefully symmetrical (Pl. 30, p. 335). The mountain is, however, penetrated on all sides by wild hollows or cwms with precipitous curving sides, and, seen from the heights of Moel Siabod (Pl. IX), is obviously the remains of a mass from which much has been scooped away. The steep cliffs which surround the cwms and the sharp ridges which separate one from another (Fig. 23, p. 101) provide attractions for the climber and striking views for the walker, as well as for those who use the mountain railway. These two areas on either side of the Pass of Llanberis are more frequently visited than the neighbouring mountain tracts, their geological structure is more clearly understood, and their geological history is more fully recorded in the rocks of which they consist.

The south-westernmost tract, beyond the valleys of Gwyrfai and Colwyn, is roughly oval in shape and has Moel Hebog and Moel Ddu near its southern end with the conspicuous because relatively isolated Mynydd Mawr near the other. Of these only Moel Hebog rises above 2,500 feet, and although the region is, in general, less impressive, it is not less interesting than those to the north-east of it.

The valleys separating these four tracts trend from south-east to north-west, but the fifth tract is isolated by a curved hollow that extends from Betws-y-coed to Traeth Mawr and includes the valley of the Llugwy, Nant-y-gwryd, Nant Gwynant, and the Glaslyn valley. Moel Siabod and Moelwyn Mawr rise above 2,500 feet but the isolation and structure of Cnicht (Pl. 4a, p. 27), some 250 feet lower, makes it more imposing than many a greater height. The western and southern parts of the area are rugged and wild. The region is cut into deeply by the Lledr valley, Cwm Machno, and the headwaters of the river Dwyryd, but it has no well-defined physical boundary to the south-east where, by way of Arenig Fawr and Arenig Fach, it merges into the main mass of the Merionethshire mountains.

The valleys which separate these great masses are as variable as the regions they delimit. Some are wild and bare, others are rugged and grand; some have wide flat floors and others include deep picturesque gorges, but the most consistently beautiful of them is, perhaps, Nant Gwynant, where a fringe of scattered oakwoods separates the lakes and the bright green meadows of the valley floor from the mountains on either side.

This, then, is the area with which the present book is concerned, and as an introduction to its natural and human history the first four chapters tell the geological story of Snowdonia as briefly and as simply as the necessity for avoiding technical language permits; they give, as well, a general picture of the processes and forces that have been concerned in the development of its scenery. A detailed description of the rocks and of the structure of the region would require many more pages than can be spared, but students who require such information will find it in the works that are mentioned in the bibliography that begins on page 437. It is felt that the needs of the visitor will be met if he is put in the position of being able to appreciate the origin and meaning of the features—the peaks and the precipices, the moors and the meadows, the cwms and the crags—that have influenced the settlement and activities of man in the region, and that have made it the resort of tourists and climbers as well as a source of pleasure and inspiration to all who can respond to the call of the wilder elements of our scenic heritage.

The needs of those who may have to be content to know the area by reading about it have not been overlooked, for they too are likely to find a general picture more useful than a mass of detail. Those less fortunate people will find their armchair tour more interesting, and the following pages more intelligible, if they make constant reference to the map between pages 6 and 7 and to maps on a larger scale such as the one-inch Ordnance Survey maps or Bartholomew's half-inch map of the region. These portray the configuration of the land and its influence upon man's movements in the region, whilst the maps published by the Land Utilisation Survey enable one to envisage the surface-pattern of woodland, farm, and moor.

PLATE III

F. J. North

Y Glyder Fawr seen from the flanks of Snowdon. Lavas form the summit
of this mountain

PLATE IV

F. J. North

a. Looking up, from the head of Llyn Peris: a U-shaped glaciated valley

H.M. Geological Survey

b. Looking down: the characteristic scenery of a glaciated valley, with a river meandering over a floor of debris left by the retreating ice

THE PASS OF LLANBERIS

2. ON UNDERSTANDING THE SCENERY OF SNOWDONIA:
THE EVIDENCE

> . . . . the mountains huge appear
> Emergent ; . . . their tops ascend the sky ;
> So high as heaved the tumid hills, so low
> Down sunk a hollow bottom, broad and deep :
> Capacious bed of waters.
>
> Milton, in *Paradise Lost*
> Book VII.

In *Fodinae Regales*, a book about the "places of the chief mines and mineral works in England and Wales," written in 1670, Sir John Pettus explained that "The usual method of Historians is to begin with the Creation, wherein I might tell you that when *God* breathed upon the face of the *waters*, that was a *Petrefying Breath*, and such *Waters* as were quiet *and calm* turned into *Plains* or *Levelled Earth*, and the *Boisterous Waters* into *Hills* and *Mountains*, according to the proportion of the *Billows*, and their *Spaces* into *Vallies*, which have ever since continued in those wonderful and pleasant Dimensions."

Put into words such a conception may seem highly amusing, but how few of those who have not interested themselves in geology, the science which seeks to reconstruct the story of the earth, could offer a better explanation for the origin of our scenery ? In almost any upland region the hills, rising one above another and alternating with one another, remind one of the undulating surface of a boisterous river or of waves that break on a shelving shore.

What Pettus did not know and in his day could not be expected to have known (for it was an age when speculation was more popular than observation), and what many people even to-day fail to realize, is that the hills and the valleys, as we see them, are not original features of the earth's surface, unchanged since the beginning of time. Valleys have been carved out, not suddenly created, and the hills and mountains are masses that Nature's agents of denudation have not as yet been able to wear away.

The first helpful clue in an enquiry into the origin of Snowdonia is provided by the more or less angular masses of rock that are so freely scattered on many of the mountain slopes, and can be matched in the steeper crags above, from which, indeed, they have fallen (Pl. 7, p. 78). These, and the screes that rise from the valley floors, half mantling the precipitous cliffs against which they rest, are evidence that the mountains have not the quality of immortality with which poets like to endow them—as when one of the bards quoted by John Jenkins in *The Poetry of Wales* (1873) wrote of Snowdon:

> Age after age
> Thou has endured; aye, and for ever more
> Thy form shall be as changeless as before . . .
> Thou hast seen many changes, yet hast stood
> Unalterable to the last ; remained the same
> Even in the wildness of thy solitude.

The mountains of to-day are built of the debris of the mountains of the past and they owe the characters for which we admire them to the fact that they are disintegrating to provide materials for the mountains of future ages. They disintegrate very slowly, it is true, because even the "oldest inhabitant" is rarely conscious of change in the number and distribution of the stones, but careful observation, especially after winter frosts, will often reveal new scars on the crags and fresh-faced blocks here and there amongst the debris.

If we look more closely we shall find that many of the rocks which break the continuity of the turf do not lie upon it but *protrude from underneath it* (Pl. 9, p. 126, Pl. XIV, p. 179). It is from "exposures" such as these that the loose blocks have been derived, and if our view is comprehensive enough we shall see that the emergent rocks and crags are arranged in an orderly fashion, making regular lines upon the mountain sides as if they were the edges of some great earth-structure that is partially concealed by the soil and the turf (Fig. 3). We are reminded of an old building, the architecture of which we try to interpret from residual fragments of masonry that are still unconcealed by debris resulting from the destruction of the rest.

Sometimes these isolated exposures of bare rock or the ridges of debris that conceal them run horizontally; sometimes they are steeply inclined and sometimes they are curved, but in no case does it require a great effort of imagination to envisage their continuation where they are lost beneath the turf, and to see in them evidence that the rocks of which the mountains are built are arranged in layers that rest one upon another, or, as geologists say, consist of beds or "strata" and are "stratified." The lower slopes of Y Tryfan (Pl. 6, p. 22) and those which rise above Llyn Peris towards Snowdon are amongst the many examples to be seen in "our area" as we may conveniently call it, following the very good example set by Edward Greenly in an essay in *The Mountains of Snowdonia* (1925). Others can be seen on the flanks of Carreg Gleision above Llyn Cowlyd, and in Clogwyn-y-geifr (The Goats' Precipice), also called Castell-y-geifr, behind Llyn Idwal.

Here and there, where the slopes are too steep for soil to rest, there are precipices of bare rock, and on them the structure of the mountains may be so clearly displayed as to make imagination temporarily unnecessary and to confirm what we have imagined elsewhere. It requires no training or special powers of observation to see the great basin-like folds in the rocks that are exposed in the face of Clogwyn Du'r Arddu (the dark precipice of the Arddu) or in those on either side of the Devil's Kitchen, and the privilege is not reserved for climbers and walkers because the Snowdon mountain train affords excellent views of the former during several minutes of its journey. When there is a light sprinkling of snow the feature can be seen from places in Anglesey that are far enough away to provide views of the main summits rising clear of the lesser heights (Fig. 4, p. 14).

Having convinced ourselves that many of our mountains are made up of more or less regularly arranged layers we cannot prevent the mind's eye from projecting into space the lines we have recognized as indicating their underground structure, and while Fig. 3a may be a record of what we actually see, our imagination—or rather our knowledge wisely applied—entitles us to draw Fig. 3c. Having

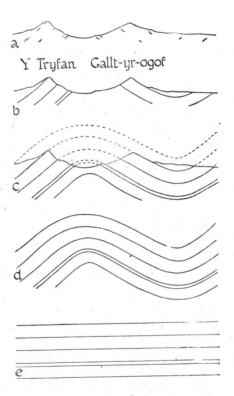

FIG. 3.— Scenery and geological history

Sections, based upon Y Tryfan and Gallt-yr-ogof, illustrating the interpretation of surface features and the inferences to be drawn from them.

FIG. 4.—Synclinal structures in Snowdonian mountains

In the cliffs behind Llyn Du'r Arddu a bed of fossiliferous limestone separates rhyolitic lavas above from rhyolitic tuffs below. In Clogwyn-y-geifr, with Twll Du (the Devil's Kitchen) in the centre, the cliff consists of andesitic basalt above and tuffs below. Bouldery screes occur at the base of each cliff.

done this we realize, perhaps for the first time, that the magnificence of our area is due less to the rocks that remain than to those which have been worn away. As a guide said to Joseph Cradock when he toured "some of the most romantic parts of North Wales" in 1776, "Aye, master, this must have been an ancient country indeed, for you see, it is worn down to the very stones." But for the action of rain and frost in disintegrating rocks, and of gravity, wind, and rivers in removing the debris, such an area would be a featureless plateau having height but no grandeur, and its surface would look very much like that of the Anglesey of to-day—undulating but not exciting. To look at Snowdonia from Harlech Castle or at Snowdon from the summit of Moel Siabod is to discover the extent of our indebtedness to the agents of erosion.

It may at first seem a matter for surprise that high mountains should be parts of trough-like folds or that their summits should, as in the case of Snowdon (Fig. 5, p. 15), possess a basin-like structure or, to use the appropriate geological term, a *synclinal* structure. An arch-like (or *anticlinal*) structure would seem more appropriate to a mountain and a synclinal structure to a valley or other area of low ground. There are, of course, anticlinal hills and mountains and synclinal valleys or belts of lower ground, but quite often—and our area provides excellent examples (Fig. 25, p. 121)—it is the reverse that applies. The reason is that when rocks are folded (due as we shall see to the operation of compressional forces), those at the crests of the folds tend to be stretched and to find relief from the strain by cracking, so that they are weakened and more easily worn away. The rocks in the trough, on the other hand, are squeezed and rendered harder and more compact; they are, in consequence, better able to resist erosion and so tend to remain as high ground when the rocks of the anticlines have been worn to lower levels (Fig. 11, p. 45). The longer an area of folded rocks has been subject to erosion the more likely are synclinal structures to be characteristic of its elevated regions.

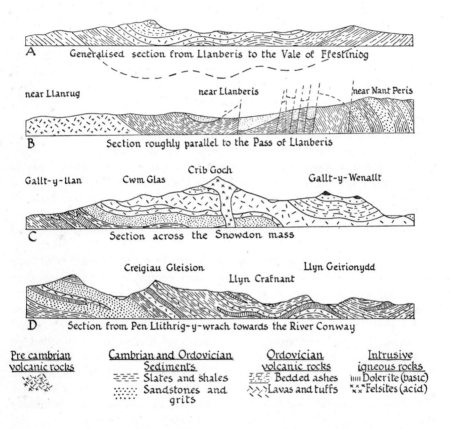

A   Generalised section from Llanberis to the Vale of Ffestiniog

near Llanrug   near Llanberis   near Nant Peris

B   Section roughly parallel to the Pass of Llanberis

Crib Goch
Gallt-y-llan   Cwm Glas   Gallt-y-Wenallt

C   Section across the Snowdon mass

Creigiau Gleision   Llyn Geirionydd
Llyn Crafnant

D   Section from Pen Llithrig-y-wrach towards the River Conway

Pre cambrian volcanic rocks	Cambrian and Ordovician Sediments	Ordovician volcanic rocks	Intrusive igneous rocks
	≡≡≡ Slates and shales	≡≡≡ Bedded ashes	‖‖‖ Dolerite (basic)
	⁙⁙⁙ Sandstones and grits	⋏⋏⋎ Lavas and tuffs	××× Felsites (acid)

Fig. 5.—The geological structure of Snowdonia

The top (generalized) section shows that the main syncline includes several subsidiary folds. The others (each of which is drawn from NW–SE for a distance of about 5 miles) illustrates, in more detail, the structure of regions in the west, centre, and east respectively of the region. B, after A. C. Ramsay ; C, after H. Williams ; D, after D. A. Bryn Davies.

It does not follow that all mountains have the simple anticlinal and synclinal structure here described, or that, having such a structure, the geology of the Snowdonian mountains is completely illustrated by the diagrams, which are necessarily simplified. The diagrams do, however, illustrate the principles involved, and we can deal with the complications as and when it becomes necessary to do so. Fig. 5 shows that the thickness of the strata is liable to vary, that their continuity may be interrupted by faults—displacements along great cracks, that the larger folds may be complicated by smaller ones, and that some rocks do not conform to the general pattern at all.

We now need to know something of the rocks that are involved in these arch-like or basin-like folds and a journey along the walkers' track from Llanberis to Yr Wyddfa enables us to do so. At first, wherever rocks can be seen not covered by soil or gravelly debris, they are grey rusty-weathering slates and sandstones; then, for about a quarter of a mile on either side of Halfway Station, there are darker slates, some of them blue-black. Beyond this, for half a mile or so, there are light-coloured massive rocks of volcanic origin, often flinty in appearance and in fracture. Still higher up, and for the last mile and a half, the route passes over more or less regularly arranged beds, of which some are speckled greenish-grey rocks, rough to the feel and deep brown on the weathered surfaces, while some are smooth and slaty.

The rough-feeling speckly rocks are made up of fragments of lava as fine as dust or as coarse as ashes: they resemble the materials that are produced as molten rock rises and falls in the crater of an active volcano. and, as it solidifies, gives rise to cindery fragments that are subsequently thrown out during eruptions. Such rocks are often called volcanic "ashes," and although we shall find it convenient to speak of ash or ashes to indicate the fragmentary products of volcanic activity, we must remember that the names, although so well-established, are not really appropriate; ash suggests burning, but a volcano is not a burning mountain in spite of the fact that its products are intensely hot and the glare reflected from the molten lava suggests a fire. In geological language, which on occasion it will be convenient to employ, rocks made up of fragmentary volcanic material are called tuffs when they consist principally of fine dust or contain particles large enough to be distinguished by the unaided eye, and those made up largely of coarser fragments—up to the size of walnuts—are called agglomerates.

Towards the summit of Snowdon there are irregular alternations of slaty and ashy beds, some of which contain the shells of marine animals or the impressions left after such shells have been dissolved away (Pl. Vb, p. 34). We could not wish for a better indication of the magnitude of the changes our land has undergone than this occurrence, at the top of the highest mountain in England and Wales, of the products of volcanic activity aid down upon the floor of a sea—and it is to the sea that we must go for the next link in our chain of evidence.

The level appearance of the foreshore, along coasts where the tide goes out for a long way, reminds us that marine sediments accumulate in layers, the upper surface of any one of which is flat and almost horizontal. From this it follows that a series of such sediments (and any associated rocks, such as the lavas and ashes of Snowdon, that conform to their general arrangement) must at one time have occurred in layers lying horizontally one above another. Their present folded condition, by reason of which they are inclined or curved in most places where we can see them, must, therefore, be the result of something which happened after their formation.

The "something" was subjection to lateral pressure, due to movements in the earth's crust that squeezed the sediments and caused flat layers to become ruckled—just as flat strips of clay or plasticine resting upon a smooth surface would be thrown into undulations if they were squeezed in such a way that their ends were brought closer together; realizing this, we are led to continue our series of sections by flattening out the curves depicted in Fig. 3 and drawing the strata as if they were horizontal. Our task, then, is to discover how rocks that began as sediments laid down upon the floor of the sea, or as lavas and ashes discharged from volcanoes, were uplifted, thrown into a folded condition, and then carved into the mountain shapes that tower above the valleys of to-day.

Most people, like old Sir John Pettus, are content to take scenery for granted, and if it ever occurs to them to try to explain it, they evoke earthquakes to account for gorges and valleys and attribute mountains to volcanic upheavals. Sometimes, confronted with what look like sea shells embedded in rocks that are far inland, or with pebbles that would look more at home on the sea shore than as constituents of rocks high on a mountainside, they explain the phenomenon by suggesting that "the sea must once have come as far as this"; but from failure to notice that the shells and the pebbles are not merely strewn upon the surface but are constituents of beds of rock that pass underground beneath other rocks, it is not realized that these shelly and pebbly strata cannot have been related to a sea that covered the land *as we know it to-day.*

The story of the building-up of the rocks from which our land has been carved is a record of the continuous operation of forces that have caused the sea floors of one age to become the land surfaces of the next; and as we learn to interpret the signs we shall be able to do what Shakespeare made his Henry IV wish he could do—"see the revolution of the times make mountains level, and the continent (weary of solid firmness) melt itself into the sea." We shall be able to say, as Ovid did in his *Metamorphoses,* nearly two thousand years ago,

> Straits have I seen that cover now
> What erst was solid earth; have trodden land
> Where once was sea, and gathered inland far
> Dry ocean shells;

we shall learn to disagree with Wordsworth, who, rather scornfully, described the geologist as

> He who with pocket hammer smites the edge
> Of luckless rock or prominent stone,
> . . . detaching by the stroke
> A chip or splinter to resolve his doubts:
> And, with that ready answer satisfied,
> The substance classes by some barbarous name,
> And hurries on,

and then thanked Heaven that

> This covert nook reports not of his hand.

Instead, we shall see him through the eyes of Huw Menai, a miner-poet whose pen-name derives from his birthplace on the Menai Straits,

> Shaking the dust from truth . . .
> Part-reading in the hard primeval sod
> The infinite biography of God.

PLATE I

John Markham

MENAI BRIDGE and the northern part of Snowdonia, from Anglesey. July

PLATE 2

a. From near Portmadoc. July

John Markham

b. From the east. July

John Markham

THE SNOWDON MOUNTAIN GROUP

3. INTERPRETING THE EVIDENCE: ROCKS
AND THEIR ORIGINS

Shall the amass'd Earth-structure appeal to me less than in early
Childhood an old fives-ball, whose wraps I wondering unwound ?
...Shall not the celestial earth-ball
Equally entertain a mature enquiry, reward our
Examination of its contexture. conglomerated
Of layer'd debris, the erosion of infinite ages ? . . .
I must wond'ring attend, nay, learn myself to decipher
Time's rich hieroglyph, with vast elemental pencil
Scor'd upon Earth's rocky crust.

Robert Bridges, *Wintry Delights* (1903)

Having, by observation and inference, been led to the conclusion that
the conditions which once obtained in our area can be illustrated by a
diagram like that given in Fig. 3e (p. 13)—in other words, having
decided there was a time when our area consisted of a great series of
strata resting one upon another in more or less horizontal layers (but
not, of course, as regular in thickness or as free from complexity as in
the diagram, which is concerned with principles and not with details),
we are in a position to set about reconstructing the geological history
of the mountains and of the valleys which separate them.

If Figure 3e represents a succession of strata resting one upon
another, the lowest must have been the first to be laid down and is
therefore the oldest of them all. This fact is so obvious that its significance is apt to escape notice, as indeed it did until a certain William
Smith drew attention to it towards the end of the eighteenth century,
and so laid the foundation of geology, as we now understand the term.
During the course of his work as surveyor and land agent, Smith came
to the conclusion that *rocks are arranged in a regular order, bed succeeding
bed in a sequence that is the same wherever the same series of strata is met with.*
He also pointed out that in the case of fossiliferous rocks *each bed or
group of beds contains a series of fossils peculiar to it.*

He did not know why that was so—the reason only became apparent
when the principle of evolution in living organisms had been established
—but he did not on that account fail to make use of his discovery.
Confirming his observations wherever he could study rocks, in shafts
and excavations and in natural cliffs, he claimed that every bed
containing fossils that were the remains of marine animals was a deposit

that must once have formed the floor of a sea. Each stratum, he said, is the record of a definite stage in the history of the earth; each tells us something of the conditions which obtained at the time it was formed and in the region where it occurs.

It would take us too far from our proper sphere of enquiry to tell the story of earlier observers and philosophers who had dimly envisaged what Smith was able to make clear, and of the later geologists who built upon the foundation which he so admirably laid. All that we need to know for the present is that his discovery made it possible to trace the outcrops or surface exposures of rocks and to recognize individual strata when their outcrops are discontinuous and widely separated. When the edges of the outcrops are drawn upon a topographical map the result is a geological map, and the crowning achievement of Smith's life was the publication in 1815 of a geological map of England and Wales on the scale of five miles to an inch. It was the first map to represent the outcrops of rocks in relation to their relative ages, and it became the basis of geological maps in general.

Smith was able to give only general information for our area because the structure was too complicated and fossils too infrequent for the details to be understood, except after much longer and more detailed research than was possible for a single individual in days when travel was difficult and when the methods and instruments of research were, according to modern standards, crude. The much greater amount of detail that is given on modern geological maps is attributable partly to improved techniques for the study of rocks and their structures, and partly to the better maps that are now available for recording field observations such as the inclination or "dip" of the strata and the boundaries between one kind of rock and another.

In order to make full use of observations upon the arrangement of the rocks of our area it is necessary to know something of the processes by which the rocks themselves were formed. If we break a piece of rock from an exposed crag or from one of the masses that are strewn upon the surface we shall find that there is a thin superficial layer differing in appearance from the material in the heart of the fragment. It may differ in colour, being either lighter or darker, and it may be softer or more porous in texture than the rock it encloses. The difference is due principally to exposure to the weather and the process is on that account called "weathering." The weathered surface of some of the volcanic rocks of our area is almost white whilst the unweathered rock beneath may be grey or nearly black; others, greenish-grey when freshly exposed, are rusty brown when weathered.

Rock weathering usually takes place very slowly and involves mechanical disintegration as well as chemical alteration. Many minerals, the constituents of rocks, are decomposed by rainwater, charged as it is with gases dissolved during its passage through the atmosphere, and some of them give rise to comparatively soft material that is easily washed away; when that is removed, the undecomposed or more resistant mineral particles, should there be any, are no longer held securely together, and they too are liable to be blown or washed away.

Some rocks are more resistant than others and the products of weathering vary according to the chemical composition of the constituent minerals, but the process eventually results in the formation of loose particles that are the essential ingredients of clay or of sand, associated with larger fragments of the rock not as yet completely weathered. Sooner or later this material finds its way into streams and is carried along until, perhaps after temporary halts in pools or in lakes, it comes to rest on the floor of the sea into which the river flows. Here, also, accumulates the material produced by the destructive action of the waves upon the rocks of the coast.

During its transport by streams, its disturbance by waves and currents along the shore, and its distribution and deposition on the sea floor, there is a tendency for the material to be sorted out according to size because, other conditions being equal, small particles tend to be carried farther and more quickly than large ones. Consequently the material derived from the wearing away of the land tends to give rise to bands of sediment arranged more or less parallel to the coast, as indicated in Fig. 6 (p. 22). The coarsest material such as pebbles (derived from fragments of more or less unaltered rock) will be found near the shore, followed by finer material, sand, and beyond that, the finest products of disintegration and decomposition will form either silt or mud, according to whether the material consists principally of very small particles of quartz, or of the compounds of silica and alumina that are the essential ingredients of clay.

In addition to the land-derived sediments, the shells or other calcareous (limy) hard parts of marine animals like corals, crinoids (popularly called sea-lilies), brachiopods, and molluscs (popularly called shell-fish) may accumulate on certain parts of the sea floor,

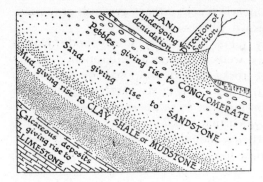

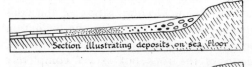

Section illustrating deposits on sea floor

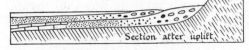

Section after uplift

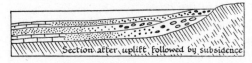

Section after uplift followed by subsidence

FIG. 6.—Diagrammatic representation of the arrangement of sediments on the sea floor

The sediments derived from a land area are spread upon the floor of the sea. The diagram illustrates the principle involved, but all the kinds of sediment will not necessarily be present on account of differences in the supply of material brought by rivers or derived from cliffs undergoing erosion. The sections illustrate the way in which different kinds of sediment accumulate one above another as a result of subsidence or elevation.

either whole or in fragments, in sufficient quantity to give rise to deposits that will eventually become limestone.

Laterally the various kinds of sediment pass more or less gradually one into another and any one or more of them may be locally absent. Their extent, if present, will vary according to local conditions, e.g. the nature of the land which is undergoing denudation—whether its rocks are easily worn away or not—and the character of the rivers which drain it—whether, flowing rapidly because the slopes are steep, they transport much, or flowing slowly because the land is low-lying and flat, they take little with them, most of it being fine mud. (The vertical scale in Fig. 6 has of necessity been exaggerated so that the bands appear to be much thicker in relation to their lateral extent than is the case in Nature. In Nature, too, the change would be progressive and not sharply defined: in so small a diagram it is only possible to indicate the conditions after subsidence and elevation have taken place, not those which obtained whilst the movements were in progress.)

If, after the formation of a series of sediments such as those described, the land region tended to rise, the sea would retreat and the zones of sedimentation would move seawards. As a result, pebbles would be deposited over a tract where sand formerly accumulated, sand would be laid down upon mud, and mud upon limestone.

If, on the other hand, the land were to sink, the sea-shore would advance upon it and the zones of sedimentation would move landwards, so that sand would be deposited upon pebbles, mud upon sand, and limestone upon mud. Since uplift and subsidence have been characteristic processes throughout the whole of geological time, we find that in any one region different kinds of sediment succeed one another in vertical sequence and occupy areas of greater extent than would have been possible with a stationary shore line.

In Fig. 6, which is based upon ideal conditions, limestone has been indicated as covering a part of the sea floor beyond the reach of land-derived sediments, but unless there are animals to extract calcareous matter from the sea water or chemical conditions to cause its deposition, limestone will not accumulate on the floor of the open sea; on the other hand, when the debris of pre-existing limestones contributes largely to the sediment, or where coral reefs occur, calcareous deposits that will give rise to limestones may be laid down near to the land or even as a shore deposit.

This description of the formation of sediments relates only, and in a general way, to deposits laid down in the sea. It illustrates the principles involved but the conditions and results of deposition are not always as simple as that; part or the whole of one set of beds was often worn away before another began to accumulate, leaving gaps in the sequence, whilst sediments were also laid down in fresh-water lakes and others originated as accumulations of wind-blown material in regions that, at the time, were deserts.

When conditions favourable to denudation and deposition were maintained in any one region for a sufficiently long time, as they often have been in past ages, sediments may have accumulated to a thickness of many thousands of feet, but the present disposition of the rocks shows that from time to time movements in the earth's crust have brought about changes in the distribution of land and sea (Figs. 15, p. 71, 17, p. 86). The sea-floor deposits of one age have become the dry-land rocks of the next; sediments that originated as mud gave rise to rocks like clay or shale; deposits of sand became sandstones;

accumulations of pebbles gave rise to conglomerates, whilst the shells or bones of animals or the remains of plants that had been embedded in the sediments are the objects we now call fossils. It is clear, therefore, that rocks tell us something of the past geography of the region in which they occur—pebbly beds (conglomerates) tell of shallow water and of shore lines; fine-grained mud-rocks with the fossil remains of animals characteristic of the open sea tell of distance from land, whilst strata with fresh-water shells are indicative of former lakes.

The processes of denudation and deposition have been in operation ever since conditions on the earth permitted the formation of oceans and of rain, and every part of the earth's crust has from time to time been subject to movements which have resulted in the elevation of land masses to provide material for denudation, and the formation of sea basins in which sediments could accumulate.

So much for the SEDIMENTARY ROCKS—that is to say, those which accumulated as sediments. There are also other important classes of rocks, a simple discussion of which presents difficulties due to the fact that a classification which has satisfied geologists for a very long time has recently been challenged. The view that has hitherto been generally accepted, and that forms the basis of the relevant sections of all standard text-books, is that certain rocks were at one time in a molten condition and cooled (a) in considerable amount and deep within the earth's crust, giving rise to *Plutonic* rocks (named after Pluto, the god of the underworld), or (b) in fissures by which the reservoirs of deep-seated molten rock communicated with the upper layers of the earth's crust or even penetrated right to the surface, giving rise to *Hypabyssal* (intermediate depth) rocks, e.g. dolerite (such as forms the dark cliffs called Ysgolion Duon, the Black Ladders or Black Pinnacles on the north side of Carnedd Ddafydd) or (c) were poured out from volcanic vents or fissures giving rise to *Extrusive* rocks, e.g. basalt, rhyolite (of which our area displays many varieties) and lavas in general. All these are called IGNEOUS ROCKS from the Latin *ignis*, meaning fire, and their relation to those of sedimentary origin is illustrated in Figure 7. The molten material of deep-seated origin differs from mere molten rock in being charged with steam and other gases; it is called magma.

There can be no doubt concerning the originally molten condition of the lavas and the hypabyssal rocks, but the view that all plutonic rocks result from the crystallization of magma has been challenged as being pure hypothesis unsupported by evidence and at variance with many observed phenomena. The challengers argue that plutonic rocks, especially granite, can be formed by the transformation *in situ* of deeply buried preexisting rocks, as a result of chemical changes due to the introduction of new constituents and the elimination of others, but without ever passing into a molten condition. Rocks formed in this way cannot be classed as *igneous* rocks, and the acceptance of the new view involves a re-definition of the term plutonic to enable it to include rocks that did not result from the crystallization of a magma.

It is neither possible nor desirable to discuss in these

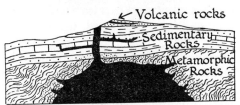

Fig. 7.—The structure of the earth's crust

Diagrams illustrating the relation between sedimentary, igneous, and metamorphic rocks, and the way in which the two last-named types may be exposed at the surface as a result of denudation.

pages the details of this interesting and important controversy but the matter is mentioned as an indication of the danger of assuming that familiarity and long usage necessarily convert an accepted view into a certainty. In any case, plutonic rocks do not make an important contribution to the geology of Snowdonia, and having indicated that the days of the old conception may be numbered, it will be convenient to continue for the present to use the terms plutonic and igneous in the sense in which they are used in current text-books of geology and petrology.

Plutonic and hypabyssal rocks may be conveniently classed together as *intrusive* rocks, the former occurring as major, and the latter as minor intrusions. They are, of course, only exposed at the surface in regions where extensive denudation has resulted in the removal of the rocks in or under which they cooled. The hypabyssal rocks are fairly abundant amongst the older strata in many parts of Wales, whilst the extrusive rocks include the ancient lavas to which the "personality" of our area is largely due.

Volcanic activity often results in the formation of vast quantities of "ash" and fine dust, because, like the soda-water in a syphon, the uprising magma is charged with gases (the most important being water vapour) dissolved or otherwise held under great pressure. When the pressure is suddenly released the gases escape with disruptive violence, disintegrating and carrying with them some of the material with which they had been associated, together with any loose fragments that may be in their path. The fragmental material may accumulate in the neighbourhood of the volcano and, either with or without the assistance of beds of lava, build up a conical mountain, but in certain circumstances it may be spread on the sea floor in such quantities as to form thick mud-like deposits, closer in chemical composition to certain types of igneous rock than to clay or shale. It is the liquid material that remains when the bulk of the vapour has been discharged that wells up more quietly and flows away as lava.

Important as are the contributions that volcanoes have made to the rocks of our area we cannot here discuss the theories that have been propounded to account for their origin. We can only note that they are associated with conditions which permit deeply-buried material to assume a liquid state. Such conditions may be related to movements in the earth's crust which locally and temporarily relieve the pressure upon material that is hot enough to melt, but is prevented from doing so by the compression due to the rocks which rest upon it. They may also have arisen from local increases of subterranean temperature due to the disintegration of deep-seated radioactive material.

Rocks, the properties of which have been materially altered as a result of the pressure which accompanies movements of the earth's crust, or on account of exposure to the heat and chemical emanations associated with the intrusion of igneous rocks, or to the heat due to deep burial beneath sediments laid down upon them, are called METAMORPHIC ROCKS. The name is derived from Greek words meaning change of form. Metamorphic rocks are well developed in Anglesey but, except for slates which owe their characters to a mild degree of metamorphism, they do not play an important part in the geology of Snowdonia.

From this excursion into the field of general geology we learn that rocks tell us something of the conditions under which they were formed,

PLATE 3

John Markham

SNOWDON RANGE from the north-east. April

PLATE 4

John Markham

a. CNICHT from near Portmadoc. July

John Markham

b. MOEL SIABOD from north-east taken at Pont Cyfyng near Capel Curig. July

and so enable us to envisage, more or less clearly, the changes which our land has undergone. They are records of seas and lakes, of deserts and mountains, that have been brought into being and then have more or less completely disappeared; but they are fragmentary records superimposed one upon another like the writings on a palimpsest. As with man's documents, so with Nature's—the older they are the more difficult they are to decipher and the less clearly can we envisage the details of the time to which they relate.

Since they occur as beds that were laid down one upon another, sedimentary rocks can be classified in the order in which they were formed and can be spoken of in terms of their relative ages; the relative age of a lava can be determined by reference to the associated sediments because it must be newer than those upon which it rests and older than those which were laid down upon it; in the case of the plutonic and hypabyssal rocks, however, the most we can usually say from field observation is that they are of more recent origin than the rocks that surround them.

Although the materials of sedimentary rocks were deposited in layers the upper surfaces of which were more or less flat and horizontal, a comparatively short journey in any part of Snowdonia would soon make one realize that the earth's crust does not consist of strata arranged regularly in a concentric manner like the coats of an onion. Movements in the earth's crust have squeezed the strata, throwing them into folds, and elevating them to form dry land. Rain, alternations of heat and cold, wind, and moving water—Nature's agents of destruction and transport—have continuously attacked the land areas, disintegrating the exposed rocks and using the debris to form new rocks elsewhere. The result is that although sediments to a thickness of many thousands of feet have been formed since the first appearance of water upon the earth, the entire thickness is not preserved in any one locality, but some part of every group into which the rocks have been divided is encountered somewhere or other amongst the strata which can be examined in natural exposures or artificial excavations, and we are able to discover, either by observation or by inference, something of the structure of the earth's outer layers—its "crust" as it is conveniently called—to a depth of about 20 miles.

Careful study of the successive layers of sedimentary rocks and of the fossils by which each is characterized has made it possible to determine the *order* in which the strata were formed, but since the

various kinds of rock—clay, shale, sandstone, limestone and so on—
have been formed time and time again some means had to be devised
whereby reference could be made, unambiguously, to limestones,
sandstones, and shales of different ages.

The early geologists realized this and one of their first tasks was to
divide the sedimentary rocks into groups based upon the order of their
formation. The groups are called *Systems* and distinctive names have
been given to them. The names and the relative duration of the periods
to which they relate are indicated in Fig. 8. The Systems that are
closely related to one another are classed together to form a few major
Groups, so that we can think of the earth-story that is recorded in the
rocks as being divided, like a book, into volumes, chapters, and
paragraphs. The period of time during which a Group of rocks was
formed is referred to as an *Era*, whilst that involved in the accumulation
of the rocks of a System is a *Period*.

The names of the Groups (and Eras)—PALAEOZOIC, MESOZOIC,
and CAINOZOIC—mean respectively, Ancient Life, Middle Life, and
Recent Life, and each relates to the life of the time in question as it is
revealed by the fossils which the rocks contain. During the Palaeozoic
Era the animals and plants were almost entirely of kinds now extinct;
the Cainozoic Era was characterized by the prevalence of animals and
plants closely allied to those now living, whilst the life of the Mesozoic
Era was intermediate in character between that of the other two.
These three subdivisions correspond approximately to the Primary,
Secondary, and Tertiary divisions recognized by the older geologists,
but while the first two of the original names have fallen into disuse,
the Cainozoic Era is still commonly referred to as Tertiary.

FIG. 8.—Table of strata

showing the sequence and approximate ages of the subdivisions into which rocks
have been divided by geologists and (in columns 4 and 5) the principal events in
the geological history of Snowdonia. The dotted portion of column 3 indicates the
Systems that are still represented amongst the rocks of Snowdonia. 1. Eras. 2. Systems
of rocks and Periods of time. 3. The age of the rocks, in millions of years. The diagram
does not indicate the relative thickness of the strata deposited during each of the Periods
and now included in each of the Systems. The thickness of sediment deposited and the
amount remaining after subsequent denudation varies from place to place. The
Eozoic Era or Eras must have been more than twice as long
as all the others put together.

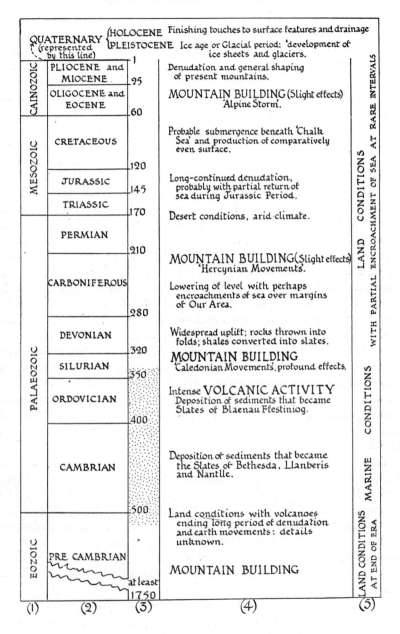

(1)	(2)	(3)	(4)	(5)
CAINOZOIC	QUATERNARY (represented by this line)	{HOLOCENE / PLEISTOCENE	Finishing touches to surface features and drainage / Ice age or Glacial period: development of ice sheets and glaciers.	LAND CONDITIONS WITH PARTIAL ENCROACHMENT OF SEA AT RARE INTERVALS
	PLIOCENE and MIOCENE	1 / 95	Denudation and general shaping of present mountains.	
	OLIGOCENE and EOCENE	60	MOUNTAIN BUILDING (Slight effects) 'Alpine Storm'.	
MESOZOIC	CRETACEOUS	120	Probable submergence beneath 'Chalk Sea' and production of comparatively even surface.	
	JURASSIC	145	Long-continued denudation, probably with partial return of sea during Jurassic Period.	
	TRIASSIC	170	Desert conditions, arid climate.	
PALAEOZOIC	PERMIAN	210	MOUNTAIN BUILDING (Slight effects) 'Hercynian Movements'.	MARINE CONDITIONS
	CARBONIFEROUS	280	Lowering of level with perhaps encroachments of sea over margins of Our Area.	
	DEVONIAN	320	Widespread uplift; rocks thrown into folds; shales converted into slates.	
	SILURIAN	350	MOUNTAIN BUILDING 'Caledonian Movements', profound effects.	
	ORDOVICIAN	400	Intense VOLCANIC ACTIVITY Deposition of sediments that became Slates of Blaenau Ffestiniog.	
	CAMBRIAN	500	Deposition of sediments that became the Slates of Bethesda, Llanberis and Nantlle.	
EOZOIC	PRE CAMBRIAN	at least 1750	Land conditions with volcanoes ending long period of denudation and earth movements: details unknown. MOUNTAIN BUILDING	LAND CONDITIONS AT END OF ERA

The Era that preceded the Palaeozoic was formerly known as *Azoic* (without life) because its rocks were supposed to have been formed before life appeared on the earth, but although no fossils have been found in the oldest known rocks of this country—rocks which undoubtedly belong to the so-called Azoic Group—it is quite certain that living things had already come into existence before the dawn of the Palaeozoic Era because the nature and variety of the fossils found in the oldest beds of the Cambrian System indicate a very long period of previous development. On this account the term Pre-Cambrian is now generally used to designate all the rocks older than those of the Cambrian System, and the term Archaean, meaning ancient, is used for the oldest crystalline Pre-Cambrian rocks. All the available evidence goes to support the view that the Pre-Cambrian rocks represent a period at least twice as long as all the subsequent periods put together.

Some of the names used in this scheme of classification refer to the districts in which the rocks were first studied or are well displayed. The Cambrian strata, for example, are well developed in Wales; the Ordovician and Silurian occur in those parts of Wales and the border counties once occupied by the Ordovices and the Silures—two of the ancient British tribes. It is with rocks of these three Systems, especially the Ordovician, that we shall be mainly concerned, and it is interesting to note the extent to which Wales provided the names for the older rock groups, because it was in the Principality that they were first intensively studied and clearly understood. Other names that we shall have occasion to use relate to the character of the rocks: Carboniferous (carbon-bearing), and Cretaceous (pertaining to chalk), refer to the great development of coal seams in the former and of chalk in the latter System.

The dividing lines between the various subdivisions which have been proposed were, of course, arbitrarily chosen by man and not fixed by Nature. Indeed, in regions where strata accumulated more or less continuously during a period that extended from one geological age into the next, or where strata of different ages tend to resemble one another and are not everywhere fossiliferous, the passage from one Series or one System into another is often so gradual that there is considerable difficulty in deciding where the dividing line should be drawn.

If representatives of all the groups of sedimentary rocks that have ever been formed were present in any one region there would be an unbroken sequence many miles in thickness, but the formation of the later rocks has only been possible because some of the earlier ones have been in part or completely worn away and re-deposited to form new rocks, so that in most districts there are usually considerable gaps in the sequence. The gap between one set of beds and another may represent a very long period of time, and the existence of such a gap is often indicated by a marked difference in the dip or inclination of the strata above and below it. The phenomenon is called an unconformity and the two sets of strata are said to be unconformable.

There is, for example, a well-defined unconformity (in this country) between Pre-Cambrian and Cambrian strata, and between those of the Cretaceous Period and those of the Tertiary Era; in each case a considerable thickness of rocks is missing owing to the fact that the older strata were uplifted and in part worn away before the newer ones were laid down: in each case, too, the geological record of our area has been partially obliterated, but while we may regret the incompleteness it has to be admitted that the reconstruction of the lost passages is a truly fascinating task.

It is of practical importance that we should be able to determine the *relative* ages of rocks, because without such information we could not understand the structure of the earth's crust—and we must do that in order to be able to discover and win for our use the rocks and minerals that it contains—but we are also able to say something about their *absolute* ages, although at present that may seem to be more a matter of satisfying legitimate curiosity than of meeting a vital need.

It is now generally accepted, even by those who have no special interest in the matter, that we can no longer say with old Sir Thomas Browne, "Time we may comprehend, 'tis but five days older than ourselves." The face of the earth is changing as the products of weathering are removed from one place and deposited in another. Except for the effects of storms, floods, or earthquakes, which, largely as they loom in human affairs, are but minor incidents in the history of the earth, the changes take place so slowly that their results in a single human lifetime are almost imperceptible, and we can only account for the magnitude of those results—for the deposition of many thousands of feet of sediments that have since become the rocks of our land areas, and for the elevation of mountains and the carving of valleys and gorges —by allowing sufficient time for all this to have taken place. But with strange inconsistency, and from the adoption of a too literal interpreta-

SN.   D

tion of the opening verses of the Book of Genesis, there has been, until comparatively recently, unwillingness to admit the possibility of a long time-scale for the history of the earth, and much ingenuity has been spent in trying to confine that history within the narrow limits allowed by estimates like that of Archbishop Ussher, to whom we owe the familiar conception of a beginning at 4004 B.C.

A century or so ago a few investigators began to realize that it was necessary to replace speculation by observation and deduction. Geologists, and later on biologists and archæologists, began to make increasingly great demands upon the bank of time, but the reader who would know more of the methods they adopted, of the disappointments they met with, and of the results they obtained must consult the books in which their work is described. We must be content here to indicate the principles upon which modern investigations are based, and the conclusions that we are entitled to draw in the present state of our knowledge.

The most recently applied, and, as we at present believe, most reliable of the methods that have been used in attempts to determine the age of the earth and to date its rocks is based upon studies of the time taken for some of the changes involved in the natural transition from uranium, by way of radium, to lead—a matter that has recently become painfully familiar because of its association with atomic bombs. The oldest known radio-active minerals are now believed to be about 1,750 million years old and the minimum age of the earth to be in the neighbourhood of 2,000 million years. There are, however, reasons for believing that the earth's age considerably exceeds the minimum (and each new estimate or calculation tends to show that it does—the latest, for example, puts the figure at 3,500 millions), but that does not concern us in this enquiry because an extension would not materially affect the age of the oldest rocks that are known to enter into the structure of our area.

The probable ages of the rocks with which we shall be concerned are indicated in the table, Figure 8, from which we see that about 500 million years have elapsed since the seas of the Cambrian Period came into being; that the volcanoes from which were poured the Snowdonian lavas died out nearly 350 million years ago; and that some 300 million years have passed since the earth-movements which threw the rocks of our area into arch-like and trough-like folds reached their maximum intensity. In comparison, the Ice Age, which saw the Snowdonian mountains covered by perpetual snow and their valleys occupied by glaciers, seems to be an event of yesterday, although it came to an end some 25,000 years ago.

It will now be apparent why the story of Snowdonia as here told is being built up on a geological foundation. Only through the medium of geology can we appreciate the significance of the scenery for which our area is justly famous, and can understand the activities of its human inhabitants.

Without knowledge of the rocks from which the mountains have been carved we cannot co-ordinate our studies of the plants and animals that have established themselves in the area, or that, as in the case of certain birds, come thither from time to time, for plants are surprisingly dependent upon soil, aspect, and elevation, and animals upon the food and cover that plants provide.

But that is not all. The student of geology needs no Time Machine and no Magic Carpet to widen his mental horizon. His studies offer rewards like that which Walt Whitman associated with the Open Road —a capacity

> To see nothing anywhere but what you may reach
> it and pass it;
> To conceive no time, however distant, but what
> you may reach it and pass it.

To look at rocks with understanding eyes is to see the inward parts of the earth as if its outer cover were sometimes the clearest glass and at others a half-revealing, half-concealing mist—to envisage the events and conditions of ages that may be just outside the limits of human recollection or may be so remote as to be beyond the measure of the mind—and, aided by maps and by memories of things seen, to do all this at any time and anywhere, not merely during those all-too-brief periods when, released from the daily round of common tasks, it is possible to travel luxuriously, receiving kaleidoscopic impressions framed by the restricting windscreen of a swiftly moving car, or laboriously but with greater satisfaction upon foot, with time to see and to comprehend.

The popular attitude towards these matters has changed but little since Herbert Spencer wrote, in 1861, "Sad, indeed, it is to see how men occupy themselves with trivialities, and are indifferent to the grandest phenomena—are learnedly critical over a Greek ode, and pass by without a glance that grand epic written by the finger of God upon the strata of the earth," and this book will not have been published in vain if it helps to bring nearer the time when that passage will have to be re-written in the past tense.

References for Chapter 1

SECTION 1
Borrow (1862), Giraldus (1188), North (1935), Pennant (1784), Pennant (1810), Roscoe (1836), I. Williams (1945).

SECTION 2
Greenly (1925), Holmes (1944), Stamp (1946).

SECTION 3
Harker (1889), Holmes (1937), North (1928), Read (1943, 1944), Stamp (1946).

PLATE V

National Museum of Wales
b. VOLCANIC ASH WITH FOSSILS from the top of Snowdon:
natural casts of the shells of the brachiopod
Orthis (Dinorthis) flabellulum

Engraving by Moses Griffith (1781) from Pennant's "Tour in Wales"
a. Y GLYDER FACH: the summit with an outcrop of well-jointed
volcanic rock

PLATE VI

F. J. North

CLOGWYN MAWR, near Llanberis: rugged outcrops of grit of Cambrian age, with shales giving rise to smoother ground

CHAPTER 2

THE ROCKS OF THE AREA
AND HOW THEY WERE FORMED

I. AN ANCIENT LAND SINKS BENEATH THE SEA

Now comes a time, when through the land and sea
Great change is wrought, all slowly though it be . . .
Lower and lower the sinking lands subside,
Deepening the mighty waters far and wide.
Till lands, that in the former days were dry,
Beneath the brine some scores of fathoms lie.

H. R. Knipe, in *Nebula to Man* (1905)

WHAT follows is a summary of work that has been done, discoveries made, and inferences drawn by many geologists who have turned their attention to our area since the days of William Smith. It will not be possible to indicate as we go along the authority for every statement that is made, and it will be easier for one not already familiar with the geology of the region to appreciate the extent of our debt to those who have helped to compile the story if we give them a section to themselves after the results of their work have been described.

The foundation rocks: The oldest rocks in our area occur in two roughly parallel lenticular bands, one of which extends in a south-westerly direction from St. Ann's near Bethesda to the neighbourhood of Llanllyfni, a distance of nearly thirteen miles, whilst the other, about eight miles long, stretches between Bangor and Caernarvon. The former is conveniently called the Padarn Ridge because it encloses the lower end of the lake of that name. The rocks are usually regarded as of late Pre-Cambrian age, but some of them may have been formed during the early part of the Cambrian Period. They are mostly pale-coloured on their weathered surfaces. Some of them originated as sheets of glassy lava and others are made up of fragmentary material ejected during explosive volcanic eruptions. Rock of a granitic type is well displayed in Twt Hill[1] at the Caernarvon end of the more northerly tract.

The lavas have now lost their glassy character, or, as geologists say,

[1]Or Twtil, the equivalent of the Anglo-Saxon Toot-hill, or Look-out hill.

have become devitrified, due to the development of a minutely crystal-line texture which makes them stone-like in appearance and opaque, whilst the fragmentary material has been converted into hard compact rocks often difficult to distinguish from the lavas. The latter can be seen to advantage in the rugged hills with innumerable relatively smooth rocky outcrops that enclose the lower end of Llyn Padarn. In geological literature, the ancient rocks of these two ridges are variously described as rhyolites, felsites, or quartz-porphyries. They are igneous rocks rich in silica (silicon dioxide, which, when it occurs naturally and in a free state, is the mineral quartz) and are members of a class called, for reasons that will appear in a later chapter, acid rocks.

Rhyolite is the name given to acid igneous rocks that were poured out at the surface as lavas. The name is derived from a Greek word meaning "to flow" and alludes to the frequency with which the rock shows signs of having flowed when in a molten condition. Felsite is an old but convenient field term for fine-grained igneous rocks, consisting of minute crystals of quartz and felspar, such as result from the devitrifi-cation of rhyolites or the alteration of fine rhyolite tuffs, whilst quartz-porphyry is a felsite in which some of the constituent minerals occur in crystals that are distinctly larger than those which form the general ground-mass of the rock. The felspars are light-coloured minerals consisting essentially of silicates of aluminum with varying amounts of potassium, sodium, calcium and barium; many different varieties are recognized but they are not all sharply defined because a perfect gradation in chemical composition exists between some of them.

Although their outcrops are comparatively small and their contribu-tion to the scenery inconsiderable, these Pre-Cambrian rocks near the edge of our area had a marked influence upon its subsequent history. They provide almost the only evidence which enables us to envisage the floor, as it were, upon which the main Snowdonian features were built. Another fragment of evidence comes from the submerged reef called Sarn Badrig which extends for about thirteen miles out into Cardigan Bay from the coast near Llanbedr, south of Harlech. It consists mostly of pebbles, but at the seaward end there are rhyolites so like those of the Padarn Ridge as to suggest that they are of Pre-Cambrian age. This justifies the belief that similar rocks are likely to lie not far beneath the surface in the neighbouring parts of Merioneth-shire, and they are, therefore, represented as occurring in that region in the sections (Fig. 17, p. 86) that illustrate the main stages in the geological history of Snowdonia. It would be going beyond the available evidence to assert that the rhyolitic rocks extend under the whole of the intervening area, and thus form the foundation of Snowdonia, but we are entitled to suggest that they very likely do.

The rocks of the Padarn Ridge are the oldest in our area, and yet the glimpse they give of the conditions which obtained when they were formed carries us no more than a third of the way back towards the beginning of geological time.

The occurrence of lavas and ashes implies the existence of a floor upon which the one could be poured and the other spread, but no trace of this floor can now be found. Indeed, wherever Pre-Cambrian rocks are exposed in North Wales, and they are well displayed in Anglesey and in south-western Llŷn[1] as well as in the regions already mentioned, they tell of still older rocks from which they were derived, upon which they were laid, or into which when molten they were intruded; they carry us back to an unknown and unknowable past   We can, however, be sure that before any of the rocks that are seen in the main Snowdonian masses were formed, the region had been occupied by a series of seas—seas that had come and gone, leaving accumulations of sediments that later became areas of dry land; we can say that the sediments had been affected by earth-movements to such an extent that they had been uplifted and subsequently eroded to form mountain chains higher and more rugged than any we now have in Britain—mountains that were higher even than the Alps, and so old that the last of them had been worn down to an almost level surface before the dawn of the Cambrian Period, nearly five hundred million years ago.

These ancient lavas and ashes tell us, too, of volcanic action as intense as any that affected Britain in later ages or that is to be seen in other parts of the world to-day. It was a bare forbidding land that sank beneath the sea to provide the floor upon which the rocks which make up the main mass of Snowdonia began to accumulate, because at that time, as far as our present knowledge goes, if land plants had come into being they were almost certainly inconspicuous representatives of the humble liverworts.

This is all we can say at present of what happened in our area during a thousand million years or more of early geological time, but it does at least give us an idea of the foundations upon which the Snowdonian mountains have been built. The first stage in the building process was

[1]Or Lleyn, also referred to as the Lleyn Peninsula.

initiated when the ancient lands began to sink beneath the waters of a sea in which the rocks of the Cambrian System were laid down and which therefore it is convenient to call the Cambrian Sea (Fig. 17, p. 86).

The advantage of using the term "our area" now begins to become apparent. In discussions involving reference to the geographical conditions of past ages we have to use modern place-names in order to indicate the relative positions of features or regions that are being described; but the county of Caernarvon or the mountains known as Y Glyder Fawr or Carnedd Llywelyn did not exist as such when the rocks of which they now consist were being formed; when those rocks accumulated the distribution of land and sea and the relation between mountain and valley were quite different from what they are to-day. It was only towards the close of the comparatively recent Tertiary Era that Great Britain began to acquire the shape and surface features with which we are familiar. When therefore, in connection with remote geological periods, mention is made of any particular district or physical feature of to-day, what is meant is that part of the earth's surface where the district or feature in question is situated, and "our area" conveniently indicates the whole of the region with which we are principally concerned, without reference to precise limits or to existing physical or topographical features.

The Cambrian Sea: The Cambrian strata appear at the surface on the north-western and south-eastern sides of the Snowdonian syncline. They rise from beneath the Ordovician strata and provide the floor upon which those strata rest. The north-western outcrop extends from near Aber to the neighbourhood of Clynnog Fawr, completely surrounding the Padarn Ridge of Pre-Cambrian lavas and ashes. It includes the mountains Carnedd-y-filiast (cairn of the greyhound bitch), Elidir Fawr (on the flanks of which the great Penrhyn and Dinorwic slate quarries have been opened) and Moel Eilio on the south-western side of the Llanberis lakes. The south-eastern outcrop extends from Portmadoc to Blaenau Ffestiniog and Arenig.

The lowest and therefore the oldest beds of Cambrian age in our area are coarse conglomerates containing pebbles of the Pre-Cambrian lavas, tracts of which formed islands in the Cambrian sea and provided the material from which pebbly beaches were made. They are well exposed in roadside cuttings and small quarries near the lower end of Llyn Padarn.

Resting upon the conglomerates there are hard grits formed from coarse sandy deposits which pass upwards into thick beds of what were originally shale, interspersed with layers of grit. Shales are rocks formed from fine-grained muddy or argillaceous sediments and they tend to break up into thin sheets or laminæ corresponding to the layers in which the sediments accumulated, but most of those in our area have been converted into slates which split much more evenly than shales and in directions that are unrelated to the original bedding. Although they were formed from sediments which accumulated in early Cambrian times it will be convenient to defer discussion of the slates until we come to consider the earth-movements responsible for their present condition. The slate areas lack the rugged aspect of the volcanic tracts and are often wooded in their lower parts, as, for example, on Ogwen Bank near Bethesda where there are old birch woods.

The slates are followed by more grits (Pl. VI, p. 35), seen on the slopes of Clogwyn Mawr above Llyn Peris and forming the summits of Elidir Fawr (from Elidir, a personal name) and Carnedd-y-filiast, and these in turn by more slates and shales (including those which form Moel Eilio), but it is not necessary for our purpose to describe all the succession in detail. What does concern us is that the Cambrian strata in our area are about 5,000 feet thick and the few fossils that have been found show that they are all of marine origin—some of them (the grits) indicating shallower water than others (the shales). Since the earlier Cambrian deposits were, in general, laid down in shallow water, it appears that we are not dealing with a deep basin that was gradually filled up, but with an originally shallow sea the floor of which was sinking, though not at a uniform rate, during a very long period of time.

The fine sediments which gave rise to slates indicate deeper water than the grits upon which they rest, and, therefore, a temporary increase in the rate of subsidence, whilst the occurrence of more grits towards the top of the Cambrian System is evidence of a return to shallow water conditions. Apart from the coarseness of grain an interesting indication of shallow water origin is provided by the wave-like ripples to be seen on the bedding planes of the topmost Cambrian grits that are finely exposed on the steep north-eastern side of Cwm Graeanog that opens out near the lower end of Nant Ffrancon. The slope of the ground here corresponds to the dip of the strata, about 48°, and there are large areas of bare rock that can be seen from considerable distances away to the north-east. The ripples have an average wave-length of about 18 inches and their profiles suggest the influence of water moving westwards. They throw light upon the geography of the time when the grits were deposited and they mark the situation of the shore of a sea that extended away to the east.

Certain fossils (*Cruziana*) in rocks associated with those that bear ripple-marks, and to be found in the loose blocks that are strewn about the floor of the cwm, are also indicative of shallow water. In a general way they may be said to look like an ornament of short pieces of slightly flattened plaited rope on the bedding planes of the rocks. A central furrow runs from one end to the other, with numerous close ridges diverging from it. It has been suggested that they may be tracks made by crustaceans like trilobites on the surface of wet silt or sand, but they may also be casts made by marine worms as they ate their way through silty deposits exposed between tide marks, as lug-worms do to-day. In either case they suggest shore deposits, and they are associated with tubular castings that are very much like the coiled piles that marine worms leave on many of our modern beaches when the tide is out.

It would unduly prolong this book to describe in detail all the animals represented by the fossils present in the various rocks with which we shall deal, and it must suffice to say that, although the Cambrian faunas are the earliest of which we have any detailed knowledge (for fossils are extremely rare in rocks known to be of Pre-Cambrian age), they include representatives of most of the groups into which invertebrates (animals without backbones) have been divided. Every group is not, of course, represented amongst the fossils from a single locality and not all of them have been recognized in the Cambrian rocks of this country. Trilobites and brachiopods, especially the former, are the most important groups represented in our area. Some of them are illustrated in Fig. 9.

Owing to the deformation which the strata have undergone since they were laid down the fossils are often fragmentary, distorted, and ill-preserved, so that photographs of actual specimens would seldom enable the non-geological reader to envisage the true shape and character of the original shell or skeletal covering. That is why Figs. 9 and 12 (p. 48) give the outlines of complete and undistorted specimens. They show what the creatures looked like and so may help the reader to see the significance of the imperfect specimens that are commonly found.

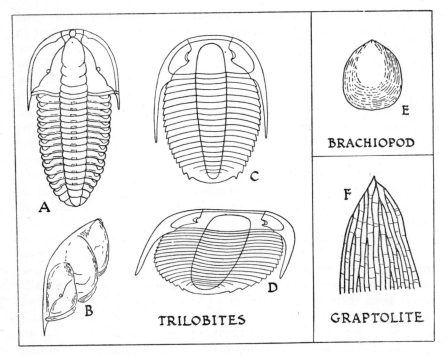

FIG. 9.—Fossils recorded from the Cambrian rocks of Snowdonia

A. *Solenopleura* [*Conocoryphe*] *viola* (H. Woodward), Lower Cambrian, Penrhyn Quarry ; restored outline. B. Fragment of the head shield of *S. viola* showing the condition in which the fossils are often found. C. *Angelina sedgwicki* (Salter), Upper Cambrian, near Tremadoc ; restored outline. D. *A. sedgwicki*, a specimen distorted as a result of pressure exerted during the formation of slate. E. *Lingulella davisi* (M'Coy), Upper Cambrian. F. *Dictyonema flabelliforme* (Eichwald), Upper Cambrian. All approximately natural size.

No useful purpose would be served by giving lengthy lists of the fossils recorded from the various strata with which we shall be concerned. Without an illustration of each one the names would convey nothing to the non-geological reader, and there are no popular names, as there are for flowers, birds, and butterflies, which would enable him to envisage them. The fossil-collector or student for whom such information may be necessary will find it in the descriptive papers enumerated in the bibliography on page 437.

The oldest fossils yet found in our area are trilobites, examples of which were discovered about sixty years ago by two quarrymen in some green mudstones (hard clay-like rocks) near the top of the slate exposed in Penrhyn quarry. The trilobites were marine crustaceans that lived only in the sea and they were mainly confined to shallow water. Externally they remind one of large woodlice in which each segment is divided by furrows into a median and two lateral portions, thus giving the creature a three-lobed appearance—hence the name. Their general form is indicated in the sketches in Figure 9, but they are often represented by isolated fragments—head-shields, tailpieces, and segments of the body region—because, as with many modern crustaceans, the external covering was moulted from time to time and, as it lay on the sea floor, was liable to be broken up by the action of moving water.

Trilobites are abundant in the Cambrian strata of many regions and their scarcity in our area may be due in part to the fact that for some unknown reason they could not easily reach it; they may, however, have been present in greater numbers in the original sediments than their present scarcity as fossils suggests, but have been obliterated by the changes that have resulted in the formation of slate. They became extinct during the Carboniferous period. Since the group underwent evolution and development during the long period of time involved, successively newer series of strata are characterized by different kinds of trilobites and can be recognized wherever they occur, either by the presence of the appropriate trilobites or else because they contain other fossils known to have been contemporaneous with those trilobites.

The brachiopods are also marine creatures (some species of which are still extant) and their two-valved shell usually has an ornament of concentric or radial lines or ribs, either alone or in combination, by reason of which they bear a superficial resemblance to some of the bivalved "shell-fish" such as cockles: some such occur in the rocks at the very summit of Snowdon (Pl. Vb, p. 34). Their internal organization is quite different from that of the mollusca and most of them live, as the extinct forms also lived, attached by means of a short stalk to the sea floor, to a stone, or to another shell. One of the most characteristic of the Cambrian forms, known as *Lingula* (or more precisely, *Lingulella*) from its tongue-like appearance, has modern representatives almost indistinguishable from it. It provides a remark-

PLATE VII

F. J. North

PENRHYN SLATE QUARRY, Bethesda. The steep, smooth faces between the terraces are determined in part by the cleavage planes and in part by joints. There are indications of the original stratification in some light and dark bands on a joint face in the lower left-hand corner

PLATE VIII

F. J. North

SPLITTING SLATE: a block of slate can be split into more or less rectangular flat slabs, by reason of the cleavage and other regularly disposed planes of weakness

able example of persistence in a group of animals that has been able to find similar surroundings in which to live throughout the ages. Certain beds in the upper part of the Cambrian System in North Wales contain these fossils in such abundance that they have been called the "*Lingula* Flags."

From their outcrops in the north-west of Caernarvonshire the Cambrian rocks pass beneath the newer Ordovician strata of the main Snowdonian mountain masses, but reappear in the belt of country that extends between Portmadoc, Blaenau Ffestiniog, and Arenig (Fig. 5, p. 15). This constitutes the northern edge of the Harlech Dome—a roughly oval region of rugged mountains extending from Blaenau Ffestiniog to Dolgelley and from Harlech to Arenig Fawr. Its structure is that of a dome-shaped fold, and, as the section in Fig. 15 shows, it is complementary to the trough or syncline of Snowdon. The ruggedness is due largely to outcrops of grit and conglomerate which occur more frequently and in thicker bands than amongst the corresponding rocks on the other side of Snowdon.

Owing largely to the greater development of grits and conglomerates—shallow water deposits, which, as Fig. 10 (p. 44) shows, tend to be thicker than those laid down contemporaneously in deeper water—the Cambrian rocks of Merionethshire are much thicker than those in Caernarvonshire and have a total thickness of about 15,000 feet, nearly three miles! The way in which the strata remain generally similar in character and vary but little in thickness as they extend from Bethesda to Nantlle, but become thicker between that region and the Harlech Dome, is shown diagrammatically in Fig. 10.

The fact that the Cambrian deposits are so much thicker and include so much more coarse material in Merionethshire than they do in Caernarvonshire suggests that the land from which the material was derived lay to the south-east. This land must have been the edge of a basin of deposition (a *geosyncline* as it is called) the floor of which steadily subsided so that although a great thickness of deposit accumulated the depth of water tended to remain more or less constant over considerable areas for long periods—as witness the comparative uniformity in size and character of the grains that make up many of the thick and extensive deposits that have been converted into slate.

Maps have been prepared to illustrate the broad outlines of the geography of the whole British region at various times in geological history (see for example Stamp, 1946) and for the more recent periods

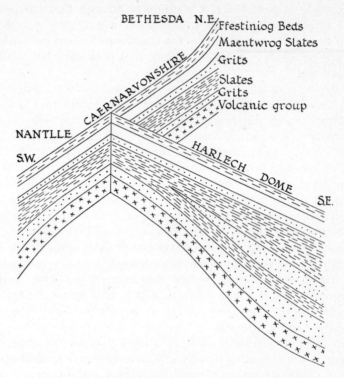

FIG. 10.—The Cambrian deposits of North Wales

Sections illustrating variations in the thickness of the Cambrian deposits from the
slate regions of Caernarvonshire to the Harlech Dome.

it has been possible to fill in the details for a few restricted localities,
but we are not yet, nor indeed are we ever likely to be, in a position to
draw a map (or rather a series of maps, because conditions were
continually changing) illustrating the geography of our area in so
remote a period as the Cambrian. The most we can hope to do is to
envisage the general characteristics of the area in those times.

The sea which occupied the site of the land on which the volcanoes
of late Pre-Cambrian times had poured their lavas and shed their ashes
was part of an ocean the shape and extent of which varied during the
long period of its existence. There were times when its western shores
were in what is now North America and its eastern limits embraced

Scandinavia. The relatively coarse deposits that were to give the Harlech Dome its special character were laid down in what began as a gulf of that sea. As time went on, and subsidence caused the gulf to lose its identity, the sediments that had originated as beach deposits or in shallow waters were covered by others laid down at greater depths. This material, having travelled farther from its place of origin and having been deposited in more tranquil water, was finer in grain and gave rise to sediments that would now be clays or shales if they had not been converted into slate.

The Pre-Cambrian land surface of our area, although much worn down, had not been completely levelled off by Nature's agents of erosion, and as it was submerged some parts remained uncovered for longer than others. These for a time formed reefs and islands in an archipelago, and it was on beaches formed around them that the conglomerates (seen near the outlet of Llyn Padarn) containing pebbles of pre-Cambrian volcanic rock began to accumulate.

As we are only concerned with the general outline of a very long story we need not discuss the local variations in the rocks due to the fact that the sub-sidence of the trough and therefore the accumulation of sediment did not take place with perfect uniformity. Sometimes the rate of move-ment increased, sometimes it slowed down, and sometimes the subsidence gave place to elevation so that newly-formed deposits were raised above sea level and were, to some extent, washed away. On the whole, however, it was a downward movement and it continued to affect the area not only during Cam-brian times, but also during the succeeding Ordovician and Silurian Periods.

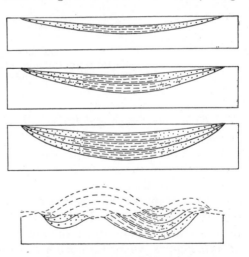

Fig. 11.—Diagrammatic representation of the formation of a geosyncline

and the subsequent uplift, folding, and de-nudation of the sediments laid down in it. The lowest section shows how mountains with a synclinal structure can result from folding followed by extensive denudation.

The long-continued but intermittent subsidence was an important feature in the history of our area because the geological record shows that the formation of a geosyncline—a trough or basin-like depression in which an enormous thickness of sediment can accumulate—has usually been followed by mountain-building movements, and the material laid down in a geosyncline of one age often forms the basis of a mountainous mass in another (Fig. 11, p. 45). The conditions associated with the formation of a geosyncline are usually an indication of instability, and already by the end of Cambrian times there were signs of disturbance leading to the crumpling of the deposits that were accumulating in the great trough—already, well-nigh 400 million years ago, it was becoming clear that our area was destined, some day, to be a region of mountains. Some of the crumpling may have been caused by the slipping, or slumping as geologists prefer to call it, of the unconsolidated sediment from the shallower towards the deepening part of the basin.

2. SIGNS OF IMPENDING UNREST

And in the change around
Is heard again the sullen rumbling sound
Of grim volcanoes, long in slumber bound.

H. R. Knipe, *Nebula to Man* (1905)

The Ordovician System and Period. The depression of the floor of the geosyncline temporarily ceased towards the end of the Cambrian Period and our area was affected by earth-movements which at first resulted in an uplift of the sea floor in the region that is now North Wales. We have already referred to the evidence of shallow water conditions in the ripple marks and fossils seen in some of the Cambrian sandstones, and the presence of the *Lingula* Flags in the Upper Cambrian strata of North Wales also indicates shallower water conditions than obtained in other areas where Cambrian deposits were formed. The modern *Lingula* burrows in the sand or silt of the sea bottom in very shallow water, and there are no reasons for supposing that its ancient representatives did not do the same. In time the earth-movements became sufficiently intense to raise some of the Cambrian sediments above sea level so that in places a considerable thickness of them was soon worn away.

The earth-movements threw the strata into alternating anticlinal and synclinal folds and while material was being worn away—removed by denudation—from the tops of the anticlines, sediments continued to accumulate in some of the troughs. Nowhere in our area is the succession of Cambrian strata quite complete and the sediments that began to accumulate as the sea re-established itself in the region mark the commencement of another period of time and a new system of rocks——the Ordovician, so named because the strata are well displayed in the region once occupied by the Ordovices, the last British tribe in Wales to yield to the Romans. Snowdon and most of the mountains of our area have been carved from rocks formed during the Ordovician Period.

As a result of the folding and denudation which preceded their formation, the Ordovician rocks in and around our area do not everywhere rest upon Cambrian strata of the same age; in other words, the relation between the two Systems is frequently one of unconformity.

The conditions which caused the Cambrian deposits to be thicker in the south-east than they were in the north-west continued to obtain during Ordovician times, for the Ordovician deposits are thinnest in Anglesey (3,000 or 4,000 feet), and thickest in the Cader Idris region (15,000 feet). In the intermediate Snowdonian area their thickness is from 8,000 to 10,000 feet, of which rather less than half is made up of grits, shales, and slates (all shown, by their fossils, to have been of marine origin), whilst the remainder consists of volcanic rocks—lavas and ashes—interbedded with the sedimentary rocks.

Since we must discuss the Ordovician strata and the events of Ordovician times in greater detail than was necessary when we were considering those of earlier periods, we must know something of the groups into which the rocks have been subdivided so that we can make use of the names by which they are known, and in order to do this we must note that whereas trilobites proved to be the most useful fossils in the classification of the Cambrian strata, towards the end of Cambrian time another animal group—the graptolites—began to assume importance in the contemporary marine fauna.

The graptolites, which became extinct soon after the end of the Silurian period, were small marine animals usually classed with the sea-anemones and corals. The individual animals or polyps were supported on slender horny rods, which were either single, divided like tuning forks, or multi-branched (Fig. 12, p. 48). Some of them lived

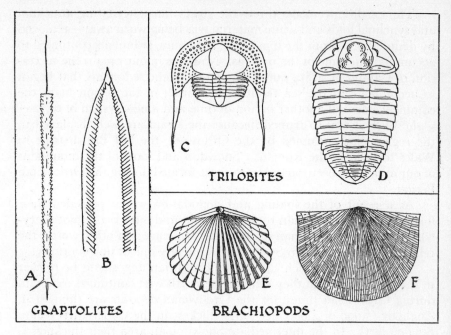

TRILOBITES

GRAPTOLITES　　　　BRACHIOPODS

FIG. 12.—Fossils recorded from the Ordovician rocks of Snowdonia

A. *Diplograptus (Orthograptus) calcaratus* (Lapworth). B. *Didymograptus murchisoni* (Beck).
C. *Cryptolithus* [*Trinucleus*] *concentricus* (Eaton). D. *Calymene brevicapitata* (Portlock).
E. *Orthis* (*Dinorthis*) *flabellulum* (Sowerby). F. *Strophomena* (*Rafinesquina*) *expansa*
(Sowerby). All approximately natural size.

attached to the sea floor or to stones, whilst others were suspended from
floating objects or from balloon-like floats of their own. Though small
and slender, the graptolite skeletons were exceptionally durable, and
in certain rocks their fossil remains are very abundant. When preserved
as fossils the rods are usually flattened and resemble fret-saw blades
because the cup-like cavities in which the individual polyps lived give
the edge a notched appearance.

On account of their floating habits some of the graptolites are very
widely distributed, and since many of the species persisted only for a
short time before being replaced by others, and are therefore
characteristic only of a comparatively small thickness of strata, they
are valuable as guides for subdividing the rocks into "zones," each

characterized by a particular species or assemblage of species and recognizable over wide areas. Their value for this purpose is increased by the fact that the skeletons of floating forms often fell on to parts of the sea floor where conditions were unfavourable to life and where, therefore, fossils in general are scarce. In many black shales, for example, graptolites are abundant whilst other fossils are rare or absent.

On the basis of the graptolites and trilobites which they have yielded —for the trilobites were still varied and numerous—the Ordovician rocks have been divided into five principal groups, each named after a place or an area where it is well displayed or was first studied; these names, like those of the older systems, indicate that the pioneer work was done mostly in Wales. Such subdivisions of a System are called Series, and, arranged with the youngest at the top, their names are as follows :—

5. Caradoc Series or Caradocian ⎱ These two together
4. Ashgill Series or Ashgillian ⎰ constitute the Bala Series.

3. Llandeilo Series or Llandeilian.

2. Llanvirn Series or Llanvirnian.

1. Arenig Series or Arenigian.

Although well represented in Anglesey and around the Harlech Dome, the Arenig rocks make no important contribution to the make-up of our area, except in the south-east where they are seen in the neighbourhood of Arenig Fawr. They are represented by dark shales with graptolites exposed along the Seiont River near Caernarvon and here and there along both sides of the Menai Straits, but they are not responsible for any conspicuous feature. It is, however, more than likely that they underlie the younger Ordovician rocks of the main Snowdonian masses, although, owing to *faults* by reason of which they are prevented from appearing at the surface, we cannot see them.

Faults are cracks in the earth's crust along which beds have been displaced for distances varying from fractions of an inch to many hundreds of yards; their effects are illustrated diagrammatically in Fig. 13, p. 50. By bringing dissimilar strata into close association they may be responsible for marked physical features and for the development of springs, and, by their shattering effects upon the rocks involved, they sometimes provide belts of strata that are easily eroded

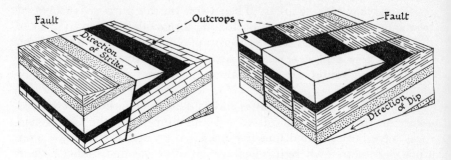

FIG. 13.—Diagrams to illustrate the terms outcrop, dip, strike, and fault

The effects of faults upon outcrops depend in part upon whether they run in the direction of strike (left) or of dip (right). The diagrams illustrate normal faults in which the strata on one side have been let down, but sometimes the strata appear to have been thrust upwards along the fault-plane carrying older beds over newer ones : such are called reversed faults and the line of fracture a thrust plane.

and on that account may locally influence the development of valleys. Although faults are abundant in our area, they have not been described in this account of it, because to refer to relatively small faults would involve entering into too much detail, whilst the effects of the great master-faults which have influenced the structure of the whole region are not yet thoroughly understood. In any case, faults in an area such as ours cannot usefully be indicated on a map of so small a scale as that included on pp. 54-55

Since we can know so little about the Arenig beds in Snowdonia, those which occur in and around the Harlech Dome are of interest because they contain the record of the early phases of the vulcanicity which at a later stage manifested itself in our area. The oldest of the volcanic rocks of the Harlech Dome are the lavas and ashes that now make up the greater part of Rhobell Fawr—carved from the relics of a volcano built up on a surface of Cambrian strata, but very largely worn away before the Ordovician sea was fully established in the North Wales region. A little later on, but still early in Ordovician times, the volcanoes responsible for the principal rocks of Cader Idris and Arenig Fawr came into being.

In each of these areas the activity continued during the succeeding Llanvirnian epoch and died out during the Llandeilian, but before the close of the latter it began to manifest itself in the Snowdonian area, where it was to play an important part in providing the rocks to which the characteristic scenery of that area is so largely due.

During Llanvirnian times most of our area was occupied by a tranquil sea in which fine-grained mud-like sediments accumulated to give rise to graptolite-bearing shales. Under the influence of the earth-movements which affected and altered the Cambrian shales of Penrhyn, Llanberis and Nantlle, the Ordovician shales also were converted into slates. They have been called the Maesgwm Slates from their typical occurrence in the Maesgwm valley beneath Moel-y-cynghorion, but they have not the economic importance of the Ordovician slates in the neighbourhood of Blaenau Ffestiniog, which have been extensively worked.

Between Nant Ffrancon and Llyn Cwellyn the outcrop of these blue-black slates varies from about a half a mile to a mile wide, but they do not as a rule give rise to craggy ground and are so largely covered by glacial debris (see Chapter 3) that exposures are not abundant. The first mile or so of the Snowdon Ranger track lies upon them, and, with their characteristic "tuning fork" graptolites, the rocks can be seen along the eastern face of Moel-y-cynghorion and in the railway cutting between Halfway Station and the railway reservoir.

Whilst these potential slates were accumulating, the volcanic activity which had already shown itself in the Harlech Dome and Cader Idris districts spread to the site of the present Manod and Moelwyn mountain groups north of the Vale of Ffestiniog, where beds of coarse ash alternate with slates, and where also, forming Moel Ystradau (Moel Tan-y-grisiau of the older Survey maps), is a mass of granitic rock that (according to the orthodox view concerning the origin of granite) was intruded when molten into the already existing strata. That it was intruded into pre-existing rocks and was not the floor on which later rocks were deposited is shown by the way in which veins of the once molten rock penetrate the covering strata in all directions, and include detached fragments of the rocks that were being invaded. Moel Ystradau provides an interesting example of the influence of rocks upon the contours of the land and upon vegetation, for its rounded heather-covered mass contrasts strongly with the rugged outlines of the grey rocks on Moelwyn Mawr and Moelwyn Bach.

At first the Llandeilo epoch saw little change in the nature and extent of the sea which covered our area, for its earlier rocks are dark shales, mudstones, and slates, differing but little from those formed during Llanvirnian times except in having different characteristic graptolites. They are, on the whole, paler in tint and smoother in texture, and, where well cleaved, they have been worked for slates, as in the Rhyd-ddu and Glanrafon quarries near Llyn Cwellyn, and the West Snowdon Quarry on Yr Aran, of which they constitute the peak.

The slates of Llandeilo Age are succeeded by beds of green or purplish grits, usually between 400 and 600 feet in thickness, but extending to about 1,200 feet on Clogwyn Du'r Arddu. These indicate the oncoming of shallower water conditions than those associated with the deposition of the muddy sediments that gave rise to the slates. From their typical development near the hamlet of Gwastadnant they have been named the *Gwastadnant Grits* and they can be traced from the Pass of Llanberis to the top of Y Garn and down the southern slope of Cwm Clyd to Nant Ffrancon and the falls of the Ogwen (Rhaeadr Ogwen) where they pass across the valley into Carnedd Ddafydd.

The shallowing which brought about the deposition of the Gwastadnant Grit was associated with the oncoming of the volcanic disturbances because several beds of lava are actually interbedded with the grits. Some of them are to be seen on the southern slopes of the Pass of Llanberis, and others alongside the Ranger track above Llyn Ffynnon-y-gwas. A further indication that shallow water conditions obtained towards the end of Llandeilo times is the fact that the lavas began to be denuded away almost as soon as they had solidified and so provided some of the material of the grits that rest upon them.

The volcanoes of southern and eastern Merionethshire had by now spent themselves and the centres of activity were all situated farther north. There were no more eruptions in the Arenig area or around Cader Idris, but lavas flowed and "ashes" were ejected from a series of volcanoes which developed along a line trending north-east to south-west from the neighbourhood of Penmaen-mawr towards Mynydd Mawr—and it is to the features which have since been carved from these rocks that our area owes most of its appeal to climbers and its attractiveness to lovers of mountain scenery and solitude. This brings us to what geologists for a long time described as the "Bala Volcanic Series of Caernarvonshire," believing the volcanic rocks to be associated entirely with sediments laid down during the Bala Epoch. It is now known, however, from study of the graptolites in the associated

slates, that although the volcanoes died out during Bala times, they arose
and probably reached their maximum intensity during the preceding
Llandeilo epoch, and so were, in part, rather older than was at one
time supposed.

3. A PERIOD OF VULCANICITY

Huge volcanoes, never long at rest, are pouring forth
Vast streams of liquid rock . . .
And down to sea the steaming lava flows.

H. R. Knipe, *Nebula to Man* (1905)

The volcanic activity was intermittent, and the fossils present in the
shales (or slates) and sandstones that are interbedded with the volcanic
rocks help us to determine the order in which the volcanoes made their
appearance. The oldest Ordovician volcanic rocks of our area appear
to be those in the neighbourhood of Dwygyfylchi and Y Drosgl; slightly
more recent are those seen between Conway and Capel Curig and
those of the Carneddau, Y Glyder Fach and Y Tryfan; the latter were
followed by a group of lavas and tuffs that is well developed in and
around Snowdon; after these came the "calcareous ashes" of Yr
Wyddfa and Cwm Idwal (as interesting to botanists as they are to
geologists), and a still later series of lavas of which small remnants
remain, amongst other places, in Crib-y-ddysgl and near Gallt-yr-
wenallt.

On the basis of the time-scale now generally accepted these
volcanoes were active between 350 and 375 million years ago. Since
then the rocks to which they gave rise have been thrown into the folds
which determined their present structures and have been so largely
removed by erosion that their scattered outcrops cover only a small
proportion of the area they once occupied. An attempt to reconstruct
the original limits of the lavas and ashes associated with the various
centres of eruption was made by the late Alfred Harker and the
essential features of his conclusions (published in 1889) are indicated

MAP 2.—Geological map of Snowdonia and the adjacent parts of North Wales

Many of the outcrops, especially of the volcanic (or contemporary igneous) rocks are generalized so that the structure of the region can be more readily appreciated. Simplified from the
maps of the Geological Survey and reproduced by permission of the Director, Geological
Survey and Museum

GEOLOGICAL MAP
OF SNOWDONIA
and the adjacent parts of
NORTH WALES
simplified from the maps
of the Geological Survey
Scale: ¼ inch to 1 mile

Sand (to L.W. mark)
Blown Sand
Alluvium

Carboniferous
Devonian
Silurian
Ordovician
Cambrian
Pre~Cambrian

Contemporaneous
Igneous Rocks
Intrusive
Igneous Rocks

ANGLESEY

Caernarvon

Nantlle

Yr Eifl

Portn
Criccieth

Pwllheli

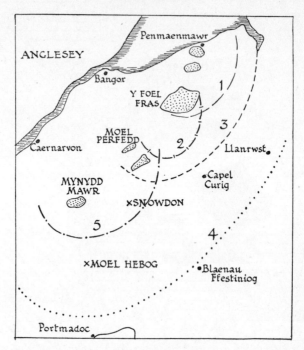

FIG. 14.—The ancient volcanoes of Snowdonia

The probable spheres of activity and the relative ages of the principal Ordovician volcanoes of Snowdonia. Also represented are some masses of igneous rock that may represent the " throats " of the volcanoes. Limits, 1, of the Dwygyfylchi lavas ; 2 and 3, of the lower and upper lavas of Y Tryfan, Y Glyder Fach, and the Carneddau; 4, of the lower (main) Snowdonian lavas ; 5, of the upper Snowdonian lavas. (After A. Harker.)

in the diagram (Fig. 14). Owing to the greater extent to which the volcanic products have suffered from the effects of denudation in the north-west their original limits in that direction are not known, but we should probably not be far wrong if we were to complete the curves by converting them into rather flattened ovals. The diagram, it should be noted, is in part the embodiment of a conception; it is not entirely a record of observed facts, for the lavas and ashes do not now survive over *the whole* of each of the indicated areas.

Along a line extending from Penmaen-mawr by way of Y Foel Fras and Mynydd Mawr to Yr Eifl (in Llŷn, outside our area), there are, here and there, what appear to be "plugs" of igneous rock that is obviously not lava; they are roughly round or oval in ground plan and rise steeply through the enclosing strata which often show signs of alteration by heat. These fine-grained crystalline rocks are derived from molten matter which cooled more slowly than if it had been poured out at the surface, but more rapidly than if it had been in as great bulk and as deeply buried as that which elsewhere gave rise to the more coarsely crystalline plutonic rocks like granite. The rock of Mynydd Mawr, for example, is described as microgranite. It contains minute crystals of riebeckite, an uncommon blue mineral consisting of silicate of sodium and iron. These masses trend roughly parallel to the ancient Padarn Ridge and some of them appear to mark the sites of the vents by means of which the molten material of the lavas reached the surface.

The rocks have been too severely denuded for direct connection between the lavas and the plugs to be traceable or even expected, and some of the plugs may represent intrusions that never reached as far as the surface, but, from their positions and the way in which the lavas and ashes become thicker when traced towards them, it seems not unreasonable to regard at least some of them as the cores, so to speak, of the ancient volcanoes. There is no positive proof that this is indeed the case and some geologists are inclined to regard the view that they are, as less well founded than it was originally thought to be.

The oldest lavas, those at the northern end of the region, are associated with the masses of igneous rock that make Penmaen-mawr, Y Foel Fras, and Y Drosgl, while Mynydd Mawr may represent the vent whence came the Upper Snowdonian lavas. The main Snow-donian volcanic rocks, which are found over so much larger an area than the others, include material poured out from most if not all of the volcanoes which were active at the time.

We have spoken of a series of volcanoes, but we must not on that account envisage conditions like those which now obtain in, say, the Andes, where centres of eruption occur here and there amongst high mountains, or think in terms of great cratered cones like Vesuvius or Etna. The Ordovician volcanoes of our area were essentially if not entirely submarine; their lavas were poured out on the floor of the sea, for they are interbedded with marine sediments, many of which are graptolite-bearing shales and slates that must have been laid down in fairly deep water and at some distance from land. An interesting

instance of marine sediment sandwiched between two sets of volcanic
rocks is a thin bed, so highly calcareous as to justify the appellation
tufaceous limestone, that separates rhyolitic tuffs from rhyolitic lavas in
the Clogwyn Du'r Arddu syncline (Fig. 4, p. 14). The rock contains
numerous fossils—brachiopods and trilobites.

The products of explosive outbursts usually mingled with or took
the place of the sediments that would normally have been accumulating
on those parts of the sea floor, but at times the piles of lava and ashes
appear to have grown high enough around some of the vents for the
summits to have risen out of the water so that the ensuing eruptions
were completely sub-aerial, or took place so near to the surface that
the ejected material was thrown into the air. This may well have been
the case with some of the "calcareous ashes" which separate the two
main series of Snowdonian lavas.

The close association with marine sediments is not the only indication that the volcanoes were submarine. It has been suggested that the
properties of some of the lavas, and the wide areas which some of them
cover, indicate that they flowed under pressure, as they would under
the water of a fairly deep sea; it is supposed that in such circumstances
they would have retained their included vapour and have remained
liquid for a longer time than if poured out on the surface of the land
under no more than atmospheric pressure.

This hypothesis reminds us that there is still much that we do not
understand about the operation and results of geological processes,
because, in spite of its plausibility, it seems to be invalidated by at
least two observed facts. One is that the evidences of flow which most
of the lavas exhibit show that they were not conspicuously less viscous
than such lavas usually are, and the other is that what must have been
some of the most fluid of the lavas, e.g. those near Cae'r-gors Farm,
Rhyd-ddu, rest on coarse grits and agglomerates, and must therefore
have flowed under water that was too shallow to have exerted any
great pressure upon them.

A more certain indication of submarine origin is the occurrence
here and there of what are known as "pillow lavas" because they
appear to be made up of pillow-shaped or sack-like masses from a few
inches to several feet across, piled upon one another and more or less
compressed in consequence.

When lavas of certain composition are erupted on the sea-floor they
retain some of their steam and become vesicular or bubbly; they are

relatively light and tend to be buoyed up in the water. By the time an extruded mass of such lava has reached a size approximating to that of a pillow its outer surface has solidified, and since further increase in size is not possible a new "pillow" begins to form; in such circumstances the sea-bed becomes covered with rolling masses that are at first kept from touching one another by reason of the steam which envelopes them. When they finally settle down the spaces between them may get filled with normal marine sediments. Such structures have been seen to form in modern times where lavas have flowed on to the floor of the sea, and the sediments with which most ancient pillow lavas are associated show that they are characteristic of the subsiding floors of geosynclines.

Since the "pillows" are separate and often removable entities, pillow lavas are apt to be dangerous to climbers, as, for example, where they occur above Twll Du, overlooking Llyn Idwal: some of the accidents on these rocks probably resulted from "pillows" being pulled out of the mass.

In the principal Snowdonian mountain tract, which preserves the products of what were probably the latest series of local eruptions, there are three main subdivisions of the volcanic rocks; a "Lower Rhyolitic Series" and an "Upper Rhyolitic Series" separated by a thick series of bedded ashes. These subdivisions were recognized by the early geologists who worked in the district; they thought, however, that the whole of the Lower Series was made up of lavas, but in 1900 J. R. Dakyns showed that there were reasons for thinking otherwise. He suggested that only part of the series was lava, of which some was nodular, some flinty-looking and well-jointed, and some strongly banded; in recent literature the banded variety is known as the *Pitt's Head Lava* because it is well displayed in a quarry near Pitt's Head, a rock overlooking Llyn-y-gader on the Caernarvon–Beddgelert road and so called from a fancied resemblance to the statesman's profile.

Dakyns found that the upper (and thicker) part of the series was made up very largely of fine fragmentary material of volcanic origin, now consolidated to form tuffs described as *vitric tuffs* because under the microscope they are seen to consist largely of fragments that were originally in a glassy condition. They are dense, hard, splintery rocks that show no evidence of bedding planes, although they generally have well-defined vertical joints.

The vitric tuffs form the sharp ridge of Llechog south of Cwm

Clogwyn, are responsible for most of the precipice of Lliwedd over-looking Llyn Llydaw, and are seen in the cliffs on either side of the Pass of Llanberis.

Where they are fully developed, as on Lliwedd, these beds are from 1,200 to 1,500 feet thick, but towards the south they become thinner and include increasing amounts of what were originally muddy sediments, and so pass into normal slates as they approach Beddgelert. The purer tuffs are grey, but as the amount of sediment increases they tend to become bluish-grey or greenish-grey. They have none of the characters (e.g. flow structure) associated with lava, and are *not stratified* like ordinary sediments or volcanic ashes. Edward Greenly, who examined them with Dakyns, came to the conclusion that they originated as showers of dust that accumulated with unusual rapidity, and suggested that they may have been the products of eruptions like that of Mont Pelée, which, in 1902, overwhelmed the town of St. Pierre in Martinique.

An objection to this view is that the dust resulting from the outburst which destroyed the West Indian town made a layer only about three feet thick, whereas the thickness of the dust-rocks of Lliwedd approaches 1,500 feet, and it is difficult to see how so great a mass of material could have accumulated without showing signs of stratification, since it is not likely to have been the product of a single explosion. The difficulty in explaining the origin of these rocks is mentioned here because it reminds us that, although we appear to know so much about the geological history of our land, many problems still remain unsolved: there is still much to engage the attention of future geologists. What seems on some grounds to be the only explanation we can offer for the origin of these peculiar dust-rocks appears, on others, to be quite unacceptable, and we can only say that if they were not formed in the manner suggested by Greenly we cannot point to any other known cause, past or present, to which they can be attributed.

Resting on the Lower Rhyolitic Series are what the older geologists called the "calcareous and felspathic ashes." These constitute the "Bedded Pyroclastic Series" of modern nomenclature, and, as the term pyroclastic (fire-broken) indicates, they are made up of material fragmented by explosive eruptions. They reach a thickness of over 1,200 feet below the summit of Yr Wyddfa, but become thinner as they are traced towards Lliwedd and Cwm Glas. They are usually dark greenish-grey in colour when freshly broken, but the weathered surfaces

tend to be brown, on which account the rocks are readily distinguish-
able from the lavas, the weathered surfaces of which are usually almost
white. Immediately below the Summit Hotel there are slaty and gritty
beds which contain many fossils, mainly the shells of brachiopods with
an occasional trilobite. Trilobites also occur in the "Bedded Pyroclastic
Series" in the neighbourhood of Twll Du. The general assemblage of
fossils suggests that the rocks belong to the lower part of the Caradocian
Series and provide evidence for dating the decline of the volcanic
activity in this region.

One of the most interesting characters of the "Bedded Pyroclastic
Series" is that the rocks are usually calcareous, that is, contain lime
(up to as much as 10 per cent). Lime is also present in comparable
amounts in some of the dolerites and andesites but in the rhyolitic rocks
and in most of the sedimentary rocks of the area its proportion rarely
reaches 2 per cent.

The presence of lime appears to have affected the vegetation which
rocks and the soil derived from them can support, for it is to the calcareous ashes that our area owes a great deal of its interest to botanists,
although the water-bearing capacity of the rocks as well as their
composition must play an important part in fostering the growth of
the mountain plants. That the richness of the vegetation depends upon
elevation and aspect as well as upon the rocks and the soil is illustrated
by the fine late-summer colouring of the hills near Conway, due to the
purple heather and golden gorse that grows upon the craggy outcrops
of volcanic rock. The vegetation is less colourful on similar rocks at
higher elevations and in more rainy regions.

The botanical interest of the area is general as well as particular,
for while the flora of certain localities presents features that are unusual
or even unique, the outcrops of many of the rocks are recognizable by
reason of the vegetation they support. The patches of heather and
bilberry that characterize the rhyolitic lavas and tuffs contrast strongly
with the greener ferns and mosses that have established themselves on
the calcareous ashes, a change that is seen, for example, at the south-
western end of Lliwedd. The ashes are, as already indicated, also
exposed in the steep cliffs overlooking Llyn Idwal, and the character
of the rock, together with the synclinal structure which ensures an
adequate supply of water, favours a luxuriant flora, on which account
one locality has been called the Hanging Gardens. The Gully of that
name is a conspicuous hollow in the cliffs to the right of Twll Du. The

effect of rocks upon plant assemblages often assists the geologist by indicating the position of geological boundaries in areas where exposures of rock are poor or absent.

Apart from these local factors, the botany of the Snowdonian region derives interest from the variety of rock types and surface conditions (crags, screes, bogs, etc.) for which the rather complicated geological structure is responsible, as well as from the considerable variation in rainfall and sunshine within short distances. Owing to the steepness of the slopes and the cleaved and jointed character of many of the rocks —factors which favour the development of slips and the formation of screes—old ground is often disturbed and new ground built up, providing opportunities for studying the struggles for settlement and supremacy that are associated with the establishment and spread of plant life.

Before ending this interpolation about plants we may note that John Williams, who wrote an account of the Llanrwst district in 1830, drew attention to the presence of the Alpine cress on waste places and walls near the lead mines; since then the association has been found to hold good in other parts of the world, e.g. in the Rhine Valley and the United States.

Resuming our account of the vulcanicity of our area we have to note that in the Nant Ffrancon district the "Bedded Pyroclastic Series" includes a thick and interesting lava-flow which makes up most of Twll Du and is seen in the hummocky ground of Cwm Cneifio[1]. The lava contains less silica than those of the rhyolitic series we have already discussed and is described as andesitic basalt. The rock contains no quartz and consists largely of the minerals felspar and augite.

Chemically the Twll Du lavas resemble the tuffs with which they are associated, and it is likely that both were derived from the same molten source—the one being erupted explosively whilst the other flowed freely at the surface. It is these lavas which, near the top of Twll Du, exhibit the "pillow" structure mentioned on page 59.

Preserved in synclinal folds on Crib-y-ddysgl and on the ridge that leads from Lliwedd to Gallt-yr-wenallt near Llyn Gwynant, there are small outcrops of an "Upper Rhyolitic Series"—largely lavas—resting on the calcareous ashes. Other small outcrops occur on the northwestern flank of Moel Hebog, but there are none on the northern side of Snowdon, for the topmost beds of the volcanic series in the Nant

[1]*Cneifio*, to shear ; perhaps a reference to sheep-shearing in the cwm in a former time.

PLATE 5

John Markham

TWILL-DU, THE DEVIL'S KITCHEN; looking north-east, with Llyn Idwal below and Llyn Ogwen and the valley of Afon Llugwy beyond. July

PLATE 6

TRYFAN, the eastern face from above Afon Llugwy. July

John Markham

Ffrancon area are the equivalents of the "Bedded Pyroclastic Series" of Snowdon proper. If the lavas of the "Upper Rhyolitic Series" ever reached as far as Y Glyder Fawr they have been removed by denudation, and the half-dozen or so small outcrops that remain are merely relics of a once large sheet or series of sheets, the outpouring of which brought the extrusive phase of the Snowdonian vulcanicity to an end.

While some of the masses of igneous material appear to have been intruded into already existing rocks and to represent the plugs or throats of some of the volcanoes, there are also other intrusive masses which make an interesting contribution to the story of the vulcanicity of our area. They seem to have arrived after the building-up of the lavas and pyroclastic rocks had been completed. In order to appreciate their significance we must refer again to the varieties and classification of igneous rocks.

We have already noted that the texture of igneous rocks is related to the conditions under which they cooled, but other characters are related to the chemical composition of the molten material or magma from which they were derived. The slow cooling of the larger intrusions, which once lay far beneath the surface, allowed relatively large crystals of various minerals to develop; the plutonic rocks are, therefore, of coarse texture and are made up of crystalline entities large enough to be seen easily with the unaided eye. Plutonic rocks that may have resulted from the alteration of other rocks *in situ* were also deeply buried and are now coarsely crystalline.

Lavas, on the other hand, which cooled rapidly, tended to solidify in a glassy condition, or if crystals developed they were usually extremely small and only to be distinguished with the aid of a lens or microscope. The molten material which filled volcanic vents, or which gave rise to wall-like sheets or *dykes* when it rose more or less vertically through the associated strata, or to *sills* when it penetrated in the direction of the bedding of the rocks and so appears to conform to the local stratification, cooled more quickly than that which gave rise to plutonic rocks and less quickly than that which flowed at the surface as lava. There was time for the constituents to crystallize but the crystals are much smaller than those of typical plutonic rocks.

On the basis of chemical composition igneous rocks are divided into two main classes—*acid* rocks, rich in silica, and *basic* rocks, poor in silica. These terms do not mean that certain rocks are acid in the sense that vinegar is acid; they were introduced because most of the minerals in igneous rocks are silicates (compounds of silica with various metallic oxides) or in other words are metallic salts of silicic acid, the silica being regarded as the acid constituent of the magma. Rocks in which it is present to the extent of over 65 per cent came to be known as acid and they usually have a certain amount of uncombined silica in the form of the mineral quartz, as in granite which is a typical acid rock.

The basic rocks are those which have less than 52 per cent of silica but more than 45 per cent; the few which have even less than this are known as *ultra-basic*. These are arbitrarily chosen divisions, for the rocks of one class pass gradually into those of the next, and the rocks of the important group in which the silica-content lies between 65 and 52 per cent are termed *intermediate*.

This brief outline of the main classes into which igneous rocks can be divided on the basis of their chemical composition will be sufficient for our purpose, although it ignores certain complicating factors such as those due to variations in the identity and relative amounts of the basic constituents that may be associated with any given proportion of silica.

In general we can say that igneous rocks include three principal groups of constituent minerals—quartz, felspars, and the ferromagnesian minerals. Ferromagnesian minerals are those which are essentially silicates of iron, magnesium, and calcium, which may or may not be accompanied by silicates of sodium, potassium and aluminium. As with the felspars there are many varieties, some of which grade one into the other. Owing to their iron content, the ferromagnesian minerals are heavier and darker than the felspars; they are often almost black in mass and greenish or brownish in thin transparent slices. The felspars, on the other hand, are pale-coloured and usually colourless in thin section, transparent when fresh and cloudy when weathered. Quartz and felspar are the principal minerals in the acid rocks, whilst the intermediate and basic rocks consist essentially of felspar and ferromagnesian minerals, the former predominating in the intermediate rocks and the latter in the basic. The acid rocks are generally pale-coloured, hard, and resistant to weathering, but the basic rocks are darker, heavier, on the whole are softer and weather more readily.

The lavas of our area are mostly of acid types but at the northern end in the neighbourhood of Dwygyfylchi and Y Drosgl they are related to andesite which is typical of the intermediate class. The lavas of Twll Du and Cwm Cneifio approach the basalts in composition, having only about 47 per cent of silica. Of the large intrusions that are regarded as representing (possibly) volcanic plugs, the more southerly ones are made up of typically acid rocks (e.g. microgranite) whilst the more northerly are less acid and sometimes are of intermediate types as in the case of part of the rock which makes up Y Foel Fras and parts of the great intrusion of Penmaen-mawr. The latter includes several rocks of varying acidity, the least acid being those near the base, as if a large molten mass had cooled slowly enough for there to have been a certain amount of differentiation in its constituents.

In general there appears to be a relationship between the hypabyssal rocks and the extrusive rocks in any one region, just as there is between lavas and pyroclastic material when they occur together; it will be remembered that the lavas and the tuffs of the "Lower" Series of Snowdon are both rhyolitic, whilst the composition of the tuffs associated with the Twll Du andesitic basalt justified the belief that both were derived from a common magma.

For the most part the rocks of our area have been built up layer by layer, some of them as sediments and others as lava flows or spreads of pyroclastic material, so that sections illustrating the structure of the country show a series of bands, which, in spite of variations in thickness and modifications due to folding and fracture, extend more or less regularly for considerable distances, but, as the Sections in Fig. 5 (p. 15) show, some rocks are intrusive and may cut across the general stratification in a remarkable manner. There are several such intrusions of acid rocks on the north-eastern side of Snowdon between Crib-y-ddysgl and Tal-y-llyn, including the great mass of Crib Goch which was formerly supposed to be a lava flow.

The rock of the Crib Goch intrusion has a distinct columnar structure, the result of contraction during cooling. In chemical composition the rock is similar to the "granitic" rocks of Mynydd Mawr, Moel Perfedd, and Bwlch-y-cywion, which in turn resemble (chemically) the rhyolites such as the Pitt's Head lava. This suggests that the microgranites of the larger masses like Mynydd Mawr, the smaller intrusions like the one responsible for Crib Goch, and the volcanic rocks (lavas) of Snowdon were most likely all derived from the same magma, the difference in the rocks being principally due to the different circumstances in which they cooled. In other words, in spite of the variation in their physical characters and in their effect upon present-day topography, the rocks all belong to one suite of ultimately common origin; they represent many separate eruptions, but are the products of one great volcanic episode.

In addition to the acid hypabyssal rocks there are also many dykes and sills of basic rock, darker and heavier than those just mentioned; a characteristic type is dolerite, which consists largely of a variety of felspar and the ferromagnesian mineral augite. These dykes and sills penetrate the Cambrian slates as well as the Ordovician lavas and sediments, and the rocks adjacent to them often show signs of having been affected by the heat of the invading magma. The slates, for example, have usually been hardened and some have been converted into hard pale green rocks suitable for honestones. There was once a small honestone quarry high on the mountain near Marchlyn Mawr, and "Welsh oilstone" from near Llyn Idwal and other places in our area has been used on account of its hardness and fine texture for grinding small blades like those of lancets. Early in the nineteenth century, rock from the neighbourhood of Cwm Idwal was exported to Dublin and London.

Features due to dolerite intrusions (some of which exceed 500 feet in thickness) are to be seen, for example, in the great crag that rises on the southern side of the pass of Llanberis near Pont-y-gromlech (Pl. IV, p. 11), in some prominent bosses of rock smoothed by the action of glaciers (*roches moutonnées*, see page 105) near the south-eastern end of Llyn Llydaw (Pl. Xb, p. 99), and in the hills rising on the southern side of Llyn Teryn on the north side of Cwm Dyli below Llyn Llydaw. A thick sheet of dolerite forms the summit of Carnedd Llywelyn and the dark cliffs of Ysgolion Duon on the northern side of Carnedd Ddafydd.

The acid hypabyssal rocks and some of the dolerite dykes and sills were affected by the earth-movements which gave rise to the anticlinal and synclinal folds and converted shales into slates, and this means that they must have been intruded as part of the main manifestation of igneous activity, before the mountain-building movements reached their maximum intensity. It appears, therefore, that as the volcanic episode drew towards its close, strains and stresses developed that were premonitory of the more intense movements that were to come later on; they caused cracks to develop in the sedimentary and volcanic rocks that had accumulated during the Cambrian and Ordovician periods, and squeezed into them some of the molten material that still remained in the deep-seated reservoirs. The magma which gave rise to the basic dolerites most likely came from lower layers than those which had been drawn upon during the earlier phases of the vulcanicity.

With certain minor exceptions these injections of dolerite and felsite (as the acid hypabyssal rocks may conveniently be called) were the last permanent additions to be made to the rocks from which our area has been carved. The exceptions include certain small dykes of dolerite (seen, for example, in Cwm Perfedd and between Bwlch-y-cywion and Marchlyn Mawr) and which, not being affected by the movements that folded the rocks and converted the shales into slates, must be of more recent origin. They are, indeed, on account of characters they have in common with certain dolerite dykes in Anglesey, Bardsey Island, and the west of Scotland, believed to have been intruded during a very much more recent period of earth-movement—that which took place during the Tertiary Era. Since they contribute so little to the fabric of our area, being at the most from 25 to 40 feet in thickness and in one case thinning away to less than 6 inches, it might be thought that they are hardly worth mentioning, but, as we shall see, they provide important evidence relating to the age of the *mountains*, as distinct from the age of the rocks out of which they have been carved.

Also amongst the exceptions are rocks of Silurian age which, although widely distributed in North Wales, only appear in the extreme eastern margin of our area. Rocks of more recent age than Silurian may indeed have been deposited in parts of the region at various times before the close of the Tertiary Era, but they have since been worn away, and the only surviving post-Silurian rocks are the superficial deposits that were spread indiscriminately at the end of the Ice Age, and the silts and gravels laid down by modern rivers.

Great as were its effects at the time, and important as are its contributions to the scenery of to-day, the volcanic episode of Ordovician times was only a stage in the formation of the geosyncline of which our area was then a part. Whilst the floor was sinking to maintain a basin capable of receiving the sediment that was being poured into it, lateral pressures began to manifest themselves, leading to occasional local upheaval and the denudation of some of the newly-formed deposits; and then, as the forces increased in intensity, and earth-waves broke against that ancient but very stable feature, the Padarn Ridge, some of the deep-seated material passed into a molten condition and, forcing its way to the surface, was poured out as lava or spread about as pyroclastic fragments.

References for Chapter 2

SECTION I
Greenly (1919), Greenly (1925), Holmes (1944), Morris and Fearnsides (1926), North (1946), Ramsay (1866), Smith and George (1935), Stamp (1946), H. Williams (1927), D. Williams (1930).

SECTION 2
Smith and George (1935), H. Williams (1927), D. Williams (1930).

SECTION 3
Dakyns (1900), Fearnsides (1905), Greenly (1905), Greenly (1925), Harker (1889), Ramsay (1866), D. Williams (1930), H. Williams (1927), H. Williams and Bulman (1930).

CHAPTER 3

THE BUILDING AND SHAPING
OF THE MOUNTAINS

I. A MOUNTAIN-BUILDING AGE

Then 'gan the sea to have a shore and brooks to find a bank,
And swelling streams of flowing flood within their channels sank.
Then hills did rise above the waves that had them overflow,
And as the waters did decrease, the ground did seem to grow.

> Ovid, *The Metamorphoses*,
> trans. Arthur Golding, 1565

SILURIAN rocks were deposited in our area but they were soon removed by denudation and it is not until we cross the Conway river that we find them making important contributions to the fabric of North Wales. The Silurian Period is, however, of interest to us, because it saw the final stages in the formation of the geosyncline and the commencement of a new series of earth-movements that, as they rose to a climax, caused the Cambrian and Ordovician deposits to acquire the anticlinal and synclinal structures they now display, that converted what would otherwise have been shales into hard and often commercially important slates, and that built up mountains where there had, for so long, been sea.

Since they play no part in determining the present features of our area we need not describe the Silurian deposits in detail or enumerate the groups into which they have been subdivided. It will be sufficient to say that they are nearly 4,000 feet thick in the Denbighshire moor country and reach 10,000 feet in other parts of Wales.

By the end of the Silurian Period the total maximum thickness of the material that had been deposited in the geosyncline—the layers of mud, silt, sand, lava, and volcanic dust and ashes—was more than 35,000 feet, and the sea, which then extended without a break over the whole of our area, had its margins not nearer than central Scotland in one direction and the English Midlands in another. From time to time, as we have seen, movements within the geosyncline had affected the nature of the sediments, had resulted in the removal of some of them almost as soon as they had been deposited, and had caused volcanoes to break out; but they were feeble movements compared with those which now began to manifest themselves.

The picture we have to envisage is that of the two flanks of the great trough approaching one another, largely as a result of pressure exerted from the south (Fig. 17, p. 86). The sediments within it were squeezed and thrown into alternating arch-like and trough-like folds, were hardened by reason of the pressure to which they were subjected and the heat to which that pressure gave rise, and great masses were displaced along lines of fracture, initiating what are now faults. The deposits of the sea floor were uplifted to form mountains resembling in magnitude the Alps of to-day and with similar if less intensely developed structures (Fig. 15).

The geosyncline stretched from north-east to south-west; so, therefore, do the main structures of the mountains raised upon its site. The earth-movements responsible for the mountains are called the "Caledonian" movements because their results are well displayed in Scotland.

The conditions at the end of the period of compression and uplift are illustrated diagrammatically in Fig. 15, but in reading the diagram we must remember that as soon as the rocks emerged from the sea they began to be attacked by the agents of erosion. The wearing-down of the crests of the arches proceeded simultaneously with, but more slowly than, the uplift, so that the conditions which actually developed during Devonian times are represented in the middle part of the diagram. The upper part is an indication of the amount of material that was carried away to make new deposits in the areas to which the sea had retreated, or that accumulated in shallow lagoons and estuaries to give rise to the Old Red Sandstone. Deposits of this age that remain in Anglesey are wind-blown dusts (the products of weathering in a region of barren rugged hills), and conglomerates that accumulated in shallow water. They indicate a dry climate and a desertlike country-side, and give us a clue to the conditions that are likely to have prevailed over our area.

We are now in a position to appreciate the part which the region that is now Anglesey has played in the development of the Snowdonian mountains. It was a land mass during Pre-Cambrian times, and although it sank to receive Cambrian deposits its land status was restored for a time before the Ordovician deposits began to accumulate; its Ordovician rocks show that it did not share in the vulcanicity of

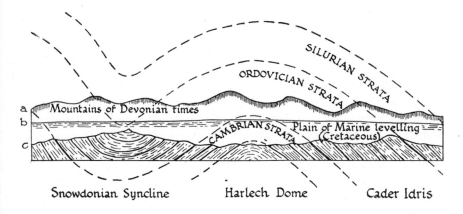

FIG. 15.—The ancient and the modern mountains of Snowdonia and the
Harlech Dome

A generalized section showing the relation between (a), the mountains of Devonian
times that resulted from the denudation of folded Silurian, Ordovician and Cambrian
rocks ; (b), the comparatively even surface that had been developed by the beginning
of the Tertiary Era; and (c), the mountains of today. The formation of the
Cretaceous plain of marine denudation was preceded by subsidence and followed
by uplift and erosion

that Period and, whilst the great pile of Cambrian, Ordovician, and
Silurian sediments of our area was being folded and uplifted during
Devonian times, deposits of Devonian Age (Old Red Sandstone) were
being laid down in Anglesey upon the worn and upturned edges of the
older rocks of the island.

The Old Red Sandstone is displayed at sea level in Dulas Bay,
Anglesey, but a line representing the base of any contemporary deposits
that may have been laid down in our area has, as shown in Fig. 17
(p. 86), to be drawn well above the summits of the present mountains:
compared with Anglesey our area has been greatly elevated. This
does not, of course, mean that Anglesey was not affected by the Caledonian movements, because the essential structure of the island was
determined by them. Its Ordovician and Silurian sediments with
their floor of Pre-Cambrian rocks were thrown into folds, in some of
which the rocks were stretched beyond the limits of their elasticity: as
a result, they fractured and were thrust along the planes of fracture.
In the north of the island, for example, a great slice of Pre-Cambrian

rocks was driven, along an inclined line of fracture, over the much newer Ordovician strata, so that in the cliffs at Carmel Head folded mica-schists of Pre-Cambrian age can be seen actually resting upon poorly cleaved Ordovician shales. Although affected to this extent, the Ordovician and Silurian shales in Anglesey were not subject to such severe compression as were the argillaceous rocks of Snowdonia.

It seems, therefore, that, compared with our area, Anglesey has been a comparatively stable block, the massive and resistant rocks of which played an important part in determining the trend and structures of the Snowdonian mountains and the present conditions of the rocks of which they consist (Fig. 17, p. 86).

The considerable influence of the apparently insignificant Padarn Ridge now becomes understandable, for we can regard it as being an outpost of the relatively stable Anglesey block and not the narrow isolated mass it would be if nothing more were involved than its present outcrop. The effects of this north-western stable block are seen even in the easternmost parts of our area—in the undulating tableland between Carnedd Llywelyn and the valley of the Conway. In this region the folding, the faulting, and the cleavage of the rocks, and the courses of the principal rivers (Dulyn, Porth Llwyd and Ddu) all conform to its alignment.

The margins of the stable north-western block provided the foundations for the archipelago around the shores of which the earliest of the local Cambrian deposits accumulated; it assumed the rôle of the immovable object against which the sediments accumulating in the geosyncline were from time to time pushed by an irresistible force; it continued in that rôle when the earth-waves of Ordovician times broke against it, thus playing an important part in bringing about the development of volcanoes and in determining their north-easterly/south-westerly trend; then, when the compressional movements reached their maximum after the end of the Silurian period, the Padarn Ridge itself acted like one of the jaws of a vice in which some of the fine-grained deposits of Cambrian age were squeezed and converted into slate. The other jaw was the great Snowdonian syncline of Ordovician sediments, lavas, and ashes.

As a result of the squeezing, the particles in the ancient mud-rocks tended to take up positions with their broader faces more or less at right angles to the direction of pressure; also under the influence of the pressure, supplemented by the heat associated with it and the heat

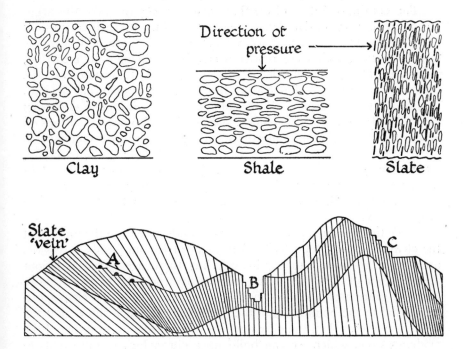

FIG. 16.—The formation and occurrence of slate

The arrangement of the particles in clay, shale, and slate : in shale they are more closely packed than in clay, and most of them lie with their longer axes parallel to the surface on which they were deposited ; in slate they lie in a direction nearly perpendicular to that in which the pressure that altered the rock was applied, and flaky crystals of mica have been developed amongst them

The lower section illustrates (a) the relation between rock folding and the cleavage of slate, and (b) the development of mountainside quarries (C), deep pits (B), or underground chambers (A) according to the conditions under which a bed of well-cleaved commercially useful rock appears at the surface

due to the depth of the beds beneath the surface (for they were then covered by a blanket of sediment that must have been three or four miles thick), some of the constituent particles underwent chemical change and minute crystals of new minerals were developed. The most important of these was a variety of mica, the most characteristic property of which is a tendency to split into thin filmy flakes.

The continued effect of all these changes was to make the argil-laceous rocks very hard and very compact, whilst, with their constituent particles (both original and secondary) all lying more or less in the same direction, they were rendered capable of being split into thin, strong, durable, parallel-sided sheets that for most purposes are the best covering for roofs that Nature has produced or man has devised. The property by reason of which slate can be split is known as *cleavage* —the Welsh name is *hollt*. Thicker slabs of slate also have their uses on account of their chemical inertness and freedom from a tendency to warp; they are in demand for making such things as billiard tables, laboratory and skin-dressers' benches, chemical vats, electrical switch-boards and insulating panels, and many other things which cannot be enumerated here but which are discussed in works mentioned in the bibliography.

Since the pressure operated regionally and came from the south-east the cleavage planes tend to "strike" more or less uniformly across the area from north-east to south-west, but there are local deviations around some of the larger masses of intrusive rock like Mynydd Mawr and the granite of Bwlch-y-cywion. In these places the cleavage is tangential to the boundaries of the igneous rock, which shows that the latter was there when the cleavage was developed—an example of the evidence upon which we can build up a chronology of the events in geological history.

We can now see why it is that such great slate quarries—the greatest in the world—have been opened in the strip of country immediately south-westwards of the Padarn Ridge. The largest are the Penrhyn Quarry near Bethesda and the Dinorwic Quarry near Llanberis, opened on opposite sides of the mountain, Elidir Fawr. The Dinorwic quarry takes the form of a series of terraces rising tier upon tier for more than a thousand feet, whilst the Penrhyn quarry, similarly terraced, extends into the mountain as a deep oval pit well-nigh three-quarters of a mile long (Pl. VII, p. 42).

There are also slate quarries in the Cambrian rocks of the Nantlle district, but these (for the most part) take the form of deep pits and chasms because the rocks do not there outcrop on the sides of steep mountains. Although smaller than the Penrhyn and Dinorwic quarries, those in the Nantlle valley are much larger than the usual run of quarries; the pits of the Dorothea quarry, for example, are nearly 600 feet deep (Fig. 16, p. 73).

The pressure which converted the Cambrian shales into slates also affected the Ordovician rocks, but the fine-grained argillaceous deposits in the latter are thinner, and the effects of the pressure were modified locally by the masses of hard igneous rocks that make up so much of the System. Consequently, the slates that were developed amongst the Snowdonian Ordovician strata have not the commercial importance that attaches to those of the older System. There are, however, several more or less parallel lines of quarries in slates of Ordovician age following the north-easterly/south-westerly trend that characterizes the structure of the region; some of them are still working but many never get beyond the experimental stage. One such line of quarries extends from Rhyd-ddu (Glanrafon and Llyn-y-gader quarries) by way of Cwm Pennant towards Llanfihangel-y-Pennant, another extends from Bwlch Cwm-y-llan, between Snowdon summit and Yr Aran, to near Tremadoc, while a third extends from Llanrhychwyn near Llanrwst to Llyn Dinas and Beddgelert.

Further to the south-east, and extending from near Betws-y-coed by way of Dolwyddelan and Penmachno to near Llanfrothen, a distance of about twelve miles with Blaenau Ffestiniog near the centre, thick and extensive beds of fine-grained argillaceous rocks of Ordovician age lay between the Snowdon volcanic series on the one hand and the Harlech Dome with its massive Cambrian rocks on the other. Such conditions were favourable to the formation of slate during a period of compression and we find, accordingly, that Blaenau Ffestiniog is another of the world-famous names associated with slate. Here the rocks are mostly blue or grey and they are capable of being split into unusually thin, even sheets of great strength.

In this district the strata are less steeply inclined than they are in the Cambrian slate belt, so that as a quarry is worked a bed of slate exposed in its face tends to pass more and more deeply beneath a covering of other rock, and this has to be removed before the slate can be won. In such cases open quarries cannot be developed except on a small scale; instead, the slate is followed underground by means of inclined tunnels and is excavated from what eventually become great "chambers"; these are separated from one another by walls of rock left to prevent the overlying strata from collapsing into and burying the working places.

Some of the slate mines in the Blaenau Ffestiniog area are the largest of their kind in the world. The chambers may eventually be as much as 300 feet long, 40 feet wide, and 100 feet high, and in one mine several such chambers are or have been worked on as many as twenty-four levels, the lowest of which is more than 1,500 feet from the top of the incline which gives access to it. In these circumstances the region has not the vast open quarries and pits that are seen on the other side of our area between Bethesda and Pen-y-groes, and the evidences of slate-working are the vast tips of waste material that disfigure the countryside, as they do wherever slate is worked.

For various reasons, most of them quite unavoidable, the production of a ton of slate, split and trimmed into the thin rectangular sheets that are spread upon our roofs, involves the quarrying of from twelve to twenty tons of rock for which there is no use. Various attempts have been made to utilize this waste and research with that object in view is still being undertaken, but we must regard the ugly dumps as the price that must be paid for the exploitation of a natural product that provides a valuable article of commerce and work for a considerable population. The quarries in our area and around its margins have always yielded from four-fifths to three-quarters of the slate produced in Britain.

The preparation of roofing slates involves operations calling for great skill, sound judgment and long experience. It begins in the dislodgment of masses of rock with the least possible amount of shattering and of such shapes and sizes that they can be split into roughly rectangular blocks of suitable size. For this purpose explosives are used, and the thunder-like roll of the explosions at blasting-time and the puffs of smoke that they produce are characteristic features of the quarry regions.

Taking advantage of the property which permits the rock to be split in certain directions, the fallen blocks are divided, by means of wedges, into masses convenient for transport to the dressing sheds (Pl. VIII, p. 43). Here, after further splitting to produce slabs about three inches thick, wide enough to yield a roofing slate and two or three times as long, the slabs are sawn into convenient lengths and split into sheets about one-sixth of an inch thick, or thicker with some slates and for some purposes. The splitting is done by means of a chisel placed against one of the shorter edges of the block and lightly struck with a mallet; when a crack appears in the direction of cleavage skilful manipulation of the chisel enables the splitter to prise off one of the thin sheets; these are trimmed to a true rectangular shape, originally (and still to some

extent in small undertakings, or where the nature of the slate is such
that machine cutting is not practicable) by hand, using a heavy knife
and a fixed straight-edge on which the slate is laid. In some dressing-
sheds the operation is performed by a foot-driven appliance with a
movable knife acting like a printer's guillotine, and in others machine-
driven rotating knives are used.

2. THE UNRECORDED AGES

" Nature has bestowed upon us an inquisitive disposition. . . .
Our vision opens up a path for its investigation and lays the
foundation of truth so that our research may pass from revealed
to hidden things."

Seneca, *On Leisure*

In our survey of the building-up of Snowdonia we had reached a
stage when the sediments and volcanic products that had accumulated
over a long period of time had been uplifted to provide an elevated
mass from which mountains and valleys were being carved by the
agents of erosion. But this brought us only to the Devonian Period,
and as the table on page 29 indicates there are no rocks in our area
to provide a record of its subsequent geological history until we come
to the Glacial Period, or Ice Age, separated from the present by only a
few thousand years.

We are, however, not altogether without means for reconstructing
some at least of the history of those *Unrecorded Ages* as Greenly so aptly
termed them, for rocks were accumulating in other parts of the country,
and from them we can infer something of what was going on in our area
and can suggest explanations for certain features which it presents.
A summary of the story for Britain as a whole will be found in *Britain's
Structure and Scenery* (L. D. Stamp), recently published in the NEW
NATURALIST series. It will be sufficient here to indicate the general
course of events and the part they played in converting the mountains
that had been uplifted and carved during Devonian times into those
which supported the ice-fields and fed the glaciers of the geologically
recent Ice Age.

At the end of the Devonian Period and during the early part of the
succeeding Carboniferous Period our area was part of a larger region
of barren hills and inhospitable wind-swept plains, but in time the

waters of a somewhat shallow sea began to encroach upon it. The calcareous deposits that accumulated on the floor of that sea contained abundantly the remains of corals, crinoids (sea-lilies), brachiopods, and other kinds of "shell-fish," and they built up the rocks that are now seen, for example, in the limestone (Carboniferous Limestone) cliffs of Great Ormes Head, in the great quarries at Llanddulas and at Penmon Point in Anglesey—that is, around the margins of our area but not within it.

By the end of Carboniferous Limestone times the sea was more extensive than the present restricted outcrops of the limestone would suggest, but it is unlikely that it covered the higher ground that still remained after the severe denudation of Devonian times: this appears to have been a peninsula projecting westwards from land occupying the site of what is now south-eastern England. It has been called St. George's Land because the St. George's Channel of to-day cuts across it, but it is not likely to have been a region of high relief with rapidly flowing rivers, because the calcareous deposits which accumulated in the neighbouring sea contained very little land-derived sediment, and on that account some of the limestone to which they gave rise derives considerable economic importance from its purity.

As time went on the sea grew shallower because its floor was no longer sinking and the deposits discharged into it gradually filled it up, and it gave place to extensive swampy regions which supported the dense forests that provided the materials of our coal seams. The Coal Measures—the shales and sandstones with coal seams that constitute the upper part of the Carboniferous System—are preserved in Anglesey and in the coal-fields of Flintshire and Denbighshire, but although they were deposited over wider areas than those in which they are now preserved they are not likely to have encroached over more than the margins of St. George's Land. We cannot say for certain that the coal-forests never extended over our area but there is no evidence that they did.

History repeated itself during the Carboniferous Period because there were, from time to time, minor oscillations due to compressive movements—precursors of great disturbances which brought the Period to a close and determined the physical conditions of the one that followed. This new series of earth-movements is called Hercynian from the fine manifestation of its results in the Harz Mountains. The drive came, as before, from the south, but having lost most of its force before

PLATE 7

John Markham

LLYN OGWEN and the head of Nant Ffrancon from the lower slopes of Tryfan. April

PLATE 8

a. LLYN-Y-CWN above the Devil's Kitchen. July

John Markham

b. CWM IDWAL, Llyn Idwal and the Devil's Kitchen. July

John Markham

it reached our area its effects were small and are not easy to recognize.

As a result of the Hercynian movements continental conditions, tending to desert-like scenery and an arid climate, prevailed over much of the British region for a long time. It is interesting to note that arid conditions prevailed on the land uplifted as a result of the earlier Caledonian movements, and that the Old Red Sandstone then deposited has much in common with the marls, sandstones, and conglomerates (also usually red) that accumulated on the lands resulting from the Hercynian movements and that constitute the Trias or New Red Sandstone.

During Triassic times our area continued to be a land region undergoing denudation and it provided material for the building up of the Triassic strata (red marls and sandstones of lacustrine or aeolian origin) that now occupy so much of the Cheshire plain and the Midlands of England. Similar deposits were, no doubt, formed in our area also, but they have since been completely worn away. This does not, however, mean that we can dismiss the Period as of no interest to us, because some of the problems relating to the age of the mountains, as we see them, depend for their solution upon our views concerning the extent to which Triassic deposits accumulated in our area, and the length of time they remained.

During the Jurassic Period many kinds of clay, shale, and limestone (including the Oolites, some of which like the Bath stone and the Portland stone are well-known building stones) were laid down in comparatively shallow water that covered much of England, but Wales remained a land region except during the early part of the period, when the sea covered the southern part of Glamorgan and received the sediments which built up the shales and limestones (Lower Lias) that are well displayed in the wall-like cliffs that overlook this part of the Bristol Channel. The nearest Liassic deposits to our area are some clays near Prees in the north of Shropshire, but since they show no signs of having been deposited near a shore-line they suggest that the Liassic sea extended considerably farther west. Where the shore-line was we do not know but it is probable that our area was then the northern part of a peninsula that projected eastwards into a sea that covered England.

Subsidence became more general during the Cretaceous Period, and Britain, in common with a much larger surrounding area, sank beneath a sea in which, eventually, the white Chalk accumulated.

The Chalk is a limestone and some parts of it contain so little non-calcareous material that they must have been deposited out of reach of ordinary land-derived sediments. This means that the sea must have been extensive, although not necessarily deep as was once supposed. For a discussion of the problems relating to the origin of the Chalk reference must be made to geological text books; our interest in the rock, paradoxical as that may seem, lies in the fact that it does not now occur in our area.

The Chalk outcrops of the British region are confined to the south and east of England, north-eastern Ireland, and the west of Scotland: it is, however, highly probable that the Cretaceous Sea covered the greater part of Wales (Fig. 15, p. 71). The highest mountain regions may perhaps have remained as islands, but it is likely that for a time even these were completely submerged.

Where the outcrops of the Chalk end off in England, the beds are tilted towards the east or the south-east, and although the general inclination or dip is small, it is sufficient to carry a line representing the base of the deposit over the tops of the Welsh mountains; this suggests that the Chalk and therefore the sea in which it was deposited may, indeed, have covered the whole of the area.

We have no proof that such was the case: the most we can say is that there is no evidence to show that there never was such a cover and that certain present features can be best explained if we admit that there was. We cannot afford space to discuss this interesting problem in detail, but whether North Wales was completely or only partially submerged beneath the Chalk sea, the present height of its surface is indicative of considerable upward movement.

The Cretaceous Period, and with it the Mesozoic Era, came to an end when this new uplift began, and the next rocks to be formed in Britain belong to the Eocene Period of the Tertiary Era—but the Tertiary Era is, for our present purpose, another Unrecorded Age, for if any Tertiary rocks were laid down over our area they have long since been denuded away. The available evidence, which is mostly of a negative kind, suggests that, except perhaps towards its close, when early Pliocene deposits may have been laid down over Anglesey and in what are now the coastal regions of the mainland, the Tertiary Era was one of uplift and denudation. It was an important Era in the history of Snowdonia because it saw the development of the mountains, as we know them, from the materials that had been accumulating during so many millions of years. By late Pliocene times—just before the commencement of the Ice Age—the prolonged denudation had given rise to a land surface that, although differing greatly in detail from that with which we are familiar, would have been recognizable in its major features.

A striking characteristic of the river valleys of our area is that their general pattern seems to be unrelated to the geological structure of the country. The great passes and the valleys leading to them—Nant Ffrancon and the Pass of Llanberis, the valleys of the Gwyrfai and the Llugwy—cut across the grain of the country, most of them with rivers flowing in a direction opposite to the prevailing dip of the strata: they pass over or cut through hard and soft rocks alike, and do not, as one might have expected, follow very irregular courses in efforts to keep to strata of more or less equal resistance to erosion.

Some streams, especially the smaller tributaries, do indeed conform to the geological structure, as do those of Anglesey and Arfon—the country between the mountains and the Menai Straits—but the dominant elements of the river system do not. The latter give the impression that they were developed independently of the geological structure of the rocks that now form the surface of the land, and if that is a correct interpretation of the evidence, the only way in which we can explain the phenomenon is by supposing that the drainage originated on the surface of rocks in which the structures that characterize the existing rocks were not developed—that is, on a surface of which no trace now remains because the rocks which provided it have been completely denuded away. In other words—in the language of physical geology—we are confronted with an example of superimposed drainage, or drainage initiated upon and having its general pattern determined by rocks that do not now exist, and that, as those rocks were worn away, was superimposed upon others with different structures. In such circumstances the older rocks and their structures began to assert themselves as soon as denudation proceeded sufficiently to expose them, but although the original drainage pattern may have been modified as to detail, its main features have not been obliterated.

This brings us back to the hypothetical covering of Chalk, for, had the old folded rocks of our area been covered by layers of more or less homogeneous material when the region was uplifted to form the central part of an elliptical dome, the conditions would have been just those required to explain the phenomenon we are considering. Radial valleys would tend to develop on such a surface and to be so deeply cut when their floors reached the older rocks beneath that the rivers flowing in them would be compelled to continue in their original courses; they would be so well established in those courses by the time the newer rocks had been completely worn away that adaptation to the outcrops and structures of the older rocks could take place very slowly if at all.

It is true that the subaerial denudation to which the older rocks of Wales had been subjected during the Mesozoic Era must have produced a fairly even surface over most of the land, and had such a surface been uplifted to form a dome the drainage is likely at first to have been radial; but the varying effects of harder and softer rocks would have been manifest from the beginning, and as the drainage developed it would have become more and more closely related to the geological structures and the radial pattern would have been destroyed. In our area, however, the radial pattern was well established before the rocks that make the present surface began to affect it, and that seems to confirm the view that a blanket of more or less homogeneous material once overspread the area and has been worn away.

There are minor diversions of the radial pattern, some of them determined by the outcrops of softer and more easily eroded rocks, and others by the abnormal conditions of the Ice Age to which we have yet to refer, but there are also major diversions that are related to certain important structural features of the region.

The effect of outcrops of relatively soft sedimentary rocks and of the scouring action of the ice are seen in the NE.-SW. trending valleys that have determined the position of the Menai Straits, in the main drainage pattern of Anglesey and the coastal fringe of the mainland between Bangor and Caernarvon. The valleys in the latter region trend parallel to the Straits and were sufficiently well defined after the retreat of the ice to have prevented what is now the River Seiont from following a direct course to the sea, compelling it, instead, to swing to the left in the direction of Caernarvon. But for this the road from the Pass of Llanberis, and later the railway, would have reached the sea in the neighbourhood of Port Dinorwic, instead of, as now, making for Caernarvon. The slate railway from the quarries at Llanberis follows a more direct course, keeping close to the 300-foot contour until within a short distance of the sea at Port Dinorwic (from Dinnorddwig, the stronghold of the Ordovices).

A major interruption of the radial pattern is the curved depression that, as we have seen (Fig. 1, p. 5), separates our area from the rest of North Wales, and, reaching the sea near Portmadoc, is continued for many miles as a depression of the sea-floor, over twenty fathoms deep, opposite the end of Llŷn.

That this great valley-arc is not merely an accidental feature is shown by the fact that another curved depression, parallel to it, runs from the Mawddach estuary by way of Bala Lake, the upper part of the valley of the Dee, and the Vale of Clwyd. For a considerable part of its length the floor of this depression is less than 400 feet above sea level and its highest point rises only to 900 feet. Between the two concentric depressions the radial pattern of the drainage again becomes apparent.

In a paper dealing with the rivers of Wales and their connection with the Thames, Philip Lake pointed out that these and other concentrically arranged valleys farther afield in Wales constitute a single series. "In a dome built by man," he wrote, "the joints between the stones or bricks are all planes of weakness whether they run radially or transversely. If the abutments yield so that the dome begins to collapse . . . there is a tendency for roughly concentric fractures to form, and in general the strip on the inner side of a fracture sinks farther than the strip on its outer side."

If we apply this reasoning to the rising dome centred about Snowdonia, we can envisage a radial system of rivers developing upon it, the partial collapse of the dome resulting in part of it sinking beneath the sea and the subsidence of the remainder in concentrically arranged strips. The positions of the concentric fractures were, no doubt, in part influenced by faults that had already affected the older rocks before they received their covering of chalk. When valleys developed along the lines of the concentric cracks, some of the radial streams, instead of continuing to flow towards the south-east (towards England) were deflected and made their way more directly to the sea. We thus arrive at a possible—indeed, a highly probable—explanation of the conditions indicated in the simplified contoured map (Fig. 1, p. 5).

However we may fill in the details of the picture we choose to envisage of the initiation of the present drainage, the essential feature is that the region was uplifted. The elevation was one of the effects of a new series of mountain-building movements—a great disturbance that has been called the Alpine Storm because it was responsible for the crumpling and elevation of the rocks from which the Alpine ranges have been carved. It was also responsible for other great mountains of the modern world, such as the Himalayas and the Andes. Britain lay too far away from the main European centre for its rocks to have been crumpled and uplifted to the same extent as were those in the Alpine areas, or those in Britain that had been affected by earth movements during previous mountain-building episodes, but the pressures were sufficient to throw the rocks of southern England into broad east-and-west-trending folds, seen, for example, in the structure of the Weald, and the Isles of Wight and Purbeck.

In our area the effects of the Alpine Storm are not easy to recognize on account of the much more intense distortions and displacements that had been produced by the earlier mountain-building movements, but we may be sure that there was renewed movement along some of the faults formed in earlier ages, and, as we have already seen, there were signs of igneous activity in the intrusion of the molten material that gave rise to some small but interesting dolerite dykes. The main British centre of vulcanicity associated with this mountain-building episode lay farther north—in Antrim and western Scotland.

The Tertiary Era is divided into four Periods, and the Tertiary rocks into four Series—Eocene (the oldest), Oligocene, Miocene and Pliocene. The names refer to the increasing proportion of animals and plants of modern types that are represented amongst the fossils which each Series has yielded. *Eocene* suggests the dawn of recent life, *Oligocene*, the occurrence of a small proportion of recent forms, *Miocene*, the occurrence of a minority of recent forms, *Pliocene*, a majority of recent forms, and *Pleistocene*, the name of the post-Tertiary epoch that includes the Ice Age, indicates that most of the fossils found in the relevant rocks belong to species characteristic of recent faunas.

It was at the dawn of the Eocene Period about sixty million years ago that the sea of Cretaceous times gave place to the land surface on which the present river system was initiated, and it was during the Miocene Period that the Alpine Storm took place. By late Pliocene times (some two or three million years ago) our area had assumed an aspect sufficiently like that which we see to-day to have been recognizable as a stage in the development of the present scenery. This is the first time in the history of the long series of submergences, elevations, and denudations that such had been the case. The resemblance would, however, have applied only to the general pattern of the coast line and the distribution of the mountain masses and the valleys which separated them. The forms of the masses would have seemed strange, for as yet there had been no Ice Age. The mountains were less craggy, the valleys were more sinuous, and it is unlikely that there were any lakes.

It transpires, therefore, that if this explanation of the even skyline we noticed when we first glanced at our area from across the Menai Straits is the correct one—that the mountains have been carved from an elevated mass with an originally even surface, then the mountains *as we know them* are, geologically speaking, comparatively recent. The *rocks of which they consist* were, indeed, formed and folded in very early epochs, but by the end of Mesozoic times the land surface for which they were responsible had been reduced to the condition of a featureless plateau, and probably covered by newer deposits, so that the *carving of the present mountains* was accomplished during the Tertiary Era.

Geologists have not always agreed upon this matter, for some have thought, and some still think, that the mountains may have been carved early in Mesozoic times and that, at the beginning of Tertiary times, the valleys were filled with Mesozoic strata; but no trace of such deposits has been found in our area. It is certain that the valleys did not exist as *hollows* in early Tertiary times, and if they were not filled with Mesozoic deposits the only other explanation is that they had not by then been carved out—that the conditions were those suggested in the diagram (Fig. 17G, p. 86).

Evidence in support of this view comes from an unexpected source and illustrates the importance of what may at first appear to be trivial observations. We have referred to the existence of dolerite dykes of Tertiary age, so insignificant in bulk when compared with the more ancient volcanic rocks into which they were intruded as to appear scarcely worth mentioning—but they have a very important bearing upon the problem in hand. Such dykes, trending NW.-SE., were recorded by Greenly in Anglesey nearly thirty years ago, and more recently David Williams discovered others in our area, trending in a similar direction, and making, with those across the Menai Straits, a series extending intermittently over more than twelve miles and undoubtedly constituting one volcanic unit.

In Anglesey the outcrops of the dykes are at somewhat low levels (between 200 and 300 feet) and those near the Menai Straits are not much higher (around 300 feet), but one in the Penrhyn Quarry reaches 1,200 feet above sea level, and others at near Marchlyn Mawr and

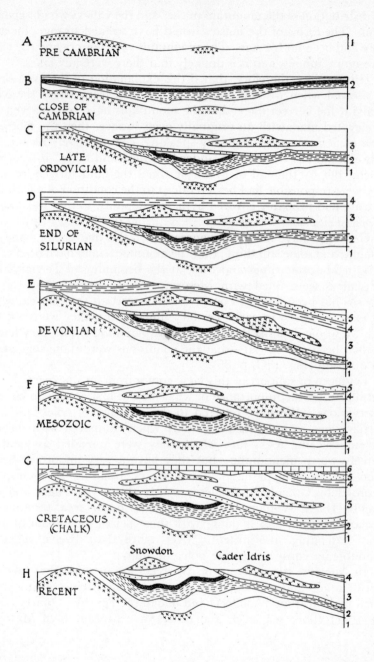

A   PRE CAMBRIAN

B   CLOSE OF
    CAMBRIAN

C   LATE
    ORDOVICIAN

D   END OF
    SILURIAN

E   DEVONIAN

F   MESOZOIC

G   CRETACEOUS
    (CHALK)

Snowdon   Cader Idris

H   RECENT

Bwlch-y-cywion, in the mountain tract between Nant Ffrancon and the Llanberis lakes, outcrop at 2,400 feet and 2,500 feet respectively. Greenly has pointed out that, for the molten matter to have retained its character and to have consolidated in dykes, there must have been a considerable rock cover that does not now exist, and such a cover, to the extent of about 1,000 feet, is available if we regard Marchlyn cwm and the surrounding ridges as having been carved from a mass of which relics are seen in Y Glyder Fawr and the Carneddau on the opposite side of Nant Ffrancon—all of them well over 3,000 feet and the latter rising nearly to 3,500 feet. Had the present relations between Anglesey and Snowdonia obtained when the molten material was injected it would have reached the surface in the areas of low ground long before it could have risen high enough to form the dykes at Marchlyn and Bwlch-y-cywion, and extrusive volcanic phenomena— outpourings of lava—would have manifested themselves. In other words, the similarity between the dykes of Anglesey and Arfon on the one hand and those of Marchlyn and Bwlch-y-cywion on the other suggests that at the time of the intrusion the land surface was, to quote Greenly, "little, if any, higher over the site of Snowdonia than it was over the site of Anglesey." If this is the case it follows that the mountain region was uplifted and the valleys carved out after this series of dolerite dykes was formed, and comparison with other areas of Tertiary vulcanicity in this country suggests that they were intruded in early Tertiary times—during the Eocene period.

Any attempt to present briefly a clear word-picture of the nature, sequence, and results of events in earth-history that were spread over a very long period of time necessarily involves a considerable degree of generalization, even at the expense of omitting important and interesting details. We have, in this chapter, envisaged the uplifting of our area and the production by denudation of a fairly level plateau from which the present mountains have been carved, but all that took a very long time and the changes did not proceed always at a uniform

FIG. 17.—The geological history of Snowdonia

Sections illustrating some stages in the formation of the rocks of Snowdonia, and the effects of folding and denudation in producing the mountains of today. (In part after W. G. Fearnsides.) The geological Systems represented are 1, Pre-Cambrian. 2, Cambrian. 3, Ordovician. 4, Silurian. 5, Devonian (Old Red Sandstone). 6, Cretaceous (Chalk).

rate; there were periods when the uplift took place more slowly than at others, and occasions when it may have ceased altogether or have been replaced by movement in the opposite direction.

Before the story can be told in full there must be much more study in the field as well as a much clearer understanding of the information we already have; but even the incomplete story now available is too long and too detailed to be included here without upsetting the balance of the book, and the matter has been mentioned only because the discontinuity of the uplift has affected the activities of man within the area.

From suitable viewpoints in and around Snowdonia one sees extensive areas over which the hills end off at similar levels irrespective of the nature of the rocks from which they have been carved. These comparatively even surfaces, now of course discontinuous, appear to be relics of platforms of erosion produced during what might be called resting-stages in the uplift and, in addition to the well-marked platform in the coastal regions that is regarded as of Pliocene age, others can be recognized at elevations of about 1,000 feet, 1,250 feet and 2,000 feet. In certain circumstances fairly level regions at moderate elevations would have provided good grazing for mountain sheep, but the rainfall and the rocks in Snowdonia are such that the drainage is poorer on the upland levels than on many of the slopes, and peat bogs rather than pastures have been produced.

3. THE ICE AGE

A frozen continent
Lies dark and wild, beat with perpetual storms
Of whirlwind and dire hail, which on firm land
Thaws not, but gathers heap, and ruin seems
Of ancient pile ; or else deep snow and ice.
. . . the parching air
Burns frore, and cold performs the effects of fire.

John Milton, *Paradise Lost*, Book II

Although much shorter than those which preceded it, the Tertiary Era lasted for more than sixty million years, so that there was ample time for the uplift of the dome we have postulated, as well as for the complete removal of any covering of Chalk that it may once have supported.

The Tertiary strata preserved in various parts of England indicate that, as in earlier eras, there were oscillations leading to changes from marine to dry-land conditions and back to marine again, but our area seems to have been dry land during nearly the whole of the time, and denudation so far exceeded deposition that no sedimentary rocks of Tertiary age, have been preserved; even if we could afford the space we could add very little to the brief conjectural summary, already given, of what took place between the emergence from the Cretaceous sea and the partial submergence at the beginning of Pliocene times.

As the Tertiary Era drew to a close our area shared in a downward movement that affected the country as a whole; the sea encroached upon the land and in North Wales eventually reached a shore line some miles inland from the present one. Its position is now marked by the rather sudden change from the undulating agricultural country that fringes the Caernarvonshire coast to the steeper and more rugged slopes of the mountain masses. It was cut largely in the relatively soft Ordovician shales and mudstones that were outside the regions of vulcanicity and of slate-formation, and it would no doubt have extended farther inland, perhaps over the whole county, making it like Anglesey or Pembrokeshire to-day, had the outcrops of the softer rocks been more extensive and the relative levels of land and sea been maintained for a longer period.

As the sea occupied this coastal strip it levelled off the old land surface, producing a characteristic "plain of marine denudation," and then, when elevation once more set in and the sea retreated—this time to a coast-line even farther out than our present one—the mountainous region was left rising somewhat abruptly from an extensive and almost level plain stretching away in northerly and westerly directions.

The magnitude of the up-and-down movements was much less than in the case of those which had affected the area in former times, because a large part of the planed-off surface—of which Anglesey and its continuation in the coastal fringe of the mainland are relics—stands at an average elevation of only 270 feet. There are also traces of other "platforms" that may indicate movement to the extent of at least 600 feet, but even that is inconsiderable when compared with the thousands of feet in which the movements of earlier ages must be measured.

These later oscillations brought about marked changes in the position of the local coast-line but their effects upon the inland regions are too slight to be discussed in a general account like this. We are, however, interested in one of the factors that accompanied them and probably had something to do with bringing them about, and that is the development of conditions that allowed snow and ice to accumulate to such an extent that for a time a large part of our country must have been a snowy waste broken only by the tops of the highest mountains. The period during which these conditions obtained was the Ice Age or Glacial Period (the Pleistocene Period of geological nomenclature) which began about a million years ago and saw the initiation of the cwms with their steep enclosing cliffs and narrow bounding ridges, and the formation of the hummocky spreads of stone-laden clay as well as many other features that contribute to the "personality" of our area.

Although the Glacial Period was so short compared with the preceding subdivisions of geological time, its story can be told in more detail because, being more recent, it has left many tangible traces of its existence; but for our purpose a general picture must suffice.

In common with a large part of northern Europe and north America, Britain during the Pleistocene period experienced a climate so cold that the summers were not warm enough to melt the winter snows, and these accumulated to such an extent that, for a long time, conditions like those now obtaining in Greenland must have prevailed over enormous areas. In North Wales the weight of snow that gathered on the higher ground eventually became sufficient to compress the lower layers until they became compact ice which tended to flow slowly away in all directions.

It was a time when, to alter the tense of a passage in one of Michael Roberts's poems (*The Secret Springs*),

> the green glacier ice
> Moved down like history, or like the huge
> Slow movement of a nation's mind.

It moved down the valleys, pushing farther, growing thicker, and coalescing on the coastal plains to form an extensive ice sheet. The margin of that sheet moved towards the Irish sea and extended into Cardigan Bay on the one side, whilst eastwards it spread towards the low ground of Cheshire and Shropshire. The largest glaciers were those in the Ogwen and Llanberis valleys. The former was over 1,000 feet thick between Carnedd Ddafydd and Y Glyder Fawr, thinning to 800 feet in the vicinity of Bethesda.

For a time each of the higher regions in Wales had its own part to play as a centre of ice accumulation and distribution. No less than six glaciers, for example, radiated from Snowdon: two of them, coming from Cwm-glas-mawr and Cwm-glas-bach, fed the glacier which moved down the Pass of Llanberis; two others coming from Cwm-y-llan and Cwm Dyli joined the Nant Gwynant glacier, whilst those originating in Cwm Brwynog and Cwm Clogwyn flowed westwards to an undetermined extent.

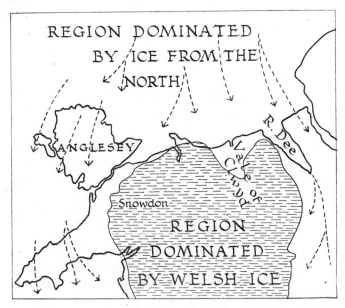

FIG. 18.—The spheres of influence of the ice that originated in Wales and of that which reached Wales from the north

(After Geological Survey)

When the glaciation was at its maximum the area as a whole was also affected by ice which came from the north and travelled across the Irish Sea (Fig. 18). On meeting the main Welsh ice the Irish Sea ice divided; one tongue made its way across Anglesey and Llŷn, thus preventing the glaciers of the Snowdonian valleys from continuing very far on their way across the low-lying ground to the north-west. All the indications of glacial activity in Anglesey extend in a north-easterly/south-westerly direction, which is at right angles to those seen in the Snowdonian valleys that open out towards the island. It was ice moving from the north-east that deepened the valleys which, when more normal conditions of climate and level again prevailed, became the Menai Straits. The other part of the Irish Sea ice invaded the Cheshire plain, leaving traces of its movement on some of the hills in north-eastern Wales.

A rather surprising indication of the passage of ice across the Irish Sea into our area is the presence on the slopes of Moel Tryfan near Nantlle, at heights of over 1,400 feet above sea level, of sands and gravels containing marine shells (Fig. 19). These represent masses of

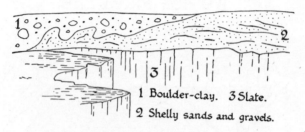

1 Boulder-clay.   3 Slate.
2 Shelly sands and gravels.

FIG. 19.—Glacial deposits on Moel Tryfan

Section illustrating the occurrence (at about 1,400 feet above sea level) of shelly
gravels carried by ice from the floor of the Irish Sea
(After A. C. Ramsay)

a frozen sea-floor scraped up as the ice travelled across the Irish Sea, and, impelled by the well-nigh irresistible force behind it, moved over the rising ground that lay in its way.

It was at one time thought that this and similar deposits were beaches formed during a period of submergence, but that would have involved a depression of about 1,500 feet, and although we have seen our area raised and depressed through much greater distances than that, we cannot regard as possible a movement of that magnitude as recently as in the Glacial Period. Had there been such movement there would have been much more tangible evidence of its occurrence than these relatively small patches of gravel. That the deposits cannot represent material normally laid down upon the sea-floor is indicated by the fact that the shells include kinds that lived in different depths of water—they could not all have existed together; besides, many of them are badly crushed. That ice from the north moved over the places where the gravel occurs is indicated by the fact that at Moel Tryfan the shelly beds were found to be overlain by clay containing boulders brought from Cumberland and Scotland.

The Ice Age, like earlier periods we have considered, had one outstanding characteristic, but, also like them, it was not a time when conditions were monotonously uniform. The formation of the ancient geosyncline was the result of subsidence, but the downward movement was not continuous and did not take place all the time and everywhere at the same rate; sometimes it stopped or was replaced by a movement in the opposite direction: the Ordovician was a period of vulcanicity, but the centres of activity shifted from time to time, and the violence and the products of the eruptions were subject to continual change: so with the Ice Age—it was not a single period of gradually increasing cold and gradually extending ice sheets and glaciers, followed by an equally gradual amelioration of the climate and disappearance of the ice. The cold waxed and waned—the glaciers advanced and retreated —and it was most likely during the second of four distinct glaciations recognized as having affected the Alps and northern Europe that the mountainous regions of Britain, including our area, began to develop their own ice caps and glaciers.

The effects of one advance by the ice were often obscured or obliterated by those of the next. Only the more normal processes of erosion operated during the warmer intervals between the cold periods, and those intervals were longer—one of them many times longer—than the whole of post-glacial time. The result is that the sequence of events is often difficult to trace and we must be content to note the evidences of ice action in our area, without enquiring closely into the chronology.

The general shape and form of the Snowdonian region had, as we have seen, been determined by the end of Pliocene times, before the coming of the ice, but when milder climatic conditions came to stay at the close of Pleistocene times and the ice melted away, many new features had been introduced: minor in a geological sense, those features would have been very striking to a human observer (had there been one) familiar with the earlier scene. Valleys which had previously been curving and V-shaped had become straight and U-shaped like Nant Ffrancon to-day, because the stone-laden glaciers had worn away the overlapping spurs, and, acting like gigantic rasps, had cleared away the soil and weathered rock (Pl. IV, p. 11; Fig. 20, p. 94). Although usually described as U-shaped, the section of a glaciated

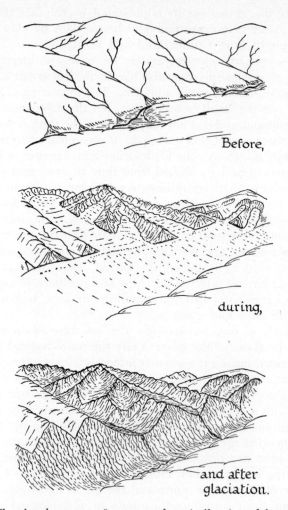

Before,

during,

and after
glaciation.

Fig. 20.—The development of cwms, arêtes (cribau) and hanging valleys
as a result of glaciation
(After W. M. Davis)

valley is, in fact, U-shaped only in its lower part, for glaciers do not
usually completely fill the valleys down which they move, and above
the limbs of the U the slopes are parts of the V-section that characterizes
valleys produced by river action.

Most of the main valleys in our area exhibit glacier-formed features in a greater or lesser degree, and it is largely to their straight and open character that we owe the fine glimpses we so often get of the profiles of the principal peaks—Moel Siabod from the lower end of Nant Gwynant near Beddgelert, Snowdon from Pen-y-groes where the straight and open Llyfni valley leaves the mountains, the pyramidal Moel Hebog from Llyn Dinas, and many others that are even better known.

The characteristics of a glaciated valley are well illustrated in Nant Ffrancon, especially when it is viewed from the flanks of Y Glyder Fawr (Fig. 21, p. 96). The valley lies wide open and straight all the way to Bethesda and its almost level floor is divided into irregular fields and unenclosed peaty patches; its cross-section is U-shaped at the bottom, merging into more normal valley slopes above, and often ending in steep bare crags. It is not surprising to learn that it was largely in this valley and in the cwm occupied by Llyn Idwal above that some of the early geologists saw the signs that first led them to recognize that Britain had once endured an Ice Age. Such a valley contrasts strangely with one that has not been occupied by a glacier —one in which the view is limited by the spurs which project alternately from either side as the river winds, and changes continually as one goes up or down the valley.

The tributary valleys on the south-western side of Nant Ffrancon have floors that at first are relatively steep so that the streams flow rapidly and give rise to picturesque but small cascades, but the valleys seem to come to an end at the edge of the U-shaped section of the main valley, leaving the streams to plunge over that edge or to flow in gorge-like notches cut into it as they make their way down the steep slopes that lead to the level floor of the valley in which the Ogwen flows, some 600 feet below.

Valleys like these, which end off in the air as it were, are called *hanging valleys* They are characteristic of, although not confined to, glaciated areas, in which they owe their origin to the fact that the ice in the main valley was much thicker than in the smaller side valleys; the greater weight of the glacier due to its greater thickness gave it greater eroding power, so that it was able to lower its valley more rapidly than its tributaries could lower theirs.

Hanging valleys are well displayed on the south side of Nantlle valley where they have been cut into the flanks of the mountains

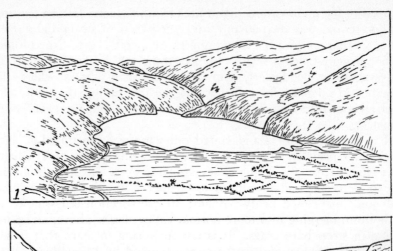

stretching from Y Garn to Carnedd Goch. Others, like that which comes from Cwm Du on the northern side of Mynydd Mawr, enter the Gwyrfai valley. Another striking example is seen in the descent from Cwm-y-llan to the Gwynant valley: the great hollow of the cwm breaks the continuity of the hills on the north-eastern side of the valley and affords a glimpse of Snowdon, with the smooth south-western slopes of Lliwedd (so different from the precipitous face overlooking Llyn Llydaw) on the right, and Yr Aran on the left (Pl. 11, p. 142).

The steep descent to the main valley is often characterized by a series of cascades, or, if circumstances have concentrated the effects of erosion in one or a few places, by large single waterfalls. The well-known waterfall (in Ceunant Mawr, the Big Ravine) to be seen from the Snowdon railway about half a mile from Llanberis, occurs where the River Arddu is cutting a little ravine at the end of a hanging valley. It does not, of course, follow that all the waterfalls in our area occur where tributary streams "hang" into glaciated valleys. Those above Aber, for example, occur where a river (Afon Goch) falls over the edge of the hard igneous mass of Y Foel Fras, which has resisted erosion to a greater extent than the softer shales into which it had been intruded.

Most of the valleys in glaciated areas begin in steep-sided amphitheatre-like hollows that are amongst the most characteristic features of such areas, and make the mountains look as if some mighty mechanical excavators had been at work upon them, scooping them away. In Scotland such a feature is called a *corrie* (Gaelic spelling, *coire*), in France a *cirque*, and in North Wales a *cwm*, although cwm is also loosely used for valleys in general. If the name "cwm" corresponds with the Anglo-Saxon *comb* or *cumb*, meaning the upper part of a valley, and with the Irish *cum*, meaning a valley enclosed, except on one side, by mountains, it would be convenient to regard it as relating especially to the kind of feature with which the name is associated in Snowdonia, thus avoiding the use of a non-Welsh term. Support for this attitude

---

FIG. 21.— Effects of the passage of glaciers down some Snowdonian valleys

In Nant Ffrancon (3), most of which traverses Ordovician sediments, the overlapping spurs of the pre-glacial valley have been almost completely removed ; they are still obvious in the Llanberis valley (2) which crosses considerable outcrops of Ordovician volcanic rocks and Cambrian grits, whilst Nant Gwynant (1), which crosses irregular and extensive outcrops of igneous rock, retains more of its original character.

comes from Jonathan Otley's *Concise description of the English lakes and adjacent mountains*, a standard early-nineteenth-century work on the Lake District. In a section entitled "Explanatory Provincial Terms" (e.g. in the fifth edition, 1834) we read that "Coom denotes a place scooped out of the side of a mountain," and it would be difficult indeed to devise a more apt definition for a Snowdonian cwm. The word has been used for many years by geographers, both Welsh and English, in this sense, with an English plural form, *cwms*, and even at the risk of appearing inconsistent (having used the Welsh plural form in other cases) it seems desirable when writing in English to use cwms instead of the Welsh plural form, *cymau* or *cymoedd*.

A cwm (using the word in its geographical sense) differs from a normal valley-head in having much steeper sides and a rounded or roughly quadrangular outline. A normal valley-head is a V-shaped trough with a sloping floor, but a cwm has been likened to an armchair with a slightly hollowed-out seat. Many cwms are occupied by lakes, e.g., Llyn Idwal, Llyn Du'r Arddu, Marchlyn Mawr (under Elidir Fawr), and Llyn Dulyn (south of Y Foel Fras), which are amongst the most striking features of our area; they are certainly the loneliest and, especially when the hollows that contain them are half obscured by rolling mist, the most awe-inspiring.

There is not complete agreement as to the origin of cwms, but an explanation that finds favour, and that it seems reasonable to apply in our area, is that they are valley-heads which once harboured small glaciers. In such circumstances, where snow and ice are banked against steep slopes, there is a tendency for a crack or crevasse (the alpine Bergschrund) to develop a few feet away from the rock-face as the movement of the ice carries the main mass away from that which is frozen to the rock behind. Such cracks tend to be inclined towards the rock wall, meeting it some distance below the surface of the ice. As a result the rock is exposed to the disintegrating effects of the ice that is produced when melt-water makes its way into cracks and then freezes. In this way masses of rock are dislodged, get frozen into the ice of the cwm-glacier, and are dragged away from the rock wall. The latter is thus made and maintained steep and the glacier becomes charged with angular blocks of stone. Those which become embedded in the base of the ice cause it to act as an abrasive, excavating a shallow basin in the floor of the cwm to provide the nucleus of a lake.

When improving climatic conditions caused the Snowdonian

PLATE IX

Dr. A. O. English

SNOWDON from Moel Siabod: an infra-red photograph showing the cwms and the ridges separating them. Llyn Llydaw is the small dark patch near the centre of the mass

PLATE X

a. Snowdon and Llyn Llydaw: beneath the top, which consists of volcanic ash, the valley of Cwm Glas Llyn runs down to the lake, its lower slopes showing the characteristic hummocky outlines of moraines

b. Glacial topography near the mouth of Cwm Dyli (below Llyn Llydaw): two prominent *roches moutonnées* are surrounded by mounds of boulder clay with scattered "erratics" on their surface. The shoulder of Tal-y-llyn rises on the left; on the right is Moel Siabod

TOPOGRAPHY OF SNOWDON

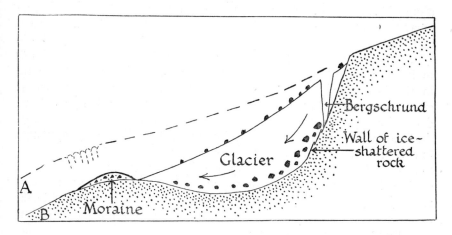

FIG. 22.—A cwm (or corrie) glacier

Diagrammatic section through a cwm showing (A), the surface of the glacier when
at its maximum, with crevasses where a steeper slope begins, and (B), a late stage
in the retreat of the glacier, with a moraine forming at the lip of the cwm. (After
W. B. Wright)

glaciers to disappear from the lower ground, shrunken remnants of
them remained in the cwms, especially those which faced northwards
or eastwards, and the rock debris which slid over the surface of the ice
from the frost shattered crags above, and that which was deposited at
the front of the glacier as it melted, often built up a small ridge or
moraine across the mouth of a cwm, producing a hollow or making
deeper one that had already been excavated in the rock floor. Since the
ice of glaciers tends to move more rapidly in the middle than at the
sides the lower end of a glacier is convex and its terminal moraine is
in consequence usually crescent-shaped.

Moraines of this nature are to be seen in the lonely Cwm-glas-mawr
above the Pass of Llanberis, where the various results of glacial action
are extremely well displayed, and in Cwm Graeanog (Graianog on the
O.S. maps). In the latter the small but symmetrical crescent-shaped
moraine lies at its mouth, overlooking Nant Ffrancon. The floor of the
valley above the moraine is covered with loose blocks and stones from
which a great deal of the finer debris has been washed away, so that
the cwm is well called *graeanog*, meaning gravelly. In Cwm Idwal
there are some moraines, now four grassy ridges, which were formed

along the side of a glacier as it gradually but not continuously shrank
away from the sides of the cwm. They were first described by Darwin
in 1842.

As the ice finally disappeared from a cwm any stones then remaining
in it were spread upon the floor and water tended to accumulate
in the hollow behind the terminal moraine, forming a more or less
circular or oval lake; some of them still remain whilst others have
drained away leaving marsh or bog in their places.

Since valleys originating on a dome tend to radiate from a central
line or point, several cwms may develop on one mountain mass—
Snowdon, for example, has six, an excellent picture of which is given
on hill-shaded or hachured maps, e.g., Pl. XXXIIa, p. 379: then,
as the precipices that form their heads are cut farther and farther back,
more and more of the original surface of the mountain disappears. In
the case of Mynydd Mawr, for example, with its hard massive igneous
rock, the cwms, including even the impressive Cwm Du on the northern
face, do not materially alter the rounded profile of the mountain, but
the extent of the little that sometimes remains is illustrated in Fig. 23,
which shows the north-western spur of Snowdon as seen from Moel-y-
cynghorion, with Cwm Du'r Arddu on the left and Cwm Clogwyn on
the right.

The surviving surface is still narrower on the ridge separating Cwm
Dwyfawr from those overlooking the Nantlle valley and culminating
in Mynydd Tal-y-mignedd[1] (Fig. 23). It is actually breached in one
place as if it were on the way towards becoming a sharp ridge like
those of Crib Goch or Lliwedd, where the walls of two cwms have
intersected giving rise to a sharp-edged serrated ridge of bare rock.

Such ridges are characteristic of glaciated mountains. A Welsh
name for them is *crib* (plural *cribau*), and those in our area differ only
in magnitude from the *arêtes* of the Alps. They are often unsymmetrical
because the slope tends to be steeper on the shady side than on that
which receives most sun and on which the action of the ice was neither
so severe nor so long continued. From their mode of origin, arêtes tend
to converge on one another, and to rise towards the culminating peak
of the mountain of which they are parts, giving it a characteristic
pyramidal outline. It is to the fully developed or potential arêtes that
we owe the ridge-walks which, for many people, are a main attraction
of our area. The higher parts of Moel Siabod afford fine views of some

---

[1] *Mignedd*, bogs or quagmires.

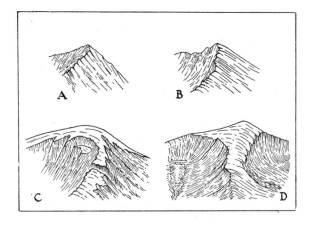

FIG. 23.—The development of arêtes (cribau),

as cwms are cut more and more deeply into originally rounded mountains.
A, Crib Goch ; B, Lliwedd ; C, the ridge leading to Mynydd Drws-y-coed near
Nantlle; D, ridge between Cwm Du'r Arddu and Cwm Clogwyn seen from Moel-y-
Cynghorion. In C the grass-covered ridge has been breached at one point.
(After W. M. Davis)

of the cwms and cribau of Snowdon—views that encourage one to
replace in imagination what erosion has removed, and to restore the
rounded contours of the pre-glacial mountain (see Pl. IX, p. 98).

Carnedd Ddafydd and Carnedd Llywelyn also have their cwms
overlooked by impressive cliffs which converge on one another. Carnedd
Llywelyn has four, Cwm Eigiau and Cwm Llugwy on the south-east
and Cwm Gaseg and Cwm Llafar on the north-west. The last-named,
which also might be regarded as belonging to Carnedd Ddafydd, is
the largest; it is a vast semi-circular hollow overlooked by dark crags
of dolerite. Here, too, the principal heights are connected by ridges
which grow narrower and sharper, from that connecting Y Foel Fras
with Y Foel Grach in the north, to that between Carnedd Ddafydd
and Carnedd Llywelyn in the south. These cwms and ridges are less
accessible and on that account less well-known than those in the more
southerly mountain tracts.

When the ice had gone from a cwm the steep rocky slope was still
subject to normal frost action and dislodged fragments of rock accumulated at the base of the cliffs, building screes that crept higher and
higher, masking and temporarily protecting the lower part of the cliff.

Scree formation is not, of course, confined to cwms; it takes place wherever steep cliffs of jointed rocks are exposed to weathering, but it is specially active where frost is frequently experienced. The sides of many of the rocky valleys of our area are more or less fringed with screes, which, being composed of loose angular material, and with their exposed faces as steep as Nature allows, are notoriously unstable, and may be dangerous to unwary climbers.

In its passage down the valleys and across the plains the ice picked up a great deal of material (soil and the disintegrated rock debris of the subsoil) from the surface over which it flowed, and masses of rock fell on to its surface from crags that it failed to cover. Then, if the end of a glacier remained stationary for a time, because the rate at which the ice moved forward was just balanced by the rate at which it melted, its burden of solid material was deposited either as a dam-like moraine stretching across the valley, or else in hummocks or ridges on the more open ground (Pl. X, p. 99).

When the ice finally melted, whether on the plains it had overspread or in the valleys amongst the mountains where it began its course, the gravel and fine rock-flour which had been produced as stones were rubbed one against another and dragged over the rocky floor, together with the stones that still remained unbroken and unground, were deposited to form a blanket of stony clay spread about in sheets, mounds, or in long sinuous ridges. This debris conceals the solid rocks beneath, and since it tends to be thicker in the hollows and to thin out over the hills, it gives rise to a surface less diversified than the one upon which it rests. The material so deposited (Boulder Clay) usually contains stones of all sizes, smoothed, but not completely rounded like the pebbles on a river or a beach; the stones are often covered with scratches and furrows made as, embedded in the ice, they were rubbed one against another or were dragged across the rock-floor over which the ice had been moving.

A collective name for all the ice-transported material, whether clayey or gravelly, is Drift, and a geological map depicting its distribution is described as a "Drift" map; one that is concerned only with the nature and distribution of the rocks that enter into the essential structure of the earth's crust, together with, perhaps, certain superficial deposits like the alluvium laid down by modern rivers and large tracts of modern peat, is called a "Solid" map.

Drift of one sort or another covers the greater part of our area, except ground above about 2,000 feet and crags and scarps too steep for loose deposits to remain upon them. This means that although the major features of the area are determined by the "solid" rocks, the nature of the soil (and, therefore, of the vegetation and the use man can make of the land) is largely dependent upon the Drift, and this may result in monotonously similar conditions extending over very large areas. Quite often the Drift, especially the Boulder Clay, gives rise to stiff, ill-drained soil that supports little more than coarse grasses and marsh plants.

Boulders and masses of rock carried by the ice were often dropped many miles from their place of origin. They are called "erratics" or "erratic boulders," and are sometimes precariously perched just where they fell off the edge of the glacier or were dumped as the ice melted away; they are then described as "perched blocks." If other signs were wanting perched blocks would be a sure indication of the former existence of moving ice, because they are so often situated in places to which they could not have rolled from the heights above owing to the undulating character of the surface, or in places such that, if they *had* rolled down, they could not have stopped where we find them, but would have bounded over into the valley below. Conspicuous perched blocks can be seen on the slopes above the Pass of Llanberis (Pl. XIc) and some others above the Idwal Slabs are well known to climbers.

The big rock called Maen Bras near the Ranger track belongs to this category, so too does Carreg Wen, a large whitish block on the top of a hill near Borth-y-gest (Pl. XIa. p. 106). The latter is a mass of Snowdonian agglomerate that must have travelled several miles in a southerly direction and have been carried over the elevated mass of dolerite that forms Moel-y-gest. Old pictures (e.g. Pl. XIb) suggest that perched blocks must once have been more numerous on the slopes than they are now: the temptation to set them rolling has probably been too great for their safety. Those which remain should be guarded as jealously as are the "ancient monuments" of man.

Masses of rock and boulders that have been transported by ice and deposited as "erratics" or entombed in the Boulder Clay often throw light upon the direction and extent of the movement of glaciers and ice sheets, for many rocks have distinctive characters by means of which the place of origin of isolated fragments can be determined within narrow limits.

Studies made (especially in recent years by Greenly) of the transported boulders in Arfon show, for example, that when the glaciers reached this belt of undulating lowland each was at first able to hold its own, for the blocks and boulders near the mouth of any one of the valleys are all of rock types that occur in it, but as one goes farther out over the coastal platform the local blocks become less numerous; their place is taken by rocks of extra-Welsh origin brought by the Irish Sea Ice, and they are rare by the time we reach the Menai Straits. The distance travelled has, as we should expect, affected their size and form, for large angular blocks predominate near the valley mouths, but smaller fragments with the edges and corners more or less rounded are found farther out on the coastal platform.

As another example of the interest and the intricacy of the glacial story we may note the contributions made to it by boulders of rock from the neighbourhood of Blaenau Ffestiniog that lie near the summits of Moel Llyfnant and Arenig Fawr. Such blocks indicate a time when those mountains, protruding from an ice sheet that covered all the neighbouring land below the present 2,000 foot contour line, were affected by an ice stream coming from the heart of Snowdonia. The retreat of the ice from this region was rapid in its initial stages because there is little morainic material on the slopes between 1,800 and 1,500 O.D. Below 1,500 feet, however, it becomes abundant again, but here the material is essentially of local origin, suggesting that the sphere of influence of the Caernarvonshire mountains had by then been considerably restricted. One of the moraines of this lower local series, lying on the north side of the Tryweryn valley, is almost as regular as a railway embankment.

Other striking indications of the former existence of glaciers in the valleys of our area are seen in smoothed rocky surfaces or "pavements" like that illustrated in Plate XII, p. 107, which lies by the side of the road near the lower end of Llyn Peris. They are parts of surfaces worn smooth by the passage of stone-laden ice and scored with furrows made by sharp fragments of hard rock pressed against them by the weight of hundreds of feet of ice. We have to remember that the sides and base of a glacier are not pure ice; they are studded with stones plucked from the side of the valley or that fell upon the surface and found their way down cracks until they reached the bottom. Here, the embedded stones, pressed heavily against the surface over which they moved, were gradually ground away. The finer debris thus produced allowed the base of the glacier to act like glass-paper on rough wood, rendering the rocks smooth and in some cases even polishing them. The larger fragments acted like the coarse teeth of a rasp and made deep scratches or furrows on the otherwise smooth rock surface. The "glaciated pavement" illustrated in Plate XII (p. 107) is one of the best and most easily accessible in Snowdonia. It is to be hoped that it will neither be defaced by tourists unaware of its interest, nor destroyed in response to a demand for a wider road.

Features due to the grinding effects of stones embedded in the ice are not confined to the bottoms of the valleys, and their occurrence high upon the sides of the flanking hills are amongst the proofs we have of the great thickness which many of the glaciers attained. About half way up the steep slope opposite Pont-y-gromlech in the Pass of Llanberis, for example, near the foot of the dark cliff formed by the dolerite sill illustrated in Pl. IV (p. 11), there are well-marked smooth furrows sloping gently in the same direction as the floor of the valley. They are indications of a time when a glacier had its sides heavily studded with stones at that level, with a sufficient thickness of ice above to have exerted the pressure necessary to make those stones score the cliffs that imprisoned the glacier.

Wherever such pavements are exposed in a valley the striae trend parallel to its sides because that is the direction in which the ice was moving. In open country, where the movement of the ice may have been influenced by a variety of causes, the striae provide a means for determining the direction in which the ice was travelling, and thus help to fill in the details of our picture of the conditions which then obtained. They tell us, for example, that while the glacier emerging from the Llanberis valley was pushed aside and deflected to the left by the Irish Sea ice, the larger Ogwen glacier was able to make its way as far as Llandegai near Bangor after the Irish Sea ice had disappeared.

Sometimes the smooth and striated rocks are conspicuously hummocky and look like reclining sheep, or like stretched-out wigs. At the end of the eighteenth century, H. B. de Saussure, a pioneer in mountain studies, gave the name *roches moutonnées* to rocks of this description, which he saw in Alpine valleys, on account of their resemblance to the moutonnées or sheepskin wigs of the time, but strangely enough he did not associate them with the movement of ice.

As the ice moved down a valley and rode over the hillocks and knobs that lay in its way, it smoothed the rocky faces that faced upstream, but on the downstream side it tended to pull away blocks that had

previously been loosened by weathering along joints. Consequently a
roche moutonnée is usually smooth on the side which faces up the valley
but tends to be rough and craggy on the side facing downwards. That
is why a glaciated valley—the Pass of Llanberis, for example—often
looks strikingly different according to whether one is going up or down.
Looking down the valley the scene is dominated by the smooth rounded
surfaces, but viewed in the other direction it still appears to preserve
much of its original ruggedness (Pl. IV). The lakes of our area also owe
their origin to the work of ice, but it will be convenient to discuss them
in another chapter.

The changes which have taken place since the close of the Ice Age
have, in the geological sense, been slight. Rivers have cut their way
into the loose superficial material that the retreating ice left on the
valley floors, and screes have grown at the foot of many a cliff. The
extensive sands of Traeth Bach and Traeth Mawr just east of Portmadoc, and the Lavan sands between Aber and Beaumaris, are an
indication of the extent to which the rivers have cleared away the
gravelly glacial debris. The completion of an embankment across the
entrance to Traeth Mawr, a project conceived by Sir John Wynn of
Gwydir in the time of James I, and eventually carried out by Mr.
W. A. Madocks, M.P., in 1815, converted what must have been a
beautiful estuary—and at high tide a mirror for the mountains—into
a tract of poor meadowland reaching nearly as far as Pont Aberglaslyn.

There have been small changes of level since man came into the
area. The net result has been a slight subsidence, sufficient to have
submerged certain low-lying coastal regions and to have converted
Anglesey into an island; this it did by drowning two NE/SW. trending
valleys that follow the "strike" of the rocks and that had, no doubt,
been deepened as the Irish Sea ice moved towards the south-west.
Indications of this change of level are to be seen in the submerged land
surfaces that occur here and there between tide marks. Some of the
clays exposed on the foreshore are associated with beds of peat and
contain the boles of trees like alder, hazel, and oak, still *in situ*, on
which account the exposures are often described as submerged forests.
They have been seen on several parts of the Anglesey coast, at Rhyl,
at Rhos, near Llandudno, and on the Lavan Sands. Writing of the
last named, about 1626, Sir John Wynn of Gwydir said, "In this greate
washe, uppon a lowe grownd ebbe, are to be seene the rootes of greate
oake and ashe, where att other tymes in the yeere ytt doth nott ebbe

PLATE XI

F. J. North

a. Carreg Wen: a block of volcanic rock from Snowdon, transported by ice from the other side of Moel-y-gest, the ridge in the distance

Engraving by S. J. Mackie in A. C. Ramsay's Old Glaciers of Switzerland and North Wales

b. Perched blocks in the Pass of Llanberis: many of these have since been dislodged
Drawn before 1859

GLACIAL ERRATIC BLOCKS

PLATE XII

F. J. North

GLACIATED PAVEMENT near Llyn Peris: a surface of Cambrian grit smoothed and scratched
by the passage of a stone-laden glacier

att all; This I speak as an eye witnes, havynge seene the rootes mysealf and taken them upp, soe that ytt shoulde seeme that this vale before the inundacion was a woodland countrey."

Local evidences of subsidence, and of coast erosion not due to subsidence although popularly attributed to it, and the discovery of objects made by early man in clays exposed on the foreshore have given rise to legends relating to a catastrophe that, in the sixth century A.D., caused the inundation of the region now occupied by the sea between Llandudno and Priestholm (Puffin Island) in Anglesey. The legend in its present form originated in the manuscript by Sir John Wynn mentioned in the preceding paragraph, and since his time a submerged seaweed-covered reef off Penmaen-mawr has been pointed out as the ruins of the Llys or palace of Helig, the ruler of what was described as one of the most fruitful and fertile vales in the land; actually, however, the subsidence which allowed the sea to overflow this vast tract took place long before the historic era and the accumulation of stones is a relic of the Ice Age—the debris of morainic mounds built up (before the inundation) where the ice from the Snowdonian mountains met that which had travelled across the Irish Sea.

Amongst the most striking of post-glacial changes are those due to the re-establishment of plant life in an area from which most of the vegetation and most of the soil that originally supported it had been removed. The flora of Britain before the arrival of the ice was generally similar to that of to-day. It used to be thought that the Glacial Period saw the destruction of all the plant life in this country except perhaps for some lichens and mosses, but it is now believed that a few plants of other kinds also survived in those parts which were not actually covered by ice, so that, amongst the so-called arctic or alpine species to be found in mountainous regions, some may actually be survivals of the pre-glacial flora. A species of *Dryas*, a member of the rose family which occurs on Snowdon, is, for example, represented in beds of peat that are interspersed amongst glacial gravels, but while certain arctic plants survived, trees were killed off or slowly migrated to regions where the climate was more congenial, to return on the heels of the retreating ice.

We are not concerned in this chapter with the history of the return of plant life to our area, as each partial retreat of the ice permitted immigration from some more favoured region farther south where the plants had been able to survive, but as part of the geological story we may note that some of the local peat beds contain the remains of trees, such as birch still retaining its silvery bark, at elevations up to 1,500 feet—considerably higher than trees grow in Snowdonia to-day, except for an occasional holly or mountain ash. Such remains have been recorded on Moel Siabod and in Cwm Dyli, and they seem to point to a change of climate which caused cold damp moorlands to replace forests: this took place early in the human era, and although it is not likely that there were dense forests at the highest levels within historic times, there must have been a considerable loss of woodland and lowering of the potential tree-level due to human activity.

The soils of Snowdonia have been produced in post-glacial times, either from the "solid" rocks, where they are exposed, or from the drift which occupies the surface over considerable areas. The character and behaviour of the soil is influenced not only by the chemical and physical properties of the materials from which it has been derived, but also by the amount of rain that falls upon it, the adequacy of its drainage, the amount and nature of the vegetation it supports, and the extent to which it is subjected to the artificial processes of management.

In an upland region like Snowdonia, where the rocks from which the soil has been derived are for the most part hard and non-calcareous, where the rainfall is heavy, and there is a poor covering of vegetation, the soluble ingredients of the soil tend to be carried downwards from the surface in solution, whilst some of the finest of the insoluble particles may be washed down mechanically to accumulate at a slightly lower horizon, which is thus enriched by what the higher layers lose. Amongst the materials so removed are compounds of iron, with the result that the soil below the humus layer is often pale-coloured due to the loss of its iron, whilst the enriched layer below may be stained brown by the iron oxides resulting from the re-deposition of the iron compounds. Soils that present a profile of this nature are called podsols or podsolic soils, from *podsol*, a Russian word meaning an ashen-coloured soil.

The process of podsolization obviously tends to produce relatively uniform soil-conditions from materials of varying character and origin. We find therefore that although the soils of Snowdonia include a wide range of types they fall naturally into two main series: (1) the shallow soils of the uplands, where the influence of the parent rock is dominated by the effects of drainage and vegetation, where podsolization is pronounced, and where there is less variation than the geological map might lead one to expect; and (2) the lowland soils, which are more variable in composition and texture because the rainfall is less and there is more cultivation—both of them factors that tend to inhibit podsolization. As a result, the general distribution patterns of the soil-texture, of types of grassland, and of arable land, all of them reflected in the pattern of the Land Classification Map, are more closely related to the contour-map than to the geological map, although in view of the relation between rocks and surface relief they do not differ conspicuously from either.

This brief note upon the soils of our area will be sufficient to indicate in a general way their influence upon the local natural history and cultural landscape; the ways in which that influence is exerted, and its effects, will appear in subsequent sections of this book. Further local details will be found in the admirable North Wales section of the Report of the Land Utilisation Survey of Britain, whilst for a concise account of modern views upon the formation and classification of soils in general, reference should be made to the chapter on Soils in Stamp's *Britain's Structure and Scenery.* Having regard to the attention now being paid to the study of soils, their improvement, and their wise utilization, it is interesting to recall a passage in the *General View of the Agriculture and Domestic Economy of North Wales* written by Walter Davies as long ago as 1810: "The more fertile soils consist of a due admixture of the primitive earths, especially the calcareous, siliceous and argillaceous. In this district, although there be instances, in several of the vales, of such due admixture; yet, in most other places, Nature seems only to have brought together the materials in detached masses, and left to the skill and industry of man to mix and form them into fertile soil by the rules of alligation—agricultural. These rules, however plain, are not sufficiently attended to."

4. THE LAKES

Crawl on old ice-worm, from the solemn hills ;
Press deep thy burrowing snout among the stones ;
Mutter and murmur with thy turbid rills.
And crush the old earth's bones. . . .
Gnaw, grind the patient cliffs with ravenous teeth . . .
Haste thee, for thou art destined to decay. . . .
And though shalt not prevail.

A. C. Benson, *By the Glacier*

A striking feature of our area is the number of lakes it contains. There are more than sixty altogether and twenty of them can be seen from Yr Wyddfa. They range from little rounded pools like Llyn Glas in Cwm Glas overlooking the Pass of Llanberis, to narrow valley-bottom lakes like Llyn Dinas and Llyn Padarn, of which the last is more than two miles long.

They occur at all elevations from as little as 176 feet above sea level for Llyn Dinas in Nant Gwynant to over 2,094 feet for Melynllyn beneath Y Foel Grach. Even more remarkable than their variation in size and elevation is the variation in the depth of their waters. At one extreme we have Llyn Ogwen with a maximum depth of only 10 feet, and at the other Llyn Cowlyd, which has given soundings of 222 feet. The greater depths are in general associated with the larger of the high-level lakes, e.g. Llyn Llydaw (190 feet), Llyn Dulyn (189) and Glaslyn (127), but even the low-level lakes are surprisingly deep for their situation, e.g. Llyn Cwellyn (122 feet), Llyn Peris (114), and Llyn Padarn (94) (Fig. 24). These considerable depths present an interesting problem. Why, we may ask, should Llyn Peris, which lies higher up the valley, be deeper than Llyn Padarn, since they are in effect one lake with a surface level at 340 feet—and normal valley floors slope continuously if not uniformly in the direction in which the stream flows?

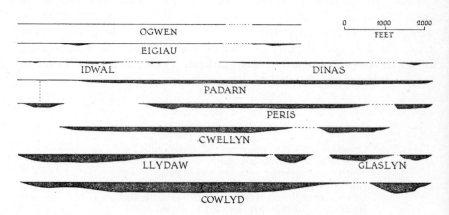

FIG. 24.—Sections across some Snowdonian lakes

For each lake there is one section in the direction of its length and another across its widest part : the horizontal and vertical scales are the same. (After T. J. Jehu)

The waters of some of the smaller mountain tarns are dammed back entirely by moraines, but many of the lakes are far deeper than can be accounted for by the thickness of the superficial deposits of glacial origin that appear along their margins. Many years ago, when the depth of the water was as yet unknown, J. B. Dakyns showed, after a careful examination of the outlets of Glaslyn and Llyn Llydaw, and noting the levels at which solid rock was exposed, that any depth of water in these lakes in excess of 40 or 50 feet could only be accounted for by supposing that the basins were partially excavated in rock. Subsequently, in 1900–01, when soundings were made by T. J. Jehu, the waters were found to be 127 and 190 feet deep respectively, showing that each lake does indeed lie in a rock-basin which accounts for the greater part of the depth. The remainder is due to a dam of morainic material resting upon the rim of the basin. This proves to be the case with many of the other lakes as well.

Such basins could not have been excavated by the ordinary agents of subaerial erosion and there is nothing in their surroundings or in the profiles of their floors to suggest that they occupy deep fissures in the earth's crust.

There can be no doubt but that the hollows in the floors of cwms were excavated by glaciers. We have seen that the ice of such glaciers was heavily charged with masses of rock derived from the gradually receding wall of the cwm, and, pressed downwards by the weight due to its own thickness and forwards by the natural flow of the ice from the centres of accumulation above, the stone-laden cwm-glacier is presumed to have been able to exert a strong scouring effect upon the floor over which it moved. This would in time lead to the scooping out of a basin-like hollow, because the effect would be greatest where the ice was thickest—that is, near the head of the glacier—and would diminish with distance from it.

As the ice melted and deposited a moraine across the cwm, the material may have accumulated in the hollow that had been excavated in the rock, partly filling it, or it may have been deposited on or beyond the lip of the rock-basin, deepening the cavity in which water could accumulate when the ice finally disappeared. Most of the cwm lakes in our area seem to occupy rock-basins and to have originated in this way, although in some cases their depth has been increased by the morainic dams. Having regard to their origin and elevation it is easy to see why the lakes which occur in cwms are impressive rather than attractive, and have grandeur rather than beauty. Beautiful and attractive are adjectives more applicable to the lakes which occur down in the valleys where the vegetation is richer and the surrounding country less severe.

Glaslyn lies in a semicircular mountain-girt hollow at the foot of Yr Wyddfa, and a stream issuing from its eastern end plunges down a steep rocky slope to Llyn Llydaw. The lake is oval and its floor slopes fairly evenly to the deepest part, which is in the middle.

Llyn Llydaw is larger than the average for the local cwm-lakes, because, although the deepest part lies in a cwm, overlooked by the curving precipice Y Lliwedd, it spreads beyond the cwm and is dammed by moraines along its south-eastern side (Pl. IX, p. 98). There are also the remains of a great morainic dam near the outlet of the lake. Boulders and loose masses of rock derived from it form islets and the huge mounds on the northern side of the lake are also of morainic origin.

Llyn Idwal, which lies in a cwm beneath the steep walls of Y Glyder Fawr and Y Garn is, by contrast, surprisingly shallow. The lake trends north and south and is about half a mile long. The water is kept back by a huge terminal moraine while some long mounds on the western side are the remains of lateral moraines. The floor of the lake is very irregular, being partly covered by large boulders and partly by mud. The lake does not occupy a deep hollow after the fashion of Glaslyn for its greatest depth is only 36 feet, and nearly 60 per cent of it is less than 10 feet deep. It is, however, likely that it was once considerably deeper and is gradually being filled up by rocks that fall from the surrounding cliffs and by sediments washed out of the moraines. The morainic dam would seem to be sufficient to account for the present depth of the water. The Marchlyn lakes, north of Elidir Fawr, have much in common with Llyn Idwal.

Llyn Dulyn, which lies under the cliffs between Y Foel Fras and Y Foel Grach at a height of 1,747 feet, in many ways resembles Glaslyn. Its depth is 189 feet and the deepest part is near the middle. The lake is almost surrounded by bare rock except on the east side where a thin covering of Drift is responsible for a grassy boulder-strewn slope. The slope to the lake bottom is steep on all sides, especially on the western side where a precipice rises sheer from the water and a depth of 55 feet was recorded only 3 feet from the rock face. The stream which drains the lake flows over bare rock.

Contrasting strongly with the lakes we have just considered is Llyn Cowlyd—the largest of the lakes in the northern-most mountain tract of our area and the deepest (222 feet) in the whole region. It is long, narrow, even-sided, occurs at the head of a valley, and lies only about 300 feet below the watershed behind it. No stream of any importance runs into it, and the contours follow the shape of the lake, the deepest part of which is in the middle. There is a comparatively shallow area near the outlet, suggesting that the lake comes to an end against a subaqueous ridge. There is no great cwm behind Llyn Cowlyd, as there is behind Glaslyn or Llyn Dulyn, in which a powerful glacier could have originated, but the lake is too deep to be regarded as entirely due to a morainic dam and it seems likely that ice moving down from the Carneddau was diverted into the Cowlyd valley in sufficient quantity to have gouged out a deeper trough than a river could have made.

Llyn Eigiau lies in the next valley to the north and about a mile and a half away. Unlike the lakes we have already considered, it does not occupy the cwm at the head of its valley, where there is only a tiny tarn, Ffynnon Llyffant, but occurs some two miles lower down. The precipitous Craig Eigiau rises on the west side, but low marshy ground on the east and flat alluvial tracts extending from the head of the lake indicate that it was at one time considerably larger. An artificial embankment, made when the lake was adapted for the purpose of a reservoir, now defines most of its eastern side. Llyn Eigiau contrasts strongly with Llyn Cowlyd in having a mean depth of only about 8 feet and a maximum of 32. The drift and alluvium which cover the valley floor near the end of the lake are sufficient to account for its depth. The bottom is to a large extent covered with stones and boulders and its margins are being encroached upon by rushes: it is gradually being silted up and represents a stage in the direction of the conditions we now see at Llyn Ogwen.

Llyn Ogwen occupies a shallow basin excavated at the head of a valley by glaciers that came from Cwm Idwal and Cwm Bochlwyd. Although nearly a mile long it is nowhere more than 10 feet deep and its mean depth is about 6 feet. It was at one time deeper but is growing shallower owing to the amount of sediment carried into it. The lake is bounded by lofty, striking mountains—the rock-strewn slopes of Y Glyder Fawr and Y Tryfan on the one side and the back of Braich-ty-du, a spur of Carnedd Ddafydd, on the other—and boulders that have rolled down from the former have built a well-marked promontory projecting from the southern shore. Also projecting from the southern side is the delta of the river which drains Llyn Bochlwyd; it will eventually cut the lake into two unequal portions. The river begins in a hanging valley and, descending more than 800 feet in three-quarters of a mile, it picks up a great deal of debris as it rushes down the steep northern flank of Y Glyder Fawr.

Extending for about half a mile from the upper (eastern) end of Llyn Ogwen there is a flat alluvial tract suggesting that the lake was once considerably larger, and the watershed separating it from the head-waters of Afon Llugwy stands at a little more than sixty feet above its present surface level.

Seen from the east Llyn Ogwen is so shut in by hills as to look as if it were part of the Llugwy valley; it is, indeed, likely that it did at one time drain in that direction for the watershed between the lake and the Llugwy is only a mound of Drift. To-day the water drains westwards through a gorge cut in the cliff-like end of Nant Ffrancon, to which it descends by the well-known Rhaeadr Ogwen. The gorge, really a gap in the original watershed, was probably initiated by water flowing beneath a glacier.

Llyn Ogwen represents a later stage in the disappearance of a lake than that encountered in Llyn Eigiau, and the carpet of mud that is being spread over its bottom is likely in time completely to displace the water, leaving a flat expanse of potential meadow in its place.

In several of the valleys of our area there are alluvial flats marking the sites of lakes that have been filled up, or that have been drained because the stream leaving them has cut through to the bottom of the dam or rock ridge that held the water back. The flat land around Beddgelert, for example, marks the site of a lake that has disappeared, so also does the much larger area which forms the floor of Nant Ffrancon. In the latter the river meanders for more than three miles through meadow-land built up of sediment laid down in a lake that must have been one of the largest the area has supported—nearly as large as Llyn Padarn and Llyn Peris together.

In common with Llyn Cwellyn, Llyn Gwynant, and Llyn Dinas, the Llanberis lakes lie at comparatively low levels. Of these, Llyn Cwellyn at 463 feet is the highest and Llyn Dinas at 176 feet the lowest. They occur in the valleys that enclose the main Snowdon tract.

Llyn Padarn and Llyn Peris were originally one lake, for the alluvial flat separating them is really an extreme development of the delta of the river Llwch. Above Llyn Peris there is a nearly flat expanse of alluvium extending to Gwastadnant (the smooth, level valley—a very appropriate name), whilst below Llyn Padarn a flat marshy tract, often flooded, extends below Cwm-y-glo. These flat regions were at one time parts of the combined lake which, at its maximum, must have been between four and five miles long. The surface levels of the two lakes are the same, but whereas Llyn Padarn has a maximum depth of 94 feet Llyn Peris reaches 114 feet.

Since the upper lake is the deeper of the two the valley cannot have been completely cut by normal river erosion. Like the cwm-lakes they must occupy basins gouged out of the valley floor by the stone-laden ice. We should, indeed, expect that the glacier would have its greatest erosive power where its flow was retarded and the ice heaped at the bottom of the relatively steep slope from Pen-y-gwryd to Gwastadnant.

Although Llyn Cwellyn stands at only 463 feet above sea level it is situated near the head of its valley—that of the river Gwyrfai—and not in the lower reaches like Padarn and Peris. The water has a maximum depth of 122 feet, with a mean of 74 feet, so that this lake, too, occupies a rock-basin excavated by ice. Alluvial flats at each end of the lake indicate that it must at one time have been about two miles long. The level land at the lower end extends for about half a mile, after which the hills close in on either side and the stream leaving the lake falls over a rocky barrier that extends across the valley. Such a barrier would have been an obstacle to the flow of the glacier and would have led to the erosion of a hollow just above it.

Llyn-y-dywarchen, the Lake of the Sod, lies some 300 feet above and about a half a mile to the south of Llyn Cwellyn, although its waters pass by way of the narrow Llyn Bwlch-y-moch to the stream (Afon Drws-y-coed) that flows into the Nantlle lakes and leaves them as Afon Llyfni. It is supposed to be the lake which Giraldus Cambrensis described as "having a floating island in it which is driven from one side to the other by the force of the wind." Later writers have, as usual in such circumstances, associated the phenomenon with a legend, but Giraldus had a simple, matter-of-fact explanation. "A part of the bank," he wrote, "naturally bound together by the roots of willows and other shrubs may have been broken off . . . and being continually agitated by the winds . . . it cannot reunite itself firmly with the banks."

Pennant claimed to have seen the floating island and confirmed the story that cattle which strayed upon it when it was near the shore were occasionally marooned when it again began to move, but when Joseph Cradock's guides "related many singular and surprising tales" concerning a floating island, and he "indulged their credulity so far as to go and inspect it," he was not impressed. He found that "the lake as they called it was somewhat bigger than a duck pond, and the island was a knotty piece of Bog, which, after very heavy rains, might very possibly float in it."

The vale of Gwynant is separated from that of Gwryd by a low watershed at Pen-y-gwryd. The comparatively gentle descent to Capel Curig (near which are the two shallow Mymbyr lakes) contrasts strongly with the steep slope into the vale of Gwynant. The glacier —and it must have been a large one—emerging from Cwm Dyli, entered the vale near its head and joined that which came from the slopes south of Gorphwysfa, with the result that the mass of ice moving down Nant Gwynant was greater and had more eroding power than that which made its way towards Capel Curig. The grass-covered tongue of land which separates the Capel Curig lakes is made up of debris that has slipped down from the hill on the left or northern side of the valley.

The lakes Gwynant and Dinas lie in the vale of Gwynant. The former is about three miles from the head of the vale and a flat expanse of meadowland stretches for about a mile from its upper end, recalling the conditions we encountered at Llyn Peris and suggesting that the lake was at one time that much larger than it is now. The hills close in towards the lower end of the lake and appear completely to shut it in. Beyond this the river makes its way through a narrow glen on its way to Llyn Dinas, about a mile and a half away.

The valley between the lakes is occupied by Drift through which the river has to cut its way. It is, therefore, heavily charged with sediment when it reaches the lower lake, in which it is building up a large delta. Llyn Dinas, too, has the appearance of being shut in at its lower end and the water leaves it by a narrow passage between rocky hills. The bottom of the lake is muddy. Its upper part is very shallow and is being encroached upon by water plants, while the whole is gradually being silted up—another reminder that lakes are, in a geological sense, temporary features of the landscape; no sooner are they formed than they begin to disappear, either because sediment carried into them gradually displaces the water, or else because a river flowing from them lowers its bed and causes the water to drain away.

Llyn Gwynant has a maximum depth of 54 feet and a mean depth of about 18 feet; the corresponding figures for Llyn Dinas are 30 and 13 feet respectively. In Llyn Gwynant the deeper water lies on the right side, which is what one would expect since that is the side on which the river enters and leaves the lake while most of the sediment-laden tributaries come from the opposite side.

Although the valley floor is to a large extent drift-covered the stream leaving Llyn Dinas flows over rock, so that here too we have an ice-deepened channel. We have already noted that below Llyn Gwynant, and again below Llyn Dinas, the valley becomes constricted by the approach of the flanking hills, and it is at such places that the movement of the glacier would be retarded. Consequently, the ice would tend to pile up and so to have greater eroding power, leading to the over-deepening of the valley floor. In other words, the lakes are situated just where they should be if we regard them as occupying rock-basins excavated by ice. The lakes were probably never as deep as those in valleys at higher elevations but their present shallowness is largely due to the fact that they are rapidly silting up. The water of Llyn Arenig Fawr is held up by a moraine of the lower (local) series formed when the main Snowdonian ice no longer reached that region.

It transpires, then, that although the lakes of our area differ in their characteristics and modes of origin, they are all relics of the Ice Age, the events of which did so much in other ways to determine the present details of the scenery, and these brief notes upon a few typical examples will help the visitor to classify for himself the many lakes that cannot be mentioned in the space available for this chapter.

Some of the lakes have been adapted as reservoirs for water supply on account of the heavy rainfall and the almost complete absence of human settlements on the gathering grounds, whilst others lend themselves to power production because they occur in hanging valleys. The fall from tributary to main valley provides the head of water necessary to drive turbines, as in the case of Afon Porthllwyd which flows from Llyn Eigiau and descends about 700 feet in a quarter of a mile when approaching the valley of the Conway. Afon Ddu, which drains Llyn Cowlyd, makes a similar entry to the Conway valley but Afon Crafnant, which carries the waters from Llyn Crafnant and Llyn Geirionydd, has cut its own valley more deeply and descends to the Conway by a step of only about 200 feet. The increased gradient of the

Llugwy as it approaches the Conway is responsible for the waterfalls near Betws-y-coed. Water from Marchlyn Mawr is used to provide hydraulic power for raising slate from the deeper parts of the Penrhyn Quarry to the level of the dressing sheds.

The lakes tend to regulate the flow of the water, so that the valleys below them are less liable than others to flooding after heavy rainfall.

References for Chapter 3

SECTION 1
Davies (1936), Greenly (1919), North (1946), Sharpe (1847), Smith and George (1935), Stamp (1946).

SECTION 2
Greenly (1938), Lake (1934), Stamp (1946).

SECTION 3
Davis (1909), Fearnsides (1905), Greenly (1919), Greenly (1942), Holmes (1944), Howell (1946), North (1928), North (1940), Stamp (1946).

SECTION 4
Giraldus (1188), Jehu (1902), Holmes (1944).

CHAPTER 4

THE PERSONALITIES OF THE MOUNTAINS AND THE COMPILATION OF THEIR STORIES

I. THE STRUCTURE OF THE REGION AND SOME INDIVIDUAL MOUNTAINS

The earth is rude, silent, incomprehensible at first—
Nature is rude and incomprehensible at first—
Be not discouraged, keep on, there are divine things well envelop'd.

Walt Whitman *Song of the Open Road*

PERSONALITY has been defined as "the sum of qualities and characteristics that constitute individuality," and in that sense we can speak of the personalities of our mountains. To the walker and especially to the climber each has individuality; one has steeper faces and another a finer array of gullies; one has a more extensive fringe of screes and another gloomier hollows; one culminates in featureless moorland and another in awe-inspiring ridges—and all these depend upon the rocks of which the mountains are built, the way in which those rocks are disposed, and the extent to which they have been affected by the various agents of denudation: in other words, the personality of a mountain is determined by its geological make-up and structure, and by the nature and severity of the geological processes to which it has been subjected.

This applies also to regions as well as to individual mountains. The great tract north-east of Nant Ffrancon and the valley of the Llugwy, for example, present two quite different aspects determined by the abundance and relationships of the igneous rocks. On the west, where volcanic rocks predominate in thick massive sheets we have high and often rugged mountains including the Carneddau and Y Foel Fras, but eastwards towards the Conway valley the hills are lower, the slopes less steep, and the precipices less forbidding, because volcanic rocks are less extensively developed. The individual lava flows and beds of ash are thinner, being measurable in tens of feet, not in hundreds as they are nearer to the centres of eruption, and they are separated from one another by sedimentary rocks (mostly slates) which make up the bulk of the series (the Crafnant volcanic series of Llandeilo age) in which they occur.

We have considered the geological history of the area and have seen how the events of far distant times have influenced the features of to-day, but it would require more pages than can be spared in this book, and would involve entering into technicalities to a greater extent than would be fair to the general reader, if we were to attempt to discuss in detail the outcrops of the rocks as they are depicted on a geological map and the way in which they are arranged and vary from place to place.

We can, however, by means of simplified diagrams based upon sections that have been drawn by various workers to illustrate the geology of various parts of our area, show the principal ways in which well-known mountains differ from one another. As Fig. 5 (p. 15) shows, the whole area is a syncline complementary to the anticlinal Harlech dome, but it includes several subsidiary folds the axes of which trend in general from north-east to south-west, so that the structure is most easily appreciated when the area is crossed at right-angles to that direction, i.e. from north-west to south-east. This happens, fortunately, to be the direction taken by the principal main roads (from Bethesda to Betws-y-coed; along the Pass of Llanberis; and from Caernarvon to the Glaslyn estuary). Only the most unobservant traveller along the first of those roads could fail to notice that in Nant Ffrancon the strata are inclined towards the south-east—that is, in the direction in which he is going, while the rocks of Y Tryfan are inclined in the opposite direction and slope towards him. The road from Capel Curig to Beddgelert follows approximately the direction of the strike of the rocks and the structure of the area is in consequence less apparent to the traveller along it.

The sections in Fig. 25 have been drawn from north-west to south-east in order to illustrate the *structure* of the mountains but they do not in all cases depict the steepest slopes or most striking profiles; to show those features the sections would need to be drawn at right angles to the main valleys which cut deeply into the region, but they would not then adequately illustrate the relationship of the rocks to the surface. A section in the direction of the strike of the rocks (see Fig. 13, p. 50) shows the succession and thickness of the strata but does not, like a section in the direction of dip, indicate their inclination to the surface.

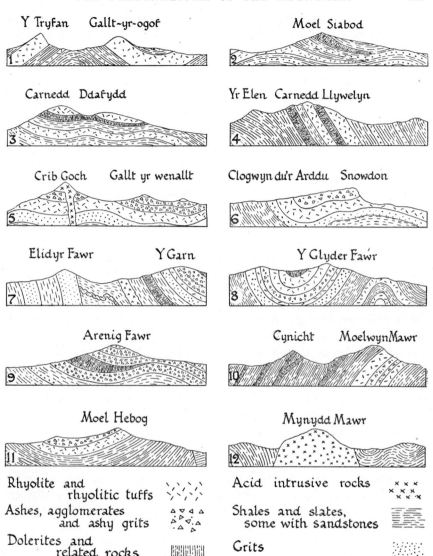

Rhyolite and
          rhyolitic tuffs

Ashes, agglomerates
          and ashy grits

Dolerites and
          related rocks

Acid intrusive rocks

Shales and slates,
          some with sandstones

Grits

Fig. 25.—The structure of some Snowdonian mountains

Each section represents a distance of about 4 miles and only the principal rock-
subdivisions are indicated.   More detailed sections upon which some of the above
have been based will be found in the papers enumerated on pages 437-8

The sections have been considerably simplified: they do not show all the groups into which the strata have been divided, nor do they give indications of all the contortions and disturbances that interrupt the regularity and continuity of the beds: they are intended to illustrate essential structures rather than details—to help a visitor to interpret what he sees, even although he makes no claim to be a geologist.

In general the more spectacular mountains in our area are those in which, as a result of folding or faulting, rocks with varying degrees of resistance to erosion have been brought together at the surface, and the steepest faces are developed where thick beds of massive rock are intersected by strong joints. The lavas and compact tuffs are responsible for most of the gully-riven faces esteemed by climbers, although suitably disposed sills of dolerite have also given rise to forbidding cliffs, as in Ysgolion Duon and the cliffs opposite Pont-y-gromlech.

Joints are the divisional planes by reason of which most kinds of rock tend to break into blocks, varying greatly in size, but often surprisingly regular, for any given kind of rock, in shape. They result partly from shrinkage as sediments dried or from contraction as igneous rocks cooled, and partly from strains to which rocks of all kinds have been subjected during periods of earth-movement They are responsible for many of the features—the wall-like faces and the deep cracks and gullies that break their continuity—that give rise to "unclimbable" precipices and at the same time provide the means whereby that description may be proved inaccurate. The Great Gully on Craig-yr-ysta is an open joint in volcanic rock, and joints are responsible for the awe-inspiring chasm, Twll Du, down which come the waters from Llyn-y-cwn (Pl. 8a, p. 79).

Where rocks are steeply inclined, bedding planes, marking the break in deposition between one bed of sediment and another, or between a lava flow and the rocks upon which it was poured or by which it was covered, may also give rise to comparatively even steep surfaces, as, for example, in Cwm Graeanog and on the western face of Y Tryfan.

On faces determined mainly by joints, such as the eastern face of Y Tryfan and the cliffs above Llyn Idwal, the bedding or stratification of the rocks may be responsible for ledges that may be horizontal or inclined, according to the relation of the face to the direction in which the rocks are dipping. When inclined, such ledges often provide convenient paths from one level to another, as in the case of those which rise on either side of Clogwyn-y-geifr with Twll Du between them.

We have already seen (Fig. 3, p. 13) that the steep face of Y Tryfan is the outcrop of a series of inclined volcanic rocks and that the corresponding rocks on the other side of a denuded anticline give rise to Gallt-yr-ogof. The sloping Heather Terrace at the base of the main cliffs of Y Tryfan follows the direction of the bedding of the rock, while the nearly vertical gullies which divide the cliffs have been developed along joints that are vertical to the stratification. Other vertical joints more or less at right angles to those responsible for the gullies determined the eastern face of the mountain and since the joints run, as joints usually do, roughly at right angles to the planes separating one bed or one set of beds from another, the eastern face is steeper than the western, which is determined by the *dip* of the strata. So built, it is no wonder that Pennant described the mountain as having "a pyramidal form, naked, and very rugged." Structurally the west facing slope of Gallt-yr-ogof corresponds with the eastern face of Y Tryfan, but it is less steep and well defined, probably because it has been less exposed to severe frost action and more exposed to rain.

Still farther to the south-west the lavas that make up Y Tryfan and Gallt-yr-ogof reappear on the flanks of Moel Siabod. Here they are near the limits of the area they once overflowed, are thinner and are not responsible for the dominating feature of the mountain, because the summit and spurs of Moel Siabod have been carved out of a large sill-like mass of dolerite.

Representatives of the Tryfan lavas occur at the summit of Carnedd Ddafydd, but there the dip is less steep and approximates to the southern slope of the mountain; so that although the volcanic rock covers a large area it gives rise to less spectacular features and Carnedd Ddafydd is more massive than shapely.

The precipices called Ysgolion Duon on the northern face of the mountain mark the outcrop of a thick sill of dolerite. The same dolerite forms the upper part of the north-western slopes and the summit of Carnedd Llywelyn, but the outcrop of the equivalents of the lavas of Y Tryfan on the south-eastern slopes of the mountain is inconspicuous. Slates of Ordovician age and not volcanic rocks are responsible for the wild-looking Yr Elen which dominates the north-western spur of Carnedd Llywelyn.

Snowdon and the less impressive Gallt-yr-wenallt provide examples of synclinal mountains; so also does Moel Hebog. Y Glyder Fawr and

Y Garn represent the limbs of a syncline in which thick sheets of lava play an important part; it is interesting to compare Fig. 25 (8) with Fig. 25 (1), in which the anticlinal structure allows the well-jointed volcanic rocks to dominate the profile.

The steepest part of Y Lliwedd and the precipice of Llechog have been carved out of volcanic rocks (the vitric tuffs) belonging to the Lower Rhyolitic Series. These rocks often show a slabby type of weathering along joint-planes, such as is well displayed in the Idwal Slabs, while flinty rhyolites of the same series are largely responsible for the cliffs of Clogwyn Du'r Arddu. The Lower Rhyolitic Series is also responsible for the wilderness of massive blocks on the summit of Y Glyder Fach. Shaped as if by art and not by Nature, and often precariously poised (Pl. Va, p. 34) these have been a source of wonderment to travellers in all ages who have recorded their impressions of the mountain. The name, which is said to be derived from *cludair*, meaning a heap or a pile, may have been suggested by the resemblance to the ruin of a stupendous edifice. The effects of joints are also well seen on the main cliff of Y Glyder Fach which appears in places as if it were built up of squarish pillars.

The sharp-ridged Crib Goch has been carved out of the largest of the masses of acid intrusive rocks that came into position towards the end of the Snowdonian volcanic episode. On the southern side the intrusive rock rises almost vertically through the ashes and tuffs that form so large a part of the mountain, but towards the north it seems to spread out until it so nearly resembles a horizontal sill, conforming to the bedding of the pyroclastic series, that it was originally interpreted as a lava flow.

The remaining diagrams speak for themselves. Arenig Fawr with its escarpment of volcanic rocks recalls Carnedd Ddafydd while Moelwyn Mawr has an even simpler structure, being one limb of a much denuded anticline—structurally like Y Tryfan, but less impressive because composed of different rocks. Cnicht is also an outcrop of steeply inclined rock—Ordovician sediments and ashes, reinforced by dolerite sills: actually a mile-long ridge facing south-east, it appears as a sharp peak recalling the Alpine Matterhorn when seen end-on, as from near Portmadoc (Pl. IV, p. 11). The summits of Elidir Fawr and Carnedd-y-filiast are determined by outcrops of Cambrian grits similar to those on Clogwyn Mawr near the head of Llyn Peris.

Lava flows (rhyolite) and sills of dolerite are responsible for the bold ribs that slope south-eastwards on the face of Creigiau Gleision as it is seen from Pen Llithrig-y-wrach[1] on the opposite side of Llyn Cowlyd. Altogether different in character is Mynydd Mawr which probably represents the plug or throat of an ancient volcano and rises as a conspicuous boss deeply cut into by Cwm Du.

Chemical change within the acid rocks, whether they are intrusions, lavas, or tuffs, has often resulted in the segregation and deposition of quartz in considerable masses or in thin veins that sometimes look like streaks of snow upon the darker rocks. The processes responsible for the deposition of quartz played a part in the distribution of ores containing metallic minerals, but their results are also of interest to visitors who may have no leanings towards geology, especially to climbers. Quartz is very hard and resistant to weathering and on that account often tends to stand out in relief on weathered surfaces and so to provide what appear to be convenient holds, but the joints which determine the face of the rock pass also through the quartz, the projecting portions of which tend in consequence to break off when least expected to do so.

With these general principles in mind the essential characters that determine the personality of the mountains in our area can usually be readily recognized. Some will remain enigmas to all but the experienced field-geologist, either because they may be so much encumbered with glacial deposits or peat, or on account of faults, the existence of which it may be difficult to recognize and the effects of which it may be difficult to interpret; besides, it is not always possible to discover or convenient to reach a view-point from which to see cliffs and crags that cut across the dip of the rocks, and thus show clearly their relation to the arch-like and trough-like folds that are the main structural features of the region.

If mountains have personality so too have lakes and rivers, and the personality is, in each case, largely if not entirely dependent upon geological factors. The lakes we have already considered, and a very brief note must suffice for the rivers. Flowing as many of them do down steep slopes in a region of heavy rainfall, their upper reaches tend to vary with the weather from rapid torrents to inconspicuous trickles —unless they are fed by extensive bogs, in which case the flow may be more regular.

The departure from a hanging valley is often marked by the develop-

---

[1]The slippery headland of the witch. There are, indeed, slippery grassy slopes, but the allusion to a witch is obscure.

ment of cascades and waterfalls, and when they reach the more level
ground of the larger valley floors the streams flow more slowly, are
deeper, and have larger and more frequent pools. These are matters
of interest to the angler, for the rapid variable streams tend to have
small active fish and an occasional deep pool, but in those parts of a
valley where the gradient is gentle, a river may be expected to meander
across meadowland and on occasion to flow beside tree-shaded banks.

One of the most striking stretches of river scenery in our area is
that to be seen where the river Glaslyn turns southwards after passing
Beddgelert and cuts across the strike of a series of massive felsitic rocks.
This feature was very well known to early tourists because, when Traeth
Mawr was still an estuary, the journey from Bala or from Harlech into
Caernarvonshire involved a detour as far northwards as the bridge,
Pont Aberglaslyn, at the lower end of the pass. It is one of the most
frequently described parts of our area and the descriptions provide an
interesting illustration of the frame of mind in which the early tourists
often made their journeys. Joseph Cradock, who wrote *An account of
some of the most Romantic parts of North Wales* in 1777, recorded his impressions of "tremendous precipices, the river roaring over disjointed rocks,
black caverns and issuing cataracts" all of which, he wrote, "serve to
make the noblest specimen of the Finely Horrid the eye can possibly
behold: the Poet has not described, nor the Painter pictured so gloomy
a retreat; 'tis the last Approach to the mansion of Pluto through the
regions of Despair." The reference to Pluto was, in a sense, prophetic,
because at that time the part played by igneous activity in determining
the character of North Wales had not been recognized.

Cradock's rather extravagant effusion may be compared with an
entry in the Diary of the Hon. John Byng, afterwards Lord Torrington.
He toured North Wales in 1784 and wrote of "Pont Aberglasslyn
. . . There are so many descriptions of this place that I must retire from
weak relation, on my part; and only exclaim that the scene is most
truly wonderful! A narrow winding road looking down on a foaming,
stoney river: and overhung by the steepest mountains." Byng's more
restrained comment may perhaps be accounted for by the fact that he
was not writing with a view to publication, at least during his own
lifetime: he was not thinking in terms of a book-buying public.
"I dread not the reviewers," he wrote, "as I shall never hazard a
book-seller's window."

This short section could easily be expanded into a long chapter,

PLATE 9

John Markham

SNOWDON from Llyn Nantlle-uchaf. July

PLATE 10

John Markham

PASS OF ABERGLASLYN with Craig-y-llan. July

but having been shown the path, the reader must be left to follow it as far and in as enquiring a spirit as his inclination dictates. To interpret the personality of our area is to enter into its secrets—to understand, for example, why it is that although volcanoes figure so largely in an account of its geological history, and volcanic rocks enter so largely into its fabric, there are no *volcanoes*, not even extinct ones, amongst its mountains. The triangular profiles, suggesting cones, are the final products of erosion, not the first products of eruptions. The crater-like hollows, the cwms, are not the orifices from which molten rock once poured and from which ashes were ejected amidst clouds of steam: they, in common with many of the details of the present landscape, are the work of frost and ice. The dreary scenery of much of the upland region is due to the covering of ill-drained and infertile morainic material.

There are, indeed, few areas where the effects of ice can be more conveniently studied, and although the last of the glaciers disappeared many thousands of years ago it is wonderfully easy, once the fact of their former existence has been appreciated, to put them back in imagination, envisaging the picture that was in the mind of the author of *Nebula to Man*, when he wrote:

> Green vales are hid, and rivers cease to flow,
> High hills are slowly passing out of sight,
> As o'er their brows great glacier streams unite,
> And Cambria holds aloft as gathering ground,
> Snowdon and Arenig.

2. MINES AND QUARRIES

> Not only corn and other fruits, for sustenance as for store,
> Were now exacted of the earth, but eft they 'gan to dig,
> And in the bowels of the earth insatiably to rig
> For riches couched and hidden deep in places near to hell.
>
> Ovid, *Metamorphoses*,
> trans. A. Golding, 1565.

To trace the history of all the mine and quarry ventures in our area would require more space than this volume can afford, and to discuss their future potentialities would involve reference to technical and commercial matters that have no place in a work dealing with natural history, but the abundant indications of mining and quarrying on the mountain-sides call for some notes upon the nature and origin of the industrially important rocks and upon the ores and the principal places where they have been worked.

Experiments that have been made to determine the weight of the earth show that its specific gravity is about 5.5 (i.e., it weighs about five and a half times as much as a body of similar size made of pure water), but the average specific gravity of the igneous and sedimentary rocks which make up its crust is between 2.5 and 3. In other words the earth is nearly twice as heavy as it would be if it consisted entirely of the rocks we see in its surface layers, and from this it is inferred that the heavier constituent elements are concentrated in zones that lie beneath the relatively thin external crust. The heavier elements are metals such as iron, nickel, lead, tin, copper, gold and the like, and their presence in comparatively small quantities near enough to the surface to be accessible to man implies the operation of processes that led to their transfer from the levels at which they normally occur. The processes associated with the formation of igneous intrusions at once suggest themselves as fulfilling the necessary conditions, for they cause material of deep-seated origin to rise through the earth's crust and even to reach the surface.

As an igneous magma cools there is, as we have already seen, a tendency for its constituents to separate out into portions of varying chemical composition, and since some of the metallic elements tend to be concentrated in those parts that are last to solidify they are often present in the material injected during the latest stages of cooling, and so may occur in association with the veins and dykes that penetrate all the earlier-formed rocks. With these residual magmas come hot vapours and solutions that, on cooling or meeting with materials with which they can interact, deposit solid matter on the sides of fissures through which they pass or in the pores of rock they may permeate.

The hot solutions, which are often rich in silica, pass out of the intrusions into cracks in the surrounding rocks and give rise to veins of quartz with varying amounts of minerals containing the metallic elements. The final disposition of workable ores depends upon contemporaneous or subsequent changes that affected the chemical composition of the minerals, their distribution, or their local concentration, but these are matters we cannot consider in detail. For our purpose it is sufficient to recall that our area has seen considerable igneous activity in past ages so that it is not surprising if we find, here and there, veins containing metallic minerals in sufficient quantity to have encouraged mining operations.

The lodes, as the metal-bearing veins are called, usually consist principally of quartz mixed with rock broken into fragments during disturbances associated with the development of faults (fault-breccia) and with metallic minerals such as the sulphides of copper, iron, zinc, and lead. The lodes vary in thickness and in their relation to the associated strata, while the proportion of metallic minerals in any one is apt to vary considerably and unpredictably so that mining operations in the region have always been speculative and sporadic.

Copper ores: One of the best known of the copper mines in our area was opened in the great precipice overlooking Glaslyn, or Llyn-y-ffynnon-las as it used to be called, meaning the lake of the green well or spring— *las* being the mutated form of *glas* of which one meaning is green. It was worked at intervals over many years but finally closed down when the waters draining into Cwm Dyli were harnessed for electrical purposes and it is now represented only by ruined buildings.

The decomposition products of copper ores are usually blue or green and the green colour to which Glaslyn owes its name was due to the fine green detritus that was discharged into the lake as a natural product of erosion or perhaps from some of the earliest of the mine workings. Pennant recorded that, seen from above, the black waters of the lake were quite green at the edges. It is interesting to note that when, during a period of mining activity in 1899, the ore was crushed and dressed on the shores of Llyn Llydaw (Pl. 30, p. 335) the waters of that lake are reported to have assumed, for the first time, a greenish hue.

The Drws-y-coed mine near Nantlle is one of the oldest in the area; Edward I is said to have visited it. This and the nearby Tal-y-sarn mine have been opened in lodes that penetrate shales and grits believed to be of Llandeilo age. The principal ore is copper pyrites (a metallic-looking mineral consisting of sulphide of copper and iron, and sometimes mistaken for gold) which has been worked from four lodes, the deepest workings (in the Drws-y-coed mine) being about 480 feet below the adit that gives access to the mine, and in the Tal-y-sarn mine over 540 feet. These mines were worked well into the present century but the most productive era for Drws-y-coed, the larger of the two was between 1855 and 1909 when the output was nearly 8,700 tons of ore averaging from 9 to 14 per cent of copper.

Other small copper mines have been opened in Cwm Ceunant and on the lower slopes of Carnedd-y-filiast, both on the west side of Nant Ffrancon, and also above Llyn Du'r Arddu and near the head of Llyn Peris, whilst numerous trial excavations are mentioned by William Williams (1802) in his *Observations on the Snowdon Mountains*.

Lead and zinc ores: Ores of lead and zinc that have from time to time been thought worth working occur in a number of places *around the margin* of our area: taking them in a clockwise direction they are between Trefriw and Betws-y-coed, near Blaenau Ffestiniog, near Llanfrothen, and near Llanllyfni.

The oldest and most important mines are those in the first-named of these regions. They are situated in the hills rising from the Conway valley towards Llyn Geirionydd. There are indications that the ores were known to the Romans and in 1625 Sir John Wynn asked Sir Hugh Myddleton, of London's New River fame, to do something about exploiting the lodes which happened to be on his estate—but not, he explained, with a view to personal profit! "My skill is little," he wrote, "and my experience none at all in such matters; yet I ever had a desire to further my country in such actions as might be for their profit, and leave a remembrance of my endeavours."

The lodes usually occupy fissures and faulted zones near the junction of sedimentary rocks (slates, believed to be of Bala age) with igneous rocks. One set runs north and south and the other east and west. The principal ores are galena (sulphide of lead) and blende (sulphide of zinc), but other metallic minerals such as pyrites (a brassy-looking mineral consisting of sulphide of iron) and copper pyrites also occur in varying but usually unimportant quantities. The ore minerals are associated principally with quartz when the lodes are in volcanic rock and with calcite (crystalline carbonate of calcium) when they are in slates. The lode material contains an average of from 8 to 15 per cent of galena and from 8 to 10 per cent of blende, and the galena sometimes contains silver, usually about 2 ozs. to the ton but occasionally as much as 18 ozs.

In all about 20 mines have been opened. The principal period of activity was the second half of the last century and the first few years of the twentieth. Nearly 1,400 tons of lead ore and over 1,800 tons of zinc ore were raised from the New Pandora Mine, south west of Llanwrst, between 1877 and 1911. Between 1855 and 1911 the Pool

Mine near Betws-y-coed yielded nearly 1,500 tons of lead ore and 700 tons of zinc ore, while during approximately the same period the Llanwrst Mine yielded over 1,500 tons of lead ore.

During the present century the most productive undertaking has been the Trecastell Mine, about three miles south-west of Conway, which, between 1900 and 1914, yielded 4,800 tons of lead ore and 9,000 tons of zinc ore. Some of the neighbouring lakes (e.g. Llyn-y-parc and Llyn Geirionydd) were artificially extended to serve as reservoirs to provide water power for the plant in which the ore was crushed and concentrated, but modern machinery and methods were introduced at some of the mines before they closed down.

Old as well as fairly recent levels have been driven to work lead and zinc ores in the Ordovician sediments and volcanic rocks on the lower slopes of Moelwyn Bach and near the Gamallt lakes in the neighbourhood of Blaenau Ffestiniog. The Bwlch-y-plwm mine near Llanfrothen church has been worked intermittently for about a century, whilst shafts and levels have been driven into rocks of Ordovician age both here and in the Llanllyfni district in the Nantlle valley. Although important in the economic life of the district the output from all these mines was small compared with the national output of lead ore and the future of the mines is highly problematic.

Iron Ores: The processes of erosion, transport, and denudation have affected ore-bearing lodes as well as the rocks with which they are associated, and, occasionally, sedimentary rocks are so rich in metallic compounds deposited with their other constituents that they yield valuable ores, especially when the subsequent action of percolating water has resulted in local concentrations of the metallic materials. One of the most important of the metals, the ores of which originated as sedimentary rocks or have been formed within such rocks, is iron. The iron ores of Cumberland, Staffordshire and South Wales, as well as those so extensively quarried in some of the east midland counties and in Yorkshire, occur in or are associated with sedimentary rocks.

Here and there amongst the Cambrian and Ordovician sediments of our area there are beds of what is for this country, a somewhat unusual type of iron ore. It is a dark heavy rock, often full of oolitic and pisolitic grains (i.e. more or less rounded grains, resembling the hard roe of fish or approximating to the size of peas or beans). The iron content averages about 45 per cent, but it may be as much as 52 per cent.

The iron is present largely as the mineral chamosite, with other members of a group of flaky minerals consisting of silicates of aluminium, iron, and magnesium, and known collectively as chlorite; but in many of the ores the chloritic mineral has been partly altered into iron oxides—either magnetite, which is black, or haematite, which is red.

It is believed that the oolitic and pisolitic grains grew *in situ* as the muddy sediments were consolidating. The iron-bearing deposits appear to have been laid down in shallow water upon an uneven surface that was sinking, for they are covered by fine-grained sediments deposited in quiet, relatively deep water. The ore-bodies usually occur as lenticular masses of small extent, partly because they were uneven in thickness when deposited and partly as a result of folding and faulting during periods of earth-movement.

Mines have been opened in several localities in and around our area although some of the ores contain too much silica and sulphur to have commercial importance. The more important of the workable occurrences are in rocks of Upper Cambrian age at Betws Garmon, where the ores are characteristically black with magnetite; those at Llandegai, which are to a large extent the red haematitic varieties, occur in beds of Lower or Middle Ordovician age, and others at Trefriw are in beds of Middle or Upper Ordovician age; similar ores occur elsewhere in Caernarvonshire outside our area, as well as in Anglesey and the Cader Idris district.

The ore bed at Betws Garmon is from 6 to 15 feet thick and in some places is triplicated, but whether this is because there are three separate beds or because parts of one bed have been displaced by faults and piled one above the other is not certain. The ore, which has been obtained from open workings or from short levels driven into the hillside, has been worked intermittently for more than a century; the first one-inch Ordnance map (1841) of the district shows an "Iron-stone Quarry" in the neighbourhood.

The mines at Llandegai are of recent origin, the first of them, the Penrhyn Mine, having been opened in 1913. The ore occurs in sharply folded beds from 4 to 14 feet in thickness and has been won from open workings and short levels. Some of the mines were active in the early half of the present century; in 1917 one of them produced as much as 300 tons of ore a week, some of which went to the steel works at Brymbo in Denbighshire while some went to those near Swansea.

Difficulties due to the chemical composition of the ores (which renders some of them unacceptable to steel-makers), the somewhat irregular disposition of the deposits (which affects both the working conditions and the estimation of probable reserves), and the remoteness of the mines (which made transport to the furnaces difficult and expensive) have all militated against the development here of a large-scale iron-mining industry.

At the eastern extremity of our area there is an interesting deposit of pyrites. It occurs as a seam or bed about six feet thick, outcropping on the steep western slope of the Conway valley about a mile north of Trefriw. It rises northwards at an angle of about 27° and separates an intrusive mass of diabase below, from black shales of Bala age above. It was extensively worked during the 1914–18 war and has been studied more recently with a view to future working but the results were not encouraging. Pyrites is principally of value on account of its sulphur, which can be used in the manufacture of sulphuric acid, but it is also possible in certain circumstances to recover the iron.

The mode of origin of the Trefriw pyrites deposit presents an interesting problem and in the opinion of R. L. Sherlock, who examined the mine when it was being worked, the ore originated as a pisolitic iron ore like those of Betws Garmon or Llandegai but was converted into pyrites as a result of the intrusion beneath it of the magma that gave rise to the now subjacent diabase.[1]

Quarries: On the whole, mining activity has not seriously affected the scenery of our area but the same cannot be said of quarrying. Slate quarries with their great waste heaps have already been mentioned, and stone quarries have completely altered the appearance of Penmaen-mawr and other mountains made up of intrusive igneous rocks. The summit of Penmaen-mawr has now almost completely gone, and with it an ancient tribal fort. The once familiar rounded profile has been replaced by the horizontal lines of a table mountain.

Consisting largely if not entirely of minute and often intergrowing crystals, the rocks of Penmaen-mawr and Yr Eifl in Llŷn are tough and resistant to abrasion and on that account are specially suitable for road making; they are, indeed, as good for the purpose as any in the country and can be delivered direct from quarry to quayside. Much as one may regret the ugliness for which quarries are responsible, it is

[1] A basic igneous rock similar in composition and mode of origin to dolerite but having certain peculiarities due to changes which some of its constituents have undergone.

necessary to remember their economic importance to the community: in 1931, for example (the year of the last census), nearly one-fifth of the males between the ages of fifteen and seventy in Caernarvonshire were employed in the slate and stone quarries.

3. HOW AND BY WHOM THE STORY
WAS COMPILED

" In attempts to improve, it is always desirable to be able to measure the distance we have laid behind us in our advance, and also that which still remains between us and the object in view."

Benjamin Thompson (Count Rumford, who inspired the foundation of the Royal Institution), 1795.

Early visitors, according to their reaction to mountains, described the beauties, the magnificence, the "terrific chaos" or the "horrid sublimity" of our area. Some found that the journey got on their nerves. The Hon. John Byng, for example, wrote, in his diary of a tour made in 1784, "I now don't sleep well at night, but am eternally climbing over rocks, descending precipices, etc. . . . wake at 4 o'clock in the morning, not to sleep again." Others wrote of stupendous summits, perpendicular cliffs, and immense cataracts; they recorded memories of mists that buried everything in impenetrable obscurity, and occasionally they remarked upon the columnar rocks, the slates, the mines, and the soils, but it was not until towards the end of the eighteenth century that anyone paid attention to what we should now call the geology of the region, or sought to explain the origin of the rocks and of the features to which they have given rise.

Pennant had seen, in the rocks of Y Glyder Fach and in pieces of what he took to be lava, reasons for supposing "this and its neighbours to have been thrown up by some mighty internal convulsion," but, in his account of a tour in 1796, Arthur Aikin began a chapter entitled *Geological Observations* by saying, "There are no proper volcanic productions to be met with in North Wales; by proper volcanic substances I mean ashes, lava, and scoriae or semi-vitrified stones such as are the peculiar products of Etna and other acknowledged volcanoes."

John Evans, who toured the district in 1798, ridiculed Pennant's suggestion partly on the grounds that, since many of the rocks have "marine shells imbedded in them, they rather support the opinion of *the action of water than the action of fire*"—an interesting example of incorrect deduction from incomplete evidence. There are, indeed, fossil shells of marine origin, but not in *all* the beds! Evans went on to say that he had never discovered in the area "anything that could possibly be construed into volcanic matter," and cited in support of his view "the testimony of a gentleman, whose name, were I permitted to use it, would add honour to these pages. He affirms *that he never could discover any volcanic matter, nor the least symptom of the action of fire amidst these mountains.*" It is, perhaps, as well for the gentleman's reputation that Evans did not reveal his name. Evans must, however, be given credit for being the first to record the occurrence of fossils in these old rocks.

According to Evans, Pennant thought that Llyn Du'r Arddu may have been the crater of a volcano. He seems to have been referring to the older author's allusion, in the original edition of his *Tour*, to "Ffynnon Las" as lying in a "horrible crater," but to speak of a crater is not necessarily to imply that it is of volcanic origin, and even if Pennant had thought in terms of a volcano he can be more easily forgiven than can Mr. Evans's anonymous gentleman who saw in the lakes and in "everything in the vicinity" evidence of "the retreat of waters towards the bowels of the earth." "Not feeling," as he wrote, "at present any symptom of hydrophobia," Evans subscribed to the once popular belief that when the waters of The Deluge subsided they found their way into mysterious subterranean caverns, and to him the cwms were the funnels, as it were, down which the waters passed. He may have been influenced by his "knowledge" that "Llyn Peris . . . is of prodigious depth, a line of seventy fathoms in places not finding the bottom"! His contemporary, W. Bingley, on the other hand, was content to describe the vale of Llanberis as containing "two small lakes or rather pools, for their size will scarcely admit of the former appellation."

It was not until early in the nineteenth century that the part played by volcanic rocks in the make-up of the region began to be fully appreciated, and even then the observations were mostly confined to a mention of the names of various kinds of rock. Walter Davies, who in 1810 wrote a *General View of the Agriculture and Domestic Economy of North Wales*, mentioned the soil, the slates, the "primitive aggregates of the siliceous class," the ores, and the minerals, but he said nothing about stratification and structure.

William Smith was not familiar enough with our area to do more than give the whole of it one tint representing "Killas or Slate" on his 1815 map of England and Wales, but he did, on his 1825 map, show that he was aware of the occurrence of igneous rocks also, for he included a narrow band of "trap rocks" trending NE./SW. in the midst of a large area of "Killas or Slate and other mountain strata." ("Trap" is an old Swedish name that was originally applied to igneous rocks of types like those now included under the terms basalt and dolerite, and early geological literature contains many references to trap rocks.)

On the geological map of England and Wales prepared by G. B. Greenough in 1819 the local rocks were indicated as "clay-slate and porphyry" with the higher ground occupied by "compact fieldspar or hornstone." On a second edition of Greenough's map published twenty years later, the area was shown as consisting of "Clay Slate with frequent beds of porphyry, greenstone, and compact feldspar"; the complexity of the geology of the area had been realized, but the details were as yet not worked out and the area was again given one tint only.

The first serious attempt to attack the geological problems of our area was made by Adam Sedgwick in 1831. He had already spent some time in the Lake District where also there were igneous rocks associated with Ordovician sediments, and in North Wales he was better able to appreciate the significance of the slates and grits and lavas than those whose geological knowledge had been gained in the south of England, where many of the pioneer geologists lived or worked.

From Sedgwick's *Life and Letters* we learn that when in North Wales he went from peak to peak, in traverse after traverse, always seeking some more easily recognizable stratum that he could adopt as a base-line upon which to build up the succession of strata and by means of which he could correlate them from one mountain mass or one exposed section to another. His physical energy and geological insight were such that at the end of his first season's work he had obtained a good grasp of the essential structures and had recognized the synclinal character of Snowdon itself. In a communication made to the British Association in 1832 he stated that "the lowest beds of these strata are composed of mica slate. . . . The highest mountains are distinctly stratified and not infrequently contain organic remains, but are associated with masses of compact felspar and porphyry, generally arranged in masses parallel to, and passing into, the true strata: the laminae of slaty cleavage, after passing through the various beds of entire mountains, are seldom, if ever, parallel to the stratification."

Describing the occasion in a letter to Murchison, he wrote, "I dwelt specially on the position of the fossiliferous trough of Snowdon and I showed on the unequivocal evidence of the sections that the fossil beds were many thousands of feet above the great slate quarries of Nant Ffrancon and Llanberis." In the following year he told members of the Cambridge Philosophical Society that "by various traverses across Caernarvonshire and Merionethshire it was ascertained that the strata of the district are bent into saddles and troughs of which the anticlinal and synclinal lines occur alternately and are all nearly parallel to the great Merionethshire anticlinal line." It would be difficult, to-day, to present a clearer picture of the structure of the area in as few words.

Sedgwick also recognized the subaqueous origin of the lavas, but he did not, at that time, make a detailed geological map, and on one prepared to illustrate a paper read in 1843 he was content to indicate the strike or trend lines of the strata and the lines of anticlinal or synclinal axes without delimiting the outcrops of the rocks.

In a letter written from Llanllyfni on September 13th, 1831, he told Murchison—then a keen amateur, but later to succeed de la Beche as Director of the Geological Survey—something of his adventures in Caernarvonshire. His first recollection was of conditions that many others have experienced since. "As the Prince of the Air would have it," he wrote, "I was almost drowned in a thunderstorm the very morning I commenced my labours . . . I have now been at real hard work, cracking the rocks of Caernarvonshire for rather more than three weeks, and can report progress." He had already realized that "Anglesey is almost as distinct in structure from Snowdonia as if they had been separated by the Atlantic Ocean rather than the Straits of Menai."

Although it is to Sedgwick that we owe the first clear description of the structure of our area, the first detailed geological map to delineate its strata was prepared by Daniel Sharpe in 1846. Sharpe's map illustrates in an interesting manner the difficulties of pioneer work in such a district. He had made a special study of slaty cleavage and showed that the strike of the cleavage planes was remarkably constant over wide areas and that their dip increased from low angles around

Blaenau Ffestiniog to nearly vertical on the west side of Snowdon, but he completely misunderstood the general structure and maintained that an anticlinal—not a synclinal—axis passed through Snowdon, and that northwards, towards the Llanberis slates, newer and newer beds appeared—not, as Sedgwick believed and as we now know to be the case, older and older ones. His mistake was no doubt due to the fact that he concentrated too much upon one feature—the cleavage—and did not pay sufficient attention to the evidence of stratification and to the fossils, which, although not abundant, and at that time less fully understood than at present, might have given him a clue.

In 1847 the Geological Survey—then a little more than a decade old—turned its attention to Snowdonia and, with several workers devoting their energies to it, detailed knowledge began to accumulate very rapidly. H. T. de la Beche, to whose vision and persistence we owe the establishment of the Survey, directed the work in North Wales, but the field work was mostly done by A. C. Ramsay, W. T. Aveline, A. R. C Selwyn, J. B. Jukes, and W. W. Smyth (who paid special attention to the minerals), while J. W. Salter and Edward Forbes concentrated upon the fossils. Andrew Crombie Ramsay was the outstanding figure and he contributed more than any other single individual to our knowledge of the geological structure of our area, its glaciation, the history of its denudation, and the development of its scenery.

He was the son of a Scottish dyer (of Haddington) who founded the Glasgow Chemical Society which later gave place to the Philosophical Society of that city. Andrew joined the Survey in 1841, became Local Director for Great Britain in 1845, and began his work in our area in 1847. He devoted most of his time to North Wales until the work there had been completed, and, after his retirement from the Survey in 1881, when he received the honour of knighthood, went to live at Beaumaris where he could enjoy the panorama of the mountains to our understanding of which he contributed so much.

The new surveys were made on the basis of the one-inch Ordnance maps and it was possible to delineate, in greater detail than ever before, the outcrops of many of the volcanic and intrusive rocks and of the sedimentary rocks amongst which they occurred. Various sheets of the one-inch geological map of the area were published between 1851 and 1854, followed by a series of horizontal sections on the scale of six inches to the mile.

A permanent memorial to the work of the Geological Survey in our area was provided by Ramsay's memoir on *The Geology of North Wales*, published in 1866. Murchison, who had by then succeeded de la Beche, expressed the opinion that it was the most important work issued since he assumed office. The field work had been completed by about 1857 and Ramsay explained that the delay in publication was due principally "to the numerous occupations that fall to the lot of one who directs all the field work of the Survey and who edits its Geological Memoirs and who has had to superintend the details of the publications of the various maps and sections issued." The volume was accompanied by a geological map of Wales on the scale of 10 miles to an inch; this demonstrates in a striking manner the progress made during the years the Survey officers had been working in the district, for it differs in but few important respects from one that could be published to-day on the same scale. The volume also contained some fine coloured sections illustrating the structure of the principal mountains and the relation of our area to the Harlech Dome. J. W. Salter contributed an account of the fossils, illustrated by twenty-six plates with over 320 drawings.

After surveying the area in the nineteen-twenties with all the advantages of modern methods in palaeontology, petrology, and chemical analysis, Howell Williams was able to say, "Considering the limited means at Ramsay's disposal he outlined the salient features in the structure of Snowdon with admirable accuracy."

The diaries and letters of some of the early surveyors give us interesting sidelights upon their work. At that time geology was still young enough for every new discovery to give a thrill. Ramsay, for example, records (June 21, 1848) "Out north to Marchlyn Mawr. While minutely examining the section and hammering along out jumped a trilobite and a lingula some 600 or 700 feet down from the 'Cambrians' as we call them. So here at one blow vanishes the idea which we all believed, that the rocks are unfossiliferous beneath the trappy series."

A similar experience befell Joseph Beete Jukes, who joined the survey in 1846 and became Director of the Geological Survey in Ireland in 1850. He wrote of an occasion when, after five weeks of hard work trying to understand a "complicated bit of ground" south-west of Conway, he succeeded only in getting on his map "as curiously complex a patchwork of incongruous colours and unnatural forms as Punch, had he turned geologist, could have devised." Then, as he was descending a steep hill after a hard day's work "in despair, as all my labour seemed to be thrown away," he wrote, "I hit upon the clue to a great fault or dislocation . . . It gave me at once the solution of all the puzzle; and in two or three days I was enabled to map the whole district with as near an approach to accuracy as the scale of the map admitted of . . . I have ever since regretted that, in my haste and joy at acquiring a right notion, I obliterated all my former work from the map which contained it; for I should have been glad to preserve it now as a curious instance of the contrast between laborious hypothesis and the simplicity of natural truth." Then, as now, the weather determined the rate at which progress could be made. "Clear hill tops," wrote Ramsay, "are so scarce that one day when they are so is worth a fortnight's foggy weather."

The Director of the Survey made a practice of visiting his assistants in the field from time to time, and such occasions were a source of great pleasure to the young men. Ramsay tells how on one such visit he went to the top of Snowdon with de la Beche and his daughter. "It was a glorious day. First all the country was partially enveloped in white fog, which, clearing off here and there, showed peeps of the country as if set in a superhuman frame. . . . Confound the tourists though, that one meets a-top, and confound the huts and coffee pots, visitors' books and guides." That was a century ago!

Several members of the Geological Survey staff began their domestic lives during the course of their work in our area. Edward Forbes and his wife made their first home in a cottage at Llanberis, and invited Ramsay to join them. That was in 1848, and in the following year Ramsay wrote that he had promised to go to Aber to look for a cottage that J. B. Jukes could occupy after *his* marriage. A year later, whilst in Anglesey, it was Ramsay's good fortune to meet the lady who, eighteen months later, became his own wife. She was Miss Williams, daughter of the Rector of Llanfairynghornwy.

Accommodation seems to have been as difficult to obtain in those days as it is now, and was, in the opinion of those who wanted it, unreasonably expensive. Jukes, for example, complained that "These confounded artists won't go away from Bettws-y-coed, and I'm almost reduced to a standstill...every house is crammed full of amateurs of scenery and salmon-fishing...I had to wait about two months for lodgings the year before last. Llanrwst would do very well, but there are no lodgings to be had there. For a poking room leading out of a kitchen, which you had to cross to go upstairs, they asked me thirty shillings per week, and it was the best room that was ever let out in the town."

Our admiration for the work of those early surveyors is increased when we remember that they had no contoured maps and none of any kind on a larger scale than one inch to the mile, while, judged by modern standards, their instruments were cumbersome and inadequate. Writing to Ramsay in 1847, when working around Capel Curig, J. B. Jukes wrote: "By the bye, both Gibbs' and my compass are spiflicated. I am going to try and remagnetise them, but fear I shan't succeed, in which case I must send them both up to London. Would it not be a good dodge to have a few spare needles and cards at the office in boxes made on purpose, which could be sent at once in such a case ? I don't think I can go on without the compass to fix myself."

The geological complexity of our area, together with difficulties arising from the mountainous character of the country, resulted in the work proceeding more slowly than de la Beche had anticipated. He still had to justify the existence of the Geological Survey and liked to be able to report each year that so many square miles had been surveyed, but his own work had been done mostly in the south where the rocks were more fossiliferous, the structure more straight-forward, and travel much easier, and he seems not fully to have appreciated the difficulties of the work in North Wales. The delay not only meant that there was little to report for Snowdonia, but it kept his men from being transferred to other districts, and we find him complaining to Ramsay, "MORE (!!!) examinations in North Wales! The very sound of such matters sets me adrift." Ramsay very wisely insisted that it was better that the omissions and errors which they discovered as the work proceeded should be amended as they went along, "rather than leave them open to amateur carpers."

The earliest published reference to a feature now regarded as indicative of ice action in our area was a note *On the Diluvial Deposits of Caernarvonshire* by Joshua Trimmer (1831). He described the shell-bearing gravels of Moel Tryfan and elsewhere, and recorded that some of the associated pebbles and boulders were to be identified with rocks found *in situ* in Anglesey, Cumberland, and Scotland, but he regarded the deposits as having been "drifted upward by some violent inundation in a direction contrary to that of the rivers which descend from Snowdonia to the Menai."

The idea of an Ice Age was introduced into this country soon after 1840 by the Swiss naturalist J. L. R. Agassiz, who had taken up with enthusiasm certain suggestions made by T. de Charpentier (in a paper to the Swiss Society of Natural Sciences) relating to the former existence in Switzerland of glaciers much larger than those of the early nineteenth century. The "glacial theory," as it was called, was first opposed and then championed by William Buckland, Professor of Geology at Oxford, who more than any one else was responsible for its adoption by geologists in this country.

Once recognized, the glacial features of North Wales were pointed out as indubitable indications of the former existence of conditions quite unlike any that now obtain, and a note by Charles Darwin shows how completely their significance had previously been overlooked. He tells of how, in 1831, he and Sedgwick "spent many hours in Cwm Idwal examining all the rocks with extreme care, as Sedgwick was anxious to find fossils in them, but neither of us saw a trace of the wonderful glacial phenomena all around us. We did not notice the plainly scored rocks, the perched boulders, the lateral and terminal moraines. Yet these phenomena are so conspicuous that a house burnt down by fire did not tell its story more plainly than did this valley. If it had still been filled by a glacier the phenomena would have been less clear than they now are."

With the appearance, in 1881, of a second and enlarged edition of Ramsay's memoir, in which he discussed the physiography of the region, the effects of ice action, and the history of its rivers, we come to the end of the first important period in the history of geological investigation in our area. By then most of the rock-subdivisions had been mapped and their relations recognized, while the parts played by volcanoes in building up the rocks, and by glaciers in shaping the surface features, had been fully appreciated. Ramsay himself had given a clear picture of the glacial phenomena in his *Ancient Glaciers of Switzerland and North Wales*, a little volume published in 1860.

The work of the next stage had, however, already been commenced when, in 1875, J. Clifton Ward began to apply the microscope to the study of volcanic rocks and described some of the "felstones" and ashes exposed along the Llanberis track and near Glaslyn. A few years later F. Rutley showed that some of the lavas were likely to be devitrified glassy rocks. Nowadays it is difficult to conceive of a geological survey of such an area being undertaken without constant reference to the

PLATE II

L. Dudley Stamp

TYPICAL SHEEP FARM south-east of Snowdon, whose top is in the clouds. Walled fields in the valley are ploughed for the growing of oats and other food crops; there is rough grazing on the hill slopes beyond. April

John Markham

RHYD LLANFAIR, the high single-span bridge, a few miles above Betws-y-coed. Built about 1780

evidence yielded by the examination under the microscope of thin sections of rock.

The last quarter of the nineteenth century also saw the publication of Alfred Harker's essay on *The Bala Volcanic series of Caernarvonshire* (1889) to which we have already referred, and the inauguration of detailed studies of the trilobites and graptolites, notably, in the case of the latter, by Charles Lapworth and others, including Gertrude Elles, who followed his lead. Their work prepared the way for the accurate correlation of the Cambrian, Ordovician, and Silurian strata by the recognition of "zones" or series of beds characterized by certain species or assemblages of fossils.

When J. R. Dakyns retired from the Survey in 1896 he went to live within reach of Snowdon, which he had known and loved from boyhood days, and he spent much of the next sixteen years in re-mapping its rocks and studying some of its unsolved problems, but he never completed the work and consequently never published his maps. This was a pity, and an account by Greenly of the events which led to this unfortunate result illustrates the extent to which the personal element may influence the rate or direction of scientific progress. There were, it appears, two large gaps in the work—one relating to the northern slopes of Snowdon and the other to an area overlooking Nant Gwynant. At the time, Dakyns was living in a house between the lakes Gwynant and Dinas, and when asked why he did not get on with his survey of the country on the north side of Snowdon he complained of the toil involved in going over the summit to do it. To Greenly's suggestion that it might be done from Llanberis he replied: "Never, that's a nasty sharky place." That may have been a reason or merely an excuse, for since Llanberis was a fairly populous place he would have found it necessary there to put on what he called "respectable clothes," and he preferred to wear his suits regardless of appearance, so long as they held together.

A sheep-dog was responsible for the failure to complete the maps for the south-eastern side of Snowdon. The animal had been condemned to death for sheep-killing but Dakyns had secured a reprieve on the understanding that he would be responsible for any damage done subsequently. One of the farmers was not satisfied; high words passed between the two men and Dakyns vowed that he would not go on that farmer's land again; neither did he. His work was not entirely in vain, however, because when Howell Williams began to re-survey

Snowdon in 1923, Greenly was able to arrange for him to have access to the then almost forgotten maps which were later presented to the Geological Society. We have already mentioned Dakyn's part in recognizing that some of the rocks which the earlier workers had regarded as lavas were really of pyroclastic origin.

In 1903 W. G. Fearnsides discovered graptolites of the tuning-fork type (*Didymograptus*) on the northern side of Snowdon in the beds now called the Maesgwm slates. This discovery showed that the lowest volcanic rocks of Snowdon lay only a little above beds of Llanvirn age, and paved the way to the realization that the volcanic episode was not, as had previously been supposed, entirely of Bala age, but was in part earlier—of Llandeilo age. Later on Fearnsides showed that the sedimentary rocks with which the main rhyolites of the area are interbedded contain trilobites suggesting that they belong to the lowest part of the Bala series. The glacial features of the area, particularly those due to erosion, were discussed by W. M. Davis in 1909.

Although the fame of Edward Greenly rests principally upon his work in Anglesey, he has turned his attention from time to time to the problems of the mainland. He played a part in demonstrating the probable dust-origin of rocks that were originally believed to be lavas, studied the glacial phenomenon of the coastal region, and as far back as 1898 initiated an investigation by the British Association of the glacial deposits on Moel Tryfan that were being rapidly destroyed by quarrying: as a result of his action we have valuable records of features that cannot now be seen. Greenly also wrote a brief popular account of the geology of the area for *The Mountains of Snowdonia*, published in 1925.

The latest phase of detailed work was begun by G. L. Elles when she described the Ordovician and Silurian rocks of Conway: thirteen years later Howell Williams published an account of the igneous rocks of the Capel Curig area. In 1926 Fearnsides and T. O. Morris described the Cambrian slate area of Nantlle, and then, for a few years, important papers followed one another in rapid succession. 1927 saw the appearance of Howell Williams's paper on Snowdon, followed in 1930 by an account of the adjacent region between Nant Peris and Nant Ffrancon by his brother David Williams. In 1931 the Dolwyddelan region was described by Howell Williams and O. M. B. Bulman, while the country between Trefriw and Capel Curig was described by D. A. Bryn Davies in 1933, and in 1934 Philip Lake revived interest in the radial pattern of the rivers of Wales, of which pattern our area constitutes the centre. In the same year Greenly discussed the age of the mountains, as distinct from the ages of the rocks out of which they have been carved. The relation between the most recent changes of level and local legends was discussed by the present writer, after an examination in 1939 of the seaweed-covered reef called Llys Helig, off Penmaen-mawr, and the relevant documentary evidence.

We now have fairly recent detailed accounts of the geology of most of the central parts of our area, but much work still remains to be done in the region surrounding the main Snowdon tract on the south-west, south, and south-east, while the great compact northern region, cut off by Nant Ffrancon and the valley of Llugwy, and including more than half the really high ground of Caernarvonshire, received less attention from the early workers than the areas more easily accessible from roads; as far as recent published work goes it is still almost unknown, except for its north-eastern and south-eastern corners.

Seneca wrote his *Quaestiones Naturales* a very long time ago, but, as we look at our area and at those who have made its geological history known to us, we can say with him, "Let us not be surprised that what is buried so deeply should be unearthed so slowly. . . . The world is a poor affair if it does not contain matter for investigation in every age . . . Nature does not reveal all her secrets at once." Opinions change, explanations that have satisfied for generations are suddenly shown to be invalid, and we are asked to add new details to pictures that have long been regarded as complete, because, as James Hutton wrote in his *Theory of the Earth* (1795), "While man has to learn, mankind must have different opinions. It is the prerogative of man to form opinions; these are often, commonly I may say, erroneous, but they are commonly corrected, and it is thus that truth in general is made to appear." Hutton was a contemporary of William Smith, and he it was who led the way in showing that, in geology, the present is the key to the past —that, by observing the effects of geological processes in operation to-day, we can envisage the conditions which produced similar effects in ages past.

4. CLIMATE AND WEATHER

" The climature of North Wales naturally divides itself into three
kinds :   that of the vales, the hills and the mountains.   The
humidity of the atmosphere, on particular seasons, which, in the
first climate, falls in rain ;   may be observed, in the second, to be
sleet ;   and in the third perfect snow."

> Walter Davies, *General View of the* . . .
> *Domestic Economy of North Wales* (1810)

Caernarvonshire shares in the mild moist climate that prevails in the
western coastal regions of Europe. It is influenced by the warm surface
waters which drift north-eastwards across the Atlantic, and by moisture-
laden winds that come from the sea. The water of the sea absorbs heat
less quickly than the land and loses it more slowly and, as a result, is
relatively cooler in summer and warmer in winter than the land. Winds
coming from it tend to cool the land in summer and to warm it in
winter, giving to maritime regions a climate more equable than that
experienced farther inland.

On the lower ground around the Caernarvonshire coast the
temperature is comparable with that of westerly regions in Britain
farther south rather than with more easterly regions at the same
latitude, for the latter are affected to a greater extent by the cold and
often dry winds from Europe than by the moist damp ones from the
Atlantic ocean; but since temperature falls with elevation above sea
level to the extent of approximately 1 °F. for each 300 feet the mountainous regions are normally cooler than the lowlands.

In winter Llŷn compares in temperature with Cardigan and
Torquay, Snowdon with Gower, and the Conway valley with Swansea
and Cardiff: in summer Llŷn compares with Pembrokeshire, and the
remainder. of the area with Carmarthenshire.

The effect of the mountains in hindering the passage of the warmer
westerly and south-westerly winds is seen in the fact that the average
January temperature in the mountainous Snowdonian area as a whole
is 41 °F. (it is of course much lower—about 30°—on the summit of
Snowdon), while for Llŷn it is just a little higher (42°), and for the
Conway valley a little lower (40°). In summer (July) Llŷn is the cooler
with an average of 59°, while the mountains and the Conway valley
experience the same average temperature (60°).

The day-to-day temperatures are influenced by the direction from

which the winds come, for those from the south and south-west are
warmer than those from the north and north-west. Within the mountainous region the mountain slopes are cooler than the valleys which
intersect them, except for brief intervals when clear sunny conditions
prevail in the height of summer.

Since the prevailing wind comes from the south-west and from the
sea, the rainfall in our area is higher than in inland and eastern parts
of Wales and England, but the actual amount of rain and its distribution
is determined principally by the mountainous character of the terrain.
When warm damp air meets the colder land and is compelled to rise
over the mountains it is cooled; condensation follows and cloudy
conditions are produced with, most likely, rain.

A generalized rainfall map of the area bears a striking resemblance
to one depicting contours. There is a coastal belt of (for Wales)
relatively low rainfall—less than 50 inches but varying from about
30 inches per annum at Llandudno and the outlying regions of Llŷn to
between 30 and 40 inches in a tract extending from Criccieth to Bangor
and round to the Conway Valley. Within this is a belt from five to
ten miles wide in which the rainfall is between 50 and 80 inches
annually, and within this again is a large triangular core, embracing
the highest ground, with a rainfall of over 80 inches. In some places
the maximum often exceeds 100 inches; in a few, more than 200 inches
are recorded from time to time.

Rainfall records were not published during the war years, but in
1939 the following amounts were recorded:—near Llyn Llydaw, 167
inches; in the lower end of Cwm Dyli, 126 inches; above Blaenau
Ffestiniog, 108; near Llyn Eigiau, 84; Criccieth, 48; Penmaen-mawr,
41; Caernarvon, 35; Llandudno, 28. In 1912 a total of 246 inches
was recorded above Glaslyn at a height of 2,500 feet. The effect of
elevation is also apparent during individual storms. On an unusually
wet day in June 1926, for example, when 7.25 inches fell in the
neighbourhood of the copper mine near Llyn Llydaw, less than half
an inch fell in Flintshire and Anglesey. The rule is not, however, an
invariable one and may even be reversed by local conditions. For
example, during the 14 years from 1931–44 the yearly average at the
Oakeley Quarries at an elevation of about 1,000 feet was about 101
inches, but at Llyn Morwynion, more than 200 feet higher and some
four miles to the south-east, it was rather less than 66 inches.

Even when no rain falls the skies are apt to be cloudy and the sunshine averages are less than those recorded for the eastern English counties, but rain is often heavy so that in the actual number of rainy days Snowdonia compares not altogether unfavourably with others which have a much smaller total rainfall. In 1939 when Cwm Dyli had 126 inches, more than one twenty-fifth of an inch of rain fell on each of 204 days. The corresponding figures for other places are as follows, above Blaenau Ffestiniog, 104 inches, 196 days; Bangor, 40 inches, 154 days; Llandudno, 28 inches, 132 days; Aberystwyth, 46 inches, 159 days; Tenby, 40 inches, 155 days; Truro, 45 inches, 160 days; Brighton, 42 inches, 157 days; Falmouth, 43 inches, 151 days.

In general the wettest months are August, and from October to January inclusive: the driest are usually April, May, June and September, but any year may show surprising variations from the general rule and only tables too extensive to print even if it were worth while to compile them would give a detailed picture of the vagaries of the weather in our area.

The approach of a "cyclone" or "depression" brings south-westerly winds and warm moist air, followed by rain, although in summer-time the higher ground may instead be enveloped in thick mist or fog which, according to circumstances, may be merely unpleasant or a source of danger to persons out upon the mountains. Sometimes it persists for long periods and at others it may be suddenly swept aside—giving glimpses of the lower hills and the valleys extending in all directions—perhaps for a moment or two, perhaps for the remainder of the day. The clouds and mist tend to obscure the sun, thus causing the temperature to fall. Often the clouds seem to rest upon the mountains so that the valleys look like vast grey-roofed caverns. Nant Ffrancon is particularly impressive when these conditions obtain.

In winter, on the other hand, an approaching depression results in a rise of temperature, and the extent of the rise is a fair indication of the amount of rain that may be expected. As a depression from the sea passes over the land the wind veers round towards the north-west; the barometer rises but the temperature falls because the air is coming from a colder northern region. It is warmed rather than cooled by the land and its capacity for holding moisture increases so that as the depression leaves the region the rain which came with it tends to become inconstant and finally to stop. The change is first experienced near the coast where the sky soon clears, but whether the mountains lose their cloud caps or not depends largely upon how long the wind blows from the direction in question.

These are general features due to the position of the region, but the weather is so greatly influenced by its mountainous character that the movements of the barometer and of the wind usually give earlier and more reliable information than the appearance of the sky, except perhaps to those with long experience, and those, like farmers and fishermen, whose work naturally makes them weather-wise.

If the general elevation of Snowdonia is responsible for its relatively high rainfall, the configuration of the land is responsible for the great local variation in the amounts of rain that fall. The cooling of warm moist air from the sea as it rises over the mountains is not only due to the attainment of a higher elevation but also to the fact that in general the mountains themselves are cooler. Some of the airborne moisture condenses to form clouds and probably also rain. It may be taken as a general rule that the greatest amount of rain falls just beyond the summits of the highest mountains that first lie in the way of the winds coming from the sea. The amount of cloud and the formation of rain are, however, influenced by the kind of weather that preceded the arrival of the south-westerly wind. After a long spell of sunshine the mountains are warmer than after a period of dull cold weather and the rain may be longer delayed.

There are, as we have seen, very large tracts of sand exposed at low tide in Tremadoc Bay and between Llandudno and Anglesey, and these probably influence the day-to-day weather even amongst the mountains. When the tide is out air passes over a considerable stretch of damp sand before it reaches the land, and if that condition obtains during the hotter part of a summer's day when there is much evaporation from the exposed surface, the air picks up a considerable charge of moisture. In such circumstances cloud caps appear on the mountains in the afternoon and there may be local showers, from whichever direction the wind may be blowing, since the sandy tracts are developed off the north coast as well as off the south. The lakes and the wide expanses of boggy country also contribute to the moistness of the atmosphere in the mountainous area.

Some of the early writers about Snowdonia spoke of its perpetual snows, but they were wrong, for, as fourteenth century Dafydd ap Gwilym wrote (the translation is by Sir H. Idris Bell), it is usually

In January's month, first of the year
God makes hermits everywhere.
Everywhere the country round,
He has whitewashed the black ground,
Clothed in white each woodland glade,
On every copse a white sheet spread.

Although snow may remain around the higher summits until May or June it rarely lasts longer than that, and even in winter, cold dry conditions are too uncertain in appearance and too short in duration to make the region a centre for winter sports. Snow remains longest in hollows and gullies high up in cwms facing northwards where it is sheltered from the sun and from the south-westerly rains; such places are found for example, here and there on the north-eastern face of Carnedd Llywelyn and the north face of Crib-y-ddysgl.

5. CARTOGRAPHY AND MAPS

" Some to beautify their Halls, Parkes, Chambers, Galeries, Studies or Libraries with, . . . some other for their own journeys or to understand other men's travels . . . liketh, loveth, getteth and useth, Maps, Charts and Geographical Globes."

John Dee : Preface to *The English Euclid* (1570)

The modern era of map-making for this country began in the fifteen-seventies, when the work of Christopher Saxton materialized in the volume of county maps (*An Atlas of England and Wales*) which he published in 1579. The honour is often accorded to John Speed whose county maps, first published in 1611 (in *The Theatre of the Empire of Great Britaine*), are more abundant and better known, but his maps are based upon earlier ones, most of them upon Saxton's. Our area is, however, represented upon older maps than Saxton's, and although it is not possible here to discuss in detail the history of the cartography of Snowdonia reference to some of the early maps that take note of it may not be without interest. Illustrations of many of them will be found in *The Map of Wales before* 1600 *A.D.*, published by the National Museum of Wales.

Giraldus Cambrensis is said to have made a map of Wales with rivers and mountains and the names of forty-three towns, but no recent student has seen the manuscript. It could not be found in 1780 by so assiduous a searcher as Richard Gough, the topographer.

Snowdon would, no doubt, have been one of the mountains Giraldus thought fit to include; it was, as we have seen, given a special place on the maps of Britain prepared about 1250 by or under the direction of Matthew Paris at St. Albans, and it was also the only mountain to be indicated by a symbol (a hill in profile), and a name, on the map of Britain (now in the Bodleian Library) prepared by an unknown worker early in the fourteenth century and usually known as the Gough Map after Richard Gough in whose possession it once was. The almost contemporary circular world map in Hereford Cathedral gives prominence to Snowdon, but it also includes a few mountains in other parts of Wales and the border counties.

These early manuscripts depict Wales as an oval mass separated from England by the rivers Dee and Severn and give no representation of Llŷn as a peninsula or of Cardigan Bay. A similar outline continued to appear on both manuscript and printed maps until well into the sixteenth century. One of them, an anonymous manuscript of 1534 in the Cottonian collection in the British Museum, has a large mountain-symbol named *Snowdone hillis* and another in central Wales in which the Severn and the Wye have their sources.

With continued copying the mountain symbols for Snowdon tended to spread into central Wales, and on what is probably the first printed map of the British Isles (apart from those after Ptolemy of Alexandria who flourished in the second century A.D.) the range of hummocks extends from near *Bangarium* halfway to *Suamsei* (Swansea). The map is attributed to George Lily and it was printed in Rome, probably in 1546.

For the first map to depict Llŷn in anything like its proper shape we are indebted to Gerard Mercator, well known by reason of a projection which he used for world maps and because he was the first to use the term *Atlas* for a collection of maps bound in a volume. It was a map of the British Isles prepared in 1564, and it was lost sight of by students until it was reprinted in 1892 from a copy found in the State Library at Breslau. Our area has a fine range of mountains extending through Llŷn from a river that has *Aberconwey* at its mouth, with other mountains running southwards on either side of the river. The latter is, however, called *Snowdon flu*, and *Snowdon hylle*, the mountain mass in which it rises, is placed in about the position of the Berwyn Hills instead of in the heart of Caernarvonshire. There are a few recognizable names like *Dalbadarn*, *Dolwytlan*, and *Maentrok* (Maentwrog), and some mistakes like *Carmarden* for Caernarvon, and *Seynt* for the river flowing by Bangor.

The next notable map that interests us was prepared by Humphrey Llwyd of Denbigh in 1568 and printed (in 1573) in the *Supplement* to an Atlas published by Abraham Ortelius of Antwerp. This map, too, depicts Llŷn as a peninsula but gives it a curious inward curve at the extremity. Mountain-symbols named *Snowden hil*, with *Y Widna* as its Welsh equivalent, occupy their correct positions between *L. Peris* and *Bethilhart* (Beddgelert), whilst other mountains are grouped about the *Lhugwy flu*, and yet others sweep round from *Peurindeudraeth* between *Penmachno* and *Festiniog*.

The quaint forms assumed by the names on most of the early printed maps are not necessarily an indication of how they were formerly spelt and pronounced, or a reflection upon the competence of those who prepared the manuscripts. They are due to the fact that the maps were engraved in the Low Countries by men as unfamiliar with Welsh—or indeed with English—as they were with the handwriting of those who had prepared the originals. There is, however, evidence that some of the map-makers made attempts at phonetic reproduction, but this is not a matter we can elaborate here.

On the maps we have already considered our area was merely part of Wales or of Britain, and their interest lies not in the detail they give but in the fact that Snowdon was indicated at all and was in many cases the only mountainous region so honoured. With Christopher Saxton the map enters upon a new phase because he devoted a whole sheet to Caernarvonshire and Anglesey, giving a map on a scale of approximately four miles to the inch.

The coastline on Saxton's map is surprisingly well delineated, although the end of Llŷn swings round too much to the south, as it does on Humphrey Llwyd's. Traeth Mawr is—as it should have been for the time—a large estuary reaching as far as *Llanwrothen*. Most of the important rivers are indicated, the Conway in some detail, as well as the more important lakes. Caernarvonshire is well covered with mountains drawn in profile: Snowdonia has almost 150 grouped around *Snowdon hill* which is very much larger than all the rest, and there are about 100 names of towns, rivers, and lakes. Having regard to the quality of the maps which preceded it, Saxton's (and this applies also to his maps of other parts of the country) surprises us by the amount and relative accuracy of the detail he included. In his days surveying instruments were crude, by modern standards, and travel was by no means easy and yet he was able to provide maps that served as a national standard for quite two centuries. Coloured reproductions of Saxton's maps were published a few years ago by the British Museum, from a very fine copy of their Atlas. The map of Caernarvonshire is unfortunately now out of print, but it should be consulted in libraries where it is available by all who are interested in the early maps of Snowdonia.

Saxton's maps were still being printed from the original plates (with alterations described as improvements and corrections, although they were really disfigurements) as late as 1690, and they were the main—often the sole—source of information drawn upon by the publishers of the "new" county maps during the whole of the seventeenth century and the early part of the eighteenth. Reduced copies of the maps (printed with due acknowledgment) were used to illustrate the last Latin edition (1607) and the early English editions (1610 and 1637) of Camden's *Britannia*: in these, Caernarvonshire was given a map to itself, well provided with symbols suggesting mountains with uneven slopes. The map of North Wales by Robert Morden used in the 1695 edition of Camden's *Britannia* was no more than a poor compilation from several of Saxton's, so also was the crude but popular map of North Wales published by Richard Blome in 1673, also in a work called *Britannia*. Each gives a much less satisfactory picture of our area than does its prototype.

John Speed devoted a whole map to Caernarvonshire, but it is so essentially a copy of Saxton's delineation of the county, with the addition of plans of Caernarvon and Bangor, as to require no further description. The first edition of the map was dated 1610 and it appeared in the *Theatre* which was published in 1611. The same map, still bearing the date 1610, appeared in the last edition of the *Theatre* published in 1676.

During the seventeenth century, maps of Caernarvonshire or of North Wales as a whole were included in the fine atlases published by the firms of Blaeu, Jansson, and Hondius of Amsterdam. The maps are well known because they are finely printed and in many cases attractively coloured (although modern attempts to enhance the price of an old map by colouring it, have, for the most part, produced crude and displeasing results), but they were all based upon Saxton's, either directly or through Speed's.

With continued copying and very little new work maps tended to
deteriorate during the latter part of the seventeenth century and most
of the eighteenth, and we may take as a typical example the *Map of
North Wales* by E. Bowen and T. Kitchin included in *The Large English
Atlas* published by T. Bowles and others in 1760. In it, mountains and
valleys are represented by shading made up of fine wavy lines but
conveying no accurate picture of their distribution, whilst the irregulari-
ties of the coastline have been so much exaggerated as nearly to sever
most of Llŷn from the remainder of the county. Except for the inclusion
of roads from Conway to Caernarvon and from Caernarvon to Traeth
Mawr the map is less informative and attractive than Saxton's, by
then nearly two centuries old.

The first map to depict Snowdonia on what may be regarded as a
reasonably large scale was published by John Evans of Llanymynech
near Oswestry in 1795. It is a map of North Wales on the scale of
about three-quarters of an inch to the mile and it depicts many of the
individual mountains by means of shading but makes most of them
appear as if they were either more or less rounded conical peaks or
long caterpillar-like ridges. The rivers are drawn in great detail and
the positions of isolated houses and farms are indicated, but one of the
most interesting features of the map is the information it gives relating
to the roads of the time.

The well-known map-publisher John Cary produced various
editions (e.g. 1809) of a map of Wales on the scale of about six miles
to an inch, but although attractive as a whole and very well engraved
the map is disappointing if studied for detail. The main roads are
clearly shown but the shading to indicate mountains is more vigorous
than accurate and gives no indication of their real forms.

The foregoing are typical examples of the kinds of maps on which,
from time to time, the topography and physiography of Snowdonia
have been indicated, and they will serve as representatives of the scores
of others, good, bad, or indifferent, that exist in manuscript, were
printed in atlases and topographical works, or were published as
separate sheets in the days before the Ordnance Survey turned its
attention to North Wales.

The earliest one-inch Ordnance Survey maps of our area, published
around 1840, are beautifully engraved and full of detail. One of their
most attractive features is the lively picture they give of the surface
relief (Pl. XXXIIa, p. 298). This is the result of carefully drawn

hachures—lines drawn in the direction of slope and varying in thickness and closeness according to its steepness: the thicker and closer the lines the steeper the slope. No lines at all are drawn where the ground is comparatively even, whether at high level or low, but where, as in Snowdonia, the higher ground consists mostly of narrow ridges, no confusion results: on the contrary, the pattern of the ridges and the grandeur of the cwms they separate are portrayed as clearly as they would be on a relief map.

On most current maps elevation and slope are indicated by contours —lines connecting all points at a given height above sea level. They differentiate between steeply and gently sloping ground, because the steeper the slope the closer they are together, but they go farther than hachures in that they indicate actual height above sea-level. Alone, however, they suggest unnaturally smooth rounded outlines for the mountains like those of Snowdonia and they are usually supplemented by a modified form of hill-shading to indicate precipitous slopes and sharp ridges.

The relief of a region is still more vividly portrayed when colours —usually green and brown, in various shades with the darkest shades of green for the lowest ground and the darkest shades of brown for the highest—are used in addition to contour lines to indicate elevation with hill-shading to indicate crags. For most purposes a coloured contoured map like the half-mile to the inch Ordnance Survey map or Bartholomew's half-inch map (Sheet 27) is the best to use when one desires to envisage the region as a whole or to enjoy a tour therein. A different purpose is served by the one-inch maps of the Land Utilisation Survey. These show, by contrasting colours, the use of the land—brown for ploughland, green for pasture, dark green for woodland, yellow for moorland, purple for houses, red for main roads and waste land. They are particularly useful for reference when reading about the scenery and human occupation of North Wales, because they show at a glance the extent of the moorland.

For serious scientific work the Ordnance Survey maps on the scale of six inches to the mile are necessary. Showing details like field-paths and field boundaries, cottages, and even sheep folds, they enable one's position to be fixed quickly and accurately and for that reason they are invaluable to ramblers also.

Our area was surveyed on the six-inch scale between 1885 and 1888 but there have been revisions up to 1920. Unfortunately the six-inch maps are not contoured above 1,000 feet, but the use of characteristic symbols to indicate different kinds of surface feature, and of "spot heights" to indicate elevation, make up to some extent for the deficiency. They enable one to envisage both the appearance and the elevation of the area represented. Differentiating between bog and swamp, between meadow and stony ground, and indicating the positions of crags and the extent of enclosed lands, they clearly present the general character of the country and indicate the elevation of all conspicuous summits.

Owing to circumstances connected with the recent war the range of available Ordnance Survey maps is now very limited, but new sheets are being published as rapidly as possible. These will include a new edition of the half-inch map, and an entirely new map on the scale of 1:25,000 or about 2½ inches to 1 mile, but some years are likely to elapse before sheets of either map are available for the Snowdon area. Sheet 107 of the new Popular Edition of the one-inch Survey map and sheet 27 of Bartholomew's half-inch contoured map cover Snowdonia.

Apart from maps of limited areas prepared to illustrate local monographs (see bibliography), there are no modern geological maps of the region, neither the quarter-inch nor the one-inch maps of the Geological Survey being now obtainable unless from stocks which may happen to be in the hands of local booksellers.

References for Chapter 4

SECTION 1
Davies (1936), Fearnsides (1905), Greenly (1925), Pennant (1810), Ramsay (1866), D. Williams (1930), H. Williams (1927).

SECTION 2
Dewey (1922), Dewey (1925), Greenly (1925), North (1946), Pulfrey (1933), Sherlock (1917), Strahan (1920).

SECTION 3
Aikin (1797), Browne (1871), Byng (1784), Clark and Hughes (1890), Evans (1800), Greenly (1938), North (1943), North (1946), Pennant (1784), Ramsay (1866), Sedgwick (1843), D. Williams (1930), H. Williams (1927).

SECTION 4
Howell (1946).

SECTION 5
North (1928), North (1935).

II

NATURAL HISTORY

By Bruce Campbell

CHAPTER 5

INTRODUCTION TO THE
NATURAL HISTORY

THE Snowdon range, whose striking scenery has been analysed by Dr. North in the preceding chapters, presents, especially in the holiday months of August and September, a somewhat enigmatic appearance either to botanist or zoologist. Great sweeps of grassland, with a limited and featureless flora, enlivened only by larks and meadow-pipits no longer in song; impressive cliffs whose rare alpine plants have now relapsed into the vegetative phase; slopes of scree over which occasional ravens and carrion-crows fly; swift rivers and deep lakes, many of them famous for their trout, and whose surface is broken by the thin spikes of the water lobelia: these are the chief elements in the landscape, which is the core of our region, and which will be the first objective of the visitor. But once Yr Wyddfa, the summit of Snowdon, clad in its customary mist, has been attained, and Llyn Idwal precariously admired through the vertical slit of Twll Du, the naturalist will probably turn to the east, to the Migneint, Wales's largest cotton-grass moor, thence to follow Afon Conwy through rapid changes of scenery until it emerges, anglicized, as the River Conway; or to deviate up the very different straths of its tributaries, Machno, Lledr and Llugwy; or even to break out of the strict boundaries of the future National Park altogether, to the sea-coast, to the Ormes with their limestone plants and sea-birds, to the sheltered, wooded shores of the Menai Straits, to the bare warrens of southern Anglesey, or to the bogs, marshes and saltings bordering Traeth Mawr.

These various landscapes and their wild life began interesting naturalists about three hundred years ago, and the next chapter covers what might be called the history of natural history in North Wales, with special reference to our region, which, apart from the classic pioneer expeditions to the summits, has not attracted nearly so much attention as the coastal districts around it.

Chapter 7 deals with the attitude of the human population generally, both resident and visitor, to the flora and fauna. This is an aspect which will become of even greater importance once the National Park is established, particularly as regards the impact of visitors, for the

Parks will be the first large-scale attempt in Britain to integrate a high concentration of humanity in wild country with the protection and encouragement of wild-life populations.

Chapters 8 to 11 contain the detailed description of the natural history of the region, as defined on Map 3 (p. 160). The area has been divided into broad habitat zones, but it is inevitable that purely ecological considerations must give way to geographical groupings, if the convenience of visitors is to be studied at all. Once such a compromise is made, two main divisions are clear: "Eryri," the Snowdon range, and "Nant Conwy," the name of an old Caernarvonshire hundred, which covered the upper part of the Conway valley and the valleys of its principal tributaries.

Eryri can be divided into three life-zones, according to altitude: first of all a semi-alpine zone, above 2,000 feet and therefore concentrated on the three principal massifs of the Carneddau, the Glyders, and Snowdon itself. This zone is described in Chapter 8.

Chapter 9 is devoted to the middle or grassland zone which extends between 2,000 feet and the natural tree-limit, varying from 750 to 1,000 feet above the sea. It contains many rock-faces and screes, some of the higher lakes, and the steep upper courses of the streams. Much of the grassland is, or has been, enclosed by stone walls, and is known in Welsh as *ffridd* (plural: *ffriddoedd*), which has become a general term for high pasture of this kind.

Chapter 10 covers the lowland zone. This includes the woodlands, the larger lakes and rivers, the cultivated farmland, and the bulk of the habitations, which exert their influence along the roadsides to form an attenuated habitat of considerable interest.

The valleys which drop away north-east and south from Penygwryd, at the eastern end of the Llanberis pass, make an obvious boundary between Eryri and Nant Conwy, the subject of Chapter 11. Although it includes Moel Siabod (2,860 feet) and the lower but rocky summits round the Ffestiniog basin, Nant Conwy can be dealt with in two principal zones: moorland and lowland. The moors, however, differ greatly in character, and the lowland zone has both extensive scrub-woods and the conifer plantations of the Forestry Commission, a good deal of farmland in the upper Conway, Machno and Lledr valleys, and the sizeable human settlements of Yspytty Ifan, Penmachno, Dolwyddelan and Betws-y-coed.

The final chapter of this section consists of a brief "tour," from

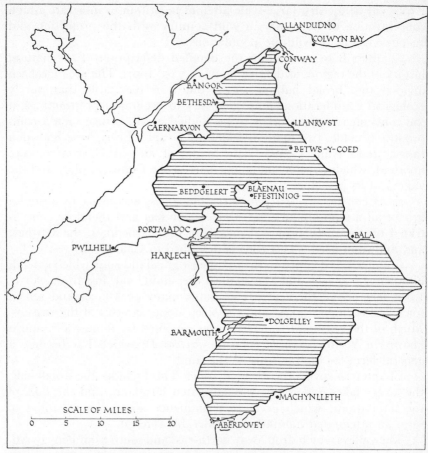

MAP 3.—The area proposed for the North Wales National Park by the
National Parks Committee

Based on the map in the Report of the National Parks Committee, July 1947. Reproduced by permission of the Controller of H.M. Stationery Office

north to south, of certain localities outside the future Park boundaries
which a naturalist on a visit to North Wales should not miss if possible;
they are all coastal and thus quite unlike anything to be seen inside
this part of the Park; one has already been chosen as a prospective
National Nature Reserve, and it is not too much to hope that others,
in view of their outstanding interest, may also eventually find themselves scheduled for conservation under national or regional auspices.

At the end of the book will be found an Appendix, in which an attempt has been made to summarize the wild life of this part of the North Wales National Park. Lists are given of all vascular plants and vertebrate animals, for whose presence in the region there is good evidence: the Welsh names for as many as possible of these species are also given. A much briefer treatment of the lower plants and of the invertebrates is dictated partly by considerations of space, and partly by our ignorance of the distribution of many of these groups in the region; lists of the more spectacular insects—grasshoppers, dragon-flies, hawk-moths and butterflies—are given as fully as possible.

The scientific names of all species listed are included in the Appendix, and, to facilitate straight reading, the scientific names of vertebrates listed are not also given in the text. But it was felt advisable to give the names of plants and invertebrates at the first mention of each species in the text as well; this, of course, also applies to vertebrates not listed in the Appendix. The sources followed for the nomenclature of each group will be found in the Appendix.

Several visits to the region in 1946 brought my knowledge of it up to date, but my indebtedness to others is great; sources are summarized at the end of each chapter and given in greater detail in the final bibliography. In addition to such acknowledgements, I should like to record my thanks to Mr. H. A. Hyde and Mr. A. E. Wade, Keeper and Assistant Keeper of the Botany Department, to Mr. Colin Matheson, Keeper of the Zoology Department, and to Miss Edwards, the Librarian, of the National Museum of Wales; their help has been continuous and invaluable. For assistance with special subjects I am grateful to Dr. William Davies and the staff of the Ministry of Agriculture's Grassland Improvement Station, and to the officers of the Forestry Commission, particularly Mr. F. C. Best and Mr. J. R. Hampson; the Welsh used in my section has been kindly checked in MS by Professor Evan John Jones, Mr. John Rees and Dr. Iorwerth Peate. Finally I must thank John Markham for the infinite trouble he took to get suitable photographs in the region, and for his companionship on several memorable occasions, and also Mr. Matthew Speake, Cefncyfannedd, for much practical help, and for information of Traeth Mawr and the south-western part of the area covered by these chapters.

The section was finally revised in October 1947, and no reference has been made to work published after that date.

CHAPTER 6

THE NATURALISTS OF NORTH WALES

EARLY Welsh literature is full of references to nature and to a number of creatures, usually those most striking to the traveller or most metaphorically useful to poet and writer. Eagles, of course, loom very large, and Giraldus Cambrensis, who has been called the first journalist, mentions several of them in relation to Snowdon. But it is the following passage, from his *Itinerary* (1188), which must rank as the first factual "Nature Note" about our region:

"Having traversed the valley, and reached the opposite side with considerable fatigue, the archbishop, to rest himself and recover his breath, sat down on an oak which had been torn up by the violence of the winds; and relaxing into a pleasantry highly laudable in a person of his approved gravity, thus addressed his attendants: 'Who amongst you, in this company, can now delight our wearied ears by whistling?' which is not easily done by people out of breath. He affirming that he could, if he thought fit, the sweet notes are heard, in an adjoining wood, of a bird, which some said was a wood-pecker, and others, more correctly, an aureolus. The wood-pecker is called in French *spec*, and with its strong bill perforates oak trees; the other bird is called aureolus, and at certain seasons utters a sweet whistling note, instead of a song. Some persons having remarked that the nightingale was never heard in this country, the archbishop, with a significant smile, replied, 'The nightingale followed wise counsel, and never came into Wales; but we, unwise counsel, who have penetrated and gone through it."

The Editor of the Everyman Series, whose translation this is, suggests that the incident took place in Nant-y-Garth, a narrow valley on the Vaynol estate near Bangor. The confusion of the Archbishop's entourage is realistic, since many reputed occurrences of the golden oriole in Britain have been traced to the green woodpecker, which in bright light has a golden tint. On the other hand the golden oriole has occurred recently in Caernarvonshire and, as it seems to have been early summer when the "Crusaders" reached Bangor, there is no inherent impossibility about the record; the bird is also associated with oak trees. Besides, Gerald may have been personally familiar with the oriole, since he had studied in France as a youth. His remark about the nightingale (*Luscinia m. megarhyncha*), incidentally, would still be true ornithologically, for though its Welsh name of *Eos* is frequently bestowed in admiration upon women singers, the bird itself is seldom heard except close to the borders of England.

But this eyewitness account remains isolated in a sea of literary semi-allegory and legend; even Leland's eagles may be taken with a grain of salt, and we have to wait until 1639 for the arrival of the first naturalist. Appropriately, in view of the principal attractions of the region, he was a botanist, the Englishman, Thomas Johnson[1].

Johnson was accompanied on his visit to Wales by three friends, one of them a Welshman who acted as an interpreter. They climbed both Snowdon and Carnedd Llywelyn—a considerable feat in those days—and did pretty well in the objects of their quest ; but they would have done better if their guide had not been afraid of the eagles of the Carneddau, a fact which has been jubilantly seized upon by all writers on the natural history of the district. Indeed, as far as the early natural history of Eryri is concerned, it is largely a history of the decline of its supposedly eponymous inhabitants (see pp. 4 and 202).

Johnson wrote in Latin, and it gives a certain unscientific pleasure to find the weather, which has been execrated so often in Welsh and English, feelingly described in the sonorous phrasing of a classical tongue. He was evidently much impressed by it, for it comes into the dedication of his account to a local landowner; nothing would please him more than again with more leisure *"benignioreque coeli aspectu"*[2] to visit places, which could show so many wonders of Nature to those diligently searching.

As to other early travellers, the scenery appeared frightening rather than impressive; the passage of *"Pen-maen-bahen & Pen-maen-mawre"* he calls *"duos horroris plenos transitus,"*[3] after which he relaxes in the cultivated beauty of *"Glynn-lhivonam"* (Glyn Llifon near Bangor), with

---

[1] whose interesting life has been the subject of a biography by H. W. Kew and H. E. Powell (*Thomas Johnson, Botanist and Royalist*. London, 1932).

[2] "and when the aspect of the sky is kinder." A translation of Johnson's original Latin was published in Bangor in 1908, apparently by Llew Tegid, though there is no name on the title page. It was called "The Itinerary of a Botanist" and a copy, bound together with other pamphlets and manuscript notes by J. E. Griffith, is in the possession of the Department of Botany, National Museum of Wales, by the kindness of whose Keeper I have been able to examine it. As a translation, however, it is somewhat inadequate, and the versions given in these foot-notes are based on it with corrections and additions by Professor E. J. Jones.

[3] "two passes full of horror."

its *"peramoena nemora,"*[1] soft and murmuring brooks, gardens adorned with flowers and herbs, and finally the view, so often enjoyed since; on one hand, *"Virgivium mare,"*[2] Anglesey, and even Ireland *"caelo sereno,"*[3] on the other *"Alpes nostrae Britannicae,"* which, rather sweepingly, he acclaims as *"montes totius insulae maximi,"*[4] and whose rigours he was soon to try.

The start of his ascent was under familiar conditions; not only the summit, but the whole mountain (Snowdon) was *"nubilis obvelatus,"*[5] and his description of the subsequent climb must be given in full: *"Hic via admodum angusta est, horroremque ascendentibus maximum incutiunt praecipitia cautibus aspera ex utraque parte, Stygiae etiam hinc & inde paludes, quarum maxima Daemonis domicilium ab incolis vocatur."*[6] Amongst the alpine flora he was, like others after him, surprised to find *"Gramen junceum marinum"* [*Juncus squarrosus*], *"Caryophyllum marinum"* [*Armeria maritima*] and *"Lychnidem marinam Anglicam"* [*Silene maritima*].

After this strenuous expedition, the party rested and also spent a few days in Anglesey, where they visited *Landhwin* (Llanddwyn) and on the way noted Newborough Warren (*"sterilem planitiem"*)[7] carpeted with a great variety of *"Jaceae tricoloris"* [*Viola curtisii*] and also *"Centaurii minoris,"* [*Centaurium littorale* and *C. umbellatum*] just as it was in 1946.

Carnedd Llywelyn seemed to impress Johnson even more than Snowdon: he calls it *"mons ille famigeratissimus Carnedh-lhewellyn"*[8] and seventeenth-century Latin could hardly go further. But the conditions for their assault on it were no more propitious; they started *"caelo admodum pluvioso,"*[9] and found themselves *"humidis & densis nubibus circumdati."*[10] However, they pressed on until their guide proved recalcitrant. The passage which describes this famous scene also brings out the contrast between the somewhat dull fescue-clad slopes and the "hanging gardens" where the alpine plants grew.

[1]"very charming groves."
[2]"St. George's Channel."
[3]"in fine weather."
[4]"the highest mountains in the whole island."
[5]"veiled in cloud."
[6]"Here the way was very narrow, and climbers are horror-stricken by the rough rocky precipices on either hand, and the Stygian marshes, both on this side and on that, the greatest of which is called the 'Abode of the Devil' by the inhabitants."
[7]"barren plain."
[8]"that most famous mountain."
[9]"in very heavy rain."
[10]"enveloped in wet and dense clouds."

"*Sed nullo modo persuasus est, ut nos ad praecipitia duceret, ubi plantae rariores solummodo crescerent; etenim colles vulgari gramine vestiti pascua satis grata ovibus & jumentis praebent. Rusticus noster illic nidificantes aquilas timebat, solent enim transversim praepeti penna in ora pascentium ad praecipitia pecorum devolantes, ea subito incusso terrore in ruinam dare praedae causa.*"[1]

He does not mention seeing the eagles himself, and he obviously did not think much of the story, but the rustic's obstinacy won the day and they had to retire and soon made their way south out of our region, still grumbling at the weather and the scenery, but botanizing indomitably.

Johnson's botanical works were published between 1629 and 1641, and they inspired Ray and Willughby to make two expeditions, in 1658 and 1662, of which the second is the more important and is recorded in Ray's *Third Itinerary*.

The travellers followed very much in Johnson's footsteps. They rode to Carnedd Llywelyn on May 20th, and only found the starry saxifrage (*Saxifraga stellaris*). There is no mention of the eagles. Coming to Anglesey, they made a first hurried ecological survey of Priestholm (Puffin Island), details of which are found in Chapter 12, as also of their visits to Llanddwyn and Abermenai, where they found the now vanished sea-cottonweed (*Diotis maritima*). At Llanberis they heard of the torgoch, and Ray reports the local legend that the fish had been introduced from Rome by "three sons of the church" and put into the three lakes "Llanberis, Llynumber [? Mymbyr] and Travennin [Cwellyn]." On Snowdon their only reported find was the parsley fern (*Cryptogramma crispa*).

The fashion continued, and it was fitting that to a Welshman, Edward Lhuyd (Lloyd), the antiquary and naturalist, fell the honour of finding the greatest rarity of the alpine flora, mountain spiderwort, which is now called after him, *Lloydia serotina*, but was at first known as *Bulbosa alpina*.

Lloyd described his find to Ray and it appears in the second edition (1696) of the latter's *Synopsis*. The National Museum of Wales has a copy of this work which belonged to Dr. Richard Richardson (1663-

[1]"But we completely failed to persuade him to take us to the precipices, where alone the rarer plants grew; for the hills, clothed with common grass, furnish very welcome pasture for sheep and horses. Our rustic feared the eagles nesting there, for they are accustomed to sweep crosswise on swift pinion before the faces of the cattle feeding on the precipices and by suddenly frightening them make them fall down the rocks and become their prey."

1741), one of the fathers of Yorkshire botany. Through the kindness of H. A. Hyde, I have been able to examine this valuable book, which has Richardson's own handwritten marginal comments. These include his description of "*Bulbosa*," which he had been shown by Lloyd *in situ*. His notes are remarkably accurate and were incorporated in the third edition of the *Synopsis* (1724).

About 1690, when Lhuyd was well established at Oxford, a rather mysterious young man called Samuel Brewer was privileged to meet him. Many years later, in 1726, Brewer accompanied Dr. J. J. Dillenius, later Professor of Botany at Oxford, on a visit to North Wales, somewhat in the capacity of a collector, for he seems to have had a poor education, but great ability in the field. This expedition and Brewer's subsequent stay in North Wales were clarified in a paper by H. A. Hyde following the acquisition by the National Museum of Wales of a manuscript copy of Brewer's diary, made by Hugh Davies of Beaumaris.

Dillenius and Brewer timed their visit badly if they wished to find the alpine flora at its best, for they did not climb Snowdon until August 20th, when the weather flattered to deceive and "fog" on the summit put an end to any searching. Two days later they were up the Glyders and had a look at Llyn-y-cwn, where they found pillwort (*Pilularia globulifera*), quillwort (*Isoetes lacustris*) and shoreweed (*Littorella uniflora*) while round Llanberis the next day they were rewarded by field gentian (*Gentiana campestris*), Welsh poppy (*Meconopsis cambrica*) and water lobelia (*Lobelia dortmanna*). Brewer then stayed on in the neighbourhood of Bangor and during the winter concentrated on mosses, sending his material to Dillenius. The next summer he made many visits to "Trigfylchau," an unidentified rock in the Glyder massif where he found most of the typical alpines, but not the already famous "*Bulbosa*," though his friend Richardson, who had given him the locality, assured him afterwards that he had been on the very rock. In courage and enthusiasm he evidently outdid his companions, for he records: "I was forced to part with R. Parry, who would not follow me up the rocks," and his resourcefulness is shown by his method of securing, with a long pole, specimens of the rare fern *Woodsia alpina*. His greatest success, however, was gained in Anglesey, where he collected the variety—at one time granted specific status—of rockrose that bears his name, *Helianthemum guttatum* var. *breweri*, and thus preserved for posterity the memory of a prototype of the professional collector, an enthusiast forced by economic circumstances to capitalize his talent as a field naturalist.

Zoological data from this period are meagre—Defoe, though he mentions the char of Llyn Peris by its correct Welsh name, seems to have given the mountains a pretty wide berth—until the massive figure of Pennant fills the canvas. We are now in the age of Gilbert White, the dawn of field natural history as we know it, though the thread from earlier writers is not lost; in fact it was Willughby's *Ornithology* (1676) that stimulated Pennant to his own four-volume *British Zoology* (1770), though for our purposes his *Tour of Wales* (1778) is more relevant. His major work was the first comprehensive account of the fauna of Great Britain, and his tours opened up to Johnsonian England the Celtic Fringe, which had hitherto in many respects been more remote and unknown than the eastern seaboard of North America.

Although Forrest points out that Eyton, who wrote the first Fauna of North Wales, appears to have been ignorant of Pennant, to most other writers on the area he was, for about a century, the *fons et origo* of much of their information, some arm-chair naturalists having a rooted preference for quoting published records, even of great antiquity, rather than for personal investigation in the field. Now we know that, with animals at any rate, status can never be taken for granted: the *Handbook of British Birds*, for instance, is no sooner published than revision begins for the next edition. Botanically, too, there are always liable to be shocks of which the discovery in 1935 (not made known till 1946) of a new locality for the mountain avens (*Dryas octopetala*), hitherto believed to occur only on one spot on the Glyders, is an example.

Dawson Turner and Dillwyn summarized existing botanical knowledge in 1805, while about the same time the Rev. William Bingley recorded a vacation ascent, in the company of the Rev. Peter Williams of Llanrug and Llanberis, of Clogwyn Du'r Arddu (1798). This, since its incentive was botanical, can well be mentioned here, although there are alpinists who claim it as a prototype of the modern rock-climb (see Pl. XIII, p. 178).[1] The Rev. Hugh Davies (1740-1821) and William Morris (1700-1765), the poet admired by Borrow, were considerable naturalists, the former being perhaps the first Welsh botanist of distinction; but the province of both was Anglesey. On the other side of our region lived John Williams (1801-1859), whose *Faunula Grustensis* (1830) was the fruit of intense activity in the Llanrwst

[1]Bingley listed 400 species "of the most uncommon Welsh plants."

area, where he accumulated over 5,000 specimens of flowering plants, grasses and mosses. Lower down the Conway flourished the genial and scholarly John Price the Elder (1803-1887), who wrote *Llandudno and How to Enjoy it,* and assisted his friend, the Rev. Robert Williams (1810-1881), with the *History of Aberconwy* (1835).

Price becomes "world news" when he records an incident on the sand-dunes near Deganwy when he and Charles Darwin killed, skinned, but did not, "for reasons never explained," eat an adder.

Darwin (1809-1882), to digress from the Welsh stream, made at least three visits to the area, a virile walking tour in his youth, when he climbed Snowdon, a riding tour with his sister, and, in 1842, the last active expedition he was ever able to undertake, his objects being mainly geological. Another "national" figure, of very different attainments, was Charles Kingsley (1819-1875). He frequently led the Chester Natural Science Society on expeditions in the neighbourhood, though, as with many other visiting naturalists and celebrities, his observations seem to have been mainly peripheral to the area of the proposed Park.

It is tantalizing to speculate what apparently trivial field notes (which could now be of inestimable use in reconstructing the wild life of 150 years ago), might have been made by the early climbers of Snowdon and its sister peaks. As it is, the alpine flora, having been recognized as of great interest, had its admirers, but the vast bulk of the area was left unrecorded—from the rounded tops of the Carneddau, possible habitat of the dotterel, to the moors of the Migneint, equally suitable for the hen-harrier.

Thomas Campbell Eyton (1809-1880) made a gallant effort to survey the entire vertebrate fauna of North Wales. This would be a large subject at any time, and he had far less material to draw on than had Forrest, when he wrote about seventy years later, so that inaccuracies, errors of identification and incompleteness may be pardoned; his familiarity with the Capel Curig district is of particular interest for this volume.

During the nineteenth century a number of naturalists made observations in North Wales, but few penetrated the Snowdon region. It is, however, of some historical interest that Henry Ecroyd Smith (1823-1888) found terns nesting at Abermenai in 1868, where we saw them in 1946, for terns fluctuate tremendously in numbers and frequently change their breeding stations.

An unusual visitor in the middle of the century was J. Gay, a French botanist whose passion was the primitive genus *Isoetes* (quillworts). I am again indebted to Mr. Hyde for introducing me to him and his remarkably frank account of the Snowdonian sites, given in a series of communications to the Société Botanique de France in 1862. He listed every lake in Eryri and obtained "échantillons" of quillwort from the vast majority, though the rare *I. echinospora* only occurs in the Llanberis lakes. The "hanging gardens" were visited by way of relaxation from his stern purpose and he has to excuse himself to his learned audience, for his levity in climbing Snowdon, by saying that he wished to see the flora so many metres above the sea. Actually, he was extremely surprised to find a number of plants, which he knew in the Alps, growing at such relatively low altitudes. He did not see the spiderwort, but was given "un échantillon," collected in 1850.

Entomological collecting went on steadily during the second half of the century and the journals had a number of accounts from W. E. Sharp, Theodore Wood, F. D. Bland, E. W. H. Blagg and others. The Lepidoptera, of course, received most attention and, while Merioneth and the Conway valley were the areas most worked, there are accounts of one or two expeditions to Snowdon. Although no book was written on the invertebrates, the standard works on the different orders, which began to appear about this time, contain a fair number of references to North Wales.

The turn of the century is a landmark both in the botany and vertebrate zoology of the region, for in 1895 J. E. Griffith published his *Flora of Anglesey and Caernarvonshire* and in 1907 came J. E. Forrest's *Vertebrate Fauna of North Wales*. The two books are in strange contrast. Griffith's was published in Bangor and contains a short list of authorities, for, as he points out in his preface, no one since Hugh Davies had taken a regular interest in the botany of the two counties. "For upwards of twenty years," he writes, "I have diligently explored these two counties and studied their flora; and not having had the advantage of local assistance, the greater portion of the work is the result of personal observation during that period."

Griffith claimed five species and four varieties of plants new to science, but six of them are brambles (*Rubus* spp.) and hawkweeds (*Hieracium* spp.). Six species, eleven varieties, and one form were new to the British flora, while his advance on the Caernarvonshire list in H. C. Watson's *Topographical Botany* (1835) included 50 species, 45 varieties and one form, not counting 32 species, 13 varieties and two hybrids of *Rubus*, and 17 species and 12 varieties of *Hieracium*. Much of his collecting was done round Bangor and in the Creuddyn peninsula, but he knew his Snowdon, and, in an introductory chapter on Geology, he indicates the more characteristic and important plants of the different soil groups in the county.

Forrest's work, on the other hand, was no solo effort, for he, as his obituary notice in *British Birds* said, "excelled in the collection and collation of the work of others." His bibliography is extensive ; he gives biographical notes on nearly thirty past authorities and acknowledges the help of 187 living contributors, of whom, it is interesting to see, not less than 84 were domiciled outside Wales.

Among his correspondents are many whose names have been "household words" in zoology well into this century; it is invidious to select out of so many famous men, but I think I may suggest that the development of our knowledge of the fauna of North Wales and the north-west Midlands of England owes a particular debt to a group of four: T. A. Coward, Charles Oldham, J. Steele Elliott and Forrest himself, the last three of whom died in the same year (1942), some years after Coward, probably the best-known of the quartet by reason of his successful three-volume *Birds of the British Isles and their Eggs* in Warne's "Wayside and Woodland" series. None of these giants lived in Wales, Oldham latterly as far away as Hertfordshire and the others on the Border, Coward in Cheshire, Forrest in Shropshire and Elliott in the Wyre Forest ; he was the only one I had the fortune to know and visit in his Tudor manor, a sanctuary with over forty species of birds nesting regularly round it, with commas flitting over the hollyhocks in the days when commas were rare, and with his own experiment —a warren of wild rabbits crossed with a white domestic strain—a pattern of luminous dots in the summer dusk up the sloping meadow.

Elliott talked sometimes of his North Wales expeditions, and I felt that he had been one of a generation of British naturalists, who, no longer quite heroic—because by their time the rigours of travelling and staying in the more unpronounceable parts of these islands had been somewhat mitigated—had nevertheless a large stature because they first mapped out in detail the distribution of our flora and fauna. At the time when Harvie-Brown and his colleagues were covering Scotland with a series of "Vertebrate Faunas," Forrest and his associates were doing this for most of Wales, and it is interesting today, when one starts investigating the literature of regional natural history, to find how often the most recent attempt at a comprehensive account is still theirs, dating at latest from the first decade of the century. No doubt interest has shifted since then from distribution to problems of ecology, behaviour and evolution, and much of their writing appears to us digressive, even garrulous, but it must be remembered that they were amateurs who wrote largely to please themselves and the select sub-scribers to their volumes.

Two others who helped considerably with material for the *Vertebrate Fauna* were O. V. Aplin (1858-1940) in Llŷn and G. H. Caton-Haigh (1860-1941) in the Traeth Mawr district; but neither gave much attention to the Snowdon range, and the same is true of the other naturalists of national status on Forrest's list.

The golden age of distributional study ended with the 1914-18 war. Immediately after it Forrest published addenda to his Fauna as the *Handbook of the Vertebrate Fauna of North Wales* (1919), and this remains the standard list for these classes of animal life.

Botanically the period since 1918 has been dominated by institutions rather than by individuals: the National Museum of Wales, the Botany Department of the University College of North Wales, and the Agricultural Departments there and at Aberystwyth. Intensive work by the Keeper, H. A. Hyde, and the Assistant Keeper, A. E. Wade, of the Botany Department at the Museum, produced in 1934 *Welsh Flowering Plants*, nominally a handbook to the collection in the Welsh National Herbarium, but actually a most useful flora, remarkable for its wealth of ingeniously compressed information. They have also written *Welsh Ferns* (1940), and Hyde wrote *Welsh Timber Trees* (1931, second edition 1935), both valuable for the student of our region in different ways, the latter revealing the absence from it of notable trees of any kind, and the former indicating the wealth of pteridophytes. *Welsh Flowering Plants* gives county lists, with a brief survey of the flora of each; Caernarvonshire is credited with 1,057 macro-species against about 870 claimed by Griffith.

In the field of applied botany, the *Survey of the Agricultural and Waste Lands of Wales* (1936), henceforward referred to as *The Grassland Survey* or *The Survey*, edited by Sir George Stapledon, must take pride of place. This vegetational survey, the first ever undertaken for the whole of Wales, was carried out by the staff of the Welsh Plant Breeding Station at Aberystwyth, under the supervision of Dr. William Davies, now

Director of the Ministry of Agriculture's Grassland Improvement Station near Stratford-on-Avon. It took several years to complete, and was thoroughly checked in 1934-35. The field records were made on maps to the scale of one inch to the mile, though detailed transects of sample areas were made to the scale of six inches to the mile. Many thousands of miles were covered by the investigators in cars and on foot. The main transects were made by cars, upon every kind of road, but these were frequently supplemented by foot transects outward from the roads. Although, with practice, the main grassland associations could be recognized from a car, especially in autumn and winter, when the colour differences are most marked, new or unfamiliar associations were investigated by field studies, an example of which is given later (p. 241).

Much work has been done from Bangor by N. Woodhead of the Botany Department and Alun Roberts, Professor of Agricultural Botany, and their students. Unfortunately, the bulk of it has not yet been published. John Rees, now in the advisory service of the Ministry of Agriculture, has made a special study of Llŷn.

These names and associations speak for themselves; botany is now in the hands of professional scientists, and the region is fortunate that there has been such a concentration of talent upon it in recent years. But the amateur spirit survives, and is well represented by Albert Wilson, E. Price Evans and Evan Roberts of Capel Curig, to whom the discovery of the new locality for the mountain avens, already mentioned, is due, and who combines his botanizing with the profession of quarry-man. Mr. Evans and Mr. Roberts seem to be heirs of the line of native Welsh botanists, descended traditionally from Hugh Davies of Beaumaris and Edward Lhuyd.

Zoologically, the transition of activity from amateur to professional hands has not been so marked. Ornithology, the most popular branch, is still predominently a recreation—and there are many who believe that it should remain so—while the study of mammals, fishes and invertebrates has been professionalized chiefly where there is an economic incentive, which in the case of our region means a relevance either to agriculture or forestry, and that rather in the negative sphere of pest control than in the field of ecological research.

However, some extremely interesting work was done from Bangor by C. L. Walton and W. Maldwyn Davies, for they went well beyond their province of agricultural zoology. Walton not only published a number of papers and pamphlets himself, but he seems to have inspired and encouraged others, including H. F. Barnes who made a study of the crane-flies (*Tipulidae*) of Caernarvonshire, identifying 37 species in 1922-23. About the same time J. M. Brown was working on the plant-bugs and frog-hoppers (*Hemiptera*) first from the Llandudno area and later in Merioneth.

Very recently J. Balfour-Browne, as a result of intensive work in 1940-41, has published a list of the Water Beetles (Aquatic *Coleoptera*) of North Wales. He personally confirmed 115 out of 146 species claimed for Caernarvonshire, but his comment that he could only find 11 previous notes referring to the county is illuminating. The butterflies and moths (*Lepidoptera*) of the region have been the concern of J. A. Thompson, who identified the two local subspecies of butterflies described in Chapter 12 (p. 286).

Many figures of the "Forrest Age" have continued to publish notes on North Wales, some of them in the *Transactions of the Caradoc and Severn Valley Field Club*, of which he was for so long the moving spirit. *The Proceedings of the Llandudno, Colwyn Bay and District Field Club* over the period 1909-1939 contain a number of interesting papers and accounts, both signed and anonymous, of field work and expeditions in the area. The National Museum of Wales, through its Keeper of Zoology, Colin Matheson, has amassed a great deal of data about North Wales, and Mr. Matheson's *Changes in the Fauna of Wales in Historical Times* (1932) does for Wales what Professor James Ritchie's *Influence of Man on Animal Life* did for Scotland.

But, whatever the reason, there are greater gaps in our knowledge of the zoology of the region than of its botany. Birds attract more observers than any other class, and many distinguished ornithologists visit the Snowdon range annually, yet in all the volumes of *British Birds* since 1919, when Forrest summarized references to North Wales in his *Handbook*, there have been only two short notes relevant to the area of the Park, as against eight articles and over 90 notes dealing with the rest of North Wales. The Appendix reveals clearly that there is plenty of room for entomologists; only the mammals and the fish appear to be fairly well covered, though in their case modern changes—afforestation and hydro-electric schemes—demand that the data should continually be revised. And though this revision will be more and more in the hands of trained biologists, doing it as their day-to-day work, one hopes that they will not forget their predecessors, who, both native and "foreign," country parson or business man on holiday, have built up through the years our knowledge of the natural history of North Wales.

References for Chapter 6

Balfour-Browne (1942), Barnes (1924), Bingley (1800), *British Birds* (1919-47), J. M. Brown (1925), Coward (1920), W. M. Davies (1934), Defoe (1724-27), Eyton (1838-40), Forrest (1907) (1919), Gay (1862), Gilmour (1944), Giraldus Cambrensis (1188) (p. 439), Griffith (1895), Hyde (1930) (1935), Hyde and Wade (1934) (1940), Johnson (1641), Leland (1536-39), Matheson (1932), Pennant (1784), Price (N.D.), Ray (1696) (1724) (1846), Ritchie (1920), Sharp (1899), Stapledon (1936), Walton (1922, etc.), Watson (1825), J. Williams (1830), R. Williams (1835), Willughby (1676), Wilson (1946-47).

CHAPTER 7

THE HUMAN FACTOR

RESIDENTS

THE previous chapter has indicated the relatively small proportion of natural history information which has been collected for our region by native naturalists; only in botany is their share significant, and this seems at first surprising when we realize the preoccupation with natural imagery to be found in Welsh poetry, whence it is supposed to have overflowed to form the loveliest element in English poetry as well.

But, in closer examination, it is found that a talent for nature poetry is not necessarily connected with an interest in scientific natural history, and that the reputedly more Celtic parts of Britain, cradles of crag-loving bards though they may be, have failed to produce as yet more than a handful of biologists. I can only advance opinions and theories to account for this. Firstly, the Celtic temperament is not by tradition exact, methodical, scientific: it is romantic, ornamental, adaptive. An animal to the Celtic mind is a point of departure for excursions in the imagination: water-monsters, one-eyed fish, eagles awaiting a carnage with prophetic regularity—these are the creatures with which native fancy peopled Eryri, until the debunkers came west from flat lands, whence even the raven had been banished.

Possibly urbanization is a spur to natural history studies; nowadays, at any rate, many leading naturalists live in towns—and a people as wholly rural as the Welsh before the Industrial Revolution may have been too busy living in the countryside to worry very much about its wild life, except to kill it off whenever its competition was feared. At all events the situation cannot be explained away, even by a lover of Wales. In the agricultural sphere, however, Welsh scientists have come into their own in their own country, and have now invaded England. This is particularly interesting, for it suggests that the intense Welsh feeling for the land is sufficient to make biology attractive, when seen in relation to farming, to the improvement of grassland and to the encouragement of the animals which graze upon it. So perhaps, in the last analysis, it is the Celt who is practical, only studying plants and creatures when that study has a definite application to economics, and the Saxon who is romantic, escaping from dull towns to collect specimens and watch birds for the pure love of it alone.

This preamble is necessary to explain the extraordinary confusion that exists over the Welsh names for natural objects and animals. Welsh is a more poetic language than English, and poetic languages do not have to worry so much about accuracy in what C. E. Montague called a paltry sense. Nor in a country where travel was so difficult, as in Wales at the time when the language was assuming its modern form, is it likely that the same name for an animal or a flower would obtain in every district; or, if it did occur, it might easily refer to quite a different species. Anyone who reads through the Welsh names of vertebrates, which Forrest painstakingly collected, will soon find the same name cropping up for several creatures, and also a wealth of by-names, which are fascinating as folk-lore material, but exasperating to the natural historian who has entertained dreams of a unified nomenclature in Welsh.

The same confusion, of course, is present in English, and no one, whose mother tongue accepts the common names house-sparrow and hedge-sparrow for two scientifically dissimilar birds, can afford to feel superior; but whereas in English the position has been reasonably clarified, and we all know that these names stand for *Passer domesticus* and *Prunella modularis* and for no other species, in Welsh the battle has still largely to be fought, for although the National Museum has courageously laid down names, its writ does not yet run throughout the country in this respect.

In our region the source of the Welsh names of plants is Hugh Davies's *Welsh Botanology* (1821), which linked them with both Latin and English. His names were largely followed by Griffith. Many were coined from the scientific names, and, therefore, are unlikely to have popular currency, though it is, of course, also unlikely that country people would be capable of that keen differentiation between species which made the coinings necessary.

The origin of the faunal names is more varied ; Forrest collected many, or they were sent in to him from all over Wales, so that those he gives are not necessarily the North Wales versions. The Museum names, I am informed by Mr. Matheson, are based on Forrest's collection, with various additions, alterations and corrections, and they were submitted to authorities on the language before being finally accepted.

There appears to be as yet no complete study of the Welsh names of plants and animals, but a booklet for schools was published in 1945 more or less with official backing. *Geirfa Natur* (A Nature Vocabulary), as it is called, is plainly not the work of naturalists, and has come in for criticism both from scientists and from authorities on folk-culture. The introduction deals largely with the domestic, agricultural or proverbial aspect of these names, and there is a final selection of proverbs, Biblical passages and Welsh poems dealing with Nature; in fact the whole production suggests a literary rather than a natural-history standpoint, which is in line with the general Welsh attitude to wild life.

However, a number of interesting facts are brought out, though few in direct relevance to our region, and the origin of the names given is not stated.

Plants were apparently much used for medical purposes in rural Wales ; one of the names for selfheal (*Prunella vulgaris*) is *Craith unnos* ("one-night scar") and *Geirfa Natur* records that in the Conwy valley it was used to cure cuts on the hands of farm-workers.

Birds figured to some extent in weather-lore; an ancient *pennill* or rhyme describes gulls in hard weather flying in *"o'r mor i ben y mynydd"*—from the sea to the top of the mountain, so that perhaps the visits of herring-gulls to the slopes of Snowdon are not only due to the English habit of alfresco meals on mountainsides. An interesting problem concerns the name *Aderyn yr Eira* (bird of the snow), which is applied both to the fieldfare and to the starling. Flocks of the former species, a winter visitor, are liable to appear suddenly ahead of hard weather, and frequently join forces with starlings, some of which may also be migrants, but of which the majority will probably be resident. It is tempting to conclude that the name was transferred from one to the other by faulty observation, but it is conceivable also that at one time, before the general increase which is believed to have taken place, starlings were only known as winter visitors in rural districts[1].

Legends equally current in the English countryside are epitomized by such names as *Aderyn Corff* (corpse-bird) for the owl and *Aderyn Anlwc* (bird of ill-luck) for the magpie, but others, *Llysiau Cadwgan* (valerian, *Valeriana* spp.), *Llysiau Taliesin* (brooklime, *Veronica becca-bunga*) and *Bran Arthur* (chough) commemorate heroes in the national

---

[1]Mr. J. L. Davies tells me that the starling is still a very scarce nesting species over much of West Wales.

sagas and *Geirfa Natur* indicates the legacy from pre-Reformation times in the number of plant names which contain the word *Mair* (Mary). The more colourful show that pleasing fancy which is often found in flower names: *Esgid Mair* (Mary's shoe) for monkshood (*Aconitum anglicum*), *Ysgol Mair* (Mary's ladder) for centaury (*Centaurium umbellatum*), *Gwniadur Mair* (Mary's thimble) for foxglove (*Digitalis purpurea*), and *Clustog Mair* (Mary's pillow) for thrift (*Armeria maritima*).

Some animal names, mainly of the more spectacular creatures or beasts of the chase, are very ancient, their meaning not easily discernible today: *Bele* (marten), *Blaidd* (wolf), *Hebog* (hawk or falcon), while a number of bird names, as is the case in any language, are onomatopaeic: *Giach* (snipe), *Heligog* (guillemot). A large class, though they may be old, are directly descriptive and easily understood by modern Welsh speakers: *Bronfraith* (thrush, literally: "speckled breast"), *Dyfrgi* (otter, literally, "water-dog"), while others are more metaphorical: *Glas-y-Dorlan* (kingfisher: "blue of the stream-bank"), *Caseg Wanwyn* (green woodpecker: "mare of spring"), *Gwas-y-Gog* (meadow-pipit: "cuckoo's servant"). Very often, however, as in English, it is the attractive and fanciful names which are regarded as local and discarded in books in favour of the more prosaic.

Names for invertebrates are even more generalized than those for the higher groups, but the farmer has, of course, recognized the pests that attack his stock and given them names, some of which are mentioned by C. L. Walton, such as *Llaw Gwartheg*, the ox-louse (*Haematopinus eurysternus*); *Trogod*, ticks, especially *Ixodes ricinus*; *Cynron Gwartheg*, warble-flies (*Hypoderma* spp.) and *Pryf Llwvd*, dun-fly or "cleg" (*Haematopota* spp.). *Pryf* or *Pry* usually means an insect, but *Pryf Llwyd* is also a name for the badger.

Geirfa Natur gives a number of names for common insects, or rather for whole families or orders. One name for butterfly is *Iar Fach yr Haf* (little hen of summer), while the dragonfly is called either *Gwas-y-Neidr* (adder's servant) or *Gwaell Neidr* (adder's knitting-needle). This formed the subject of a correspondence in *Nature* some years ago in which W. Maldwyn Davies and Charles Oldham joined; both names apparently have their counterparts in the English-speaking world.

One interesting result of the dominant part played in North Wales natural history by non-Welsh naturalists and sportsmen is that in many cases the English rather than the Welsh names are used by Welsh speakers, because their only interrogators have been English-speaking;

PLATE XIII

Photograph and interpretation by Dr. J. Menlove Edwards

CLOGWYN DU'R ARDDU: scene of one of the earliest rock-climbs (after rare plants), showing the modern network of climbers' routes on the 500-ft. cliff:—

EAST BUTTRESS

1. East Gulley
2. Sunset Crack
3. Piggott's Climb
4. Chimney Route

5. Curving Crack
6. Pedestal Crack
7. Direct Finish
8. Birthday Crack

WEST BUTTRESS

9. West Wall Climb
10. Longland's Climb
11. Narrow Slab
12. Bow-shaped Slab
13. Great Slab

PLATE XIV

John Markham

PLANT ASSOCIATION OF A ROCK OUTCROP in moorland, about 1,400 ft. above sea level
Caernarvonshire, June

this is probably most true of game-birds and wildfowl, but is found in the case of smaller Passerine birds as well, as *Pinc, Titw* and *Robin Goch* show, while other names, though their constituent words are Welsh enough, suggest a translation from the English replacing an original name, for example, *Aderyn Du*, which is literally "black bird," instead of *Mwyalchen*, and *Aderyn-y-To*, "bird of the roof" (house-sparrow), instead of *Golfan*. The use of *Grugiar*, literally "heather-hen," for moor-hen, could only be due to a wrong idea of the meaning of "moor" in this connection[1]. *Iar Ddwr*, "waterhen," given by Forrest and others is much more sensible, but one wonders whether the old Welsh name for such a common bird may not have been lost altogether.

The importance of the gamekeeper in a rural area such as the Park has undoubtedly helped in the anglicizing of wild-life names, for the majority of keepers locally have been Scots or English, and have often been men of considerable personality. Matthew Speake, for instance, who guards Ystumllyn and its neighbourhood so vigilantly, is a Shropshire man though most of his professional life has been spent in Wales, and he is a keen and observant naturalist. He secured several specimens for G. H. Caton-Haigh (see p. 297) and is well informed about the local distribution of birds and mammals. Holiday naturalists come and go, but the gamekeeper is there all the year round and in time becomes the focus of information about wild life and, while ornithologists deplore the loss of rare birds of prey through game-preservation, the control of the crow family and of carnivorous mammals is an aid to the smaller species, as well as to game, and it seems reasonable to attribute the abundance of these on well-keepered estates at least partly to the keeper's rule.

The heyday of preservation did banish the harriers from North Wales; Forrest shows a photograph of the last nest of the Montagu's harrier in Merioneth—the birds had already been shot! But the other predators held out either on the high hills or on the sea-cliffs and it is somewhat surprising that Forrest did not know anywhere where the buzzard nested on the coast, since elsewhere it has been a favourite retreat of this species; in fact one is tempted to think that the secret of the survival of raven, buzzard and peregrine as against the disappearance of the harriers, honey-buzzard, kite and osprey, is that they had an alternative habitat where men did not pursue them, whereas the latter group were restricted to inland moors and woods.

[1] The name properly refers to the red grouse.

But the recovery of the golden eagle and loss of the sea-eagle in Scotland is rather damaging to this theory, and it may be safer to suggest simply that large birds which nest entirely or frequently in rocks have a better chance against gamekeeper and collector than ground and tree nesters.

Game-preservation is not a powerful factor in the destruction of wild life at the moment and probably never will be again, but one aspect of the encouragement given to agriculture during the 1939-45 war has been an intensification of the farmer's and smallholder's normal guerilla warfare against the imagined enemies of their stock. We talked to a man in North Wales in 1946, who described a harrier quite accurately to us. I mentioned that it was of the greatest rarity, but that did not affect his stated intention to shoot it, if he got the chance, in defence of his chickens. Again, near Penmachno, Markham and I were told of a supposed pine-marten's attacks on sheep; no one had set eyes on the creature, but the bites on the corpses were said to be unlike anything ever seen before locally and so the "invisible" rarity was given the blame. In August 1946, a considerable stir was caused by a short note in our most distinguished daily paper about the number of pine-martens said to have been killed by one keeper near Capel Curig. This story was investigated and shown to be a colourful concentration: a lifetime's killings attributed to one season, but the incident served to show that the old idea of indiscriminate destruction dies hard and that, with public opinion unaroused, such statements can be published without apprehension in reputable newspapers.

The most hopeful sign of a new attitude to wild life in North Wales comes from that interest in agricultural science already indicated. In 1943, when I was speaking on birds at a Youth Course, a Young Farmers' Club official from Caernarvonshire asked me about the supposed connection between starlings and the conveyance of foot-and-mouth disease; the fact that he bothered to inquire, instead of accepting a facile condemnation on superficial evidence, seemed to me a hopeful sign, and it is only right that a new and co-operative attitude towards wild life in Wales should spring from the traditional Welsh attachment to the land, brought up to date with scientific advances and given, in our region, every assistance by the future administration of the National Park.

VISITORS

Part of the region included within the boundaries of the future National Park is already one of the most popular inland holiday areas in Britain. The Snowdon range, of course, is the focus, with radiating narrow strips along the principal roads, especially the main road down to Capel Curig and Betws-y-coed. Strategically placed at the foot of ascents of Snowdon, Llanberis and Beddgelert rival the remoter Betws in attractions, and for sheer numbers of visitors Llanberis undoubtedly wins, since it has the lower terminus of Britain's only mountain railway, which runs to the highest point south of the Grampians.

Visitors are of several distinct types; there are those who make long stays in hotels, boarding houses and farms: fishermen, artists, walkers of the leisurely kind, and family parties, much the same sort of people that are found elsewhere in scenic Britain. Then there are the climbers, in the restricted, specialist sense, concentrating on the famous hotels at Pen-y-pass and Pen-y-gwryd, on the Idwal Hut Youth Hostel, on their own club huts, and on guest-houses and cottages at Capel Curig and Nant Peris. They merge into the other active holiday-makers, the cyclists, ramblers and "youth-hostellers," who seldom stay more than a night or two in each place and usually make some sort of round tour of the region. Distinct from all these are the day-trippers, perhaps the most remunerative of all to the locality, who may drive direct from the large towns of East Lancashire or the Midlands in the special coaches, or may come up from the coastal "resorts" on excursions. For these the Snowdon Mountain Railway, the Swallow Falls near Betws-y-coed, and Beddgelert (legend and all) are the principal places of call.

Generally speaking, the natural history interest and knowledge of these visitors decreases in the order in which I have mentioned them; that of the day trippers may be illustrated by an episode at the Miner's Bridge, another Betws beauty-spot. We met a bus-load who had braved the muddy path from the main road and were now gazing over a wire fence into the Forestry Commission's property, where their mentor, the driver of the coach, was brandishing a stick. There were whispers of a snake, and one or two of the party were obviously full of admiration. We crossed the fence and found a limp grass-snake amongst the heather. The weather being wet, it was at first thought to be torpid, but when picked up the shudder it aroused in the crowd suggested that the driver had given bloodcurdling warnings and then gone into action against the monster: an interesting contrast to the attitude of J. S. Elliott, who wanted to reintroduce adders into his estate!

Campers and youth-hostellers form the group which, above all, will benefit by the establishment of a National Park, for the *Report of the National Parks Committee* makes it clear that to increase the accommodation suitable for the holiday-maker who likes "roughing it" on a small budget should be one of the first tasks of the Park administration. At present there is a fairly high concentration of Youth Hostels, a number of privately owned camping sites and the large hostel of the Forestry Commission near Beddgelert, intended for all types of visitor.

As far as the appreciation of Nature is concerned, the Youth Hostels of North Wales do not appear to be a very active agency of propaganda, although their clientele, predominantly of intelligent young people from the urban areas of England, is just the type which ought to be most responsive. A measure of financial assistance from the Parks Authority, allowing separation of the functions of catering manager and warden in each Hostel, and giving the latter time and opportunity to develop the "cultural" side of hostelling, would enable the movement to fulfil its original aims in this direction. This will be more important than ever in an area where the wild life is being deliberately conserved ; and, though it does not directly concern natural history, it may be suggested that a closer approach by the Hostels to the Welsh life around them would increase their value considerably.

While applauding the Parks Committee's recommendation that camping sites should be properly organized, campers of the tougher sort will also expect a degree of freedom and encouragement to bivouac at high altitudes. Max Madders, who has led many parties of Birmingham students on expeditions to Snowdon and other mountain areas, has suggested to me that stone huts and shelters above the 2,000-foot contour would add greatly to the "amenities" of the hills; they would also be of use to naturalists who might wish to remain "on the tops" for several nights while making continuous observations.

The rock-climbers have built up, at Penypass and Penygwryd, a long tradition of their particular brand of intellectual and at one time almost monastic athleticism, and it seems that the sport, or art, more or less originated on Snowdon and was thence transplanted to the Alps.

Climbing ability has some relevance to natural history. Perhaps the classic literary account of their combination is C. E. Montague's short story, *In Hanging Garden Gully*, but Brewer's and Bingley's botanical ascents have already been mentioned (pp. 166 and 167), and Orton suggested that the skill of the alpinist had sometimes been suborned by the egg-collector, where nests of raven, peregrine or buzzard were concerned.

At all events the mountain naturalist should be a good scrambler and able to use a rope, if only for lowering to difficult sites. But this is altogether different from the highly developed sport of rock-climbing, which should not be attempted by anyone without expert leadership. Plate XIII (p. 178) shows the variety of routes evolved on one famous face, Clogwyn Du'r Arddu, where Bingley made his pioneer climb, and which is still as renowned for alpine plants as for alpine ascents.

The fisherman is often a bit of a naturalist as well and, after mountaineering, fishing is the sport most associated with our region. *The Mountains of Snowdonia* gives a remarkable table of the contents of all the lakes, tarns and rivers, the majority of which hold brown trout. Salmon and sea-trout fishing is important in the Conway, Glaslyn and the western rivers, and an attempt is now being made to bring salmon right up the Llugwy and Nant-y-wryd by hatching fry at Pen-y-gwryd. Details of the biology of the Welsh char, now apparently confined to Llyn Peris and Llyn Padarn, and which has its own admirers amongst both anglers and trenchermen, are given in Chapter 10. As a general comment, it seems likely that the more accessible waters, for example Llyn Ogwen and the Llanberis lakes, are over-fished, and that some of the hill tarns are rarely visited.

Shooting has never been of comparable importance locally. In the lowlands of Caernarvonshire there has been considerable game-preservation in the past on large estates, and there are some first-class duck and rough shoots. There is one small grouse-moor in the Snowdon range, and others on the Penmachno moors (see p. 260), where the bird is more numerous. But the dry moors of Denbighshire are the true grouse-gardens of Wales.

The various interests of residents and the different groups of visitors will set the future Park administration some problems in adjustment. It must be remembered, however, that the National Parks are not Nature Reserves, as the term has now been defined, though the administration may establish Regional Reserves within their boundaries ; in the Parks generally the interests of the human population are paramount. Fortunately, in a sense, as the opening words of this section suggested, there is not a great deal of natural history importance to be seen over much of the most popular walking and climbing ground, especially at the time when the majority of people take their holidays. The wild-life of the Snowdon and Nant Conwy areas is, as I hope the following chapters will show, full of interest and variety, but it is, on the whole, not of a kind to suffer from generous human use of the countryside, though the sites of the rarer alpine flora may need special protection. A benevolent "educational" policy as regards plants and animals will, of course, be needed throughout the Park, but this is something for which ample provision is made, both in the National Parks Committee's Report, and in that of its sub-committee on the conservation of nature.

References for Chapter 7

Bingley (1800), Carr and Lister (1925), H. Davies (1821), W. M. Davies (1929), Forrest (1907), *Geirfa Natur* (1945), Montague (1923), National Parks Committee (1947), Oldham (1929), Orton (1925), *Report of National Parks Committee* (1947), Walton (1927).

Communications from J. L. Davies (1947), Madders (1946).

CHAPTER 8

THE ALPINE ZONE

RATHER under one-twentieth of the area of Caernarvonshire lies over 2,000 feet above sea-level, 4.7 per cent as against 2.6 per cent of Merioneth, the next most mountainous of Welsh counties. Except for the summit of Moel Siabod and the Caernarvonshire side of the Moelwyns, the whole of these 17,000 acres is found in the Snowdon range proper, and it is the area which forms the subject of this chapter, for it may be said that, except possibly in the Central Highlands of Scotland, semi-alpine conditions in Britain begin at the 2,000-foot contour, and, indeed, may be found somewhat below that altitude on north-facing cliffs in Eryri.

THE CARNEDDAU

The main block of high-level ground is in the northernmost part of the range, that massif dominated by the peaks of Carnedd Ddafydd, Carnedd Llywelyn, Foel Grach and Foel Fras. The plant cover of its eastern slopes has been analysed in detail by Dr. Elfyn Hughes in relation to the underlying soils; externally, however, most of it appears to be grassland dominated by mat-grass (*Nardus stricta*) in the areas of Llyn Eigiau and Llyn Dulyn and changing on the drier, less peaty north-eastern slopes to fescue (*Festuca* spp.), while in the valleys generally moor-grass (*Molinia caerulea*) and rushes (*Juncus* spp.)with some cotton-grass (*Eriophorum* spp.) dominate the vegetation. The summits of the big hills are seen as islands of "detritus"—very obvious to anyone who has stumbled along the razor-edge connecting the two Carneddau—surrounded by a considerable spread of blanket-peat, in which bilberry (*Vaccinium myrtillus*), mat-grass, cotton-grass and, at lower elevations, heather (*Calluna vulgaris*) form the principal cover.

The western slopes of the massif have much the same character, though their pitch is rather steeper. Formidable cliffs, however occur on both sides : on the east around Llyn Dulyn, Melynllyn, Cwm Eigiau (site of the famous Craig-yr-ysfa climb) and Llyn Cowlyd; on the west immediately below the top of Carnedd Ddafydd, the whole mountain falling away in the sheer Ysgolion Duon (Black Ladders) to the rushy glen of Afon Llafar.

It must have been somewhere here that Thomas Johnson came in 1639 (see p. 164) and most of the characteristic flora is to be found on the Carneddau, both Craig-yr-ysfa and Ysgolion Duon yielding a number of interesting records. All the same, botanists seem to concentrate on the Glyder and Snowdon cliffs, and A. Wilson's recent paper shows how relatively poorly represented is the alpine element, even at the highest altitudes, on the eastern side of the Carneddau, owing to the lack of lime in the rock-formations. For people in a hurry access is also a factor; the foot of the Devil's Kitchen (Pl. 5, p. 62) can be reached literally in a few minutes of hard walking from the macadam of A5, and in the same short space of time one can be among the rigours of Crib Goch; but to reach the best sites on the Carneddau a long and tedious pull is necessary, and it is perfectly possible to walk to the tops and to see, as Johnson did, "hills clothed with common grass" and little else.

The alpine zone on the Carneddau can be reached fairly directly from Talyllyn Ogwen up the tumbling course of Nant Lloer. On the occasion of a June visit, our welcome to it was by a solitary coal-tit; how this sedentary little bird of the woodlands came to be flitting amongst the boulders is puzzling—it was an adult and could not, therefore, be excused as a juvenile which did not know its ecological place. The normal birds of the hillside were ravens, carrion-crows, meadow-pipits, ring-ousels, wheatears and a dipper—all, it may be noticed, of the Passerine order. Mat-grass and fescue formed the broken sward, with lousewort (*Pedicularis sylvatica*), tormentil (*Potentilla erecta*) and milkwort (*Polygala* spp.) a conspicuous pattern of pink, yellow and blue. This trinity of acid-indicators is general over the Snowdonian grassland at all levels. Heath bedstraw (*Galium saxatile*) on the wetter, and wild thyme (*Thymus serpyllum*) on the drier, situations were also noted, with bitter cress (*Cardamine flexuosa*), speedwell (*Veronica officinalis*) and wood-pimpernel (*Lysimachia nemorum*) all common. Under boulders grew clumps of parsley fern (Pl. 16a, p. 207), while stonecrop (*Sedum anglicum*) associated with heather on the ledges of those small faces less accessible to grazing animals. Along Nant Lloer the starry saxifrage appeared in profusion well below our delimiting contour, and, in the frequent small bogs, butterwort (*Pinguicula vulgaris*) sought from the small flies of the mountain the salts denied it by its habitat.

This continued to be the characteristic flora up the interminable

PLATE XV

John Markham

THE MOSSY SAXIFRAGE, *Saxifraga hypnoides*; an abundant plant of the screes (note the *Carabus* beetle on the extreme right). Caernarvonshire, June

PLATE XVI

John Markham

a. Black Slug, *Arion ater*. Betws-y-coed, July (× 1)

J. Armitage

b. Emperor Moth, *Saturnia pavonia*, female. May (× 1·2)

PROMINENT SNOWDONIAN INVERTEBRATES

broad flank of Carnedd Ddafydd, that is to say up to at least 2,750 feet. Mosses began to increase, and increasing exposures of detritus encouraged them and lichens, amongst which the unusually coloured *Cetraria aculeata* was prominent.

On the summit ridge the western blast blew strongly and we trod precariously along the chaos of stones; in patches of moss grew deer-hair sedge (*Scirpus caespitosus*), heath rush (*Juncus squarrosus*)—in dwarf habit—bilberry and cowberry (*Vaccinium vitis-idaea*). But if the flora was undistinguished, the fauna was confined to sheep and ponies, to traces of foxes, and to a solitary lesser black-backed gull, scavenging below the summit of Carnedd Llywelyn. As we crossed the saddle towards the second highest hill in Wales, a wren sang, well over 3,000 feet above the sea.

The wrens of Eryri have long been considered, to quote Professor Kennedy Orton, "rather a mystery, for wrens are sedentary or non-migratory birds and sensitive to hard winters. It is not uncommon to find half a dozen wrens frozen in a hole after severe weather. Yet, when every other bird has gone, the wren will be met throughout the winter months in the mountains, where even in mild winters there are at least snaps of hard weather. When every stream has been frozen silent, I have seen and heard the wren at the mouth of the Twll Du (1,700 feet) in January. Possibly only the majority move down to the lowlands, leaving a few . . . who find both shelter and hibernating spiders or other toothsome insects in the deeper hollows and crevices."

As regards spiders, the wrens of Carnedd Ddafydd can include a rarity in their diet, for *Entelecera errata* is said by Bristowe to have its only North Wales station on this hill. Of other high-altitude invertebrates, the rare springtail, *Tetracanthella wahlgreni*, was taken here in 1933 by W. Maldwyn Davies. The coleopterist has also been active on the massif ; in 1898 W. E. Sharp collected over 40 species, representing 27 genera of beetles, including a red-legged form of *Pterostichus madidus*, from what corresponds to our alpine zone.

Beyond the top of Carnedd Llywelyn stretches the most likely bit of "dotterel ground" in Wales, and it may be from here that the records of its occurrence on passage come. Here, too, if anywhere, one might expect there to be ptarmigan, but, as Matheson says, the evidence "so far as the historic period is concerned," is no more than "unsatisfactory hearsay," and was thoroughly investigated by A. G. More (1881), who found that the only evidence was a statement by Latham, which was probably a misquotation.

The most likely alpine vertebrate to be met on the Carneddau is not a bird but a mammal, the introduced mountain-hare, which survives here better than elsewhere in Eryri. One recent writer says that they keep this territory and leave the Glyders to the herd of goats descended from those released by a local innkeeper. But as the same authority generally sees a "whole flock of great grey shrike" in Nant Ffrancon Pass about the New Year, one may expect an unusual element in his pronouncements.

After this somewhat negative expedition to the summits, I decided to spend the night in the zone in the hopes of seeing some of the fauna, of penetrating the cloak of invisibility which surrounds so much of the Snowdonian wild-life. Having anticipated the usual occupants in my choice of a resting place, I was left, when the sheep had moved disconsolately off, to the remarkable evening silence of alpine Britain. The ring-ousels, which had been gathering food for a brood in the morning, the wheatears, anxiety for whose fledged young had evoked such violent displays, had completely disappeared.

In the hollow below me lay Ffynnon Lloer, on which a fisherman was still casting. This tarn, about 2,200 feet above the sea, is the highest of any size in Eryri and is credited with trout in the *Mountains of Snowdonia* list; the molluscs *Ancylus fluviatilis* and *Pisidium milium* have both been found in it. Melynllyn, in the north of the massif, is also over the 2,000-foot contour, but several of the famous tarns, Glaslyn below Yr Wyddfa, Llyn Marchlyn Mawr below Elidir Fawr, and Llyn Du'r Arddu, are all just under it.

The sunset, and the dusk as it fell upon Tryfan and Y Glyder Fawr, which I could see from where I lay, provided an experience which was impressive and, from the naturalist's point of view, indirectly of interest, for the beauty was strangely lifeless and impersonal: I might have been looking at a landscape in the moon.

Next morning, on top of Carnedd Ddafydd before 6.0 a.m. B.S.T., a wheatear from under a stone was the only sign of life, apart from the inevitable sheep, and this condition obtained right round the semi-circular ridge which culminates in the variously-named bastion, Craig Ddu or Pen-yr-oleu-wen, at the head of the Nant Ffrancon. The steep slope down its side to Llyn Ogwen is typical acid "heather fell." Bilberry, common even at 3,000 feet, is associated with the heather as a sub-dominant; both bell-heather (*Erica cinerea*) and cross-leaved heather (*Erica tetralix*) occur, with wild thyme, goldenrod (*Solidago virgaurea*), hawkweeds (*Hieracium* spp.) and parsley fern; the principal grass appears to be sheep's fescue (*Festuca ovina*).

THE GLYDERS: THE ALPINE FLORA

Although eighteenth-century travellers had difficulty in locating the "Glyder Mountain" (Pl. III, p. 10) and even confused it with Yr Eifl in Llŷn (see pp. 398-9), which is little more than half its height, it is, as seen from Anglesey (Pl. 1, p. 2), the most striking section of the whole range and, apart from the attraction of Snowdon's greater altitude, the most interesting when examined in detail. The area of ground over the 2,000-foot contour is considerably less than in the Carneddau, and is very irregular in outline, consisting not of a solid block, but of a series of separate peaks with connecting ridges.

Botanically the massif shows the same general features as those described on the Carneddau: fescue sward on the gentle slopes, heather on the pronounced acid soils and on the "fells," leading up to mountain-top detritus, with the charmed circle of cliffs round Llyn Idwal holding, on rocks of calcareous origin, some of the most famous climbs and rarest plants in Wales.

It was unfortunate, but in keeping with June 1946, that Markham's and my attempts respectively to photograph and to examine this outstanding flora coincided with some of the most atrocious summer weather in which natural history field-work could be attempted. Our first visit to the Devil's Kitchen, in fact, was the worst day on which I have ever been out of doors in my life and made me think that, had the locality not already so appropriate a name, we should have had to invent it.

It was not surprising, therefore, that our search for the mountain spiderwort was less sustained and as vain as Brewer's (see p. 166); but we did manage to see the majority of the other characteristic flowering plants of the "Gardens." Llyn Idwal (Pl. I, p. 2) lies only 1,223 feet above the sea, but the cliffs of the Kitchen face more or less due north, and so the alpines begin to appear soon after one leaves the lake; in fact, all of them can probably be seen below our somewhat arbitrary 2,000 feet. With them, however, are associated a number of typically lowland, even woodland, plants, which add to the striking effect of the whole community: to look at nettles (*Urtica dioica*), dog's mercury (*Mercurialis perennis*) and hogweed (*Heracleum sphondylium*) on the one hand, and at moss campion (*Silene acaulis*), Welsh poppy (*Meconopsis cambrica*) and northern rock-cress (*Arabis petraea*) on the other, to see the tremendous competition between species in progress on this sheltered face, so obviously that the least crack in the rock seems to hold a plant of butterwort or starry saxifrage, to realize that celebrated botanists have admired this sight for several hundred years, all combine to impress the amateur with the importance of the habitat, even in a mixed deluge of rain and rock-drippings. Some thirty species of flowering plants and ferns were identified on the main face east of the actual chimney of the Kitchen, the famous Black Hole (*Twll Du*) (Pls. 5 and 8b, pp. 62 and 79); the majority of these we had seen a few days previously on Clogwyn Du'r Arddu below Snowdon. These are probably the two best-known localities in the zone, but, for certain rarities, special and secret stations elsewhere must be visited.

Professor Farmer suggested that "the key to the wealth of species, and to the main facts of their distribution, will be found to be in the existence of the Ordovician limestone which caps most of the higher mountains," though Hyde and Wade believe it is as much the drainage of this formation as its chemical composition which enables these rarer plants to survive. The geology of what are now to be called the "Bedded Pyroclastic Series" is dealt with by Dr. North in Chapter 2, where on pages 61-2 he links it to the vegetation, which is not without importance to the geologist as a guide to underlying conditions. The contrast between the plant cover of the acidic and basic rocks, as far as the plants of the latter are concerned, is quite clear-cut, and Farmer named purple mountain saxifrage (*Saxifraga oppositifolia*), mountain sorrel (*Oxyria digyna*) and spring sandwort (*Arenaria verna*) as particularly good indicators of lime-richness, though a fern, the green spleenwort (*Asplenium viride*), is perhaps the most sensitive of all, being "hardly ever found off the rocks rich in lime." The converse, of course, is not true; the typical plants of the acid rocks, heather, bilberry, hard fern (*Blechnum spicant*) and beech fern (*Thelypteris phegopteris*) spill over on to the limestone, and no plant is commoner, in countless niches and cracks of the face, than the butterwort, which has evolved its own highly specialized method of surviving in wet acid conditions. In this connection Tansley quoted Price Evans, who, in his ecological study of Cader Idris, suggested that the presence of these "calcifugous" plants was "due to the formation of acid humus on some of the rock ledges and also to the soil produced by acidic beds interspersed with the calciferous lavas."

Griffith attempted a rough classification of the rocks with the chief

PLATE 13

John Markham

RAVEN'S PERCH above Llanberis Pass. April

PLATE 14

b. WELSH POPPY, *Meconopsis cambrica*. North Wales. June

John Markham

a. WREN'S NEST amongst ivy-leaved toadflax, *Linaria cymba-*

John Markham

vegetative characters of each group, and his "acidic rocks," "intermediate rocks," "sedimentary rocks," "intrusive sheets of basic rocks"
and "calcareous volcanic ash," correspond roughly with the rock
categories recognized by petrologists, as outlined on pages 63-4.

As well as the calcifuges, there is on the typical limestone face the
important group of plants normally seen in hedgerow and woodland:
wood anemone (*Anemone nemorosa*), violets (*Viola* spp.), red campion
(*Melandrium dioicum*), wood sorrel (*Oxalis acetosella*), herb robert
(*Geranium robertianum*), moschatel (*Adoxa moschatelina*), primrose (*Primula
vulgaris*), foxglove, early purple orchis (*Orchis mascula*) and several
common ferns. Under boulders, on the screes, in shady recesses and, in
the case of the red campion and the orchis, on ledges alongside the moss
campion and the saxifrages, they are flowering at the end of June,
causing the observer to wonder whether he has not suddenly stepped down
a thousand feet in altitude and backwards a couple of months in time.

The globe-flower (*Trollius europaeus*)—whose heavy flowers are
expressively known as "bombels" in parts of South Wales—forms
brilliant yellow clumps and can be confused at a distance with the
Welsh poppy (Pl. 14b), whose seeds have been carried down to form
riparian colonies all the way to Bangor. In spite of its name, Griffith
considered the latter an alien, but it is now regarded as truly native;
in fact, no species of introduced origin have established themselves
on these faces, though it seems that there have been deliberate attempts
to "plant" certain alpines from time to time. Another local species
found on these rocks is the Welsh goldenrod (*Solidago cambrica*), which
is now considered to be a subspecies or variety of the common goldenrod (*S. virgaurea*), also abundant on faces of all types.

The moss campion and the saxifrages provide the authentic arctic-
alpine element. Excluding four segregates, six species of *Saxifraga*
occur, three of them being, like the moss campion, confined in Wales to
Caernarvonshire. The purple mountain saxifrage (Pl. 15, p. 206),
which has a superficial resemblance to the campion, is also found in
Merioneth and in two localities in the Brecon Beacons. Its great
attraction is its early flowering, for it is well in bloom in March, a
sort of floral counterpart to the raven, near whose nests it may often
be found. Both the mossy (*Saxifraga hypnoides*, Pl. XV, p. 186) and
starry saxifrages are widely distributed in Wales, and may be found
at low altitudes as well, the former in stony and the latter in wet
situations. The rare species are *S. caespitosa*, which has no English

name and closely resembles *S. hypnoides*, the alpine saxifrage (*S. nivalis*), a typical arctic plant, and the yellow mountain saxifrage (*S. aizoides*), a common plant in the Scottish Highlands, whose status in Eryri is somewhat obscure. Farmer actually considered it absent and includes it in a small group of British high-altitude plants which do not appear in this region. A particularly interesting example of these is the alpine lady's mantle (*Alchemilla alpina*)—which is also very common in Scotland and which has once appeared in Wales apparently planted. Farmer suggested that these species had failed to recolonize after the Ice Age, owing to the absence of intermediate areas of calcareous rocks.

One plant that has established itself, but very restrictedly, is *Dryas octopetala*, the mountain avens, for over one hundred years believed to grow only on Y Gribin, a ridge of the Glyder massif; its second station in the Carneddau, found in 1935 by Evan Roberts, but only just revealed, has already been mentioned (see p. 167). *Dryas* occurs in Scotland and in Galway at sea-level, while the mountain everlasting (*Antennaria dioica*) accomplishes the transition of habitat even more quickly, being found both on Y Gribin and on the dunes of Newborough Warren (see p. 294). The exchange between sea-shore and high altitude is two-way; Johnson was surprised at finding maritime species on Snowdon (see p. 164); but both sea-campion and thrift are common on the ledges of the Hanging Gardens.

The connection between the two habitats should not be unexpected; ability to withstand very adverse conditions characterizes the flora of mountain rock-faces and summits on the one hand, and of sea-cliffs and exposed shores on the other, but it is interesting to note that the same tendency appears in a few birds even in Britain, particularly in the case of the dunlin, which nests both on hill-tops and on littoral mosses and waste ground, and recently, to a very limited extent, of the fulmar, a typical sea-bird, which has been found breeding on an inland cliff in Northumberland. It has, of course, long been realized that the alpine zone descends as one goes north. Gay's astonishment at the low altitude of the Snowdonian alpine flora, compared to that of the same species in the European Alps (see p. 169), would have increased had he penetrated within the Arctic Circle and found them at sea-level.

A good example of this is the mountain spiderwort itself. *Lloydia*, as it can safely be called, for it enjoys a genus all to itself, is confined in Britain to the Snowdon and Glyder massifs, and, while it occurs in the arctic, its chief European stations are in the Alps, and thus its survival, in, or colonization of, Eryri is even more difficult to explain than that of *Dryas* (see p. 107) and other rarities, for which more reasonable stages of progress, by way of Northern England and Scotland, exist. Its world distribution has been comprehensively discussed by Woodhead (1929). *Lloydia* flowers in June—Griffith suggested the 12th as the best date for it—and as its leaves are thin and grass-like, it is difficult to detect at other times, though an experienced field-worker like Evan Roberts can recognize it. The four petals are white and waxy, and the whole plant has an air of delicacy not inappropriate to its exalted status. Owing partly to collectors, many of its present sites are now only accessible to skilled climbers, which was the case many years ago with some of the rare ferns.

A large number of plant families and genera are represented by one or two species on the Snowdonian rocks ; some of these are true alpines, such as alpine saw-wort (*Saussurea alpina*) and alpine scurvy-grass (*Cochlearia alpina*): others have established themselves well out of their normal habitat, such as the nettle, and even more remarkably the lake-plant shoreweed, which Griffith found growing in Cwm Idwal with barren flowers on the leaves. The situation is also unfavourable to the tree habit, and the least willow (*Salix herbacea*) and the dwarf juniper (*Juniperus nana*)—which is one of the few rarities of the acid rocks—are specially adapted. The small rowans (*Sorbus aucuparia*) which we saw on sheltered ledges were not unexpected; more interesting is the occurrence of bird-cherry (*Prunus padus*), first recorded by Griffith and confirmed recently by Roberts.

Ferns, mosses, liverworts and lichens form the background to the more obvious array of flowering plants, and are apt to be overlooked except by the specialist. The ferns, however, include over half the species known to Wales, with some of outstanding scarcity. Evan Roberts has paid a good deal of attention to this group, but he has never yet found the Killarney or bristle fern (*Trichomanes speciosum*), which was so rare in Griffith's day that he only knew of it in one site, found by his friend, Professor J. Lloyd Williams, and did not even mention the neighbourhood. Hyde and Wade report it from two or three localities in Caernarvonshire and Merioneth. Almost as hard to find are the woodsias (*Woodsia ilvensis* and *W. alpina*), two arctic-alpine ferns here in their most southerly British stations. Both are mainly confined to the pyroclastic series, and it was of the alpine woodsia that Griffith remarked that it could only be reached with ropes in the two localities where he knew it; Roberts has found both species recently, and also the holly fern (*Polystichum lonchitis*), whose disappearance Griffith feared.

Two interesting species are the filmy ferns, *Hymenophyllum peltatum* and *H. tunbrigense*; the latter is considered by Hyde and Wade to be found on acidic rocks, though Farmer describes both as forming "matted sheets of vegetation" in the rock caves of the Twll Du screes. Of the commoner ferns that will take the eye of the general visitor are the oak fern (*Gymnocarpium dryopteris*), beech fern, considered by Farmer to prefer an acid habitat but recorded from most of the stock limestone cliffs, brittle bladder fern (*Cystopteris fragilis*), broad buckler fern (*Dryopteris dilatata*), and, above all, the parsley fern, which Markham has caught effectively in early spring, when the new fronds emerge from the bright brown debris of the old (Pl. 16a, p. 207).

The allied club-mosses (*Lycopodium selago*, *L. clavatum* and *L. alpinum*) are found, like the parsley fern, not only on the rock-faces, but in suitable habitats all over the higher pastures; they may be seen near to the road at Pen-y-pass. All the species are not usually seen close together as they appear in Plate 16b; when they do, they recall in miniature a landscape of Carboniferous times, especially if the observer is young enough to put his eye at ground-level.

Mosses and other lower plants are prominent in any arctic-alpine flora. The grey cushions of woolly fringed moss (*Rhacomitrium lanuginosum*) are a general feature of the region, alike amongst the mountain-top detritus and the retrogressive bogs of Migneint (Pl. 22, p. 255). Farmer remarks on the black tufts of the moss *Andraea* on the high cliffs and on the mats formed by the hepatic *Anthelia julacea*, on which flowering plants take root. The indefatigable Griffith listed between 70 and 80 lichens, 80 to 90 mosses and nine liverworts which may fairly be attributed to the highest zone of our region, though many of them grow on the peat and not on the rock-faces. He collected the majority of them himself, and most interesting historically, perhaps, is "Griffith's Alpine Collared Moss" (*Oedipodium griffithii*), which was at one time supposed to be confined to Great Britain. Pennant, who seems to have been more interested in the utilization of plants than in their biology, remarks on the use of lichen dyes in North Wales.

Ecologically, as we have seen, the Hanging Gardens present, not a clear picture of dominance, as does the heather-bilberry association of the acid rocks, but of an intensive struggle between a variety of plants representing all types of normal habitat. These were classified nearly a hundred years ago by H. C. Watson in his *Cybele Britannica*, but they still form a useful basis for broad ecological classification. Watson defined their function—"for expressing the usual situations of the species with respect to shade or exposure, humidity or dryness, the mechanical condition of the soil and the propinquity of the haunts of man and animals"—and Hyde and Wade assign almost all the flowering plants of Wales to one or more of the fourteen types he suggested. Analysing the list of species, which are indicated by an asterisk in the Appendix (pp. 406-21) every type is found to be represented by at least one species of flowering plant. Naturally, the rupestral (walls and rocks) type is the strongest, claiming 32 species and a share in eight others out of a total of 90. The ericetal (heath) type, consisting mainly of plants from the acid rocks, has 14 full species and shares seven, while the uliginal (moors and bogs) type has nine, including two saxifrages. The sylvestral (woodland) type has eight species and shares eleven, chiefly with the septal (hedgerows), which may be regarded as closely related, since the flora of the hedge-bottom is really an extension from the woodland. These form the bulk of the lowland element, which, with half-a-dozen species of pratal (meadows) and pascual (pastures) type, amounts to about a third of the population of the rock-faces by species.

Numerically it is much harder to give any estimate on the basis of published information; the adjectival comments, "occasional," "common," "abundant" of former observers really mean very little— though constant use is made of them—unless they are standardized as in modern ecological studies. One ledge may show a local domination by the Welsh poppy, on another a great cluster of globe-flowers is surrounded by meadow rue (*Thalictrum* spp.) to be replaced a few feet away by a cushion of moss-campion, or, in a trickle of water, by closely packed rosettes of starry saxifrage, while on the screes the humps of mossy saxifrage often establish a marked ascendancy, with ferns under the larger boulders. In fact, as the popular name for the faces implies, natural competition in a favourable environment insures that variety and diversity which man maintains by his control in a well-planned garden; both result, from the human point of view, in a whole which is highly decorative.

Before leaving the plant life of this highest and most fascinating zone, the chief characteristics of its flora, in terms of the distribution-types also defined by Watson, may be noted. These types were primarily based on the number of vice-counties in which each species occurred, and thus are relevant only to these islands. His "Scottish" and "Highland" types penetrate further south in Wales than they do in England, and Hyde and Wade show that of the 37 species of Highland type—most of them in the rupestral habitat-type—known to Wales, 34 are found in Caernarvonshire and 18 of these only in Caernarvonshire; practically all the 18 are confined to the zone under consideration.

It does not appear that a list of the alpine and rock-face flora of Eryri has ever been published. Those marked by an asterisk in the Appendix include all the rarer species for which localities are given in *Welsh Flowering Plants*, *Welsh Ferns* or by Griffith. But information is not so easily forthcoming as regards the commoner species, for while the occurrence of plants outside their normal habitat is of considerable interest to the modern ecological botanist, it was not thought so important by the older workers. Some of these species have been noted personally, others added by Evan Roberts, and from references in Farmer's chapter in the *Mountains of Snowdonia*, in Woodhead's papers, notes kindly lent by G. W. Temperley, and in Griffith's introductory sections. Incomplete as the list is, it may give those who have not previously examined the region an idea of the range of species which they can expect to see in or around the "Hanging Gardens of Eryri."

Like Carnedd Ddafydd, Y Glyder Fawr has its particular spider, whose identification by Dr. A. R. Jackson in June 1915, at an elevation of over 3,200 feet, caused amongst arachnologists an excitement comparable to that roused in botanists by the spiderwort, for *Micaria breviuscula* (*alpina*) was then known no nearer than the Alps. Subsequently the slightly lower summit of Cader Idris in Merioneth has also claimed it. Other high-level arachnids are *Tetragnatha montana* and *Hilaira frigida*. A humbler group of invertebrates, the Collembola or springtails, also have a focus of interest in the Glyder massif. They were intensively studied by W. Maldwyn Davies, who listed 30 species in North Wales, of which six were new to Britain. Four of these, *Tullbergia bipartita*, *Tetracanthella wahlgreni* (see p. 187), *Sminthurides schotti* and *Onychinus alborufescens*, were identified on the top of Tryfan (Pl. 6, p. 63), in other respects a peak sacred to climbers, except when, according to Kennedy Orton, mistle-thrushes ascend it to feast on bilberries.

But, apart from creatures of such extremely local distribution—and this may be "local" only because similar habitats have not been investigated elsewhere—the animals, like the majority of plants, are common to all three major sections of the Snowdon range, and can best be considered in one account, after a short description of the alpine areas surrounding Yr Wyddfa and Moel Hebog.

SNOWDON AND MOEL HEBOG: THE ALPINE FAUNA

The area over 2,000 feet round the summit of Snowdon—for which the Welsh name Yr Wyddfa is a useful particularization—is only about half the size of that on the Glyders, and is shaped like an irregular swastika with its centre at the actual summit. The famous syncline of Clogwyn Du'r Arddu has a flora almost the equal of Cwm Idwal; Cwm Glas, a high valley draining into the pass of Llanberis, is specially famous for one or two rarities, and notable localities occur all round Crib Goch, and on the faces of Yr Wyddfa and Lliwedd, which stand over Glaslyn and Llyn Llydaw respectively (Pl. 30, p. 335), though there are repeated alternations with the poor flora of the acid rocks.

The alpine zone of the Moel Hebog massif is composed of islands, of which that round Carnedd Goch (2,301 feet) is actually larger than that of Moel Hebog (2,566 feet) owing to the latter's shapely cone. A locality for the very rare bristle fern is given in this area, but there are few other records of note; whether this is because the massif has been insufficiently worked, in view of its lesser altitudes, or is genuinely unproductive, it is hard to say.

Entomologists have covered the summit of Snowdon itself rather thoroughly, and were rewarded by the discovery of a beetle of considerable beauty and "Lloydian" rarity, for it is known nowhere else in Britain. *Chrysomela cerealis* has been a coleopterist's prize for a number of years in this one locality, where Fowler says Dr. J. W. Ellis had taken it "lately" (presumably between 1880 and 1890) in some numbers. It is found on thyme, and is a most striking insect, its upper surface being of "a brilliant fiery red or coppery colour, with three bands on the thorax and the suture and two or three bands on each elytron purple, freely edged with golden green." In June 1906, Horace Donisthorpe and Sir T. Hudson Beare took a dozen specimens each and, by wringing out moss, collected another 21 species of beetles, including two previously unrecorded in North Wales. The locality for *Chrysomela cerealis* is now a closely kept secret and there seem to be no more modern references to it in the literature of entomology. But quite recently another new insect was identified on the slopes of Snowdon, and although it strictly belongs to the next zone, the interesting point which its discovery raises can best be discussed here. On June 10th, 1933, H. W. Daltry and H. Britten, collecting on the side of Crib Goch above Llyn Llydaw, found, between 1,600 and 1,900 feet above the sea, two males and two females of a homopterous insect, a "froghopper", which was at first thought to be *Cixius sticticus*, of Mediterranean range. This was sufficiently remarkable, but, upon dissection, the genitalia of the Snowdon specimens were found to be distinct enough to warrant specific status, and the insect was accordingly described and named *Cixius cambricus*. W. E. China, of the British Museum, in publishing the data, suggests that the new species had evolved in isolation, from *C. sticticus*, a relic of the Lusitanian fauna which occupied Britain in Cretaceous times, and which retreated before the Ice Age, attempted recolonization afterwards, and retreated again, to leave a small colony in this one spot, which enjoys one of the highest rainfalls in Britain, and therefore favoured its survival by providing conditions suited to it. He further suggested that, if a close dissection of *Chrysomela cerealis* were made, it might be found also to have evolved sufficiently far from the Continental type to warrant specific status. These ideas remind one of the systematic problems of the Welsh char, which are dealt with in Chapter 10 (pp. 251-2) and of the importance to the geologist and geographer of the flora and fauna which are residual in Britain from former climates.

Beetles and spiders seem to make up the bulk of the high-level invertebrate fauna. Theodore Wood, in June 1901, collected nine species, though not *Chrysomela*, within a hundred feet or so of the summit of Snowdon, and another was added in 1907. On the other hand K. J. Morton, also in 1901, found the Snowdon area "unproductive" for Trichoptera and similar orders; records of moths are also few from the alpine zone, but F. C. Best informs me that five species of butterflies may be met within it, though presumably none of them breed there. They are the small heath (*Coenonympha pamphilus*), probably the most abundant species in the whole region, the common blue (*Polyommatus icarus*) and green-veined white (*Pieris napi*) of resident butterflies; to which he adds occasional migratory red admirals (*Vanessa atalanta*) and painted ladies (*V. cardui*), which are scarce in North Wales. James Fisher has also seen small tortoiseshells (*Aglais urticae*).

Altogether, therefore, there is a comparatively rich insect life right to the tops of the highest hills, which explains why the predominant small birds are all insectivorous; Britain's highland finch, the twite, is only known on passage; apart from one record in Merioneth, it has never been seriously suggested as a breeding bird, although, for some reason, it is a species to which imaginative bird-watchers are very fond of according an exaggerated status. The snow-bunting is reported to be a winter visitor to the hills, but not in large numbers or very regularly. Forrest quotes records from Snowdon in 1904 and from Y Garn in April, 1913.

Few detailed accounts of the bird-life of the Snowdonian summits exist. Quotations have already been made from the chapter, similar to that on the botany by Sir J. B. Farmer, contributed by Professor Kennedy Orton to *The Mountains of Snowdonia*. This deals with most of the species mentioned on page 186, but surprisingly omits the wheatear, one of the characteristic birds of the zone, except from a rather misleading list at the end, which, since it includes the dotterel as a nesting species, evidently refers to hill country all over Britain.

But the wheatear (Pl. XVIIIa, p. 211), "a small and seemingly tender bird," was seen by Pennant on Snowdon. Overlooking the meadow-pipit, he believed it to be the only small bird, apart from the "Rock-Ouzel" to "frequent these heights." Today the wheatear nests in the screes below Twll Du and Clogwyn Du; we saw broods in both localities in late June and birds on the top of Snowdon early in April; while on Carnedd Ddafydd I watched that momentary hovering which has been recognized in the past few years as a habit in at least some males of this species, apparently as a form of display. When the wheatears first arrive and the males are occupying their territories, the stony hillsides seem alive with their jerking black-and-white tails and re-echo with the rather rattling but appropriate song. In June, when feeding young, they seem to forage in the grassland at some distance from the nest; one pair which I watched at a considerably lower altitude were collecting food in a hayfield and then flying up the long screes by stages from perch to perch, before disappearing into the nest at the foot of a rock-face.

By September the wheatears have abandoned their territories, but meadow-pipits are still to be seen on top of Snowdon. This is the typical small bird of British moorland and rough pastures and may be met at any level in our region; on a sunny day in spring males are con-

stantly flying up a few feet and sailing down to earth, uttering a song
which seems to suit the action, the whole performance being on a
meagre scale compared to that of the tree-pipit. When young are in
the nest or recently fledged, the parents set up a monotonous chant as
long as an intruder is in the vicinity, and as one is continually passing
through fresh territories, a walk on the hills in June can be quite
upsetting to a sensitive ornithologist.

Wherever meadow-pipits are, there will the cuckoo usually be, and
it can, therefore, be included in the breeding birds of this zone, for
Orton and others record eggs laid in pipits' nests at about the 2,000-foot
contour.

If the wheatear is the bird of the Snowdonian screes and the
meadow-pipit of the grassland, the rock-faces are shared by ring-ousel
and wren. Modern observers may be interested in the survival of the
wren, as we saw above, but to the older naturalists the ring-ousel was
the ornithological wonder of Eryri, second only to the eagles. Gibson
in his 1722 edition of Camden's *Britannia* says the "British Alps" produce
several plants and animals "as particularly Merula saxatilis Aldrovandi,
called here as in Merionethshire, Mwyalchen y Graig i.e. Rock-ousel
and in Switzerland Berg-Amsel or Mountain Blackbird." Bingley
observed "the Black Ouzel, *Turdus torquatus*, of Linnaeus: it is a not
unusual inhabitant of these alpine regions," and in 1849 the fourth
edition of Lewis's *Topographical Dictionary of Wales* has, in reference
to the "Snowdonian chain of mountains" the statement: "the ring,
or rock ouzel, in most places a migratory bird, here takes up its constant
abode," which is probably an echo of views current in the days of
Pennant and White, three-quarters of a century earlier. Certainly,
when a ring-ouzel is heard singing in April 3,000 feet above the sea,
perched on a heather-clad ridge amongst the rocks of Yr Wyddfa, it
seems the embodiment of the wilderness, which it is difficult to believe
is only just being re-occupied after the bird has spent five or six months
in North Africa, though it is only fair to say that individuals have been
recorded in winter from Britain. The vegetation of the acid rocks
forms a very suitable habitat for the ring-ousel in the nesting season
and James Fisher has told me how, in the middle of a difficult climb
on Lliwedd, he has been amused by seeing a cock ring-ousel scolding
a tiercel merlin perched a few feet from it.

A few sky-larks, and an exceptional pair of dippers or grey wagtails—
such as those Markham found with young in July right up the Twll

Du chimney—make up the total of small passerines breeding in this zone, and, although raven, peregrine and buzzard figure so largely in any description of Snowdonian birds, it seems unlikely that any buzzards or more than one or two peregrines now have eyries above the 2,000-foot contour, while the early nesting date of the raven does not favour a very elevated site. However, as the raven is so numerous along the range—it is the only large bird that one can count on seeing at all seasons—competition is likely to drive it up from the more sheltered rocks in the great valleys, which are probably its favourite habitat. (Pl. 13, p. 190.)

The raven has been associated with Eryri since mythological times, sharing with the eagle a leading part in the sinister proverb: "The eagle knows the place but not the time; the raven knows the time but not the place." Its name is said to occur in numerous rocks, but none are of sufficient importance within the Park area to be marked on the Ordnance Survey's one inch to the mile maps. The peregrine, on the other hand, can claim Moel Hebog for its own, and, now that the eagle has gone, the raptorial mantle has, so to speak, descended on it. When Kennedy Orton wrote, not twenty-five years ago, both raven and peregrine were apparently in a precarious position; he considered the raven "the most persistently and continuously persecuted bird in this country" and said that very few of its traditional cliffs (*Clog-y-fran*) were still in use. He suggested that its present sites might, therefore, be new, or had only been visited in former days after the birds had left in the height of summer. Generally, he thought that there were "few places below the 1,000-foot contour where raven, peregrine or buzzard can hope to hatch or raise their young in the mountains of North Wales," which is rather different from the impression formed on visits in 1946.

Orton describes the fidelity of the raven towards backward young ones and a tendency to take them up to the remoter part of the mountains after fledging. To one who has found the Snowdonian summits more frequented than anywhere else in the range, this seems a little strange, and, now that persecution has ceased—at least on the scale Orton believed—it is likely that the very popularity of the tops is an attraction rather than a deterrent to a bird which, as he himself points out, is an "admirable scavenger." Nowadays, several ravens always seem to be about the peak of Snowdon, which has during the summer months the densest human population for miles around, while in

South Wales ravens have nested for many years in rocks and quarries grimed with the smoke of the collieries.

The peregrine may prefer the absence of humanity, but, provided its eyrie is inaccessible, it tolerates a certain amount of passing interference with its solitude. The one North Wales nest which I reached in 1946 was in a disused quarry, but people constantly passed and disturbed the falcon. In spite of a special campaign against it during the 1939-45 war, owing to its inroads on carrier pigeons, the peregrine seems to be holding its own everywhere; on one day round about Snowdon in April, we saw a pair at their eyrie and heard another awake the echoes of Clogwyn Du. But, after the nesting season, the higher ground is deserted for the more profitable coast-line, and the raven is left in possession of a bleak kingdom.

The buzzard will be discussed in the zone in which it seems most numerous today (see page 236), but the disappearance of the golden eagle can be reconstructed here, since its eyries were presumed to be about the 2,000-foot contour, although Clogwyn-yr-eryr above Llyn Eigiau is only 1,828 feet high, and the eyries which I have seen in Scotland have all been well below that altitude.

It will have been noticed that Dr. North cites an eminent Welsh authority on the derivation of Eryri, and though it therefore seems that *Eryr* (eagle) is only a development from the same root and not the origin of the regional name, yet the latter view has such a long tradition —far longer, incidentally, than Pennant's vulgarism "Snowdonia"— that it seems justifiable still to equate Eryri with "the eyrie," which was the sixteenth-century view of the inhabitants, according to Camden, and may have thus become a *de facto* meaning, because of the close association of the mountains with the birds. Johnson's account (see p. 165) has been taken as proof of the eagles' presence in the seventeenth century, but it is clear from the Latin that he did not see them himself and Willughby in his *Ornithologia* (1676) also gives the information at second-hand. In the late eighteenth century Pennant (though he repudiated the "Eryri"="eyrie" view on the grounds of their scarcity) still believed they nested occasionally, but no one seriously suggested it after 1800, and Lewis sums up the probable position in the middle of the nineteenth century, when he says that the golden eagle is known to have bred among the Snowdon mountains, "but those which are seen there [now] are occasional visitors in quest of prey."

Authentic recent records are very few, because of confusion with the white-tailed eagle, which, though it has ceased to nest anywhere in Britain for many years, still seems to be rather commoner as a vagrant in the south.

The last bird to be described is the only one with real alpine claims: the chough. Although in these islands it is normally found on sea-cliffs, another race (*Pyrrhocorax pyrrhocorax erythrorhampus*) and another species, the alpine chough (*Pyrrhocorax graculus*) are found commonly in the European Alps, where they are to the mountain hotels and huts rather what jackdaws are to rubbish heaps at low altitudes in Britain. North Wales is now the only part of Britain where choughs are regularly found inland, and their presence is some compensation for the absence, as nesting species, of the snow-bunting, dotterel and ptarmigan of the higher Scottish hills. Glossy black all over, with rose-red bill and bright red legs, the chough (Pl. XIX, p. 218) is a striking bird, familiar in pictures, and as a symbol of Cornwall, to many who have never seen it. It soars with widely separated flight-feathers, more like a small raven than a jackdaw, which it resembles in size. Like many rare birds, it is remarkably indifferent to man, often allowing a close approach and, in a few nests which I have seen, going fearlessly in and out when under observation. No localities can be given for a species of such scarcity, but outside the breeding season small parties may be seen on many of the hills, including Snowdon, although they may be miles away from their nesting places.

Other birds, which are daily visitors to the zone, are the flocks of rooks, which, according to Orton, frequent the grassland between 2,000 and 3,000 feet up on sunny days in late summer. James Fisher thinks that bilberries are the object of their visits; however, we saw a large number well up Cwm Brwynog in June, before the berry season. As the Snowdonian rookeries are few and small, the birds probably come from the agricultural districts along the Menai (see also p. 246). Scavenging herring- and lesser black-backed gulls have already been mentioned, as has the mistle-thrush, earlier in this section. Orton says that the nightjar may also be heard at a high altitude on warm summer evenings; Forrest notes chaffinches on the summit of Snowdon in April 1914, and swifts commonly over the mountain-tops in summer.

Only one exceptionally rare bird ever seems to have been recorded in the alpine zone, but that one was appropriate enough, for Wales' only alpine accentor was seen by Howard Saunders beside the Llanberis track up Snowdon on August 30th, 1870.

Except for the mountain hare, few wild tetrapod animals visit this zone, and none which cannot be dealt with in a later chapter. Forrest says that frogs often spawn at high altitudes, and he gives a surprising record of a hedgehog found by J. Lloyd Williams at 2,500 feet on Y Garn in the Glyder massif.

References for Chapter 8

Bingley (1800), Bristowe (1939-41), Camden (1733), Carr and Lister (1925), China (1935), W. M. Davies (1934), Donisthorpe (1906), Druce (1932), A. E. Ellis (1940), Farmer (1925), Fisher and Waterston (1941), Forrest (1907) (1919), Fowler (1887-91, 1913), Griffith (1895), Hughes (1940), Hyde and Wade (1934) (1940), Ingham and Salmon (1936), Lewis (1849), Matheson (1932), More (1881), Morton (1901), Orton (1925), Pennant (1784), Pounds (1942), Price Evans (1932), Savory (1935), Sharp (1899), Tansley (1939), Willughby (1676), Wilson (1946-47), Wood (1901), Woodhead (1928) (1929) (1933).

Communications from Best (1946), Fisher (1947), E. Roberts (1946), Temperley (1933).

CHAPTER 9

THE GRASSLAND ZONE

THE zone which has been described in the previous chapter is that, for obvious reasons, least affected by man. Grazing occurs to the tops of the highest hills, but it is unlikely that, at these altitudes, it compares with the weather as a controlling factor on the flora, while the plant-life of the rock-faces is relatively safe from disturbance by animals, although, as Dr. Scott points out (pp. 342, 398), goats, because of their ability to reach the rocky ledges, formed quite an important part of the primitive stock of the North Wales farmer and some of their descendants lead a feral existence on the hills today.

But, as we come down the contours, human interference with the original habitat increases and the modification which this has brought about means that only in odd corners without any agricultural or other economic importance can the outline of the natural community be seen; for the greater part of the area, it is a question of studying the adaptation of the wild-life to the enormous changes resulting from the establishment, through many centuries, of some sort of civilization in the valleys and on the hillsides of Eryri.

To gain the fullest understanding, therefore, of this complex position, the following chapters of this section should be read in close conjunction with those for which Dr. Scott has been responsible. Cross-references to specific points will be given, but, for a general impression, the whole of the historical section will be found to be relevant, and especially those passages which deal with the development of agriculture.

As an introduction to the problem of the grasslands, one cannot improve on the remarks of the authors of *A Survey of the Agricultural and Waste Lands of Wales*, for their work is the most detailed account of the whole of the vegetation of our region which has yet been published (see Map 4, p. 214-215).

"It is likely," they observe, "that the primeval vegetation over the greater part of Wales, and especially that occurring below the 1,500-foot contour, was deciduous forest. Alder swamp must have been common in the lowlands, while birch increased in prominence with altitude. The present-day peat bogs, even at elevations in excess of

1,500 feet, almost always contain woody remains of birch, hazel, and often of oak, representing present-day species, although these are no longer common at high altitudes. Even though many coniferous trees do well after planting, it is unlikely that conifer forest ever made any important contributions to the early forests of Wales."

"It has often been supposed," they continue, "that the disappearance of forests in Britain and their replacement by peat bogs and heath has been chiefly a function of a change in climate. The work on Scottish peat mosses appears to confirm this viewpoint. There is justification, however, for regarding the biotic factor (human as well as the grazing animal) as one of fundamental importance in this connection. Indeed, the disappearance of forest in Wales might quite well be due entirely to man and his grazing animal. Even today such trees as oak, ash, hazel, hawthorn, sycamore, mountain ash, birch and even beech can be made to grow on some of the least promising habitats on the Welsh hills. Birch and mountain ash are so easily grown that they form a complement to most of our mountain homesteads, and are today a characteristic feature marking the spot where a cottage has stood in the past, even though no trace of stone or earthbuilt wall now remains. This aspect of tree maintenance could well be amplified; the intention here, however, is to suggest that climate is not a necessary factor when accounting for the alleged change from primeval forest to grassland and moorland in Wales."

They go on to point out, as Dr. Scott says in Chapter 13, that the thickly afforested valleys were avoided by Bronze Age man in making his settlements, probably because his tools were not adequate for large-scale felling, and they believe that these oak forests survived to "late historical" times, when military requirements were largely responsible for their destruction (but see Chap. 21, pp. 371-2); it was only natural that they should then be replaced by agricultural land.

On the hills, which are the zone with which this chapter is concerned, the forests were cut originally by early man, before he had become a cultivator; and the authors of the *Survey* consider that the natural tendency to regeneration of woodland was soon in conflict "with the rapidly growing and progressively canalized biotic factor. Once the forest was felled, grass and other herbage would spread rapidly and form a more complete ground cover than in the forest phase. This in itself would slow up succession and thus make regeneration more difficult. Add to this the important fact that the spread of

PLATE 15

John Markham

PURPLE MOUNTAIN SAXIFRAGE, *Saxifraga oppositifolia*, and mosses near the summit of Snowdon. April

PLATE 16

John Markham

b. CLUB-MOSSES, *Lycopodium selago*, *L. clavatum* and *L. alpinum*, the three growing together below Glogwyn du'r-arddu

John Markham

a. PARSLEY FERN, *Cryptogramma crispa*: the young fronds appear through the dead foliage. Near Llyn Llydaw

grass herbage would make possible a corresponding increase in the number of domestic and wild animals, that, in addition to eating the herbage, would browse upon as well as crush underfoot any tree seedlings that became established."

In remarking that present-day vegetation anywhere in this country is not in a state of equilibrium, the *Survey* introduces a passage which is applicable particularly to our region, where the fences of the Forestry Commission have recently enclosed areas of hillside well above the apparent limit of native tree-growth. Although the farmer, by maintaining his stock in a certain manner, preserves an appearance of sward stability, once let him "change his system, either by decreasing or increasing the number of his animals, and almost immediately the so-called equilibrium is upset and there follows a sharp floral change. It is just this which has occurred everywhere in the hilly districts of Britain during the past two or three decades, and it has presented us with a host of new and important problems. Mountain ponies, cattle beasts and four-year-old wether sheep at one time provided an important source of revenue on these hills. They have since become unprofitable and are no longer being maintained, with the result that bracken-fern, gorse, heather and bilberry are spreading at an alarming rate in many parts of the country.

"Where plots of ground have been entirely shut off from the grazing animal the balance of vegetation is extraordinarily quickly upset. On the mountain fescue and *Nardus* pastures heather spreads rapidly, and it is only a matter of years before woody vegetation, such as birch, mountain ash and hawthorn makes its appearance. The succession from grass to heather, gorse or fern is the natural phase in development towards forest. On the open hills the progress is now, of necessity, slower because, with a relative scarcity of trees and other woody vegetation, the centres of spread are distant and new local centres have not become established. The elements of the post-grass phase (fern, heather and gorse) are, however, abundantly distributed everywhere, so that the process of succession from grass to the next ecological phase can be, and often is, a fairly rapid one." A good example of these processes in action can be seen on the right-hand side of the road from Capel Curig to Pen-y-gwryd, before the hill farm of Dyffryn Mymbyr is reached. Here bracken, with a certain amount of gorse, is well established over a wide stretch of hillside, and numerous bushes of hawthorn are growing amongst it. This would seem to be an old area of enclosed ffridd, or hill pasture; the process is not evident above the bounding wall.

In conclusion the *Survey* gives its opinion: "Having regard to all the evidence there are considerable grounds for suggesting that were the biotic factor in terms of man and his domestic animals removed entirely from the Welsh hills, forest of a kind would establish itself even under conditions of present-day climate. There is, therefore, no real necessity to rely upon possible climatic changes of the past in order to explain the destruction of forest in the hills of Wales."

The *Survey* continues by discussing some of the features of the moorland which has succeeded the ancient forest. "Following upon the destruction of the forest cover, it is to be expected that peat would accumulate readily on soils with impeded drainage, and this peat, once formed, would tend further to impede the drainage. Deep peat formations must have been laid fairly rapidly or else woody structures (trees, twigs and fruit) could never have been preserved in them in so excellent a condition as that often met with. Furthermore, soils with free drainage on the Welsh hills have almost invariably a layer of peat sometimes only a few inches thick. Over this is a mat of only semi-decomposed vegetation (immature peat), and this mat is one of the most characteristic features of the dry as well as of the wet moorlands. The 'mat' presents itself as one of the most efficient impediments to drainage, for even in very wet weather, when well-drained soils are soggy, the soil on the hillside immediately below the surface mat may be quite dry. Water finds great difficulty in penetrating the mat, and it, therefore, has to run off to lower levels without ever making contact with the soil. It goes either into the already saturated bog or direct into the hill stream. Peat formation has obviously been a much slower process on the hillside than in the flush bog, and it is seldom that one finds woody remains of tree life on the slopes. The present-day hillside habitat is, however, likely to be no less conducive to the growth of trees than is that of the peat-filled hollow below it."

Good examples of variation in drainage conditions occur along the early stages of the popular Snowdon Ranger path from the Youth Hostel of that name up the mountain, and also, though it actually falls in the Nant Conwy section of our region, in the rough walk across the moors south of Moel Siabod from Roman Bridge to Penygwryd.

These authoritative quotations have made it clear that in this zone we are dealing with an artificial situation, resulting from the impact of man-made rather than of climatic factors. In Caernarvonshire "rough grazings," the category which most nearly corresponds to the zone under consideration, amounted in 1935, according to a Table in the *Survey*, to 173,466 acres, which was 48 per cent of the area of the county and 53 per cent of its agricultural land; similar percentages for the whole of Wales were 34 and 38 respectively, so that in our region this zone is relatively more important than in the country as a whole.

The *Survey* distinguishes the following main types of rough grassland on the hills of Wales:

(a) FESCUE-BENT. Fescue usually dominant, but bent (*Agrostis* spp.) may be co-dominant. There is almost complete absence of leguminous plants. Areas invaded by bracken (*Pteridium aquilinum*), gorse (*Ulex* spp.) and scrub are included in this group, also the ffridd. Example: between Capel Curig and Dyffryn Mymbyr (see p. 207).

(b) MOUNTAIN FESCUE. Sheep's fescue dominant, associated with mat-grass; formations of bent-grass, mountain hair grass (*Deschampsia flexuosa*), heath-grass (*Sieglingia decumbens*), heather and bilberry occur. There is a restricted flora, with Leguminosae again absent. Example: Cwm Dyli, above Llyn Gwynant, and the gentler slopes of Snowdon generally.

(c) MOOR-GRASS—MAT-GRASS MOORLAND. This includes mountain flush bogs as well as the usual associations of dominant species. There is marked zonal distribution and any species may be dominant locally, e.g. on dry knolls mat-grass or heather; in wet hollows, moor-grass, rushes or even cotton-grass. Example: lower slopes of Snowdon massif above Llyn Cwellyn.

(d) COTTON-GRASS (INCLUDING "DEER GRASS"—DEERHAIR SEDGE) MOOR. This is found in wet, waterlogged hollows, indicative of stagnant conditions. The cotton-grass may be completely dominant, forming a dense surface vegetation, or where more open, it may co-habit with deerhair sedge, cross-leaved heather and bog-mosses. It is the least useful, economically, of the moorland associations. Example: slopes of Moel Siabod range above Pen-y-gwryd; generally in Migneint.

(e) HEATHER MOOR. Heather dominates but usually in association with grasses, especially mat-grass, sheep's fescue, mountain hair-grass and heath-grass. Tormentil, bilberry and heath bedstraw are almost always present, even in dense heather. Heather will invade mat-grass and mountain fescue pastures, suggesting a succession analogous to that of bracken and fescue-bent lower down. Example: upper part

of Forestry Commission block on Roman Bridge–Ffestiniog road (protection by fence from grazing); slopes of Moel Eilio above Llanberis.
(f) HEATHER FELL.   Heather is dominant but usually in association
with grasses, especially mat-grass and sheep's fescue, though locally,
and especially lower down, bracken, western gorse (*Ulex gallii*) or
scrub may be more abundant.   Typically it is a rocky and steep habitat
strewn with large boulders and, in places, with small precipices.
Example: Pass of Aberglaslyn.

The transitional Rushes and Lowland Fescue types are not important in acreage but four types from cultivated land, rye-grass pastures,
bent–rye-grass pastures, bent-grass pastures and rush–bent-grass
pastures will be described in the next chapter (p. 241) and must be
mentioned here to explain the headings given in Table VII in the
Survey, from which a modified extract follows:

GRASSLAND TYPES

Comparison between Caernarvonshire and the whole of Wales
(After Table VII of the *Grassland Survey*)

Grassland Type	Caernarvonshire (328,000 acres)	Wales (4,469,000 acres)
Cultivated Land		
(a) Rye-Grass	—	1 %
(b) Bent and Rye-Grass	9 %	14 %
(c) Bent (and White Clover)	35 %	46 %
(d) Bent with Rushes and Sedges	2 %	1 %
	46 %	62 %
Transitional		
(a) Rushes	< ½ %	1 %
(b) Lowland Fescue	2 %	1 %
	2 %	2 %
Rough Grazings		
(a) Fescue Bent	7 %	9 %
(b) Mountain Fescue	33 %	4 %
(c) Moor and Mat Grass	5 %	17 %
(d) Cotton-Grass	2 %	1 %
(e) Heather Moor	1 %	4 %
(f) Heather Fell	4 %	1 %
	52 %	36 %

The figures are percentages of the acreages given, which represent the

PLATE XVII

Eric Hosking

a. Male at nest-site; Radnorshire, June

John Markham

b. Typical habitat; Denbighshire, near Betws-y-coed, July

THE REDSTART: often an associate of declining agriculture

PLATE XVIII

John Markham

a. Wheatears; male approaching nest-hole with food, female leaving it with excreta from the young. Taken in Inverness-shire, May

Eric Hosking

b. Common Sandpiper; female on nest. Radnorshire, June

TYPICAL SUMMER VISITORS to the Snowdon region

total agricultural area of Caernarvonshire and of Wales. Temporary leys and arable acreages are included in types 1 (a), (b) and (c) and it must be emphasized that they refer to the period before the 1939-45 war.

Wartime cultivations, however, do not affect the zone under consideration, in which it will be seen that, compared with the whole of Wales, there is a far higher percentage of fescue pastures, and a good deal less of the mat–moor-grass association. Commenting on this in the paragraphs devoted to Caernarvonshire, the *Survey* remarks on the diversity in topography and rainfall, varying from 40 to 150 inches per annum, which characterizes the county. The principal pasture of the high ffridd shows mat-grass, fescue and the heath rush in association; mat-grass tends to dominate the drier and steeper slopes and is replaced by moor-grass and rushes in the damper flushes. But moor-grass is seldom dominant over large areas and is usually stunted; the large tussocks, which are such a feature in South Wales, are never common.

The earliest attempt to analyse the constitution of the grassland seems to have been by Pennant, who commented on "rushes, scirpus and carex" in Cwm Brwynog, and said that the hay of lower meadows consisted of "fine bent grass, *Agrostis capillaris* [? *A. stolonifera*], *Aira caespitosa* [? *Deschampsia flexuosa*], *Festuca ovina*, *Poa alpina* [? *P. annua*]." He recognized that there were viviparous forms on the higher pastures.

The tendency of the last half-century to contract the total number of hill-farms results in the dereliction of many holdings, with the advance of bracken and scrub. The desertion of homesteads has interesting ecological consequences; not only do mosses, ferns and stonecrops increase their hold on the walls, while weeds of field and wayside, nettles, willowherbs (*Epilobium* spp.) and ragworts (*Senecio* spp.), occupy the yards and pens, but, in the buildings, such birds as redstarts (Pl. XVII) and little owls find congenial breeding sites once man has gone, taking the sparrows, swallows and house-martins with him.

The collapse of walls and hedge-banks allows further inroads by bracken and heather; the value of these artificial barriers can often be noticed where fields end against the moorland, and, as the *Survey* points out, it is the best pasture which shows the effect of invasion most deeply, particularly where bracken encroaches on drier ground, while the wetter fields, which depended for their sward on man-made drainage, soon fall a prey to rushes.

The great stretches covered by rushes are one of the vegetative features that will strike those who visit North Wales for the first time. One of the commonest methods by which rushes advance gives the impression, from a distance, of a roughly circular blotch or smear, and those who see things with the eye of a hill-farmer will be struck by its similarity to some dark, fungoid growth, spreading over the pale face of the grassland.

Those more botanically minded may attempt a specific identification; for many years it seems to have been assumed that *Juncus conglomeratus* was the dominant rush in our zone, but Tweed and Woodhead have recently shown that this is far from being the case. *J. conglomeratus*, in fact, is extremely rare in North Wales and could be found only at a height below that with which this chapter is concerned. *Juncus effusus*, on the other hand, proved to be much more frequent at high altitudes than had been generally believed, with the variety *compactus* abundant or dominant. Caernarvonshire records show that *J. effusus* is found up to 1,100 feet in Nant Ffrancon and up to 1,400 feet in the Migneint. It is a species of the mountain slopes, retrogressive pastures and open spaces in woods, and its "sere and brown appearance over long periods of the year" is responsible for the sinister impression described above.

The flora of these *Junceta* (rush-dominated associations) is composed largely of mosses and a typical example from between the 750- and 1,600-foot contours fits conveniently in the zone under consideration and gives an idea of other detailed ecological data on the region which await publication.

Juncetum effusi compacti

Juncus effusus var. *compactus*	d.	*Eurhynchium praelongum*	v.a.
J. articulatus	o.	*Sphagnum cymbifolium*	a.
Galium saxatile	o.	*Hylocomium splendens*	a.
Agrostis alba (*stolonifera*)	o.	*Polytrichum commune*	a.
Chrysosplenium oppositifolium	o.	*S. cuspidatum*	a.
		S. acutifolium	a.

The right-hand column consists entirely of mosses; with the two rushes are associated heath bedstraw, white bent grass and opposite-leaved golden saxifrage; the symbols are d=dominant, v.a.=very abundant, a=abundant, o=occasional.

Generally speaking, this zone in Eryri suffers from being intermediate; it lacks the exciting character of the alpine zone or the greater diversity of the woodlands and valley bottoms. The flora of the ffriddoedd, as the associations described above indicate, is not conspicuous for variety or for rarities and, as regards the fauna, most of the more interesting species can be more properly treated in the higher or lower zones, or, in the case of such birds as the golden plover and grouse, in the chapter on Nant Conwy, where they are much more numerous. There is one small grouse-moor on the western slopes of the Snowdon massif: the area of Moel Eilio, already mentioned as an example of typical heather moor (see p. 210), and there are a few pockets of bog where a pair of golden plover may nest.

Nevertheless, one mammal belongs predominantly to the grassland, which has been to a large extent created for it and by it: the domestic sheep, whose history in Eryri is described by Dr. Scott (see p. 377). Although domesticated, the sheep, as a victim of parasites, is of interest to naturalists and especially to agricultural zoologists. C. L. Walton in his comprehensive paper on *The Agricultural Zoology of North Wales* listed 26 species of worms, ticks and insects which had been recorded attacking sheep in the North Wales counties between 1920 and 1926. The most serious of these was the liver-fluke (*Fasciola hepatica*), a flat worm which "occurred in enormous numbers in 1920-21 and caused the death of thousands of sheep, while another outbreak of lesser extent occurred in 1924-25." A map, prepared by Walton, is exhibited in the Zoology Department of the National Museum of Wales and shows the incidence of the epidemic; the higher blocks of mountain seem to have been relatively immune, but Eryri was intersected by a band of high incidence running through Nant Ffrancon, Llyn Ogwen and the Llugwy valley. No doubt the range of the disease coincided with the range of the host snail (*Limnaea truncatula*), a freshwater species "very abundant on the heavier and damper types of land." The snails were effectively destroyed by means of copper sulphate disseminated in various ways. The majority of the other parasites were cestode or nematode worms, though not all are harmful; a nematode *Trichuris ovis*, for example, seems to occur in 60 per cent of the sheep "but does

MAP 4.—The grasslands of Snowdonia and the adjacent regions of North Wales

Based on the map of the *Grasslands of Wales* in : *A Survey of the Agriculture and Wastelands of Wales*, edited for the Calm Hill Improvements Scheme by R. G. Stapledon in 1936. Reproduced by permission of Messrs. Faber and Faber Ltd.

Legend:

(grid pattern)	Agrostis with Rye Grass pastures
(vertical lines)	Agrostis pastures
Jc Jc (vertical lines with Jc)	Agrostis with Rushes
Jc (box)	Lowland Bog
×F×× F×F	Fescue – Agrostis pastures with Bracken Fern or Gorse
××× ×××	Fescue pastures (including Mountain Fescue & Lowland Heaths)
(dotted)	Dunes and Blown Sand
(cross-hatch dark)	Heather Moor
(diagonal hatch dark)	Heather "Fell"
(horizontal lines)	Molinia–Nardus zone
-Ja-	Mountain Flush Bog (usually Molinia with Rushes etc.)
-Jc-	Molinia–Nardus with common Rush, usually at low elevation
JL JL	Cotton Grass and Deer Grass Moor
(horizontal lines with marks)	Molinia–Nardus zone of Cotton Grass & Deer Grass
F (vertical lines with F)	Bracken Fern scattered zone of Agrostis pastu...
H	Scattered areas of He...
G	Gorse in considerabl...
(wavy lines)	Open water (lakes et...
(solid black)	Urban areas

SCALE: ¼ inch to 1 mile

Menai Strait

CAER...

Yr Eifl
1849

NEVIN

PWLLHELI

LLANDUDNO

BEAUMARIS

BANGOR

Ja

Ja

Ja

Jc

Jc

Carnedd
Dafydd
3426

Cliffs

Glyder
3279

Cliffs

Cliffs

Siabod
2860

Snowdon
3571

BEDDGELERT

Pine Woods

Vale of Conway

Woods

R. Conway

R. Conway

LLANRWST

F G
G
F G F F
F

G

G

F

F

H

FFESTINIOG

H

H

TRAWSFYNYDD

H

Gylchedd
2164

Jc

Arenig
2800

Jc

Jc

Jc

Jc

Jc

Jc

MADOC

H

not appear to be injurious." Arthropod pests included the tick *Ixodes ricinus*, controlled with arsenical dip, and the sheep-maggot-fly (*Lucilia sericata*), which may be serious in its attacks in moist summers, especially near woodland or amongst bracken, another indication of the negative value of this cover to the farmer.

Of the more attractive insects, there is a greater variety of butterflies to be seen in this zone than in the highest. The most interesting is the marsh-fritillary (*Euphydryas aurinia*), which flies in May and June in meadows where its food plant the devil's bit scabious (*Scabiosa succisa*) grows. Although not amongst the rarest British fritillaries, this is a scarce species with an interesting distribution in Britain, for there seem to be two main centres, one in the South of England and a lesser one in central Scotland, with a blank belt in the north of England. Wales comes almost in this belt and J. A. Thompson, who reported finding several nests of larvae in September 1940, at an altitude of 750 feet in the southern part of the Snowdon range—presumably the Hebog massif—claimed that there was only one other Welsh colony, in Merioneth; but F. C. Best has found it "locally common" in Nant Conwy and believes that it occurs elsewhere. As its colonies are extremely small—Thompson's nests were all within half an acre—it seems likely that they are sometimes overlooked. A commoner fritillary of bogland, though usually at the level of tree-growth, is the dark green (*Argynnis aglaia*), a large and finely marked insect, which is on the wing rather after the marsh-fritillary, in July and August.

To the common species noted in the previous zone can now be added the orange-tip (*Anthocaris cardamines*), the ubiquitous meadow-brown (*Maniola jurtina*), the small copper (*Lycaena phlaeas*), the large and dingy skippers (*Ochlodes venata* and *Erynnis tages*), all grassland species of general distribution, and the green hairstreak (*Callophrys rubi*), which it may surprise English visitors to find in an open habitat well above the hedgerows and woodland edge but where its food-plant gorse is growing. I have not seen it in Eryri, but on a South Wales mountain at about 1,000 feet I once found it swarming over a bracken slope with small clumps of gorse.

The hairy caterpillars of the eggar-moths are almost as characteristic of the Snowdonian grassland and moorland as the great black slug, *Arion ater* (Pl. XVIa, p. 187), which, with the sheep and the meadow-pipit, make up the bulk of the visible fauna. The northern oak-eggar (*Lasiocampa quercus* var. *callunae*) has the large brown larva with black bands on which are conspicuous white patches; the smaller and very common fox-moth (*Macrothylacia rubi*) larva is black, with a brown dorsal mane, which comes off and can cause an irritation when the caterpillar is handled. The fox-moth caterpillar hibernates for one winter and pupates in the following spring but the northern eggar has a two-year cycle, hibernating the first and pupating the second winter in the brown, blimp-shaped cocoon, about an inch long, which is often seen woven into a sprig of heather. The brown imagines are burly and swift on the wing in May and June, appearing rather later than the magnificent emperor-moth (*Saturnia pavonia*) (Pl. XVIb, p. 187), whose plump green caterpillar, with black bands and pink spots, feeding on heather, is the prize of the young lepidopterist on a summer holiday in scenic Britain; the imago may be snapped up in April by a stonechat hardly bigger than itself.

Two of the smaller tiger-moths, the ruby (*Phragmatobia fuliginosa*) and the wood (*Parasemia plantaginis*) are colourful members of the grassland lepidoptera which may be seen in the daytime; Ashworth's rustic (*Amathes ashworthii*), however, is the lepidopteral rarity, not only of the zone, but of the region, for it is a confined species, only known in North Wales, where it has three stations. It is probably happier on limestone, but on Snowdon its habitat is slatey scree. The larvae may be taken on heather in April; methods have been amusingly discussed by A. J. L. Bowes in *The Entomologists' Record*. The vapourer (*Orgyia antiqua*), a small brownish moth with white spots on the forewings of the male, was the subject of a remarkable observation at Penmaen-mawr by H. F. Barnes, who has been responsible for much interesting entomological work in the region. On 28 August 1942, he found an area of bilberry moor being completely defoliated by the larvae; a rough census revealed a density in the neighbourhood of 1,250 caterpillars per square foot. 2,500 of the larvae were removed to be bred under observation, and brought with them three parasites, one of which had never before been recorded attacking the vapourer. The moth is by no means confined to such a habitat; its choice is catholic, and it is particularly at home in London, where, as Fitter points out, the caterpillars with their "grotesque tufts of hair" are common on the plane trees.

The grassland birds and mammals are disappointing; the common birds are those also found in the alpine zone and though snipe, curlew and lapwing may nest, I found no evidence in 1946 to suggest that they were in any strength at moderate altitudes in the main Snowdon range. The field-vole is the characteristic rodent, and is described, justly no doubt, by Forrest as common, but no special observations appear to have been made on it locally (see also p. 275). The common lizard is found throughout the grassland up to 1,500 feet.

THE LOWER ROCK-FACES

The flora of the lower rock-faces, which are included in this zone, in so far as it is alpine, has already been dealt with at length; in so far as the prevalent siliceous rocks are concerned, their association is much the same in composition as at the higher altitudes. The only new feature on either is the appearance, in clefts of the rock, of holly (*Ilex aquifolium*) and yew (*Taxus baccata*); the latter is commonly an indicator of lime-richness.

To the birds nesting in the rocks the carrion-crow and kestrel can be added in this zone, and though the former may normally build in trees, it is certainly at these levels what the raven is on the tops, the dominant large bird. Forrest records that the mistle-thrush nests up to 1,500 feet in gullies, and that the song-thrush occasionally builds on the moors above the tree-limit. The rocks are also the retreat of the fox, stoat, weasel, polecat and pine-marten. But except for the powerful hill foxes, which are often exported to England to enliven sport in the Shires, none of them are often visible and all are probably more numerous below the tree-line, from which they raid higher ground after voles and such rabbits as inhabit the screes and heather.

LAKES AND STREAMS

There is, however, one habitat within the zone which needs a more detailed description : that of the tarns, "alpine lakes" and streams, for it is generally in the neighbourhood of water that a varied wild-life persists at relatively high altitudes in Britain.

The flora is not extensive, but in and around Llyn Anafon, in the north-east of the Carneddau and at a height of 1,600 feet, Griffith did a good deal of successful collecting, whilst the shallow Llyn Ogwen, between Y Carneddau and the Glyders, and Llyn Idwal and Llyn Bochlwyd in the latter massif, have all received attention; few important records come from further south; although Llyn Llydaw is passed by hundreds of visitors annually, amongst whom there must be some botanists, its bare stony shores (Pl. Xa, p. 99) and sudden

PLATE XIX

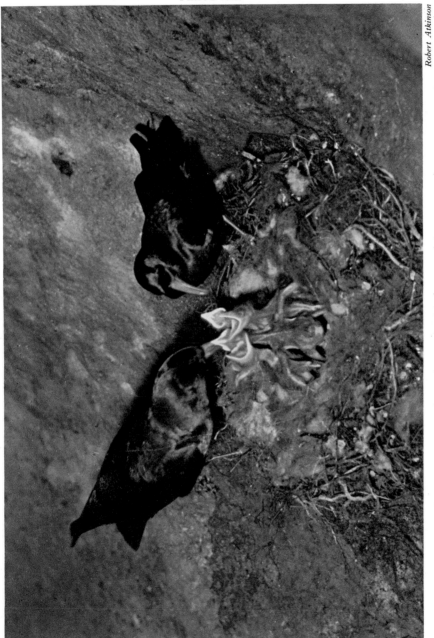

Robert Atkinson

CHOUGHS AT THE NEST: rare birds seldom photographed with success.   North Wales, June

PLATE XX

Eric Hosking

PIED FLYCATCHER: a typical bird of the North Wales scrub-woods; male at nest
Radnorshire, June

depth do not favour either riparian or lake-side plant growth, and the same is true of the legend-haunted Glaslyn and of many other tarns of the heights, whose extraordinary depths have been discussed by Dr. North (pp. 109 *et. seq.*).

Characteristic lacustral—floating or submerged—plants of this zone are the water awlwort (*Subularia aquatica*), a strongly modified crucifer, water starwort (*Callitriche intermedia*), water lobelia, shore-weed, already noted as occurring on land in Cwm Idwal, floating bur-reed (*Sparganium angustifolium*), lesser duckweed (*Lemna minor*) and floating water-plantain (*Alisma natans*), reported from Llyn-y Dywarchen, more renowned in story for its floating island (see p. 115). There are also several pondweeds (*Potamogeton* spp.), of which, in 1883, Griffith discovered an apparently new species in Llyn Anafon. This was named after him, *Potamogeton griffithii*, but is now considered to be a hybrid. More primitive plants such as the quillwort, in which Gay was so interested (p. 169), *Chara fragilis* var. *capillaria* and *Nitella opaca*, often attain a local dominance over all other vegetation.

Of all these the water lobelia is without doubt the most striking, taking the place in these higher waters of the water-lilies of lower altitudes.

Round the margins or along the streams may be found two species of crowfoot (*Ranunculus trichophyllus* and *R. hederaceus*), the attractive small variety of the marsh marigold (*Caltha palustris* var. *minor*), water blinks (*Montia fontana*), water purslane (*Peplis portula*), ivy-leaved bellflower (*Wahlenbergia hederacea*) the rare bog (*Hammarbya paludosa*) and the white frog (*Leucorchis albida*) orchids, a cotton-grass *Eriophorum vaginatum*, several sedges (*Carex* spp.), the peculiar fern, moonwort (*Botrychia lunaria*) and the fern-ally *Selaginella selaginoides*, while at Llyn Ogwen Hyde has found the white beakrush (*Rhynchospora alba*).

If the flora is not very unusual, "these mountain tarns" were considered by Forrest to be "remarkable for the paucity of their fauna; almost all contain trout, but few have any other fish; in one or two of the more secluded a pair of Greater Black-backed Gulls nest on some rocky islet, while in winter Mergansers and other wandering Anatidae pay them flying visits. There is one bird that equally affects the shores of the Welsh lakes, whether upland or lowland—the Common Sandpiper." He also recorded that the otter visited most of the higher lakes, and that the water-vole was common "up to a moderate elevation," which presumably covers some of the waters in this zone.

Going beneath the surface, we find that a small range of mollusca has been identified, a number of water-beetles and a few insects with aquatic larvae, such as the dragonfly, *Libellula depressa*, whose stout, brown-bodied imagines are common round Llyn Ogwen in June. The trout of this lake have been famous for at least a hundred and fifty years, for William Williams, whose fondness for the strange and superlative is rather marked, wrote in his *Observations on the Snowdon Mountains* (1802) that it "is well stocked with trout, which in colour and flavour surpass all fish of this kind known in any of the mountain lakes; their colour is a bright yellow; but in all other waters these fish have a darker or blackish cast externally, and when dressed are in general more white internally; but the Ogwen trout cuts as red as a salmon in full season. It has also in it excellent eels." According to Forrest, the sea-trout reaches the lake, while the only other fish found throughout Eryri, the humble minnow, also occurs.

Of amphibians, frogs, as has been mentioned, are common up to the alpine zone, while on the shore, a little time spent by Llyn Ogwen (Pl. 7, p. 78)—undoubtedly the most interesting, as it is the most accessible, of all these lakes—reveals a number of birds which, if not specifically riparian, seem to derive a good part of their food or their nesting cover from the proximity of the water.

In early April, there is little to be seen except the first wheatears, but, by the end of May, pied and grey wagtails are well on in their breeding season, and whinchats have established territories from Tal-y-llyn, the head of the lake, over the watershed and all the way down the boggy upper Llugwy valley, where they are associated with curlews in what may be that species' deepest penetration of Eryri. A short walk along the bank, much frequented by fishermen in quest of the wonderful trout, was sufficient to flush a sandpiper (Pl. XVIIIb, p. 211) off its nest under a projecting boulder. Returning in June, I was mobbed by the parents: they had evidently succeeded in hatching successfully in spite of the anglers, and the voices of other pairs were to be heard across the water.

At the head of the lake, in a stretch of protected bog where moor-grass and bog myrtle (*Myrica gale*) have been allowed to form a thick cover with bushes of heather, a pair of whinchats had young. This summer visitor is found on all kinds of rough ground, railway embankments, thorny heaths, bracken slopes, or, as here, a typical *Molinietum* (moor-grass association), which seems to be its chosen habitat in the region, as it is in the west Highlands of Scotland. We saw it up to about the 800-foot contour in several localities, particularly above the Snowdon Ranger Youth Hostel. The Ogwen pair, at nearly 1,000 feet, was about the highest. The stonechat, however, was strikingly absent, except on the coast, and this seems to be the position everywhere in Wales since the winter of 1939-40, when the small residents on the higher ground suffered in the ice-storm. Similar decreases were noticed in the nineteenth century and in 1917 in North Wales. Before 1939 the whinchat was generally considered the scarcer of the two, and its migratory habit seems in this case to have been of definite survival value. But in December 1946 I was surprised to see two male stonechats in a few minutes near Capel Curig.

By June several wheatears had families of young in the vicinity of the lake and swallows, which nest in the byres of most of the remaining occupied holdings, were obviously nesting at the farm of Tal-y-llyn, whose fields, with a mass of buttercups in flower, were a vivid patch below the grey-green ffridd. The swallows hawked up Nant Lloer, meeting the dipper, a more characteristic bird of such a stream along whose rocky course, in sheltered corners and ledges, were growing foxgloves, lady's mantle (*Alchemilla vulgaris*), wood sorrel, sweet vernal grass (*Anthoxanthum odoratum*) and, in a calmer pool, the pondweed *Potamogeton oblongifolium*. Bracken and gorse cover the slopes on either side, and here meadow-pipits, under a heap of dead fronds, were nesting in a site more reminiscent of the tree-pipit.

Although the pied wagtails of Llyn Ogwen are often seen by the lake, they really belong to the habitat of the main road which skirts it (see p. 255). Having found an empty nest in the wall close to the water, I watched the bird, in whose territory the nest seemed to be, patrolling a 300-yard stretch of the road. Normally it kept to the top of the wall, whence it made sallies into the air, on to the road surface, or to search the stones of the wall. At the end of its "beat" it showed excitement, especially if it had to fly back past me. I checked this observation elsewhere and noticed the same procedure and found a nest site within the beat.

Black-headed gulls visit Llyn Ogwen in summer, cormorants probably occur at all times, the goosander has been recorded occasionally in winter, and, as Forrest suggests, other ducks may put in an appearance. Both mallard and teal nest by some of the tarns; the latter has been seen on Ffynnon Llugwy, 1,786 feet up. But, in the main, the bird-life is passerine, and lacks the variety of the Scottish hill-lochs.

While the pied wagtails might remain at the height of Llyn Ogwen without the help of what American ecologists call an "anthropic" habitat, the presence of man at the Nant Ffrancon end of the lake and the planting of a belt of conifers and other trees there have brought a number of small birds to a height which they would not normally reach in this treeless land. Chaffinches, willow-warblers, robin, dunnock and a family of blue tits were all to be seen in June and all may well breed in the vicinity. James Fisher, however, tells me that vegetation is not necessary for dunnocks in this region; he has found them commonly associated with sheep-fanks up to 1,500 feet.

Man-made cover is also found at Pen-y-gwryd, together with a rush-fringed artificial lake. Here, as early as April 3, a willow-warbler sang, evidently on passage, for this, like the Ffestiniog–Lledr pass, has been claimed as an important overland route, while chaffinch, pied wagtail, great tit, mistle-thrush, dunnock, wren and moorhen were all identified. In September, a robin sang, while in mid-winter chaffinch, song-thrush, blackbird, robin and dunnock were still present, although the Ogwen area appeared quite deserted.

Those who need convincing of the truth of the theories advanced at the beginning of the chapter should pause at Penygwryd, gaze first at the bleak landscape, and then admire the substantial sycamore (*Acer pseudo-platanus*) which stands at the crossroads, nearly 1,000 feet above the sea and exposed to all the winds blowing over the pass; the trees round Ogwen Cottage, though less imposing, are at the same altitude and several of the hill-farms in this area, for example Dyffryn Mymbyr, are surrounded by well-grown shelter-belts. Man, in these isolated cases, shows the true potentiality of a zone which has, through his doing, been for the past two centuries recognized as a bare and forbidding waste, fit only for hardy sheep and resolute holiday-makers.

References for Chapter 9

Anon. (1909), Barnes (1942) (1943), Bowes (1942), Fitter (1945), Ford (1945), Forrest (1907) (1919), Griffith (1895), Hyde and Wade (1934), Pennant (1784), South (1939), Stapledon (1936), Thompson (1940), Tweed and Woodhead (1945), Walton (1927), W. Williams (1802), Woodhead (1926) (1928).
Communications from Best (1946), Fisher (1947).

CHAPTER 10

THE VALLEYS

THE grasslands, which comprise nearly half the land area of Caernarvonshire, effectively split the other main ecological zones. The alpine areas are seen as islands round the summits of the higher hills, while the valleys, which are now to be considered, tend to be separated from each other by great tracts of bare country, and to look outward, along the courses of their rivers, to the surrounding lowlands.

An exception is the deep cut between Snowdon itself and Moel Hebog. Here the summit of the "pass" is only 651 feet and tree growth, natural or planted, is more or less continuous between the Seiont valley on the west, and the Glaslyn on the east side. At Beddgelert on the Glaslyn, the one large village of Eryri, in the sense in which the name is used in this section of the book, the altitude is only 125 feet above the sea, and lowland conditions obtain along the Glaslyn or Nant Gwynant valley right round the back of Snowdon, so to speak, to within a mile of Pen-y-gwryd and Pen-y-pass, the gateways to Snowdon and the Glyders.

If the Glaslyn is followed to its mouth, a district is reached which is as much the junction of distinct habitats as it was once of human trade routes (see p. 312), though little of it is included in the proposed Park. The Glaslyn region, however, is the largest area of low-level ground in Eryri. Leaving it and going along the future Park boundary north by west, we come successively to the Pennant and Nantlle valleys, cutting deep into the Moel Hebog massif, and then to the Seiont already mentioned. North again is the Llanberis area with its lakes, which, though only 340 feet above the sea, are usually regarded as subalpine. The boundary runs between them, but Llyn Peris (Pl. 29b, p. 334) cannot be treated without Llyn Padarn, especially as far as its most important inhabitant, the Welsh char, is concerned. Below the lakes the Cwm-y-Glo neighbourhood was the scene of more of Griffith's botanizing, and his records can scarcely be omitted from our account.

In the next valley north, the slate town of Bethesda is outside the Park, but the lower part of Nant Ffrancon, in appearance if not in memories the Welsh counterpart of Glencoe, is naturally inside, while the slopes of the Carneddau, with the celebrated glen behind Aber, and the Sychnant pass near Conway, are also included and fall within the present zone. Finally, by way of our demarkation with the Nant Conwy section over the foothills from Trefriw to Capel Curig, the last pocket of lowland Eryri is reached.

Although its parts are so isolated, four main types of habitat are discernible within the zone and can conveniently be treated separately: the woodlands, the farmlands and open country, much of which is similar to the grassland of the previous chapter, the habitations and the riparian associations. Through them all run the roads, and there are, as Griffith points out, a number of plants which do not seem attached to any one soil or situation, and also odd records of rarities, both floral and faunal, which will be noted where it seems most appropriate; they can, of course, be found in their systematic place in the Appendix.

THE WOODLANDS

The causes of the disappearance of the natural woodlands are discussed elsewhere (see pp. 205-6 and 371-2). The process, as Dr. Scott shows, was complete by the days of the early travellers, who therefore tended to rhapsodize over what was left, particularly in the Gwynant valley, where woodland, calm lakes and cultivation are sharply juxtaposed to the rocky bastions of Snowdon. It was here also that some of the most important early attempts at re-afforestation were made.

I am indebted to Dr. Scott for notes from a MS. in the University College Library at Bangor, from which she also quotes (see p. 385). Vawdrey's friend, Dr. Thackeray, was guardian to a minor with large estates in Merioneth and Denbighshire, abutting on the region we are considering. On these estates planting began in 1804. It is interesting, in the light of modern efforts, to see what sort of ground was tackled. It consisted chiefly of "mountains, declivities of hills or dingles incapable of being improved by ploughing. Part of the land is of a thin, boggy nature . . . and part a nut-brown soil of middling depth." In other places the soil was thin and rock-strewn; in fact, the conditions were much the same as those with which the Forestry Commission is now trying to deal.

By 1810, 261 acres had been planted with nearly one and three-quarter million trees; an increase through the years in the number of trees per acre seems to indicate that conifers were being increasingly used, instead of "amenity" trees; in 1805-06 "Gilead Fir" (presumably *Abies balsamea*) and spruce (*Picea abies=P. excelsa*) are mentioned.

On the other side of Eryri, Lord Penrhyn was active between 1780 and 1797, though on a smaller scale, planting about 600,000 trees in this period and preserving his old woodland, while other landowners followed suit with what Hall, the author of the MS. quoted above, called "very florid plantations," though he noted on the Brynkir estate near Llanfihangel-y-Pennant, that the woods, which "at no very remote period were in a flourishing condition, have totally disappeared, nor is there elsewhere in the parish either wood or promise of plantation to mitigate the loss."

Of native woodland, Hall recorded an old oakwood about a mile from Beddgelert on the Caernarvon road, while Walter Davies (1797) speaks of an oak and birch wood at a good altitude on the Vaynol estate, which may be the same one. This great property had about 200 acres of woods, but most of them would be outside the strict confines of our region. Pennant said there was "very little appearance of vegetation at Pont Aberglaslyn" and all these accounts indicate that very little woodland was left by the end of the eighteenth century, though it is possible that scrubwoods were not included in the totals.

This seems to be confirmed by an examination of the figures in the Agricultural Returns quoted by J. Emrys Howell in the North Wales section of "*The Land of Britain.*" In 1881-95 there were 1,068 acres of plantations (woods planted or replanted) in Caernarvonshire, and these sank, even without wartime fellings, to 187 acres in 1905-15. But the 1924 Census of Woodlands undertaken by the Forestry Commission reported 13,145 acres of woods in the county, of which 60.3 per cent was described as "high forest." Most of this must, therefore, have been scrub-wood, which had evidently staged a considerable recovery during the long agricultural depression. But there was virtually no managed woodland of economic value in Eryri when the Commission began planting their Forest of Beddgelert in 1926.

This unit consists of only 2,771 acres, of which 865 are classified as permanently unplantable; about two-thirds of the remainder has now been afforested. The plantations lie mainly in the valley between Beddgelert and Llyn-y-gader, though the Forest extends in name up the north-eastern slopes of Moel Hebog, Moel Lefn and Trum-y-ddysgl right to their summits, well over the 2,000-foot contour, and there is a detached and recent acquisition sandwiched between Llyn-y-gader, Llyn-y-dywarchen and Llyn Cwellyn.

Beddgelert is considered to be a difficult forest; most of the planting has been done on deep peat moors which, before treatment, were difficult even to walk over. The first process in this treatment is open draining, if possible tapping and running off the water coming into the bog from the hillsides as well. The surface sods or turves cut out when draining are then upturned, spaced out, and in these, or in specially ploughed furrows, the young trees are inserted and their roots spread out on the ground underneath. Norway and Sitka spruces (*Picea sitkensis*) react best to these conditions and are extensively planted with pines on the drier slopes and a few Japanese larch (*Larix leptolepis* =*L. kaempferi*). Where the trees have succeeded and formed a canopy, they establish their own drainage; effective consolidation can already be seen in the Cwm Du plantations.

As one of the Commission's "problem children," Beddgelert has been the centre of considerable research, particularly into draining, manuring (to give the young trees a chance against the natural vegetation) and high-altitude planting. As part of a National Forest Park, planned before the 1939-45 war, the area may be visited by the public, who can see for themselves some of the experimental side of a form of land utilization which is becoming yearly of more significance in rural Britain. Some of the other problems of afforestation are mentioned in connection with the far larger Gwydir Forest (p. 266).

The remaining woods of the zone exhibit the gradual assimilation by the native scrub of the relics of the old private planting. Birches and other wild trees occupy gaps in the plantations, while rhododendrons escape from the gardens and shrubberies and colonize the rocky ledges in successful competition with the heather. This may be well seen in the neighbourhood of Vawdrey's old home at Plas Gwynan, round Tan-yr-allt above Tremadoc, and near other large houses. Beside the actual buildings there is order: flower-beds, cut lawns, ornamental shrubs and trees. Then, by a pleasing gradation, the wilderness encroaches: honeysuckle tumbles over a cypress, marring its sedate outline, a bed of foxgloves occupies a clearing, there is a dense jungle of raspberry canes—wild or domestic, nobody now knows—and finally, through a tangle in which brambles, bracken and rhododendrons compete under a broken canopy of exotic conifers and intruding birches, one enters the bare mossy floor of a typical hillside oakwood.

Sessile oak (*Quercus patraea*) is still the principal species of native trees, sometimes dominant, as near Capel Curig, at the foot of Moel

Siabod, behind Tanyrallt and at several places in the Nant Gwynant valley, but usually shading into association with ash (*Fraxinus excelsior*) and birch (*Betula* spp.) at the margin of the copses, which in Eryri are seldom big enough to be called woods. Ash is particularly prevalent round Llyn Gwynant, and often occurs by habitations or as an isolated tree along walls or hedges, as in Nant Peris (Pl. IVa, p. 11) and Nant Gwynant, perhaps from a stock planted by Dr. Thackeray or his contemporaries. Birch, in spite of much that has been written, is not as abundant as might be expected of a highland region; it nowhere grows on the same scale as in Scotland, and its stronghold seems to be in Nant Conwy. Still it is, of course, a very common tree, not often in pure stands, but rather on the fringes of the oakwoods, and indicating boggy conditions where it is associated with and, on wetter sites, replaced by alder (*Alnus glutinosa*).

Gwern (alder-swamp) is one of the commonest constituents of Welsh farm and field names, showing in the latter case that a former site has been felled, drained and brought into agricultural use. But the alder still holds its own, marking the course of the streams and circling the lower lakes; it has numerous insect associates and in winter the "cones" provide food for small finches and tits, while Daubenton's bat is traditionally fond of alder cover over the pools where it flies.

Hazel (*Corylus avellana*), which forms the understorey in the more open woodland and is common in hedgerows, hawthorn (*Crataegus monogyna*), whose rôle in the succession from grassland to woodland has been discussed (p. 207), and sallows (chiefly *Salix atrocinerea*), locally dominant on boggy sites, are the three most abundant species of bushy habit.

Beech (*Fagus sylvatica*) is not regarded as native to North Wales, and is not found to any extent in the scrubwoods, as it is in South Wales, but it forms a fine stand above the Glaslyn, along the Aberglaslyn–Tremadoc road, between Cerigrhwydwr and Prenteg (Fair Wood).

The mountain ash or rowan is characteristic of all parts of highland Britain; its white flowerheads, bright berries and often isolated position give it a prominence out of all proportion to its numbers. Like the common ash, it is seen close to deserted human settlements, and has no doubt been frequently planted or transplanted: Pennant said that a drink, *diodgriafol*, was made from the berries. Attractive as it may look against a grey ruin, standing in a green sward still free from the advancing bracken, the rowan is best seen on a steep slope, broken by rocky outcrops, on whose ledges particoloured mats of woodrush— dead brown and live green leaves—and shaggy tufts of heather, safe here from sheep and hill-fires, trail over their settings of moss. Gripping the rocks, across which its exposed grey roots seem to writhe, the rowan grows outwards at an angle into a bushy mushroom of divided leaves, studded with brilliant clusters of berries, a favourite diet of the autumnal flocks of mistle-thrushes.

Several of the other rosaceous plants which attain tree habit are confined to the lowlands of Caernarvonshire or to special habitats. The appearance of the bird cherry in Cwm Idwal has been noted (p. 193); the gean (*Prunus avium*) is not uncommon individually or in small groups, but the wild cherry (*Prunus cerasus*) is rare. Blackthorn (*P. spinosa*) on the other hand, is abundant and widespread in this zone, particularly in the hedges.

The willows and sallows (*Salix* spp.) form another group of closely related species, which to the amateur are all one. *Salix atrocinerea* is probably the commonest sallow, but *S. aurita* occurs with it, and a specimen collected near Tremadoc was thought by A. E. Wade to be a hybrid between them. Most of the willows, except the alpine dwarf, *S. herbacea* (p. 193), are found outside the Park, or along the Conway.

The wych elm (*Ulmus glabra*) is scattered through the scrubwoods, as is the holly and, to a lesser extent, the yew, which, as Dr. Scott points out (p. 350), is a notable churchyard tree throughout the region, but is not found by farmhouses as it is in mid-Wales. A famous avenue of yews and hollies existed at Gorddinog, Llanfairfechan, in the last century, finally dying out in 1914. About 1900, the biggest holly was 42 feet high, and Pennant noted a yew of 27 feet girth at Llandeiniolen.

The only alien hardwood which is seen at all generally is the sycamore, but this again is principally near habitations, as the specimen at Pen-y-gwryd (p. 222), though it can and does regenerate freely in Britain; Griffith noted it as a constituent of the hedgerows. The native small-leaved lime (*Tilia cordata*) reaches Denbighshire and Merioneth, but not Caernarvonshire, except as an introduction.

Of conifers, the yew and dwarf juniper (p. 193) have been mentioned; the Scots pine (*Pinus sylvestris*), native in the Highlands, has been planted in North Wales for many years and small clumps are now an accepted part of the scenery; what photograph of the Pass of Aberglaslyn (Pl. 10, p. 127), would be complete without them ? It is somewhat strange that there is no evidence for a recent indigenous stock of this species in the region where it is now quite at home; natural regeneration may be seen in the roadside clump opposite the Royal Hotel at Capel Curig. The other coniferous species, which have been introduced by private estates or by the Forestry Commission on a plantation scale, are described in the next chapter (pp. 266-9).

So much for the trees of Eryri, considered separately or in their principal associations. A good example of a mixed aggregation—it cannot be called a wood—of minor species can be seen on either side of the road up Nant Gwynant to Pen-y-gwryd, as it rises above Llyn Gwynant. Here, on the steep slope, are ashes, hazel, alders, hawthorns and blackthorns, which will be in flower early in April, with sallows in the narrow glen.

The principal woodland ground flora in Eryri is that of the oak-woods. In the fine stand at Tan-yr-allt, which included some ash and beech, and had a closed canopy, there was no bracken or tufted hair-grass (*Deschampsia caespitosa*), but a carpet of moss, in which were growing chestnut (*Castanea sativa*) saplings from trees lower down, male fern (*Dryopteris filix-mas*), sweet vernal grass, honeysuckle (*Lonicera periclymenum*) and wood-sage (*Teucrium scorodonia*). Down the slope the canopy opened and brambles (*Rubus* sp.), bracken, bilberry and dog's mercury appeared.

Of the smaller flowers of the oakwood none is more attractive than the cow-wheat (*Melampyrum pratense*), a relative of the foxglove and of the speedwells. Its lowly habit makes it inconspicuous but the pale yellow flowers, like narrow trumpets with lipped mouths, are blooming from May to September and in some places the plant forms quite a carpet; it may also be found under heather on the drier moors. Even more common is the trailing tormentil (*Potentilla procumbens*), an acid-indicator like its grassland relative, *P. erecta*.

"Bluebell woods" are not a feature of the region, though the bluebell (*Scilla non-scripta*) occurs on open rocky sites as well as in woodland; the foxglove, however, provides some memorable displays in suitable clearings after tree-felling, and one of them is shown on Plate 18 (p. 243). Honeysuckle also is found generally in the wood-lands, hedgerows and marginal land, often in magnificent clusters; a type, in which the basal tube of the flower is dark-red, is noticeable in the southern part of the region.

Numerous wet patches occur in the oak-birch woods, and in one of these, near the upper limit of the habitat, Tweed and Woodhead, while investigating the identity of the Snowdonian rushes, found the following community:

Juncus effusus	(large plants) d	*Eurhynchium praelongum*	v.a
Galium saxatile	f	*Hypnum cupressiforme*	a
Filipendula ulmaria		*Campylopus pyriformis*	f
Cardamine flexuosa			
Epilobium palustre			
Holcus lanatus			
Ajuga reptans			
Mentha aquatica		d = dominant	
Circaea lutetiana		v.a. = very abundant	
Stellaria uliginosa		a = abundant	
		f = frequent	

Compared with the *Juncetum* of the grassland zone (p. 212), the number of species of flowering plants (the left-hand column) is seen to have increased considerably.

Other patches may be filled by a relatively open *Molinietum*, with bog myrtle and bog asphodel (*Narthecium ossifragum*). Near such a bog, but shadowed by oaks and sallows, M. Speake showed us a remarkable plant of the royal fern (*Osmunda regalis*). The tallest of the fertile fronds—it was then in full "flower"—reached ten feet in height, and made an impressive centre, round which the sterile fronds formed a dense circle. No other plant was able to survive close to it, and it was ringed by open black bog. More normal plants are to be found in many of the wet woods, but Hyde and Wade now consider it a rare and decreasing species in Wales.

Fungi, which, owing to their edible possibilities, have lately come in for popular attention, are numerous in scrubwoods, where there is always so much decaying timber. None is more striking, for example, than *Amanita porphyria* which forms semi-circular brackets on the birches, but the one recent mycological survey of the region was done from Betws-y-coed, and will be considered in the next chapter (pp. 265-6).

The animal life of the woodlands is the most varied yet described. Not only are there a vast number of insects, and a characteristic association of birds, but here may properly be considered the rarest mammals yet surviving in Eryri, and the memories of others that have vanished.

In spite of the richness of the insect life, which is apparent to the casual visitor, there does not seem to have been systematic collection locally of those orders which compose most of the woodland fauna, always excepting the popular Lepidoptera; but even moths and butterflies have been studied more round Betws-y-coed and the Conway valley than in the lowlands of Eryri.

Geometers are especially numerous amongst woodland moths, and the variable clouded magpie (*Abraxas sylvata*, Pl. 19b, p. 250) is typical of this habitat in western Britain; our specimen was photographed in oakwood near Aberglaslyn. The typical butterfly is the speckled wood (*Pararge aegeria*); it is characteristic of the shady conditions, to which its wing pattern is so well adapted as it flutters down a sun-dappled pathway. The silver-washed fritillary (*Argynnis paphia*) is here on the edge of its range, and in woodland bogs may be found the high brown fritillary (*A. cydippe*) and the ringlet (*Aphantopus hyperanthus*) as well as several of the commoner species abundant on the open grassland. On the edge of the oakwoods one may look for the purple hairstreak (*Thecla quercus*) before it flies up tantalizingly out of reach, and this is probably where the brown and white-letter-hairstreaks (*T. betulae* and *Strymonidia w-album*) used to be found; there have been no recent records of these in the region.

The bird population of the sessile oakwoods of Britain has an element which is constant, whether the wood be in Argyll or in south Devon; it is interesting, therefore, to see what species are added in each region. Basically the association consists of: chaffinch, tree-pipit, tree-creeper, great, blue, coal- and long-tailed tits, spotted flycatcher, willow-warbler and wood-warbler, mistle-thrush, song-thrush, blackbird, redstart, robin, wren, tawny owl, sparrow-hawk, wood-pigeon and woodcock, to which, after their recent general increases, can be added greater spotted woodpecker and buzzard. In Eryri nearly all the possible additions occur: jay, nuthatch, goldcrest, pied flycatcher, garden-warbler, green woodpecker and pheasant. The black grouse may probably be called "marginal" for it prefers birch-woods and feeds largely upon young conifers, where these are available. Its status in the region at present is rather obscure; Best never saw it in the Forest of Beddgelert, 1935-38, and its local stronghold seems to be in Gwydir, where the afforestation has been much greater (see p. 271). It is almost certain that the Snowdonian stock is of introduced origin, though perhaps from no further than Montgomeryshire, which, as Matheson and Gladstone point out, is the only North Wales county where it is truly indigenous and has been continuously resident.

In the Tan-yr-allt oakwood already described (p. 229), many members of the association were observed during an hour's visit in June: jay, chaffinch, tree-creeper, great, blue and coal-tit, pied fly-catcher, willow-warbler, wren, buzzard and wood-pigeon, together with such marginal species as carrion-crow and blackcap, while the owner, Capt. Livingstone-Learmonth, informed me that the greater spotted woodpecker nested close to the house. No wood-warblers were seen, but not far off, in the beechwood of Prenteg, several were singing. This is also a favourite habitat, but the bird is equally common, in Wales at least, in open oak and birch, especially where the tufted hair-grass is growing; in fact, the majority of the few nests which I have seen have been under tussocks of this grass, which, like the bird, was absent at Tan-yr-allt.

The scrubwoods vary tremendously in density and hence in the strength of their underwood; there are few areas of continuous "high forest" and the woodlands are often narrow and straggling belts. This is reflected in the range of habitats demanded by the bird community, and allows many species to occur which would be excluded from large uniform woods. Also, a number have adapted themselves to several habitats and good examples are furnished by some of the summer visitors.

Perhaps the tree-pipit is the most various in this respect, for it may nest in quite thick oakwood, where there are very small clearings; it is particularly fond of woodland bogs in which small birch trees, moor-grass and heather predominate, but is equally at home on exposed bracken slopes or railway embankments, as long as natural or artificial song-perches are provided.

The willow-warbler is more catholic than the wood-warbler in its habitat selection, being found almost anywhere in Britain where scrub of some sort occurs. Generally speaking, it is less tolerant of shade than the wood-warbler, while the chiffchaff—the third British breeding "leaf-warbler"—cannot be regarded as a woodland species; it is essentially marginal, nor, though common throughout lowland Caernarvonshire, does it penetrate into Eryri in such numbers as its congeners.

Of the other warblers, the garden-warbler is perhaps more of a woodland bird than the blackcap, though the distinction is fine. Low bramble cover is the minimum requirement of both, and will be found to be the favourite nest site in our region.

The redstart (Pl. XVII, p. 210) is a typical highland scrubwood bird, whose range may extend above the tree-line to derelict farms (see p. 211), straggling hedgerow trees and stone walls bounding the firidd. There did not seem to be as many redstarts in Eryri as I had anticipated: as a general observation, all these small woodland birds appear to be more strongly represented in similar country in mid-Wales.

The flycatchers have been left until the last of the summer visitors, because they are the most interesting birds of this category in the Snowdonian woods. Visitors will look first for the pied flycatcher, because its restricted and unusual distribution in Britain makes it something of a rarity. But the spotted flycatcher is worth study too, since it is here not associated mainly with habitations and hedgerow trees as it seems to be in more civilized districts; it nests also in the woodland, on the sides of trees or on small rock-faces, though it requires a clearing into which to make its sallies after flies and hence is often found along the roads.

The male pied flycatcher (Pl. XX, p. 219), though it may momentarily give the impression of a house-martin or of a pied wagtail, is really difficult to confuse with any other British bird; the female, grey-brown above, and with white wing-bars, might be taken for a hen chaffinch, though the thinner beak and absence of prominent white outer tail-feathers are sufficiently diagnostic. The males arrive first and their simple song is a little like that of the redstart, with whom they share many of the same habits and site preferences—in fact the relationship between flycatchers and redstarts seems, to field observers, much closer than that recognized by systematists. The pied flycatcher is said to like a territory near running water, but whether this is because of the superior insect life in such a habitat, or because hollow alder trees are a riparian feature, or just because many scrubwoods extend only by a stream, it is difficult to say. Its recent large-scale colonization of nesting-boxes in the Forest of Dean has no connection with the proximity of water. The nesting site may be from ground-level to 20 to 30 feet or, exceptionally, higher; holes in walls are used, as well as those in trees, and other species may be evicted, though probably old woodpecker's holes are the most popular and safest choice. Up till the time that the young are fledged the pied flycatchers are much in evidence, and go to the nest boldly with food, but in July and August they are much more elusive, and the late summer visitor to the Park will be lucky to see any. At the height of the nesting season, however, they may be found throughout the woodlands.

The resident element in the population contains species more restricted to a woodland habitat than are most of the summer visitors. As an example of what may be seen on a midwinter walk, in December 1939 my diaries record, between Beddgelert and Aberglaslyn, jays "chattering angrily," a few chaffinches, bands of tits with long-tailed tits prominent, a song-thrush singing and a green woodpecker calling; while in hard frost at Capel Curig in 1946 chaffinch, great tit, blue tit, mistle-thrush, fieldfare, blackbird and robin were in evidence.

Although the jay is the most sylvestral—to use Watson's botanical terms ornithologically—of the crow family (for the carrion-crow and magpie usually choose small clumps, hedgerows or solitary trees), its appearance in the open scrubwood is a little surprising; like the bull-finch, with whom it shares such analogies of plumage as a black tail and a white rump—presumably of recognition value in dense cover—it normally prefers lowland thickets and conifer plantations. The chaffinch is the true finch of the scrubwoods, where its diet, particularly in the breeding season, will be mainly insectivorous, and it frequently associates with the tits in the flocks which keep this bare habitat alive in winter. The closely related brambling is a scarce winter visitor reported from Beddgelert.

The tits and their allies are the core of this woodland bird community. The tree-creeper is believed to be one of a group of species which adapted themselves from a pinewood habitat when the coniferous forest receded ; it is now one of the typical birds of deciduous woodland, where the nuthatch is equally well-established in North Wales, though its colonization is of more recent date; its spring call may be heard right to the Anglesey side of the Menai, where it seems to have arrived in 1921. As usual in highland districts, the numerical dominance of the blue tit over the great tit and coal-tit is not as marked as it is in the lowlands ; all three may nest in fairly open habitats, but in winter they form the principal constituents of the flocks in the scrubwoods. Both marsh-tits and willow-tits are found in the region, but neither are so much birds of the oakwoods as of the *gwern* (see p. 227) and the hedgerow. Since the willow-tit occurs in Scotland, where the marsh-tit is virtually absent, it will probably be found to be the more numerous of the two in the highland habitats of North Wales; that is certainly my impression in the Bala and Dolgelley districts of Merioneth, where I failed to see marsh-tits at all. The long-tailed tit not only winters in the woods, but may build high up in oak and birch trees, a very different site from the brambles and holly bushes where it is usual to look for its nest. The goldcrest is still generally a conifer associate (see p. 255), but joins up with the tit flocks and nests also in the ivy (*Hedera helix*) which often infests hardwood trees.

Like most very common birds in Britain, the thrush family and what may be called their allies—dunnock and wren—may be found in many habitats, most of them man-modified, but they are all, except the dunnock, also woodland birds, and to them can be added the winter visitors, fieldfare and redwing, which, though generally seen feeding in open fields, also occupy high-level birch copses corresponding to their summer habitats. The mistle-thrush nests up to the tree-limit, and on rocks beyond it, while the family parties go up to the highest zone in late summer. A rock-sited nest found in an oak-wood was a massive affair of moss and sheep's wool, which trailed down for a yard below the ledge, and, waving perpetually in the breeze, defeated efforts to take an adequate photograph of a perfect Snowdonian habitat. The pugnacious nature of the mistle-thrush is well known, but Livingstone Learmonth recounted an outstanding local instance of it: a kestrel, which had attacked and seized one bird of a pair, was forced off it by the mate.

Both song-thrushes and blackbirds use rock and bank sites for nesting in highland districts, and Coward remarked on the abundance of the latter "on the rough hillsides and wooded *cwms* of North Wales," where its range overlaps that of the ring-ousel.

So far all the birds considered have been of the passerine order, and, as is usual in British inland habitats, they provide the main strength of the population, although the representatives of other orders, of which the three woodpeckers are good examples, may be of more interest to the visiting bird-watchers.

Best and Wainwright now regard the lesser spotted woodpecker as fairly common, but in coastal Denbighshire it is reported by I. Whittaker to be "resident but uncommon": there was no Caernarvonshire record up to 1919, but by 1926 it had reached Llŷn. Though usually a bird of orchard, hedgerow and garden, it does occur in scrub-woods, at any rate in winter. Its larger relative is far more characteristic of this habitat, in which it has made its startling advance through the Scottish Highlands in recent years. Both it and the green woodpecker are striking birds and should be seen by visitors throughout the zone at all seasons. The tawny owl, nesting in hollow trees, old crows' nests or rocks, and feeding largely on the wood-mouse, is another typical species, but the barn-owl is rather more marginal in its choice of habitat, and the little owl markedly so; the latter established itself in Caernarvonshire about 1930, but was rather surprisingly checked at the Menai and is still absent or very rare in Anglesey.

Amongst diurnal birds of prey the sparrow-hawk is to the woods as the tawny amongst the owls, although like many of the species in the deciduous woodland community it is also at home in the conifers (see p. 273). A glade, giving free access and a good view, will often be the nesting site, and will be used year after year, though Speake assured me that in parts of the Moel Hebog hills sparrow-hawks nest regularly on ledges of long heather, a habitat which has no record in the literature of British ornithology, and which it would be of great interest to confirm.

Throughout inland districts of mid-Wales, the Welsh border and in Devonshire, the buzzard is a woodland bird; in Eryri determined claims are made for it as a bird of the rocks (see p. 201) and while it may use extremely open sites at times, most of the few birds which I met in 1946 were in the woods. Probably Kennedy Orton was right when he suggested that the bigger birds were happier at lower levels and were striving to regain a foothold there, and it may have been persecution that made buzzard's nests in trees rare when Forrest wrote. The raven has not yet, as far as published evidence goes, taken to tree-sites in North Wales, though this is becoming quite common elsewhere.

When Orton wrote, the buzzard, even with the respite of the 1914-18 war, was at a very low ebb. He estimated that there might be only about twelve pairs in "North Wales," although he describes it, with the raven, as the most commonly seen large bird on the mountains, to which he considered it confined, and where he kept an eyrie at 2,500 feet under observation "for many years." To say the least of it, the position is very different today, except that the numbers still seem low. Although seeing ravens every time I visited the mountain areas in 1946, no buzzards were observed above the 1,000-foot contour, nor any evidence of high-level nesting found. Perhaps the decline in bersecution, accentuated by the 1939-45 war, has really allowed the puzzards of Eryri to come down to the tree-line.

The woodcock's breeding strength in our region is in Nant Conwy (see p. 272); as a winter visitor it is not so much a bird of the woodlands as of bushy pockets along the moorland streams. It is fairly numerous in Caernarvonshire; average bags for recent winters reported to the Woodcock Enquiry of the British Trust for Ornithology were 38 over 35,000 acres and 53 over 30,000 acres.

The wood-pigeon is widespread though not abundant throughout the scrubwoods and the pheasant is found near large houses where preservation was formerly practised. Both are interesting, as forming the small vegetarian element in an insectivorous or carnivorous population, though the jay, of course, takes acorns, which, with beech mast and ivy berries, are the wood-pigeon's chief food in the woods. A final rarity to be mentioned here is the hooded crow, which nested "between Aber and Llanrwst," presumably in this zone, in 1917.

Although bats are more closely connected with the riparian tree fringe and with habitations, other insectivorous mammals—the shrews and the hedgehog—are common. The typical rodents are the wood-mouse, bank-vole, red squirrel and to a lesser extent the rabbit. The grey squirrel has not yet reached our region, and the dormouse described by Forrest as generally distributed and common at Beddgelert, is not normally a highland species. The red squirrel, however, may be looked for "up to moderate elevations" and this may be taken to be the tree-limit, since in mid-Wales it is found in isolated clumps well over 1,000 feet above the sea. The rounded dreys, of which each pair builds several, are the usual indication of the presence of squirrels, and they are particularly fond of hazel scrub, since the nuts are an important part of their diet. The 1944-45 parish survey of squirrel distribution, organized by the Bureau of Animal Population, showed that only 23 out of 53 parishes in Caernarvonshire were occupied, but as this includes the great, almost treeless, headland of Llŷn, such a low proportion is not unexpected; in Merioneth there were squirrels in 37 out of the 39 parishes.

The wood-mouse is an obvious "mouse," with long tail, prominent black eyes and pointed nose. It is a far better jumper than the voles and with its russet, black-tipped fur and white belly rivals the dormouse and harvest-mouse as our most attractive small mammal. It may make a nest at a fair height, perhaps in a hole previously occupied by tits, and collections of seeds, hips and cherry-stones found in such places may usually be attributed to it. The bank-vole, short-tailed, snub-nosed, is more terrestrial, tunnelling freely in woodland banks and hedgerows, where it is a favourite prey of the weasel.

Mention of the weasel leads to the carnivores, but while the weasel and stoat are probably found wherever there are voles and rabbits, the polecat and the pine-marten, two of the principal rarities of the Park, probably survive best in the most difficult terrain for their enemy, man, a steep and rocky scrubwood. There is little doubt that the polecat is commoner in mid-Wales than in the north, and even now it turns up quite regularly as far south as Monmouthshire. But confusion with escaped ferrets, to which it is so closely related, is always possible in records from unexpected localities.

We were not able to get on the track of any of its present-day haunts in our region, but, through the kindness of Professor Brambell and Mr. F. H. Jacob, of the University College, Bangor, we were able to visit the spot where a young marten had been trapped in 1945. The farmer, whose name, like that of the locality, must in the interests of the martens remain unpublished, told us that he first noticed something unusual in the way his chickens reacted to the edge of a wood, about a hundred yards from the house, where they regularly foraged. On investigation of the cause, martens (Pl. XXIa, p. 290) were seen; other observers, similarly privileged, have reported that the animals disappeared in a flash, but in this case they appeared to be quite curious themselves, and used to run along the boundary wall of the wood, "popping up" to look at their visitors, which, of course, is a common action of the weasel. The farmer thought that, in all, one adult and two young were seen. Eventually a muffled trap was set by the hole under the big boulder in the photograph (Plate XXIb), and one of the young ones was caught. This was about July 7. The marten was taken to Bangor shortly afterwards and kept under observation by Professor Brambell for several weeks; in his words it was "amazingly tame from the day that we got it," but constantly defeated attempts to photograph it. Eventually it was released in the grounds of a large house not far from where it had been captured.

While in the farmhouse, the marten took water through the meshes of its cage. Professor Brambell suggested to us that the animals had been attracted to the spot by the group of gean trees, whose trunks can be seen in the photograph, but whether this was because of the cherries themselves, or because of the birds which were attacking them, could not be ascertained. The farmer told us, however, that no traces of food, tracks or droppings were seen; the hole was located by his dogs. The chickens were not, in spite of their alarm, attacked by the martens.

After photographing the site, Markham and I waited for some time in pouring rain, but without seeing anything to arouse the suspicion that the martens were still in the wood. Nor, as far as we know, did they subsequently appear. Other information about their recent occurrence in the region is given on pages 274-5, and in 1932, while Colin Matheson had records of about five hundred polecats killed in Wales during the previous five years, the same lists mention less than a dozen martens. This relative abundance seems to rob the polecat of "news value" locally; people often talked to us about martens, but we did not get any reliable recent information about polecats; F. C. Best considers them less numerous in the region than they are in mid-Wales.

The woodland zone was also the last resort of species which have vanished from Eryri, if not from Britain altogether. At first sight the most perplexing of these disappearances is that of the roe-deer, for it is quite common in similar country in the Scottish Highlands today, and Matheson's thorough investigation shows that it was once widespread in Wales. In 1573, Humphrey Llwyd, the topographer, reported *"cervorum & capreorum maxima in excelsis montibus cernitur multitudo"*[1]—the mountains being in Merioneth and Caernarvonshire. But, by Pennant's day, it existed only in memory. Since the roe is more completely an animal of the woodland habitat than any other mammal or bird which has been mentioned, and does not seem anywhere to have adapted itself to other habitats, as has the red deer, it looks as though its disappearance from our region—and from Wales as a whole—can be directly correlated with the destruction of the woods, which, as Dr. Scott shows, reached its climax in the sixteenth and early seventeenth centuries, leaving the barren aspect familiar to Pennant and his contemporaries. Modern surprise at the roe's absence suggests that the scrub cover has definitely increased at low altitudes in the past two hundred years. Over the much larger area of the Scottish Highlands, the deforestation, though extensive enough to banish the squirrel, can never have been so thorough as in North Wales, and there must have always been sufficient cover for a roe population to survive there in reservoirs whence, profiting by the large-scale private planting that took place in Scotland, it set out to recolonize much former territory, even in the Lowlands, where it is found today.

The red deer, though now associated with the highest Scottish hills,

[1] "Red deer and roe are seen in great numbers in the high mountains."

SN.   R is really a forest mammal, and Professor Ritchie remarked that "the destruction of the forest has impelled the Red Deer of Scotland on a downward path, limiting its numbers, decreasing its range and whittling away its former dignity by steps of physical decadence." The greater area of the Highlands and the recognition of the red deer's sporting importance probably saved it; in the much smaller region of the North Wales hills the process was carried to its logical end and Matheson concludes that the animal was extinct as a wild species by the close of the seventeenth century. It is, therefore, only of melancholy interest to note that Leland, in writing of the scarcity of corn in the Snowdonian hills, remarks: "if there were [any] the deer wolde destroye 't."

The wild cat is another mammal which survives elsewhere in Britain after being lost to North Wales, though Matheson considered in 1932 that "specimens which show certain Wild Cat characteristics, descendants of the former union of Wild Cats and feral domestic cats, are perhaps even now barely extinct." The position is confused by the use of "wild cat" or "wood cat" to describe the pine-marten in old records written in English; the Welsh *cath goed* seems, however, always to refer to the wild cat and to show that it was considered to be a woodland animal, though Forrest, when he summarized its latest occurrences in 1907, thought its last resort was the mountains, as is the case in Scotland.

Of the large mammals that have disappeared entirely, the wolf (*Canis lupus*) survived perhaps to the early seventeenth century, to linger much longer in tradition and to be remembered in place-names, e.g. *Cae'r Blaidd*, which are a less reliable guide to the former haunts of the brown bear (*Ursus arctos*, in Welsh, *Arth*); "arth," which often appears in names, it not necessarily the same word at all. Bears were gone at latest by the tenth century, the true wild boar (*Sus scrofa*) by the sixteenth, while wild cattle (*Bos primigenius*) or their "modified descendants" may have held on even later in the wild state in Wales, though not in our region. All these may be considered relics of the forest fauna of prehistoric times.

THE FARMLANDS

The farmland habitat in this zone includes rough grazings, both open ffridd, as in the previous zone, and in the form of fields; arable land; hedgerows; marginal land and farm buildings. The *Grassland Survey* describes four main types of pasture in cultivated land in Wales:

(a) RYE-GRASS PASTURES in which perennial rye-grass (*Lolium perenne*) forms 15 per cent or more of the herbage. White clover (*Trifolium repens*) is usually sub-dominant or an important associate, while bent-grass, dogstail (*Cynosurus cristatus*), cocksfoot (*Dactylis glomerata*), rough-stalked meadow grass (*Poa trivialis*), red fescue (*Festuca rubra*) and other species occur. It is probable that this, the best-quality grassland in Caernarvonshire, is found only in the lowlands outside the Park.

(b) BENT–RYE-GRASS PASTURES. Normally bent-grass is dominant with 5 to 15 per cent perennial ryegrass. Yorkshire fog (*Holcus lanatus*), red fescue, rough-stalked meadow-grass, cocksfoot and white clover may each be co-dominant or sub-dominant to the bent-grass.

(c) BENT-GRASS PASTURES. Perennial rye-grass absent or never more than a trace. Red fescue, Yorkshire fog, sweet vernal grass, white and suckling clovers (*Trifolium repens* and *T. dubium*) are the usual constituents, and each, though usually subordinate, may be as abundant as bent-grass on particular fields.

(d) BENT-GRASS AND RUSHES. Poor pastures invaded by rushes, sedges and miscellaneous plants associated with wet and waterlogged conditions. Yorkshire fog, fescues and vernal grasses are the commonest species in that order; perennial ryegrass is usually absent. Leguminous plants are not numerous and bird's-foot trefoil (*Lotus corniculatus*) replaces white clover. These fields may once have been in cultivation.

As is often the case, such types of grassland are botanically of interest in inverse proportion to their economic value. The *Survey* gives examples of detailed examinations in Caernarvonshire, where E. J. Roberts analysed bent–rye-grass pasture near Aber in 1935 as follows:

Agrostis spp.	25%
Holcus lanatus	9%
Festuca spp.	9%
Lolium perenne	10%
Cynosurus cristatus	7%
Dactylis glomerata	5%
Trifolium repens	11%
Other plants	24%
	100%

A "flush bog" near Roewen, which would represent an extreme condition of type (d), gave:

Agrostis spp.	5%
Festuca spp.	5%
Molinia caerulea	5%
Nardu stricta	5%
Juncus "communis"	15%
J. articulatus etc.	25%
Carex spp.	trace
Potentilla erecta	trace
Other plants	40%
	100%

The "other plants," which show a great increase in the second example, are those which, unimportant to the agricultural botanist, provide the chief attraction to the pure botanist, and the analyses should be compared with those of the *Junceta* already given; they illustrate clearly the two approaches to the subject.

Throughout the zone the better pastures and hayfields are distinguished in June by a wonderful display of buttercups (*Ranunculus* spp.) in flower. These may not, ecologically speaking, be dominant, but from a distance they present a solid orange-yellow sheet. The common daisy (*Bellis perennis*) is also abundant. On the poorer pastures, which are the last to be cut for hay, there is a colour change to a mixture of purple-red and dark blue supplied by knapweed (*Centaurea nigra*) and devil's bit scabious. It was probably in this sort of association that Dillenius and Brewer found the field gentian near Dolbadarn Castle (p. 166). Many other common meadow flowers appear but are hardly of significance in our region, being representatives of the lowland and not really out of their normal habitat, like those noted on the Snowdonian rock-faces. For this reason they have often been overlooked and hence it is much harder to make a list of the common plants of Eryri than of the rarities, such as white bryony (*Bryonia dioica*) found "east of Llyn Gwynant" by R. C. Roper, the white frog orchis which Griffith found at Capel Curig in 1908, and the narrow-leaved helleborine (*Cephalanthera longifolia*) first recorded at Llanberis about 1830.

The character of the wetter fields is similar to those seen elsewhere in Wales; meadowsweet (*Filipendula ulmaria*) appears to be more abundant in highland districts such as Eryri; along the hedges and ditches, where conditions approach those of the riparian habitat, it is seen to advantage with such other large species as the water dropwort

PLATE 17

W. S. Pitt

TORGOCH OR WELSH CHAR, *Salvelinus alpinus perisii*, from the Llanberis lakes. December

PLATE 18

John Markham

Foxgloves, *Digitalis purpurea*: dense growth on a felled slope near Tremadoc. July

(*Oenanthe fistulosa*), marsh thistle (*Cirsium palustre*) and occasional patches of purple loosestrife (*Lythrum salicaria*), perhaps the most striking of all the commoner marsh plants.

The history of the principal crops is traced by Dr. Scott (pp. 340, 372, 383). Cultivation has certainly introduced many lowland and some alien plants to the region, though here again it is hard to find out what has occurred actually in Eryri; more details can be given from Nant Conwy, where Evan Roberts, E. Price Evans and A. Wilson have accumulated a great deal of modern information (pp. 275, 280).

Hedgerows are seldom as important in a highland as in a lowland region. Where loose stone is easily available or can be quarried there is usually a tradition of dry stone work, and stone walls are a feature of the Snowdonian landscape. Although the hawthorn is a common bush on the hillsides, what hedges there are tend to be of hazel, and in any case a thick growth, covered with bramble and briars, is extremely rare. Thus their importance as wild-life cover is much reduced. A common compromise, particularly on the western slopes of the range, between the typical hedgerows and the stone wall is a low bank or stone dyke, covered with grass and mosses and with a growth of gorse along the top. Gorse is widespread throughout the rough pastures at lower altitudes all round the Park, though nowhere is it more prevalent than on the reclaimed land of Traeth Mawr between Aberglaslyn and Portmadoc. In fact it is likely that the spring visitor to Eryri will carry away the impression of blazing clumps of gorse, sometimes interspersed with blackthorn (Pl. 20a, p. 25), as second only in his memory to the grandeur of the great hills. It has been suggested by Alun Roberts, quoted by Tansley, that *Ulex europaeus* is not native to North Wales, and was introduced from Ireland in the eighteenth century for cattle fodder, the plants being cut every other year. It has proved an apt colonist, though not without its disadvantage to the farmer, for the *Grassland Survey* points out that "isolated blocks of rough grazing provide a last refuge for the rabbits, thus playing an important though adverse part in lowland agriculture," and it is fairly certain that such isolated blocks in this zone will be covered or dotted with gorse bushes.

Although sheep are everywhere in this zone, cattle and other stock become much more important than at higher levels, and consequently the invertebrate life includes a large number of pests. Walton notes 19 worms, mites and insects attacking horses, 22 attacking cattle and a number on pigs, rabbits, poultry and dogs. The protozoan *Babesia bovis* caused serious outbreaks of red-water fever between 1921 and 1927, and a map illustrating its incidence and similar to that compiled for the liver-fluke (p. 213) was presented to the National Museum of Wales. Most of the worst centres were outside the Park or on its boundaries, but there is an interesting patch marked on the lower slopes of Snowdon above Llyn Cwellyn, an area whose bad drainage has been mentioned earlier (p. 208).

A large number of pests on cultivated plants of all kinds were identified by Walton and his associates; of these the most important are those attacking oats, which, at the time his work was being done, accounted for 61,000 acres in four North Wales counties, against 11,000 acres of barley and under 3,500 of wheat. The two families of the green-flies (Aphididae) and of the "daddy-long-legs" (Tipulidae) were the subjects of special study; in 1923 Theobald and Walton listed 72 species of aphids in North Wales, increasing this to about 100 by 1927, when they had identified one genus and ten species new to science. H. F. Barnes tackled the tipulids, and in 1923 listed 100, including one new species, for Caernarvonshire alone. A serious oat pest is the frit-fly (*Oscinella frit*), while the gout-fly (*Chlorops pumilionis*) attacks barley up to 700 feet above the sea.

Most of the vegetable pests, however, as is shown by the examples given, are prevalent only in the lowland agricultural area, and are not of importance in the region of the Park, though the small greenish-blue beetle *Lema melanopa* is associated with upland districts; a severe attack on oats was reported from Penmachno in July 1920, when it also occurred at Rhyd-ddu and Dolwyddelan. The slug-like larva eats away the surface of the blades of corn. Flea-beetles (*Phyllotreta* spp. and *Chaetocnema concinna*) have attacked fields of roots up to 750 feet, while no less than 26 pests of potatoes are given, the most common being the aphids *Myzus persicae* and *Macrosiphum gei*, and the most interesting the death's head hawk-moth (*Acherontia atropos*), whose larvae have been taken near Llanberis.

Thirty-six types of pests on flowering plants are listed, while on fruit 21 were recorded for apples alone. Again, these are not important in highland areas, except possibly where bush-fruit is concerned, and the gooseberry saw-fly (*Pteronidea ribesii*), the most destructive of insect pests, is found up to 800 feet. Tree pests will be dealt with in the next chapter, in connection with the Forest of Gwydir.

Finally Walton made another special study of the economically useful humble-bees (*Bombus* spp.), publishing a paper on them in 1922. This described 14 species as occurring in North Wales, six being abundant. The flowers visited by each species were noted, and, in some cases, the frequency of visitation.

The Orthoptera, since it includes the grasshoppers, is a typical insect order of the lower grassland; common species are *Chorthippus bicolor* and *Omocestus viridulus*.

Several butterflies make their appearance in the open country of this lowest zone of our region, and all those already met continue to occur. The wall-butterfly (*Pararge megera*) is characteristic of dry hedge-banks and lanes, and exposed earth generally, while the grayling (*Eumenis semele*) prefers a stony habitat; it is local in the region, and its dwarf subspecies on the Great Orme is described in Chapter 12 (p. 286). The wall-butterfly, on the other hand, has been considered by some collectors to be the commonest species in certain areas. Over rough pastures in May and June fly the beautiful little pearl-bordered fritillaries (*Argynnis euphrosyne* and *A. selene*), finding their food plants of the Violaceae on bracken banks and along hedge bottoms; the nettles inseparable from marginal farmland are the breeding-places of colonies of small tortoiseshells and the peacock (*Nymphalis io*), while their relative, the once-rare comma (*Polygonumic-album*) is also found. Along the hedges and in gardens in spring the holly-blue (*Celastrina argiolus*) flies—collectors have known it locally for many years—and the grizzled skipper (*Pyrgus malvae*) is found in much the same situations as the small fritillaries, where it feeds on plants of the rose family.

The three common white butterflies (*Pieris brassicae, P. rapae* and *P. napi*) are, of course, included amongst the pests of farm and garden crops, but the brimstone (*Gonepteryx rhamni*), whose hibernated individuals are the earliest butterflies on the wing, is considered by Best to be scarce, owing to the rarity of its food plant, buck-thorn (*Rhamnus* spp.). The migratory clouded yellow (*Colias croceus*) is seen in the summers of "good" years, of which 1947 was certainly one.

Probably the best locality to see what wealth of butterflies this zone possesses is a wet field near woods. The tall spikes of marsh thistle are a particular attraction and, in their season, are visited by the pearl-bordered fritillaries, the high brown and dark green fritillaries, as well as by the ubiquitous green-veined white, the most attractive insect of its genus. Here, too, the common blues and small coppers fly with the abundant members of the brown family (Satyridae). The picture will be completed by a few day-flying moths, by several dragonflies, including large members of the genus *Aeshna* or, in some localities, the fine *Cordulegaster boltonii* (Pl. 19a, p. 250) and by humble-bees.

The farmland birds of this zone do not present a compact community, like those of the woodland; to a foundation of species that are common everywhere there will be added most of the grassland birds seen in the previous zone and others which are associated with open country of various types at low altitudes.

The rook is essentially a farmland bird—so much so that, with the wood-pigeon, it was selected for war-time enquiry by the British Trust for Ornithology with the assistance of a Government grant. From 1944 to 1946, as part of the investigation, a sample census of rookeries was carried out, but unfortunately Caernarvonshire and Merioneth were not covered. The connection between rookeries and agricultural land is evident when driving round in early spring, before the leaves come out. In 1946 we noted, without attempting a serious survey, rookeries at Llanfairfechan and Aber, at the Caernarvonshire end of the Menai Bridge and one north of Port Dinorwic, where 127 nests were counted in 1945. Between Caernarvonshire and Dolbenmaen, in a country of small upland farms, there was a dispersed rookery round Pant Glas, covering perhaps several square miles, a handful of nests being built in each of the few clumps of high trees round farms or in the hedges: the same effect may be seen at the other end of Wales, near Solva in Pembrokeshire. As compared with this peripheral abundance, we only saw small colonies within the Park boundaries: at Capel Curig in conifers, above Llyn Cwellyn on the lower slopes of Snowdon, in a glen filled with pines and oaks, and six nests in one tree at Betws-y-coed. In the agricultural lower valley of the Conway the rook becomes numerous again, and a 1945 census of the east (Denbighshire) side of the river by the Ministry of Food Field Club revealed 321 nests in nine groups. A previous study of this area by Mitchell showed that there were no rookeries more than 600 feet above the sea and that three-quarters of them were near water or buildings. It seems certain, therefore, that the great numbers of rooks which are reported to come high up the hills of Eryri in summer, presumably when crops in the lowland area are at their least attractive (i.e. after sowing and before harvest), are mainly drawn from the big lowland rookeries (see p. 203).

Many of the finches, which are weakly represented in the deciduous woods, are typical farmland birds, nesting in the hedgerows and feeding on weed seeds and corn "gleanings" in the fields. Greenfinch, chaffinch and yellow bunting are the commonest species, and form, with house-sparrows from the villages and farmhouses, the main constituents of the winter flocks. The yellow bunting appears to be of restricted distribution in Caernarvonshire, absent from the heather habitat where it is found in the Scottish highlands, though several were present above Capel Curig in mid-winter 1946, and it is found in some numbers at Llanberis.

Linnets and yellow buntings are closely associated with gorse in the breeding season; linnets usually keep to flocks of their own kind, but may be found with other finches on the stubbles in autumn. One remarkable ornithological record from gorseland in the region is of a male Dartford warbler which was observed by D. C. Barber at Tremadoc in May 1932. It appeared in a large farmhouse garden, which gorse had invaded from a common outside, and remained for two days. This seems to be not only the first Welsh record, but the most northerly record of the species for Britain.

In this zone the sky-lark really comes to its own and is found all over the farmland, together with the lapwing, which does not seem in Eryri to favour the high altitudes from which it is reported in Scotland. Gulls, especially black-headed and herring-, with common gulls in the autumn, are all seen on the farms; in September, many herring-gulls are to be seen on the lakeside fields at Llanberis; in December, gulls still range well up the Glaslyn and Llugwy valleys.

As well as the lapwing, the curlew seems to prefer the fringe of the massifs to the wilder moors. Along the Llugwy pairs occupy territory on moor-grass ground up to 1,000 feet, but they are also common on fields of bent-grass and rush type, which are particularly extensive in Traeth Mawr; hence in Caernarvonshire the curlew's spring song is associated in my mind with the golden banks of gorse, against a background of Cnicht and the Moelwyns. The snipe occurs in similar habitats, though Wainwright considers it quite uncommon, and there are few cases of the redshank penetrating inland as a breeding species, though it has probably nested in Caernarvonshire for eighty years.

The bracken-clad lower slopes of the hills have, like the gorse patches, a limited community of birds within the larger association of the grasslands. Tree-pipit and nightjar are typical members; on the slopes of Moel-y-gest, which, though outside the proposed Park boundaries, resembles exactly many hillsides within it, Markham and I found two tree-pipits' nests more or less by chance in one afternoon, and there were other territories which we did not enter; the nightjar was reported as common, though we only met it in Nant Conwy.

Finally there are two birds which are considered to be characteristic of normal farmland; the partridge in arable fields and the corncrake in hay. In spite of the lack of arable crops, partridges used to be numerous in Llŷn and to penetrate to the edge of the moors, as about Dolwyddelan, where J. A. Bucknill used to shoot them "high up the mountain," and said they fed on heather like grouse. The opinion now seems to be that they are scarce, in spite of the wartime increase in ploughing. The corncrake is as likely to be heard in marsh or bog as in hay in North Wales; in view of its present scarcity, it may be regarded as one of the minor ornithological attractions of North Wales, although it is probably commoner in the low ground of Llŷn and Anglesey than in Eryri.

Practically all the small total of Snowdonian mammals have already been considered, but this zone is pre-eminently that of the rabbit. The first warrens were coastal, and some facts of the history of the rabbit in North Wales are given on page 371. It has spread generally, but is not abundant at higher altitudes at present. The most interesting recent work on the rabbit in Caernarvonshire is that of Professor Brambell, who investigated its astonishing pre-natal mortality in 1941–42, when 64 per cent of deaths were discovered at about the twelfth day of gestation. His recent important paper on the reproduction of wild rabbits was the result of a study of Caernarvonshire material and he notes that the breeding season in the county is a sharply defined period from January to June. The hare is to some extent the mammalian counterpart of the partridge, and appears to be fairly numerous, sufficiently so to be described in the *Journal of the Ministry of Agriculture* in 1930 as damaging mangold crops in the county.

The few reptiles of the future Park may also be mentioned here. The common lizard may be found generally on moorland and grassland; the slow-worm prefers a dry habitat, roughly the same as that favoured by the wall-butterfly (see p. 245), while the grass-snake is usually, though by no means always, associated with wetter conditions. It has been reported from Aberglaslyn and Beddgelert, though Forrest was doubtful if it occurred at Llanberis. The adder, which he described as common, is now said to be scarce and local. The former occurrence of the sand-lizard will be dealt with in Chapter 12, and the list closes with the attempted introduction at Portmeirion, a mile or two outside the Park to the south, of the green lizard (*Lacerta viridis*), which is native to the Channel Isles, but not to Britain itself. Twenty lizards were released about 1929 and were seen for some years, but there is no recent information about their progress.

THE LAKES AND RIVERS

The third main habitat-type of the zone is that of the lakes and rivers; it is one that, scenically, will prove particularly attractive to visitors, and hence its wild-life will be noticed even by those who are not necessarily enthusiastic naturalists.

The aquatic flora is not much richer than in the previous zone, and no species of great rarity occur. Most popular interest will centre on the water-lilies, both white (*Nymphaea alba*) and yellow (*Nuphar lutea*) which are not so much a feature of the larger sheets of water, as of backwaters, small ponds and peat-hags; Griffith recorded them from Cwm-y-Glo, with many other species of this habitat. The most striking of these is the greater spearwort (*Ranunculus lingua*), an outsize buttercup which may reach a height of six feet or more; other lacustral buttercups have been recorded from the Glaslyn and Ogwen rivers, where the globe-flower, which we last saw on the Snowdonian rock-faces, also grows. The monkey flower (*Mimulus guttatus*), an alien which has established itself all over Britain, is a plant of the Ogwen valley; its tubular yellow flowers with their deep-red blotches add considerably to the riparian scene, while another striking flower of general distribution is the yellow iris (*Iris pseudacorus*), whose clumps of light-green leaf blades must be familiar to the most casual walker, though, outside the flowering season, they are often thought to be some kind of reed.

Four species of bur-reed are found in different localities, and several club-rushes (*Scirpus* spp.), relatives of the common deer's-hair sedge of wet moorland. White beakrush is found by Llyn Dinas and Llyn Gwynant, while sedges are general. The common reed (*Phragmites communis*) is rather scarce, but can be seen in Llyn Cwellyn and as a thin growth elsewhere; nowhere in the Park does it form "reed-beds." Of more primitive plants, horsetails (*Equisetum* spp.) are common, and the rare quillwort *Isoetes echinospora* has been found in the Llanberis lakes. The general paucity of luxuriant water-plants is perhaps the reason why even the lowest Snowdonian lakes are regarded as sub-alpine in character, more fittingly surrounded by bogs in which bog-myrtle, moor-grass and bog asphodel are prominent, as at the side of Llyn Peris below the road.

Records of mollusc and other invertebrate life are meagre. The principal exception is in the case of the water-beetles, which have been recently studied by J. Balfour-Browne. He could only find eleven previous notes referring to these insects in Caernarvonshire, when he began work in 1938. Continuing intensively in 1940–41, he confirmed personally no less than 115 species out of 146 credited to the county, and he accepted a further eight from other recent workers. This result was in line with the general suggestion that a lack of observers rather than of creatures is responsible for the present apparent weakness of the lower fauna in the zone. The Ogwen river has long been known as a locality for the fresh-water mussel (*Unio margaritifer*), though it is not as famous in this respect as the Conway. In the Ogwen valley, in July 1899, was taken an alien plant-bug, *Elasmucha ferrugata*, for the first time in Britain; possibly it came from the docks at Port Penrhyn.

Thirteen species of dragonflies, given in the Appendix (pp. 424-5), occur in Caernarvonshire; the commonest are probably *Enallagma cyathigerum* and *Ischnura elegans*. *Libellula quadrimaculata* is found by the Llynau Mymbyr and there is one locality for the large *Aeshna mixta*.

The common fish of all the lakes and rivers is, of course, the trout. Sea-trout and salmon run up the Glaslyn, on which Pennant noted a salmon-leap at Aberglaslyn, to Llyn Dinas and Llyn Gwynant; up the Gwyrfai to Llyn Cwellyn and, sea-trout at least, to Llyn-y-gader; up the Ogwen; and up the Seiont to the Llanberis lakes, the home of the Welsh char or torgoch, which is unique in being the only sub-species of vertebrate animal confined entirely to North Wales; not to Eryri, however, as it is also found in Llyn Cors-y-gedol in Merioneth.

Most reference books place the torgoch in "three mountain lakes" in our region, traditionally Llyn Peris, Llyn Padarn and Llyn Cwellyn; it was still supposed to be in the last when *The Mountains of Snowdonia* was written less than twenty-five years ago, but in 1946 Mr. Brymer Roberts, of Llanberis, who was responsible for securing the specimen, now in the London Zoological Gardens Aquarium, which is shown in Plate 17 (p. 242) told me that it was extinct there. The earlier distribution was evidently much wider. Ray, as we have seen (p. 165), was told

PLATE 19

John Markham

b. CLOUDED MAGPIE, *Abraxas sylvata*, a moth of western woodland. Aberglaslyn. June

John Markham

a. DRAGONFLY, *Cordulegaster boltonii*, one of the larger species in North Wales. June

PLATE 20

John Markham

a. FLORA OF THE WASTE LAND: gorse and blackthorn in bloom in the lower
Conway Valley. April

John Markham

b. FLORA OF THE ROADSIDE: stonecrop, *Sedum anglicum*, ivy, mosses and lichens on
the wall; ferns at its foot; hawkweed, *Hieracium* sp., in the grass verge
Near Pen-y-groes. July

that it was also in what are obviously the Llynau Mymbyr and in "Travennin," which is an attempt at the old name of Llyn Cwellyn. Willughby, in his *Historia Piscium,* gave these waters, and Festiniog and Bettus (presumably Betws-y-coed) in Caernarvonshire, as well as "Casageddor" in Merioneth, in which Llyn Cors-y-gedol can be recognized. Forrest found an old diary for 1778 with an entry recording that four char were put in a pool south of Abergele in Denbighshire, but when he wrote the *Vertebrate Fauna,* he could, in addition to those in which the char survives today, only attribute it to three other waters: Llyn Cwm-ffynnon, in the Glyder massif above Pen-y-pass, Llyn Cwellyn and "a lake near Trawsfynydd where they are said to have been introduced by the Romans." This gradual extinction is characteristic of other races of char all over Britain in recent times, and may be due to their inability to compete with an artificial increase in the number of trout in the same lake.

The torgoch has always had an element of mystery about it. William Williams, whose colourful observations on the Llyn Ogwen trout have already been quoted, said of Llyn Cwellyn that it held "besides the common trout, those red-bellied Alpine trout, called Char, which are in season about Christmas." But he also believed that at Llanberis "the minework, which is close to the upper end of the upper lake [Llyn Peris] has destroyed most of the fish in both, especially the char, in which they used to abound. It was remarked that after they disappeared, some of the fish were caught in the sea at the mouths of rivers on this coast." In this fortunately false supposition, also put forward by Bingley, Williams appears to have been following Pennant.

The alpine association of the char was probably first suggested by Willughby and Ray, who supposed it to be the same as the "roetal" of alpine lakes on the continent of Europe. This theory was supported by C. Tate Regan, who described the range of the chars as of great zoogeographical importance, for they are more arctic and alpine than the trout and are chiefly restricted to deep, cold lakes, where they survived in colonies formed from migratory ancestors, which were cut off from the sea. The anatomical relationship of the types in the different colonies to each other provides evidence of kinship which assists in the reconstruction of former river systems and mountain barriers.

The various types were considered by Regan to be sufficiently distinct to be accorded specific status, whereas all forms of "brown trout" and "sea-trout" or "sewin" are not even racially distinct, owing to the common access of most stocks to the sea, and the very recent isolation of others. This view, though it does not command unanimity amongst authorities—some "lumpers" (including J. B. Norman, compiler of the British Museum List, whose nomenclature is being followed throughout this book) regarding all the British char as one species—is based on the structural differences between the char colonies, in which the number of vertebrae, for instance, varies from 58 to 64, while colour and shape show wide divergence. The torgoch has 61 vertebrae and an "acutely conical snout"; other features of the external morphology can be well seen in the Plate, which is from the first colour photograph ever to be taken of this fish.

The torgoch was first described scientifically by Gunther in 1862. Accounts of its life-history are rather bare, and the following is a synthesis of the remarks of Tate Regan, who has been largely copied by other writers on fish, of Forrest, and of Brymer Roberts, who knows the char better than anyone else today. Forrest's information came mostly from W. Brinckman, who lived near Llyn Peris.

The char spawn either in the river between Llyn Padarn and Llyn Peris, or in the shallows of Llyn Peris, which they begin to visit by night in October, remaining all day in November. In the breeding season the male is red-bellied, the female silvery. After spawning is over, there is no indication of their movements, until they appear in shoals "about the second week in June" (Brinckman), often on the surface of the water, "their back-fin just showing; on being approached by a boat, down they go with a splash only to reappear a few yards off." At this time one or two are taken on the fly, but by the late summer they are in deep water at 15 to 20 feet and are caught on maggots; in September and October they come closer in.

The torgoch is a small species, attaining a length of 9 to 10 inches and a weight of between four and eight ounces. It is an extremely "chancy" fish from the angling point of view, for while Regan records catches totalling 45 lb. and Roberts of 300 fish in a day, the next day may be quite blank in the same spot. Brinckman told Forrest that there were only certain parts of the lake where they occurred and that they took best in frosty weather. They seem to have reached a *modus vivendi* with the trout in the Llanberis lakes, where they are evidently as numerous as ever; possibly the greater area of these waters compared with that of other Snowdonian lakes is a factor in this accommodation.

The bird-life of the lower lakes does not differ a great deal from that of Llyn Ogwen (see p. 220), though in winter they appear to attract more duck, such as wigeon, pochard, tufted duck, scaup and goldeneye, with possibly occasional visits from the wild swans which are reported on the coastal marshes. In summer their insect life is preyed on by the house-martins, swallows and swifts which nest in the farms and villages. Sitting by the roadside at Llyn Gwynant in June, I noticed these three summer visitors, also pied wagtails, black-headed gulls and a cormorant. A preening sandpiper on a stone disappeared surreptitiously into the grass and was subsequently flushed from a nest a couple of yards off the road under a small alder tree; that there should be a nest close to a random stop indicates the abundance of the "summer snipe" in the region. Of what may be called lacustral birds, a few pairs of coots are said to nest on some of the lakes, though those we saw on Llyn Cwellyn early in April were probably migrants.

The riparian sallows are as attractive to lesser redpolls in Caernarvonshire as is the gorse to linnets; the rather bulky nest is not difficult to see and is ornamented with the fluff off the sallow flowers. When at the nest, the birds allow a near approach and the pink suffusion of the male's breast may be seen; no doubt this, rather than its singing abilities, has been responsible for the redpoll's popularity as a cage-bird. In winter the redpolls change their habitat slightly, from the sallows to the alders where, with other small finches and a few blue tits, they may be watched at short range.

At the other extreme of size, the heron is also a riparian bird, and, like the cormorant, individuals are to be seen by most of the lakes and rivers. The heron is one of the few British birds on whose numbers and colonies we possess accurate data on a national scale, collected regularly over a number of years. W. B. Alexander, who organizes the annual census of heronries, has kindly given me full information about those in Caernarvonshire and Merioneth. All those in the latter county are remote from our region, and the seven recorded in Caernarvonshire at the first census in 1928 are peripheral to it, the closest being at Aberdunant near Portmadoc. This held five nests in 1928; since 1935 annual reports have been made, showing a fluctuation from 4 (due to wartime activities in the vicinity) to 19 nests. The 1946 figure of nine suggests that a recovery is in progress. Bearing in mind on the one hand that the total for the whole county in 1928 was only 44 pairs (presuming each nest to represent one pair of birds), and on the other the relative frequency with which herons are observed, it can be seen that a small population of a large and striking species may give an appearance of numbers which is quite misleading, and shows that vague adjectives of quantity are of no more value in describing the status of birds than of flowers (see p. 195).

The slow-flowing lower reaches of the Glaslyn, where it runs through the reclaimed land below Aberglaslyn, provide the only riparian section of the kind in Eryri (Pl. 4a, p. 27). Here reed-bunting, mute swan, mallard and moorhen are typical birds, with the red-breasted merganser as a winter visitor (Wainwright). Mallard and probably teal nest in this habitat, while Captain Livingstone-Learmonth told me that tufted duck had attempted to nest a few years ago on a small dam above Tremadoc. This is the first record for Caernarvonshire, but as ducks generally are on the increase in Britain, it is possible that it and other species will come to the Snowdonian lakes.

Scarcer birds of this habitat are the reed-warbler—if, indeed, it was not recorded in error—and the kingfisher, to which the normal Snowdonian river does not appear suited. Of vagrants, the unfortunate osprey, shot within recent years near Capel Curig, a gannet in 1880 at Llanberis, and a little auk on Llyn Dinas may be noted. Observations on waders are conspicuously lacking inland, but of the large number of species which are noted regularly or have been met with along the coast-line of Caernarvonshire and in the estuaries of Traeth Mawr and Traeth Bach, some must occasionally penetrate up the valleys or use them as passage routes, and it is probable that wagtails, the arctic tern and green sandpiper may use the Glaslyn.

The otter is the typical mammal of the habitat, but, while it is generally agreed to be common, nothing of any interest about it locally seems to have been written; the tradition of the beaver in the region is referred to on pages 278.

HABITATIONS AND ROADS

Most of the species of interest which occur in this essentially artificial habitat have already been described in the woodlands and the farmlands. Rare plants near houses are suspect in origin, though they may acclimatize themselves successfully after introduction, as the rhododendron has done. Exotic trees have been planted round big houses and hotels and to their cover many species of insects and birds may adapt themselves.

PLATE 21

John Markham

PENNYWORT, *Cotyledon umbilicus-veneris*, a characteristic plant of walls and rocks at low altitudes in Snowdonia. Coed-y-ffynnon. July

PLATE 22

John Markham

DISINTEGRATING PEAT-BOG near Llyn Conwy; typical habitat of the golden plover; the Arenigs in the background. June

Visitors will not come to Eryri to observe such urban associates as the cockroach (*Blatta orientalis*) and house-cricket (*Gryllulus domesticus*), both of which were reported to Walton as over-abundant even in remote farms, or the house-mouse and brown rat which are both common; they will be more interested to hear the pied flycatcher singing in their hotel garden, as I did the first time I stopped at Beddgelert. Most of the common woodland birds occur in large gardens and here the dunnock, though found amongst stone walls and in wild heather country, is also typical. Species particularly associated with buildings are the jackdaw, starling, house-sparrow, house-martin and swift, though the first and last are also cliff nesters locally. The tree-sparrow was seen at Llanberis by Forrest, probably in an "anthropic" habitat of some kind, while the association of the goldcrest with the yew trees, described by Dr. Scott as so characteristic of the churchyards of the region (Pl. XXVIII, p. 347), is very close; another species which, for breeding at least, is largely dependent on human surroundings, is the goldfinch, which is probably on the increase in Eryri as elsewhere in Wales.

The habitations are connected by roads, whose verges therefore carry an extension of that modified environment through other habitats. Since railways, except for the Betws-y-coed–Ffestiniog line, lie outside the proposed Park, the roads are the chief means by which certain plants have, or are likely to, spread; the New Zealand willow herb, *Epilobium pedunculare*, found by Evan Roberts between Pen-y-gwryd and Pen-y-pass, and therefore over 1,000 feet above the sea, is a recent and interesting example of this.

The continuity and shelter enjoyed by the roadside vegetation enables it to withstand some of the effects of altitude. A typical lowland stretch is shown in Plate 20 (p. 251), but the species seem to be much the same throughout. Mosses and lichens, ferns, especially maidenhair spleenwort (*Asplenium trichomanes*), wall-rue (*Asplenium ruta-muraria*), and polypody (*Polypodium vulgare*), stonecrops (*Sedum anglicum*, etc.), ivy-leaved toadflax (*Linaria cymbalaria*) and pennywort (*Cotyledon umbilicus-veneris* Pl. 21, p. 254) on the walls, an attenuated strip of meadow vegetation along the verges, with foxgloves and gorse at the junction of wall and ground, seem to be the standard floral features. The stones give cover for a wealth of insect life, which is also attracted by the road surface, hence probably the close association of the pied wagtail with this habitat, of which it is by far the most characteristic bird. In

SN.   S

moorland the wheatear, and in woodland the spotted flycatcher and coal-tit are also often found. The redstart, on the other hand, is less in evidence in this habitat than might be expected, and while many other small passerines nest along the roads, these five species are the most typical of the stone walls and rock-cuttings, which are themselves typical of the Snowdonian highways. The walls are attractive to mice and voles, and so to their predator the weasel, and the whole of this interesting community can be seen along the most obvious route into the Park, between Pentrevoelas and Betws-y-coed, on Telford's road from London to Holyhead.

References for Chapter 10

Alexander (1945-47), Balfour-Browne (1942), Barber (1943), Barnes (1923), Bingley (1800), Brambell (1942) (1944), Campbell (1947), Carr and Lister (1925), Coward (1920), W. Davies (1797), Elwes and Henry (1906-13), Forrest (1907) (1919), Gladstone (1924), Griffith (1895), Hall (1810), Hyde (1935), Hyde and Wade (1934) (1940), Leland (1536-39), Llwyd (1584), Longfield (1937), Matheson (1932), Mitchell (1939), Orton (1925) (1930), Pennant (1784), Ray (1696), Regan (1911), Ritchie (1920), Sharp (1900), Shorten (1946), Stapledon (1936), Tansley (1939), Tweed and Woodhead (1945), Walton (1925) (1927) (1928), Whittaker (1942), W. Williams (1802), Wilson (1946-47), Witherby et al. (1938-41), Woodhead (1926), Zuckerman (1935).

Communications from Alexander (1947), Best (1946), Fisher (1947), Learmonth (1946), B. Roberts (1946), Smith (1946), Speake (1946), Wainwright (1947).

CHAPTER II

NANT CONWY

SO much that has been said of the three main zones in the Snowdon range applies also to the eastern part of the Park that it is unnecessary to divide it in the same way; it seems better to emphasize in this chapter those features which, if not peculiar to it, are more characteristic of Nant Conwy than of Eryri. These are, primarily, the great cotton-grass moor of Migneint, and the extensive natural and planted woodlands round Betws-y-coed; while, outside the strict boundary of the Park, the lower Conway valley is of great interest, though rather more perhaps to the agriculturist and the historian than to the naturalist.

THE HIGHLANDS

The difference between Eryri and Nant Conwy is best seen when driving from west to east along the Holyhead–London road. Coming from England the mountains are before one, and the lower hills seem to build up naturally to the famous skyline. But, in the reverse direction, the change as one debouches from the shadow of Tryfan and the Carneddau is striking, and though the peak of Moel Siabod stands transitionally between the two districts, it is obvious that Eryri is "alpine" and Nant Conwy "highland" in character. Siabod's 2,860 feet challenge the highest in Eryri, and several peaks in the Moelwyn chain are well over 2,000 feet, but south and east of the Lledr that height is not attained again until Gylchedd is reached, in the very corner of the region at present under consideration.

Alpine plants grow on the top of Siabod, where Evan Roberts, who lives at its foot, has found the purple mountain saxifrage, while the Moelwyns are famous for their "wild" goats, a herd of great antiquity and shyness. These scenic peaks are the locale of a Welsh proverb about the fox:

"Mae ei wal yn y Moelwyn,
Y mae yn lladd ym Mhen Llŷn"

["His earth is in the Moelwyn,
He kills at the end of Llŷn"]

which seems a vulpine version of "The mountain sheep are sweeter";
on the Ffestiniog side of the range, near the famous Tanygrisiau quarry,
a very pale pine-marten was trapped a number of years ago; this has
recently found its way into the National Museum of Wales collection.

Much of the grassland of the Siabod and Moelwyn massifs is similar
to that of Eryri, and the same types of association occur, with a great
deal of heather fell on the western and southern slopes of the Moelwyns.
Siabod is famous for its bad drainage, and the plateau around Llyn
Diwaunedd is covered with rushes to an extent unusual even in North
Wales. Alongside the road from Dolwyddelan to Ffestiniog, above an
isolated Forestry Commission block, is a considerable stretch of mat-
grass, in a hollow of which we found a huge tussock of the sedge *Carex
paniculata*. In late summer this area is extremely lifeless; crossing the
moors from the bwlch above Blaenau Ffestiniog to Pen-y-gwryd in
September, all we saw were occasional ravens and carrion-crows, a few
meadow-pipits, sky-larks and wheatears and a kestrel. On the other
hand Forrest gives a number of interesting records from the general
area of Dolwyddelan: meadow-pipits are abundant and attract a
number of cuckoos, while both grasshopper-warbler and corncrake nest
or used to nest up to the 1,000 foot contour on the moorland edge.
He also reports the wood-mouse up to about the same altitude, or at
least its nests in "bushes on the moors." This probably means the
low hazel scrub, where we noticed several woodland birds, chaffinches,
tits, and even traces of pheasants, a bird which I have known survive
in the same sort of cover in the west Highlands, long after the protecting hand of the gamekeeper had been removed.

Migneint is a true moor, in the restricted ecological sense. The
lowest plant layer consists of woolly fringed moss (*Rhacomitrium lanuginosum*) and lichens (*Cladonia* spp.) on the drier and of *Sphagnum*
mosses on the wetter ground. The grass-type cover runs from mat-
grass through moor-grass, cotton-grass and deer's-hair sedge to rushes
along the slow-running peaty streams. Heather dominates stretches
of the drier ground, and is found less thickly in the bogs—though highly
developed on the hummocks of disintegrating areas. Here it is associated
with cross-leaved heath, which tends to be replaced by bell heather
under drier conditions. The generally acid reaction favours adapted
plants, and rosettes of the carnivorous sundews (*Drosera* spp.) with their
hairy, paddle-shaped leaves are prominent amongst the mosses. In
several places the peat cap is breaking down and being washed away,

giving rise to a wilderness of hummocks, the cracks between which are lined with the bare soft peat. This can be seen particularly well near Llyn Conwy, in the angle of the roads from Cwmpenmachno and Yspytty Ifan which meet at Ffynnon Eidda (Pl. 22, p. 255).

This whole area is the largest of its kind in Wales, according to the *Grassland Survey*, though it is a habitat well known in Scotland and northern England. Apart from the *Survey*, Migneint has not attracted field-workers to any extent, and the dearth of published information about the wild-life of these moorlands makes the slender data for Eryri seem quite copious.

F. C. Best, however, has recently done some entomological collecting in the neighbourhood. Even more interesting than his discovery of colonies of the marsh-fritillary, already referred to (p. 216), is the finding of the large heath (*Coenonymphia tullia*), which he calls locally common, for the race is the typical *tullia* and not *philoxena*, the race found in the north Midlands and south Lancashire, and which seems therefore to separate the Welsh colony from the main range of *tullia* in northern England and southern Scotland. Superficially the large heath is a bigger, darker insect than the small heath, which is abundant in this habitat. Amongst moths, Best reports the beautiful yellow underwing (*Anarta myrtilli*), golden-rod-brindle (*Lithomoia solidaginis*), light knotgrass (*Apatele menyanthidis*) and the rarer scarce silver Y (*Plusia interrogationis*), all of which feed on heather, bilberry and other common plants of acid moorland.

The birds of the peat moor form a small community which is not met in its full development elsewhere in the Park region. The breeding species of the open moor are sky-lark, meadow-pipit, merlin, snipe, curlew, dunlin, golden plover and red grouse; round the peat-hags and tarns reed-bunting, mallard, teal, and possibly other ducks, sandpipers and colonies of black-headed gulls may be expected. Twites may occur on passage and Best once saw a quail above Penmachno, which was certainly out of its habitat. If left in peace, short-eared owl, at present a scarce winter visitor to North Wales, and hen-harrier are not impossible additions to the breeding birds.

A first point of interest is that the dominance of passerine species, so noticeable on the grassland and mountain-tops of Eryri, no longer obtains, and waders, in number of species if not actually in population, form a much more important element; thus there is an approach to a more northern type of community, which is common on the Scottish

"mosses" and reaches its climax on the arctic tundra, where probably
the majority of the world's waders nest. This "set-up" has little to
do with altitude, except as it affects the growth of heather and associated
plants, for it is also found at sea level in Scotland.

Not all the members of the community are common, and they can
all be seen to better advantage on the drier moors of Denbighshire
outside the Park; for example, along the Pentrevoelas–Denbigh road
near Llyn Aled and Llyn Alwen. Near Llyn Conwy in June, where
before 1914–18 the annual bag was from 1,000 to 1,500 brace (Best),
I could not flush a grouse, though droppings and feathers were everywhere, but I was soon under the surveillance of a pair of golden plover,
evidently with young. They kept watch, flying or running from
hummock to hummock, and a touch of comedy was added when I
crouched, for the female immediately stood up and stretched her neck
to keep me under observation. When I stood up again, she quickly
flattened herself, and this jack-in-the-box reaction was repeated several
times. By the shores of Llyn Conwy sandpipers also had young; these,
with the inevitable meadow-pipits and a singing sky-lark, were the only
birds to be seen on the peat-cap. For merlin or dunlin a thorough
search would have to be made, the former here nesting probably in
patches of the longest heather, and the latter in small colonies in the
wet bog.

The gull colonies of the Nant Conwy area present rather a mystery
historically. Pennant, who speaks of these "black and moory mountains," describes in Llyn Conwy "three islands, one of which is the
haunt of *black-back* gulls [*sic*] during the breeding season. They are so
exccedingly fierce in defence of their young, that I knew of a man who
was nearly drowned in an attempt to swim to their nests, being so
violently beaten by the old birds . . ." Forrest quotes this passage under
the heading of the *great black-backed* gull, but also gives Pennant as an
authority for the nesting of the *black-headed* gull on Llyn Conwy, and
on Llyn Llydaw below Snowdon, though in this case as well the actual
term used is "black-backed gulls." The absence of islands on Llyn
Conwy at present—though it is possible they were temporary formations
of peat, like the famous floating island of Llyn-y-dywarchen—slightly
weakens the first-hand quality of Pennant's testimony, and though
there is modern evidence that the great black-back does occasionally
nest inland in North Wales, it seems far more likely that the smaller
species, which as Forrest points out frequently changes its sites, was the

real occupant, and this view was taken by P. A. D. Hollom when reporting on the survey of it made in 1938.

The traditional gull colony of the region is at Llyn-yr-adar on the western slopes of the Moelwyns. Pennant does not mention it, but the impressionable William Williams wrote: "Llyn-yr-Adar by Orphwysfa, being in a solitary hollow, is frequented by large sea-gulls, which are supposed never to quit it: but it is said, with more probability, that they are there during the breeding season only: however I have seen them there at other times." Martin's (1864) "near Beddgelert, on a little mountain tarn, is a marvellous colony," quoted by Forrest, seems likely to refer to Llyn-yr-Adar also. When Forrest wrote his *Fauna*, however, there was no known gullery in Caernarvonshire or, apparently, the adjacent parts of Merioneth and Denbigh nearer than Llyn Mynyddlod above Bala and the Aled valley. His supplementary *Handbook* (1919) reports no change, but by the 1938 Survey there were three small colonies totalling 140 pairs on adjacent pools in the foothills east of Capel Curig: these were the only known stations in Caernarvonshire, apart from Ystumllyn (see p. 295). By 1946 a colony had been established at Llyn Elsi, the Betws water-supply, where pollution by the gulls causes the council fathers of Britain's smallest Urban District some anxiety. Eastward into Denbighshire a "clot" of five colonies was recorded in 1938; two of these were in the 101–1000-pair grade. No doubt many gulls from these sites are amongst those which range far and wide over the upland farms and along the valleys during the nesting season. Numbers were to be seen early in April 1946, on the hill road between Llanrwst and Pentrevoelas, and they are always about Betws, where in the June dusk Markham and I watched what we thought at first were a pair of barn-owls, but which turned out to be two gulls hawking silently over a field of mowing grass.

The only mammal of interest on the moorland is the introduced mountain-hare, which probably does better here than in Eryri, though it is said to have established itself most firmly on the rounded Berwyn mountains, a parallel to its remarkable success on similar dry hills in southern Scotland and northern England, where it is far more numerous now than in its native sub-alpine habitat of the Highlands.

Proceeding from Llyn Conwy, the river flows in a wide valley of great charm; changes of grassland type can be seen clearly demarcated. Pont-ar-Gonwy, where the road from Ffestiniog to Yspytty Ifan crosses the infant stream, is still in the heather zone, but this soon gives way to fescue-bent, with patches of rushes not only along the bottom, but stretching up the distant slopes in blotches and fingers. With the rushes mat-grass rather than moor-grass seems to be the principal associate. In the drier grassland tormentil, lousewort and milkwort provide colour and an indication of conditions still acid. Bracken is noticeably absent. Along the small tributaries, which may cut deep ravines, appear gorse bushes, bilberry, heather, small rowan trees and ferns, but an even more interesting habitat is that of the low outcrop which runs across from north to south to make several little falls on the river below Pont-ar-Gonwy. The rock faces east over the open moorland towards Arenig Fach, and here in June bluebells were still in flower on ledges crowded with vegetation which included sallow and rowan bushes, honeysuckle, heather, bilberry, crowberry, woodrush (*Luzula sylvatica*), male fern, beech fern, and common polypody, the whole making a vivid green band against the dark browns of the surrounding moorland (Pl. XIV, p. 179). Such luxuriance, on an obviously acid site, is evidently the result of abundant moisture and protection from the prevailing winds. These rocks frequently provide nesting places for birds of prey, and enable us to add carrion-crow, kestrel and buzzard to the general moorland association, which is completed by the presence, from Pont-ar-Gonwy downwards, of the four highland riparian birds. Grey wagtail, ring-ousel, dipper and sandpiper can all be seen along the upper Conway in a typical setting, although the ring-ousel may prefer the seclusion of one of the tributary glens, where, guided by the food-carrying parents, I found a nest of five young, well-hidden on a bilberry-covered ledge. The wagtails had a nest at the Pont-ar-Gonwy falls, where it was delightful to watch the adults balancing and bobbing on the stones; here also I watched a sandpiper "working" a slope above the stream, pulling out worms from the wet ground.

Amongst the rushy flats, and on the peat moor above, curlews in 1946 were in greater strength than we saw elsewhere in the Park region, but the lapwing only appeared right on the boundary, in boggy fields east of the Conway, between Yspytty Ifan and Pentrevoelas.

The Ffestiniog road south-west from Pont-ar-Gonwy to Ffynnon Eidda passes through the heart of the Migneint; small tarns are numerous, some of them converted into reservoirs, but on their natural history there is negligible information. At Pont-ar-afon-gam the grassland is reached again with the main Bala–Ffestiniog road and close to the spectacular waterfall of Rhaiadr-y-cwm, whose sides are clothed with heather, woodrush and a considerable bed of the decorative *Sedum reflexum*, the large yellow stonecrop so popular in rock gardens. Like many of its genus an alien, it is now well established on dry, rocky sites in Wales; it was not out here in June, though I had already seen the flowers in a sheltered situation below the cliffs at Tan-yr-allt. Colour, however, was provided by large flowers of a buttercup, perhaps the mountain form of *Ranunculus acris*. Carrion-crow, grey wagtail, meadow-pipit, wren, cuckoo and kestrel were noted in the neighbourhood.

The heather moorland returns along the Cynfal river down to Ffestiniog and merges with the upland farms, which are broken by ridges of rock, causing in the deeper pockets flush bog conditions, with bogbean (*Menyanthes trifoliata*), cotton-grass and *Sphagnum* mosses the characteristic plants (Pl. 23a, p. 270).

THE VALE OF FFESTINIOG

The industrial slate-mining centre of Blaenau Ffestiniog is omitted from the proposed Park, but "Llan" Ffestiniog, and the north bank of Afon Cynfal and Afon Dwyryd down to, but skirting, Penrhyndeudraeth, are to be included, and it may be as well to deal with this area before considering the woodland zone of Nant Conwy proper.

"The vale (of Ffestiniog)," wrote Pennant, "is composed of rich meadows; the sites edged with groves; and barren precipitous mountains close this gem, as it were, in a rugged case." Today the sides of the valley are attractively wooded, both with oak scrub and with some private conifer plantations. These do not differ essentially from woods which have been or are to be described elsewhere, though the neighbourhood, as a whole, belongs both politically and topo-graphically to Merioneth.

Since botanical records tend to be grouped by counties, it is difficult —especially as there is no published *Flora* like Griffith's available—to find out what plants may be peculiar to this corner of Merioneth, and the same is largely true of faunal data, though reports of several entomological expeditions are contained in nineteenth-century publica-tions. For example, E. W. H. Blagg, in May–June 1896, collected 160 species of macro-lepidoptera, mainly in the county, but the localities are not given. As regards vertebrates, G. H. Caton-Haigh piled up a great many records during his residence by Traeth Mawr, though most of them refer to tidal waters outside our province. However he recorded seven species of bats round Penrhyndeudraeth, this being a group of mammals in which Coward, Oldham, Elliott and Forrest, who quotes Haigh's records, were particularly interested. The species were the noctule, pipistrelle, Natterer's, Daubenton's, whiskered, long-eared and lesser horse-shoe-bats; several specimens were sent to the British Museum from the neighbourhood.

Our own observations suggested that the woodland birds are well represented in the Ffestiniog basin, with the nuthatch much in evidence; in fact, we saw one in a tit flock exploring thorn-bushes along the open road near Manod, and others called continually in September round Cae'r Blaidd, just north of Llan Ffestiniog. On the farmland the yellow bunting appears to be common, while the quarries and habitations of Blaenau mean an abundance of jackdaws, which are common over the hills at Cwmpenmachno, where slate has also been worked. Precipitous rocks hang right over Blaenau Ffestiniog, and in September heather and western gorse were blooming brilliantly on the "heather fell" above the town roofs. Past the quarries, on the road to the Lledr valley, goldcrests called in strength from a clump of conifers, and we met the fiercest and most virulent midges (*Ceratopogonidae*) in Wales; we did not stop to identify them specifically. Local records were, however, published a number of years ago by F. W. Edwards.

THE WOODLANDS OF NANT CONWY

The woodland character of the country round Betws-y-coed has been recognized even when the region as a whole was most denuded. Walter Davies records that from the Gwydir Estates in 1754–60 no less than £50,000 worth of oak was floated down the Conway, while in the parishes of Ysbytty (*sic*) and Penmachno 85,000 trees were planted in 1795–97.

Although, from the picture in Pennant's *Tours*, there appear to have been no woods round the Conway falls of Rhaiadr-y-graig-llyd in his day, the traveller Hall (1809–11) noted the sylvan beauty of the scene as one descended the Llugwy from Capel Curig, "the country now darkened by the spread of foliage. The birch more particularly flourishes," and "from above the lakes of Capel Curig to the neighbourhood of Gwydir House, a strong principle of vegetation manifests itself in despite of continual attacks on it by the cattle." At Gwydir there were proper fences and "the rocks and eminences on the west side of the valley are most beautifully covered with plantations in a very thriving condition. The firs are particularly prosperous." There were two nurseries near the Bridge of Llanrwst "one for public accommodation; the second for the use of Gwydir property." In Penmachno he observed: "Here, as in many other parts, the woods are abandoned to the cattle; but on the properties of Plas yn Cwm Glas, of Havodurig, Penarth, Digod and Delasse it is protected and has attained the character and value of timber. Wet meadows and straggling patches of wood occupy the lower parts of the parish near the Conway and immediately upon that river is a good deal of recent and flourishing plantation." Down the Conway, in the parishes of Llangelynin and Gyffin, he reported "patches of wood not very studiously protected."

If the oak-woods were not felled, they were often coppiced for various purposes; the resultant secondary growth is well seen in Coed Soflen on the Llanrwst–Pentrevoelas road, where Plate 24a (p. 271) was taken. There is an encouraging stand of very young oak above the road in the same locality.

But felling, coppicing and grazing between them have reduced most of the native woods to the general category of scrub. This can be seen on both sides of the Llugwy from Capel Curig to the beginning of the Forestry Commission property at Glyn, on Gallt-y-pandy above the Fairy Glen, in which the oaks reach their best development (it is interesting that Pennant mentions the "noblest oaks in all Wales" at Carreg-y-gwalch near Betws), and up the Conway thence in a narrow belt for several miles (see Pl. XXX, p. 371, which shows the interior of typical oak-wood). Close to the rivers the alders grow, with birches on the margins of the woods, though both combine in a remarkable clump beside the "Beavers' Pool" and near the Betws–Dolwyddelan road. But to see the birch at its most abundant one must go up the Conway beyond Yspytty Ifan. Here it is the common tree along the banks or fences between the fields and forms several copses in which hazel and holly associate with it. All the other trees described in Chapter 10 are found in Nant Conwy, as well as a number of exotic hardwoods planted along the roads for amenity purposes by the Forestry Commission. Specimens of two poplars, *Populus trichocarpa* and *P. generosa*, by the old road from Betws to the Lledr valley, are said to be the largest trees yet produced by the Commission; they were planted in 1926.

Anyone who walks through scrub woodland will be struck by the number of fungi to be seen, especially by the roots of the trees and on

dead branches and stumps. It is not surprising that the Betws neighbourhood has received attention from the British Mycological Society,
who made their autumn "Foray" there in September 1924. Concentrating on the Gwydir Woods (it must be remembered that the Forestry
Commission were then only beginning their activities), the Hafod
Woods on the Denbighshire side, and the valleys of the Llugwy and
the Conway about the Fairy Glen, the Society recorded 175 species of
fungi. Such common species as *Amanita porphyria* on birch, *Daedalia
quercina* on oak, and *Fomes annosus* on conifers do not need expert
mycologists for their discovery, but a detailed investigation of old
sawdust heaps at Betws yielded many interesting mycetozoa, of which
no less than nine species were new to Wales, one being the rare
Cienkowskia reticulata. *Diderma lucidum*, first identified at Trefriw in
1860, was duly rediscovered; this slime-fungus is found in Merioneth,
and there is a colony in Ceylon provisionally included in the same
species, an astonishing distribution. *Amaurochaete cribrosa* made its
fourth appearance in Great Britain, while above the woodland,
Microglossum atropurpureum was found on heathy slopes, and *Ramsbottomia
lamprosporoides* on moorland above the Llugwy.

In addition to the fungi, H. H. Knight identified about 100 species
of lichens, as against Griffith's total of about 370 for the whole county.
There seems to have been no more recent large-scale field work in
these groups of lower plants within the region of the Park.

The Commission's Forest of Gwydir, founded on the woodlands of
the former private estate, covers 18,000 acres—28 square miles—in
several separate blocks. Seven thousand acres had been afforested by
1945 and a further 6,000 acres will probably be planted. The rest is
either scheduled for smallholdings or is unplantable. Generally
speaking, the Commission aims to utilize the otherwise unproductive
slopes above the farmland of the valleys and below the areas which
can be left as sheepwalks.

When the Forestry Commission took over the first sections of the
Forest in 1920, the old estate woods had mostly been felled in
the 1914–18 war and it was necessary to begin again altogether on the
empty sites, while, on the open ground which was also taken in, the
natural vegetation was the only guide to timber possibilities. Following
the Commission's usual practice, pines have been planted on the higher
and drier ground, spruces in the hollows and bogs, and larches and
Douglas fir on the better drained slopes, areas corresponding approxi-

mately to those originally covered respectively by heather and gorse, by moor-grass and rushes, and by bracken and scrub.

The successful establishment of a tree-cover anywhere in Britain is no easy matter. Effective fencing from sheep and rabbits is essential; this leads to the striking floral changes already described in Chapter 9, and these in their turn cause fresh problems, for the vigorous growth, especially of heather and gorse, which springs up on the hillsides, provides formidable competition for the young trees—usually planted out when about four years old and eighteen inches in height. In Gwydir, western gorse is prevalent and constant weeding is therefore necessary until the young trees rise above the natural vegetation and suppress it themselves.

Ditching, as was seen at Beddgelert, must often be extensive, but even then in some hollows afforestation fails, even where the indicator plants, e.g. moor-grass, appear favourable. J. R. Hampson believes that a perched water-table, with impeded drainage well beneath the surface, is the cause; shrub growth is possible but nothing larger.

Naturally economic considerations control the choice of trees planted by the Commission. At present Japanese larch and Sitka spruce are the popular species, but a number of others are used, and Gwydir is noted for its variety. Some points of identification should be learned by all visitors to the Park and, indeed, to the country generally, for these trees, whatever their effect on rural beauty, will become in a few years as familiar as the native hardwood species are at present.

Although it is difficult to tell from the European larch (*Larix decidua*) when in leaf, in winter the rich red-brown shoots of the "Jap" larch contrast strongly with the pale yellow-brown of the European, which, though providing better timber, is out of favour owing to its liability to disease. Japanese larch can be seen throughout the Forest, and in its pure stands certainly adds to the colour of the winter landscape.

Both Sitka and Norway spruce are remunerative crops, but the former, a west American species, does better in the climate of western Britain. Trees planted in 1925 near the Swallow Falls are already of forest height. The spruces bear their needles singly on short woody stems and those of the Sitka are generally longer, sharper and with a bluer tint than those of the Norway; they also have a rich blue-white "bloom" on the under side. The Serbian Spruce (*Picea omorika*) has also been planted in Gwydir and can be seen on the road from Gwydir Castle to the old lead mines; in its young stages, at any rate, it has a very narrow habit.

Also of "Christmas Tree" shape, but with curiously soft needles and brown buds rather like those of the beech, is the Douglas fir (*Pseudotsuga taxifolia*), another west American species, which, however, needs better conditions than the Sitka spruce; it will be found extensively planted on the lower slopes.

The Scots pine, owing to its native tradition in Britain—though it probably became extinct in Wales at least 3,000 years ago—is used on many unpromising sites with shallow soil and heather cover. Pines are, of course, known by their long needles, borne in bunches, and the Scots is distinguished specifically at a distance by its reddish bark and blueish foliage. The Corsican pine (*Pinus nigra* var. *calabrica*) is a greyer-trunked, greener-leaved tree, common in parks and gardens and fairly popular in economic forestry; good examples in Gwydir are to be seen near the Swallow Falls and there is a fine group of trees, dating from the days of estate forestry, opposite the gate of Gwydir Castle. Here the pines are mixed with noble firs (*Abies nobilis*) and the two redwoods (*Sequoia gigantea* and *S. sempervirens*). Strong natural regeneration of the pines and firs can be seen in the vicinity. The American lodgepole pine (*Pinus contorta*) has already been planted in Gwydir and is to be used more extensively in future.

The silver firs, whose flat boughs bear flat, blunt needles, may recover their popularity if *Abies noblis* and *A. grandis* maintain immunity from the insect pest *Chermes* spp. which ravages the European *A. alba*, once a favourite ornamental tree. A plantation of *A. grandis* can be seen above the road from Betws to Gwydir Castle, where it is doing well; both it and the noble fir can be seen near the Miner's Bridge on the Llugwy.

The hemlock spruces (*Tsuga* spp.) are the most graceful of all conifers. Their flattened needles somewhat resemble those of the yew, but the tapering habit and the curving-over of the apex of the stem is quite characteristic; this apparent weakness is really the strength of the tree, for its branches are resilient and throw off the snow in their native American habitat—also any climber who is unlucky enough to lose his grip. Hemlocks will be seen along the Llugwy valley, where they have been used for marginal effect.

Cypresses and thuyas are superficially similar and recall the cemetery rather than the forest to the ordinary observer, but both groups give good timber. *Thuja gigantea* has been used on a plantation scale about half-way between Betws and Capel Curig on the south side of the road, and Lawson's cypress (*Chamaecyparis lawsoniana*) is also to be seen.

The possibility of these exotic conifers reseeding naturally is of prime importance to British forestry. Near the old lead mines, Hampson showed me a clump of Sitka spruce and Scots pine planted by the Gwydir Estate. Snow had made a clearing in which an extraordinary vegetation had grown up. In the midst of heather, gorse, brambles, bilberry and willowherb, were young trees of birch, oak, sweet chestnut, and of the two conifers which overshadowed the spot. If these economically important species, with protection from grazing animals and a certain amount of weeding, can really regenerate on the forest scale, then not only will the costly process of planting, with its concomitant of forest nurseries, be largely eliminated, but a natural type of forest will succeed the uniform blocks at present inevitable.

Some twelve acres of oak have been planted in the Machno valley; otherwise hardwoods are only used for amenity planting, though the native scrub-wood is now left on rocky faces and outcrops, which adds greatly to the attractiveness of the landscape. Also the practice of ringing the bark of scrub trees and leaving them to die, in order to clear the ground cheaply, has at last been abandoned. The unsightly grey skeletons of woods so treated probably aroused more "aesthetic" criticism of the Commission than anything else. Now, however, the sparing of marginal scrub and the existence of larger woods alongside the Forest boundaries has resulted, round Betws-y-coed, in a blending of native and planted woodlands which is as yet quite unusual in Britain, and in which the green fields of the hill-farms and the forest holdings stand out like continental "alps."

Large-scale forestry often means pests on the epidemic scale, but Gwydir has so far escaped. The Honey Fungus (*Armillaria mellea*) has transferred its attentions to conifers planted on old hardwood ground, while such common animal pests as *Chermes* spp., which attacks Douglas as well as silver firs, and the green spruce aphis (*Neomyzaphis abietina*) also occur; on the top above Diosgydd I saw spruces which had been attacked both by frost and by this aphis. The pine weevil (*Hylobius abietis*) had been known in the area long before the Commission came, as had the defoliating moth *Tortrix viridana*, whose larvae, responsible for widespread attacks on oaks and other hardwoods, were noted by Caton-Haigh as a favourite food of the willow-warbler. Recently the Forestry Commission has become interested in the possibility of insect control through the encouragement of bird predators, and experiments begun in the Forest of Dean by the saturation of sample areas with nesting boxes, may be extended in the near future to Gwydir.

The general insect life of the woodlands and valleys of Nant Conwy is probably the richest in North Wales, and Betws-y-coed has been the centre of entomological collection in the region; most of this, as elsewhere, has been primarily concerned with the Lepidoptera. Outside this order, the most striking woodland insect is the giant wood-wasp (*Urocerus gigas*), whose terrifying appearance has no doubt broken up many a picnic party by the Swallow Falls or Fairy Glen. This insect, introduced originally in foreign timber, is, however, neither dangerous —what looks like a gigantic "sting" is really the ovipositor—nor confined to woodland, for it has been met with on the top of Cader Idris. In the Diptera may be noted the not unexpected occurrence of the fungus gnat, *Mycomyia prominens*, while a number of the ninety-odd species of Hemiptera taken by J. M. Brown in 1924 were from Betws and Llanrwst. Of the orders with an aquatic association, some of North Wales's few recorded Ephemeroptera (May-flies) and Trichoptera (Sedge-flies) were collected by D. E. Kimmins in 1931–33 from the Llugwy and the Lledr (see Appendix). In the latter river, in 1898, W. E. Sharp discovered a large population of the beetle *Harpalus latus* in flood refuse; 75 per cent were found to be of a new variety, *erythrocephalus*. Balfour-Browne's recent work on the aquatic Coleoptera has been mentioned in the previous Chapter (p. 250); an earlier collector, E. A. Newbery, found the shingle-beds at the confluence of the Llugwy and the Conway "very profitable" for beetles. The principal species of dragonflies in the region were mentioned in the previous Chapter (p. 250).

At the end of the last century, F. D. Bland was an active lepidopterist in this area, combining this hobby, like many other naturalists, with fishing. In 1899 he reported that moths of all the main families were plentiful round Betws, taking 20 species of Noctuidae, and reporting a humming-bird-hawk (*Macroglossa stellatarum*) at rhododendron flowers. He had previously collected near Trefriw, where he found the tributary valleys to have a rich lepidopterous fauna, including 22 species of butterflies. He describes the comma as common, which is extremely interesting in view of its restricted range in the early part of the present century. Of the larger moths he mentions the poplar-hawk (*Laothoe populi*) and the ghost-moth (*Hepialus humuli*) as abundant in

PLATE 23

John Markham

a. SMALL FLUSH BOG, showing bogbean, *Menyanthes trifoliata*; rushes, *Juncus*; cotton-grass, *Eriophorum*; and *Sphagnum* mosses. Ffestiniog. June

John Markham

b. RIVERSIDE IN THE UPLANDS; lesser redpolls in the sallows, sand-martins in the river-bank, corncrakes in the meadows. River Conway near Yspytty Ifan
September

PLATE 24

John Markham

a. Young coppiced oaks, Coed Soflen. April

John Markham

b. General view of young conifers with patches of scrub oak left on steep slopes
Near Betws-y-coed. July

FORESTRY IN SNOWDONIA

the Conway valley, the clouded buff (*Diacrisia sannio*) characteristic of moor-grass bogs, as local, and the alder-moth (*Apatele alni*) as rare; in fact his discovery of it is no doubt responsible for South mentioning Trefriw in his description of the species.

Before leaving the invertebrates, the important field work of the Rev. Hilderic Friend in respect of the little-studied Annelid worms is relevant here, for, though operating mainly from Colwyn Bay, he made some particularly interesting discoveries under the bark of a tree stump at the Swallow Falls. Out of 33 species which he listed for Wales, he found 13 in this area, one of which, the potworm *Fridericia magna*, he had first described in 1899 and found again in 1926, with five other species of the same genus. He also identified a new variety, *dendroidea*, of the Venetian worm (*Eisenia veneta*), a species which appears to be in a very unstable state, giving rise to several forms in Britain alone. It is also of interest that he failed to find the true earthworm (*Lumbricus terrestris*), its place being taken by the related *L. castaneus* and *Allolobophora chlorotica*.

The bird life of uniform conifer forest is recognized as one of the weakest in Europe. An area such as Gwydir, however, which consists of separate blocks, has a considerable linear distance of forest-edge, an ecological boundary where all the woodland birds described in the previous chapter can maintain themselves in the marginal cover. Nesting boxes in the pure stands of firs would no doubt encourage the tits and their allies which roam through them to remain to breed, but the "beneficial effect" of insectivorous birds is not yet by any means an accepted fact. Until much more is known about the relationships of insects to each other, and of the birds' diet—for many prey on the Ichneumonidae and other parasites of defoliating larvae—wide generalizations as to their value are likely to be misleading.

Two game birds are favoured in the early stages of afforestation; when the heather grows up after enclosure, red grouse increase, and, once the trees begin to grow, they are replaced by black grouse, which Best says are well established on the somewhat broken plateau between Betws and Llyn Cowlyd. Unfortunately young conifer shoots form one of their favourite foods, and it is difficult to decide sylviculturally between their sporting and amenity worth, and their harm as forest pests.

When the young trees are competing with the surface vegetation in a close and tangled thicket, many other species are temporarily favoured, especially the warblers: chiffchaff, grasshopper-warbler, blackcap, garden-warbler and whitethroat; the chats: stonechat and whinchat; and the woodcock. But when the plantations grow up, and the ground flora practically disappears, only the woodcock remains. In a self-seeding forest, however (see p. 269), all stages of growth would be present within one block at the same time, and hence a much richer bird-life would be retained than is possible in an artificial stand.

Although reports sent from North Wales to the Woodcock Enquiry organized by the British Trust for Ornithology were scanty, Betws-y-coed seems now to be the centre of the breeding area of the woodcock in North Wales; Best has seen two nests close together within a hundred yards of the main road, and "kipping" flights were a feature of the dusk in June 1946. In winter the area, according to W. B. Alexander's summary of the Enquiry, does not carry a heavy population, and numbers are stated to have decreased of recent years.

Besides the tits, a staple group of all woodland in Britain, the coniferous woods are more frequented by finches than are the hardwoods, since several of these strong-billed birds can extract the seed successfully from fir cones. Two finches are among the four special birds of the "Caledonian" pine forest: siskin, crossbill, crested tit and capercaillie; but since there is no evidence for the recent existence of this forest in North Wales, the possibility of a native stock of any of these surviving hardly arises. In spite of this, there is a persistent tradition in early Welsh literature of a "Ceiliog Coed" (Cock of the Wood), which was reaffirmed by Pennant, and which Matheson and Peate believe did refer to the capercaillie, though the nearest remains to Wales were located physically in Somerset and temporally ascribed to Romano-British times. Even in the Scottish pine-woods the capercaillie died out and had to be reintroduced, while the crossbill and crested tit developed into local subspecies. But the planted coniferous woods of East Anglia have been colonized for many years now by typical crossbills from the Continent, and recently the siskin seems to have begun a southward spread as a breeding species to areas where, as a visitor in winter, it is already well known.

The crossbill has periodically irrupted right across southern Britain, actually nesting near Penmaen-mawr in 1890–91 and wintering at Betws in 1898, reaching the Menai in 1927, and again reported in Caernarvonshire in 1942–43. Such winter visits have often been the prelude to colonization, which has unfortunately seldom persisted. Its breeding habitats in Scotland and England are open woods or hedgerow lines of old pines, and it seems unlikely that the present Forestry Commission plantations would suit the crossbill: large gardens with an artificial "succession" of exotic conifers are a more promising environment. But it might be attracted to a self-regenerating forest, comparable to the old Caledonian woods. The same is true of the siskin, though there has been a certain amount of evidence of its occasional nesting even at present. Forrest, who listed nineteenth-century records, thought that it did so from time to time, while in July 1945, J. C. S. Ellis watched a female feeding on dandelion (*Taraxacum officinale*) seeds by the roadside in the Lledr valley, and on September 11th 1946, we watched six birds on knapweed heads at Llan Ffestiniog. Two were certainly juveniles and there was a garden with ornamental firs close by. It is easy to say that these were immigrants, but the date is definitely early for such, and, taken in conjunction with the 1945 observation only a few miles away, there can be at least a suggestion that one or two pairs are nesting in the region. If they continue to do so, there will be a nucleus ready to colonize the forest areas once they form a suitable habitat.

The crested tit is such a sedentary species that the hopes entertained for the siskin and crossbill in Gwydir and other Commission forests cannot be extended to it, but the tits of deciduous woodland—great, blue and long-tailed—are already in occupation of the young conifers; the coal-tit, often associated even with isolated pines in hardwood areas, is already predisposed to the habitat. In the Lledr valley a flock, mainly of blue and coal-tits, swept through the isolated block above Roman Bridge as we passed along the road in September, while round Betws they can interchange freely between the old scrub and the new plantations. Although not so much of a woodland bird, the willow-tit is reported to be common in the neighbourhood, and was first identified in Caernarvonshire at Capel Curig in 1910, soon after its recognition as a distinct species in Britain.

Sparrow-hawk and long-eared owl are the typical birds of prey of the fir woods, but the status of the latter is rather obscure in North Wales. Forrest reports it as resident in Caernarvonshire and Denbighshire, but his records are all from localities peripheral to the proposed Park. It is quite probable that it has now colonized the new woodland, for of all the British owls it is the most likely to escape notice. The tawny owl is common also in the oak-woods, where Markham and I were shown a remarkable open nest on the top of a low alder stump close to the Conway.

Of other larger woodland birds, the Llugwy valley was noted by Forrest for the abundance of the greater spotted woodpecker, a species which will find the conifers an acceptable habitat, while wood-pigeons are also common and form considerable winter flocks.

Though covering all types of country, the "vermin" records from the Penrhyn Estates near Betws, quoted by Forrest, may be mentioned here. They are for the years 1874 to 1902 and include 464 ravens, 16 peregrines, 1,988 kestrels and 738 sparrow-hawks; figures for rarer species are not given, but no doubt anything with a curved beak was added to the bag, for Forrest refers to a hobby shot in 1880 and a rough-legged buzzard in 1881 near Dolwyddelan, both "in the collection of Mr. Foster," who appears to have been the organizer of this holocaust. It seems possible that the same hand was at work in the case of the black tern, which Forrest "examined shot at Betws-y-coed early in May" 1909; probably and rather more justifiably in the case of two out of a covey of Virginian quail (*Ortyx virginianus*) which turned up, bewildered and bewilderingly—for none were ever known to have been released in North Wales—near Llyn Elsi in 1898; and certainly in the recording of the hooded crow, great snipe, Montagu's harrier and occasional shags, which rashly came inland to feed on small lakes near Betws. An earlier record, which seems to have escaped Forrest, is of the possible nesting of the honey-buzzard near "Capel Kerrick" in 1835: there are two eggs with these data in the National Museum of Wales.

Interesting as are the ecological problems which afforestation provides for the ornithologist, Forestry Commission areas have usually an even more striking effect upon the mammal population, and are accused, by Mr. Foster's spiritual descendants, of harbouring "vermin" of all kinds. In the first place, though rabbits and sheep are excluded, voles multiply in the improved ground cover and attack the young trees. Later it frequently happens that rabbits do get into the plantations, and with them the larger carnivores, so that it is not surprising that there have been a number of records of pine-martens in the Lledr valley since 1938, and F. C. Best believes that the plantations may have brought them back. Foster's figures, quoted by Forrest, are of interest here, since they date from the palmy days of game preservation and private forestry; between 1874 and 1902, 13 martens, 98 polecats and 2,310 "cats" were destroyed on the Penrhyn estates, indicating both that, even in the stronghold of the marten, the polecat was then at any rate by far the commoner species, and also that the bulk of the damage to game must have been done, not by these two rarities, but by ornaments of the domestic hearth gone wild.

Of foxes Best writes: "We have been accused of harbouring foxes and there is no doubt that large areas of forest make fox destruction difficult, but having lived all my life in North Wales I know that the increase in foxes started with the 1914–18 war and has continued thereafter all over North Wales for no very apparent reason other than the decline in game preservation." Badgers, once believed almost extinct in North Wales, have always been fairly common in the Conway and Lledr valleys; some were seen near Betws in 1946; stoats and weasels are numerous; so, J. R. Hampson informs me, is the red squirrel, which, for all its charm, is regarded with suspicion by foresters.

The relationship of the different mammals to each other in afforestation areas is complex. Major vole plagues have not occurred in Gwydir, and Hampson believes that the normal population of stoats and weasels exercises a sufficiently rigid control and that it is not necessary to presume any increase of these predators on that account. This is supported by A. D. Middleton, who has done much work on voles in North Wales, and told Best as recently as January 1947 that "from his knowledge of the rodent population he was definitely of the opinion that an increase in voles usually takes place following afforestation, due to the increased vegetation growth, but that he has no evidence that this is followed by any increase in the numbers of predatory birds or carnivorous animals." Certainly there has been no report of the appearance of the short-eared owl in strength, a bird which is believed to be very closely linked ecologically to the field vole. In Scotland this bird has responded to vole plagues both with increased numbers and remarkably increased clutch size, for example in 1874–76, 1891–93 and 1936.

The principal constituents of the vegetation in the early stages of afforestation have been described; under the closed canopy of evergreen conifers, undergrowth should disappear entirely, and even under the deciduous larches it is reduced to grasses, a thin growth of bracken, bluebells and wood-sorrel. The general flora of the scrub-woods has also been dealt with, but notes kindly given me by Evan Roberts cover some of the scarcer plants of the district, which, except for the vicinity of Llyn Crafnant, hardly appears in Griffith's records.

Some of these plants, from lower altitudes, though not necessarily from the woodlands, are: thyme-leaved sandwort (*Arenaria serpyllifolia*) and red sand-spurrey (*Spergularia rubra*) at Capel Curig; tutsan (*Hypericum androsaemum*), the shrubby St. John's wort, which is both native and a common garden escape; bog St. John's wort (*H. elodes*), burnet rose (*Rosa spinosissima*); grass of Parnassus (*Parnassia palustris*) from Llyn Crafnant, where Roberts has also found the rare Welsh stonecrop (*Sedum forsterianum*); the sundews *Drosera longifolia* and *D. rotundifolia*, the rarer of the enchanter's nightshades (*Circaea alpina*); great valerian (*Valeriana officinalis*), the massive alien elecampane (*Inula helenium*) at Betws-y-coed; tansy (*Tanacetum vulgare*), but never far from habitations; yellow loosestrife (*Lysimachia vulgaris*) at Capel Curig; great mullein (*Verbascum thapsus*), lesser skullcap (*Scutellaria minor*), orache (*Atriplex* sp.) and the wild hop (*Humulus lupulus*). It is equally interesting to note that Roberts has not met with two shrubs, the spindle (*Euonymus europaeus*), which Griffith called "rather common," and alder buckthorn (*Rhamnus cathartica*), whose rarity has already been given as the cause of the comparative scarcity of the brimstone butterfly (p. 245).

Orchids are one of the families which attract almost anyone with an interest in botany. In the Betws area Roberts has found twayblade (*Listera ovata*), spotted orchis (*Orchis fuchsii*), early purple orchis, fragrant orchis (*Gymnadenia conopsea*), great butterfly orchis (*Platanthera chlorantha*), and, in September 1946, the little green bog orchis, previously only reported from the other side of the Snowdon range. He has not found the rare twayblade, *Listera cordata* or the marsh gentian (*Gentiana pneumonanthe*), known near Llyn Crafnant to Griffith, who reports that the Rev. A. Ley found the clustered helleborine (*Epipactis purpurata*) in woods near Trefriw; its only other Welsh station is in Cardiganshire.

Pennant, who thought himself no botanist, noticed the abundance of bog-myrtle near Trefriw; he said it was used as a yellow dye, to keep off moths and fleas and as a "vermifuge." The association of the alpine cress (*Thlaspi alpestre*) with the lead mines in this area has already been mentioned on page 62. These few extracts give some idea of the variety of the flora in the Gwydir district of Nant Conwy, where representatives of all distribution and habitat types (see p. 195) meet. The recent paper by A. Wilson, whose observations cover part of this area, is dealt with on page 280.

The wooded neighbourhood of Betws divides the agricultural area of Nant Conwy into two clearly differentiated parts: the upland farms of the Llugwy, Lledr, Machno and upper Conway valleys, and the lower Conway valley, which includes some uplands in the foothills of the Carneddau, and the alluvial lowlands along the river.

THE UPLAND VALLEYS

The upper Conway and its tributary valleys have each their own character. Very little detailed natural history field work seems to have been done in any of them, but the farms and their associated wild-life do not differ greatly from those in the valleys of Eryri, except perhaps round Penmachno and Yspytty Ifan, where smoother contours allow a more spacious agriculture. There is some fairly good grassland, and we were asked by one farmer to identify a certain "herb," which proved to be lady's mantle. He told us that store cattle feeding on pastures which contained much of it invariably did better than those which did not include it in their grazing; no official explanation of this phenomenon is forthcoming. Also in this neighbourhood—Evan Roberts has found it near Penmachno—the mountain pansy (*Viola lutea*) is quite common. This is one of the plants which Farmer notes as unexpectedly absent from the Snowdon range. It is here too that the introduced but now thoroughly acclimatized bridewort (*Spirea salicifolia*) becomes prominent in the hedgerows and in dense clumps elsewhere, especially along the streams.

Along these valleys the corncrake is still to be heard, in fields which in June are golden with buttercups. The Lledr continues to flow in a luxuriant setting as far up as the wide basin at Roman Bridge, where the interesting fern ceterach (*Ceterach officinarum*) grows on the roadside walls. Dolwyddelan was a breeding station of the yellow wagtail according to Forrest's informant Bucknill, though this bird is definitely rare as a nester in North Wales; other characteristic birds are the redstart and the swift. The latter has its strongholds in the slate-grey villages; from these bases birds hunt far and wide, right to the tops of the hills, though there has been evidence that cliff-nesting is quite usual in North Wales up to a considerable altitude.

The upper part of the Machno valley is much bleaker than that of the Lledr. There has been quarrying here and, as often is the case when man operates in a wild environment, his derelict enterprises make it seem even more desolate. From the cottages at Carog a very rough road leads up a side valley to the moors of the Migneint (see p. 259). The slopes here are clothed with bracken, fescue and rushes, which change in places to a varied scrub of hawthorn, hazel, birch, rowan and sallow. This means a richer bird-life over the several associations: chaffinches and song-thrushes in the thicket, tree-pipits and whinchats in the bracken, ring-ousels, wrens and birds of prey on the rocky outcrops.

The upper Conway has already been described in its different stages through the open moorland. At Blaen-y-coed it is joined by the Afon Serw from the region of Gylchedd and Arenig Fach and flows, still in a glen, below wet, rushy fields and straggling birch woods. At Yspytty Ifan its course is much slower and admits of shingle beds and low mud banks in which there are small colonies of sand-martins (Pl. 23b, p. 270). As Forrest points out, this is "generally speaking, a lowland species," and though it may occur elsewhere in the Park, it is certainly not numerous; possibly it is only in level uplands of the Denbighshire type that it finds the soft banks suitable for burrowing. The sallow bushes seen in the Plate inevitably attract lesser redpolls, and, of the highland riparian group, the sandpiper persists. The habitat is unsuited to the requirements of the other three—ring-ousel, grey wagtail and dipper—though the last two reappear when the Conway begins its rush down the gorges of the Fairy Glen to Llyn-yr-Afanc, the Beaver's Pool.

This seems an apposite place to remark briefly on the history of the Beaver (*Castor fiber*) in North Wales (see also p. 371). Confusion with *Afanc*, used in the sense of a water monster, is considerable; *afanc* is certainly accepted in modern Welsh as equivalent to beaver, though the descriptive *Llostlydan* (Broadtail) is also used. The Llyn-yr-Afanc tradition, quoted in *The Mountains of Snowdonia*, is that a monster was dragged from the pool and over the Siabod range by two oxen, who led it on an iron chain to the shores of Llyn-y-ffynnon-las (Glaslyn), into which it disappeared. Forrest says that evidence for the existence of the real beaver is purely documentary, no actual remains having been found. Nor was North Wales apparently its stronghold, for it had disappeared there by the time of Giraldus Cambrensis' visit in 1188, though still found on the Teifi in Cardiganshire, and Dafydd ap Gwilym, the great fourteenth-century poet of South Wales, who deals much with nature, writes as if he had watched beavers himself. Matheson, summarizing the position, refers to the beaver remains in

Pleistocene deposits in South Wales and to the discovery of a supposed "beaver-trap," similar to those found elsewhere in Britain and on the Continent, in Carmarthenshire. To the Conway Llyn-yr-Afanc, he adds Sarn-yr-Afanc (the Beaver's Causeway) in Nant Ffrancon.

Perhaps this is what led various authors and, of course, William Williams, that connoisseur of the taller stories, to twist "Ffrancon" into some connection with the beaver. In his own words, "it is supposed that the river was formerly much frequented, especially that part of it which runs through Nantffrancon, by that amphibious animal called by the ancient Britons and by the present Welsh Afange, in English the Beaver; and that Nantffrancon, or perhaps more properly, Nant Afangcwn i.e. the vale of the Beaver Dogs, took its name from that circumstance." His contemporary Bingley went one better, for he claimed that beavers had been seen "within the memory of man."

The tall alders by the Beaver's Pool are the remains of the woods which were felled in these valleys in the sixteenth century, when the inhabitants had cleared most of the hillsides and wanted more land.

Water, woodland and caves or habitations make up a favourable habitat for most of the British bats; all these constituents are found at Betws-y-coed, so that it is not surprising that the district is as rich in these elusive little mammals as the Vale of Ffestiniog. Noctule, pipistrelle, Daubenton's and the whiskered and long-eared bats are common to both areas, and the lesser horse-shoe-bat has been found near Conway; these are the majority of the species known to North Wales, and it seems unlikely, from their known ranges, that many of the others found in England will occur in our region, though the distribution of bats well deserves more research.

THE LOWER CONWAY VALLEY

Below Betws the countryside, flat, cultivated and with thick hedgerows, is unlike any habitat so far described. It is hard to believe that once deer from the Snowdonian hills raided across to the streets of Llanrwst (see p. 361). Today this area does not suggest an unusual wild-life and is for the most part outside the Park boundary. Below Trefriw, however, the vegetation of the old commote of Arllechwedd Isaf has been studied by Dr. Elfyn Hughes in a paper mentioned in Chapter 8. He notes and maps no less than sixteen types of vegetation, related to the soil, from the summits of the Carneddau to the dunes opposite Deganwy, and the tidal marshes of the Conway. The special

which characterize these habitats have all been met repeatedly in the
region; it is the variation in their proportions according to the changes
in the soil which is of interest, though Hughes does not give actual
percentages. He suggests that on gley soils alder and not oak was the
dominant tree; there can be little doubt that it is numerically second
only to the oak in North Wales today.

The principal plants of the alluvial tide-washed soils are the common
reed, red fescue, sea plantain (*Plantago maritima*), sea arrow grass
(*Triglochin maritima*), sea aster (*Aster tripolium*), a rush *Juncus gerardi*
and perennial rye-grass. During the period of most intense agricultural
activity from the sixteenth to the nineteenth centuries drainage and
the scythe drove back the reeds and red fescue became dominant. Since
the beginning of the century, however, there has been considerable
retrogression, and the reeds have returned.

At the northern extremity of the Park stands Conway mountain,
divided from the Snowdon range by the famous Sychnant pass. On
its dry slopes Hughes notes a flora of heather, bell-heather, thyme and
sheep's fescue. The lower rainfall of the Llandudno district distinguishes
it clearly from the areas which we have considered; the Sychnant pass
seems, ecologically, the frontier of a new region.

A systematic study of the local flora has just been published by
A. Wilson. He calls his area "a Portion of north-east Caernarvonshire"
and it extends over the western tributaries of the Conway as far as
Llyn-y-parc, about a mile north of Betws-y-coed. Thence his boundary
runs west to Pen Llithrig-y-wrach and the summit of Carnedd Llywelyn,
and his notes on the semi-alpine flora have already been mentioned
(p. 186). From this highest point the water-shed is followed to the
shore at Conway, so that the "Portion" corresponds closely to Hughes's
Arllechwedd Isaf.

Generally Wilson considers the flora not remarkable and reports
that aquatic vegetation in the hill lakes has suffered from their conver-
sion to reservoirs. His list comprises 667 species, of which 86 are
introduced species and many only occur round Conway and in the
lowlands outside the proposed Park. Most of his records are from
personal field-work, but observations made by E. Price Evans and Evan
Roberts are included, as well as some from his previous papers.

As an example of a plant community occupying one square yard
may be quoted that from near Llyn Geirionydd at 620 feet altitude.
The following ten species were identified:

Viola palustris	*Myrica gale*
Succisa pratensis	*Narthecium ossifragum*
Erica tetralix	*Juncus bulbosus*
Calluna vulgaris	*Carex* sp.
Pedicularis palustris	*Molinia caerulea*

Among the principal weeds of cultivation in the area are treacle mustard (*Erysimum cheiranthoides*), which is common, sharp-leaved fluellen (*Linaria elatine*), classed as frequent, the locally common weasel-snout (*Antirrhinum orontium*) and the rare English catchfly (*Silene anglica*), all introduced species.

Other points of interest in the lower Conway valley are the occurrence of wild daffodils (*Narcissus pseudo-narcissus*), which can be seen from the road at Farchwel near Caerhûn, the comparative abundance of the yellow bunting and the survival of the corncrake in the cultivated land. There is some evidence, according to Forrest, that the harvest-mouse has occurred here. The slower course of the Conway below Betws is framed by willows and sallows ; amongst the herbage Evan Roberts reports the indomitable colonist Indian balsam (*Impatiens glandulifera*), whose tall hollow stems bearing heads of intricate globular pink flowers are now becoming a familiar sight along the rivers of Britain. In the river itself the freshwater-mussel is found (see p. 308), and it is the nearest point to which various marine creatures can approach our region. The Conway is famous for its salmon and sea-trout; the humble flounder ascends as far as Trefriw, the smelt and sturgeon have reached Llanrwst, and whales—(*Globicephala melaena*)—have been stranded well above Deganwy.

The tidal stretches, whose common flora has been mentioned, attract many birds of estuarine habits. Near Caerhûn in April we saw mallard, cormorants, gulls, curlews, redshank, and one species—the shelduck—which has not as yet been attributed to the region, but which links it with the peripheral and coastal localities to be described in the next Chapter.

BETWS-Y-COED

To give some idea of the wild-life of the Betws-y-coed neighbourhood at first hand, this Chapter concludes with observations made in June on the hillside above the Conway and about two miles from the village. The house, apart from its fine view up the Lledr, formed an ideal base for naturalists; its garden, full of conifers, soon merged, by way of a rhododendron shrubbery, with scrub oakwood up the steep rocks behind. To one side was a stand of pure oak, to the other an open bracken-clad hillside at the foot of some formidable rocks and screes. Below the main road were grass fields sloping steeply to the wooded Fairy Glen, while a few minutes walk uphill led out into a derelict farm amongst rocky knolls and pockets of bog; in fact, as good a selection of habitats as could be wished.

In the garden were nesting or had nested chaffinch, goldcrest, blackcap, song-thrush, blackbird, robin, dunnock and wren, with spotted flycatcher and wren again (Pl. 14a, p. 191) on the house itself. In the surrounding woodland and shrubbery were bullfinch, nuthatch, tree-creeper, great, blue, marsh- and long-tailed tits, willow-warbler, wood-warbler and garden-warbler, mistle-thrush and wood-pigeon. Swallows, swifts and probably goldfinches nested at a neighbouring farm. The only mammals we actually saw or heard were shrews and bats.

To get on terms with the inhabitants of the rocks, I slept out for two nights—the only two without rain during this particular visit. The expected nightjar was heard reeling at 11.0 p.m. b.s.t. the first evening. The second night, spent in the bracken below the screes, narrowed its territory down, the bird being vocal at quite close range at 4.0 a.m. The following evening we watched a male with bright white wing-patches chase off a much duller bird and then reel in triumph on a rocky bluff, before returning to its original area. Passing through this we were mobbed at close quarters by the female, which hovered, churring quietly, close to us, or, between her attacks, plumped down on stones in full view. Finally, with John Morris, who had shown us the tawny owl's nest (p. 274), we made a thorough search and Morris, who had found the nest the two previous seasons, flushed the female off two young in a small bare patch amongst the screes. As we were looking at them, both parents returned and scolded us, and we noticed that their reels were of a different pitch. But the nightjars were only one of the features of the hill. In the rocks there was a jackdaw colony; they were not active very early, though a peculiar subdued whistling heard at dawn may have been due to them. A pair of swifts were seen to fly up to the face and may have been nesting there; a stock-dove certainly had a nest-scrape behind a gorse-bush. As regards early song, song-thrush, willow-warbler and wren were singing before 4.30 a.m. on 21 June, while a redstart scolded me—as on another occasion a tawny owl—before singing itself. On the 23rd, song-thrush, blackbird, robin and wren sang by 4.0. a.m., but on both days the tree-pipit started rather later. On the 23rd a cuckoo called, while from a very early hour black-headed gulls were passing over the hill, evidently between Llyn Elsi and their feeding ground on the Denbighshire uplands.

The gentler slopes, with a grass-cover principally of fescue, proved on examination to be studded, between the bracken fronds, with twayblade and butterfly orchids. Here, too, glow-worms (*Melampyris noctiluca*) performed and completed the traditional picture of a summer dusk, suggested by reeling nightjars, kipping woodcock and hooting owls.

The moors on the hill-top were covered with fescue, gorse, bracken and heath-bedstraw, with pure patches of bell-heather; in the boggy pockets were rushes, cotton-grass and sphagnum mosses. Meadow-pipits and curlews were the birds of this different world, which looked east, away from the secluded hollow of Betws-y-coed, to the sweeps of moorland and high pasture beyond Pentrevoelas.

References for Chapter 11

Anon. (1909) (1924) (1945), Alexander (1945-47), Bingley (1800), Blagg (1896), Bland (1897) (1899), Brazil (1925), Brown (1925), Carr and Lister (1925), W. Davies (1797), Edwards (1920) (1941), J. C. S. Ellis (1945), Farmer (1925), Forrest (1907) (1919), Friend (1926-28), Giraldus Cambrensis (1188) (p. 439), Griffith (1895), Hall (1809-11), Hollom (1940), Hughes (1940), Kimmins (1933) (1934), Knight (1924), A. Lister (1925), G. Lister (1924), Newbery (1899) (1903), Peate (1934), Pennant (1784), Sharp (1899), South (1939), J. Williams (1830), W. Williams (1802), Wilson (1928) (1930) (1946-47), Witherby *et al.* (1938-41).

Communications from Hampson (1946), E. Roberts (1946), Smith (1946).

CHAPTER 12

THE COAST

THE contrast between the localities whose wild-life is now to be briefly described and the actual region of the National Park is tremendous; in the Park there is a relatively low concentration, at any rate of the larger and more visible forms, over a great area of highland country, much of it difficult of access. Many individual plant and animal species, as well as ecological groupings, of great interest are to be found, but they take a good deal of looking for, and, with the exception of the rock-face flora of Eryri, are not always immediately impressive. On the coasts of Caernarvonshire and Anglesey, however, the impact of life in each spot at the appropriate season is intense, and the observer need not be a skilled naturalist to realize that he is in the presence of important gatherings of plants and animals.

CREUDDYN

Probably the Creuddyn peninsula, which juts out on the east side of the Conway estuary, is the most remarkable from all points of view, not the least of which is the survival of so much life in the vicinity of a popular holiday resort like Llandudno, sprawling between the two limestone masses of Gogarth and Rhiwleden, the Great and Little Ormes. The area has attracted field-workers for years; Griffith did much of his collecting not only on the Ormes, but in the productive Gloddaeth Woods and on the dunes along the Conway. Records of all groups of invertebrates are fuller for the Creuddyn than for anywhere else in the county, while the birds, interesting rather for their numbers than for their rarity, are being constantly admired.

The limestone flora reveals some of its attractions as soon as one begins to follow the circular drive round the Great Orme: at the roadside in June the banks were covered with rockroses (*Helianthemum nummularium*), which indicated clearly the underlying conditions and made an ideal setting for the delicate spikes of that refined meadowsweet, the dropwort (*Filipendula hexapetala*, Pl. 25b, p. 286). On the cliffs above, the happily acclimatized red valerian (*Centranthus ruber*) shared the ledges with bushy wild cabbage plants (*Brassica oleracea*). Except for the clumps of nettles and slopes of bracken, two pests that it would be difficult to exclude from any floral Eden, hardly a plant was the same as those with which we were becoming familiar inside the boundaries of the Park.

The unusual species of the Creuddyn are many; a few of the more notable may be mentioned here. A number of cruciferous plants are maritime in habitat and are found on the Ormes, but the wild cabbage and rock pepperwort (*Hutchinsia petraea*) are probably the most interesting, while Evan Roberts has found the sea-kale (*Crambe maritima*), which Griffith apparently considered extinct, and, in the Resedaceae, wild mignonette (*Reseda lutea*), which Griffith calls "very rare."

The hoary rockrose (*Helianthemum canum*) occurs as well as its commoner relative. Among the Pinks are the maiden pink (*Dianthus deltoides*), found recently by Roberts, and the night-flowering and Nottingham catchflies (*Melandrium noctiflorum* and *Silene nutans* var. *smithiana*). The typical St. John's wort is *Hypericum montanum*, and the tree-mallow (*Lavatera arborea*), though not rare in Wales, is a striking plant of the rocks. Of the Leguminosae, however, the horseshoe vetch (*Hippocrepis comosa*), is scarce in Wales, its only other stations being in Glamorgan and Monmouthshire.

The Rose family here includes the rare spring cinquefoil (*Potentilla verna*), relative of the ubiquitous tormentils of Snowdonian grassland and woodland, and, most remarkable of all, the cotoneaster (*Cotoneaster integerrima*), which is native in Britain only in this one spot, where it was discovered by J. W. Griffith in 1783, and where, as Gardner reported in 1909, it has been on the verge of extinction. Cotoneasters are common garden shrubs and two introduced species, *C. microphylla* and *C. simonsii*, also grow on the Ormes.

The teazel (*Dipsacus fullonum*) in Creuddyn is only of interest because it is rare elsewhere in Caernarvonshire. The related small scabious (*Scabiosa columbaria*) is one of the typical restricted plants of the limestone, on which it is locally common. The large daisy family claims two rarities second only to the cotoneaster and now confined in Wales to this locality : the goldilocks aster (*Aster linosyris*) and spotted cat's-ear (*Hypochaeris maculata*). The milk thistle (*Silybum marianum*) is common in the peninsula, while, of the gentians, the yellow-wort (*Blackstonia perfoliata*) is found in several places, not only on the headlands. Of the numerous speedwells, the spiked (*Veronica hybrida*) is the limestone species, with a sporadic distribution up the west side of Britain from the

Avon gorge near Bristol to the Lake District. It occurs in nine Welsh counties, but the Creuddyn colony is the largest. The typical labiate is the white horehound (*Marrubium vulgare*).

The rare orchid of the Creuddyn is the dark-flowered helleborine (*Epipactis atropurpurea*), which is known in only two other Welsh counties, and is amongst Roberts's recent records. Another monocotyledon, the vernal squill (*Scilla verna*), is common on the Ormes, as on many Welsh headlands; its miniature bluebells lighting up the bare windswept sward earn it a special place in the affection of those whose appreciation of flowers is aesthetic as well as scientific, and to whom the abundance of attractive common species on the Ormes is as important as the existence there of the rarities.

Careful work has been done on the invertebrate fauna of the Creuddyn; the molluscs, for example, have been the subject of special papers, and of 43 freshwater and terrestrial genera recorded for Caernarvonshire in the National Museum, no less than 19 appear to be confined to the district, but whether this is due to the richness of the fauna or to a concentration of observers, is, as so often in natural history, not quite clear. Many insect genera and species are localized in this small area, and there have been individual occurrences of great rarity. Of particular interest is the evolution of two local races of butterflies on the limestone rocks of the vicinity. These are the subspecies *thyone* of the grayling (*Eumenis semele*) and *caernensis* of the silver-studded blue (*Plebejus argus*). These have been studied by J. A. Thompson, who is responsible for the subspecific titles, and whose information is quoted by Ford.

Both races are dwarf; the grayling is the only form found on the Great Orme, to which it is entirely confined. The nearest colony of the normal race is about a mile and a half away. The blue is even more interesting, for both its habitat—limestone cliffs instead of lowland heath—and its food plant, rockrose, are distinct from those of the normal British race, which occurs elsewhere in the county though not in the Park. Scattered colonies of *caernensis* are found outside the Creuddyn on other cliffs, and it associates with the brown argus (*Aricia agestis*), a typical butterfly of the limestone which does not extend to the highlands. Ford discusses the genetic variation responsible for the dwarfing and early emergence of the two races and explains that in the blue there is a colour distinction in both sexes from the normal subspecies (*Butterflies* p. 221).

PLATE 25

John Markham

b. Dropwort, *Filipendula hexapetala*, Great Orme's Head
June

John Markham

a. Marsh violet, *Viola palustris*, Ystumllyn
April

PLATE 26

John Markham

VAYNOL PARK; "wild" white cattle and red deer stags; the Snowdon range behind. September

The Ormes are the homes of large colonies of sea-birds, as those who
have been by sea from Merseyside along the North Wales coast must be
aware. Herring-gulls are everywhere, nesting above the road round
the Great Orme, as well as on the steeper faces; amongst them, in
June 1946, we noticed a very few lesser black-backed gulls. On the
higher ground are jackdaws, magpies, starlings, rock-pipits and house-
martins, the last nesting against the rock cutting of the road—one pair
were optimistically building at head height in full view of the many
passing visitors. On the ground which slopes away to the final drop
were more herring-gulls, with pairs of oyster-catchers and occasional
great black-backed gulls. But, as a sight, they were only subsidiary
to the great cliffs on which the cormorants, shags, guillemots, razorbills
and kittiwakes breed. The kittiwake is confined in Wales to the
Creuddyn, the coasts of Llŷn and Anglesey, and to Pembrokeshire,
although it has recently attempted to colonize Glamorgan.

The peregrine still nests on these headlands, as it did in Pennant's
day. His account of the locality is perhaps the first given by a naturalist.
He does not say much about the plants, and the cotoneaster was not
discovered until a few years after his visit, but the sea-birds obviously
impressed him. He describes the razorbills, guillemots and "gulls" on
the lowest parts, the cormorants, and finally the herons occupying
"the highest regions." This colony on the rocks, the only one so sited
in the county, has long vanished, as have the few black guillemots.
These he noticed with the puffins, which have never been numerous
here. The black guillemot is now only a very occasional visitor to Welsh
waters, while the chough has also been lost for some years as a breeding
species here. Pennant commented on the abundance of "rock-
pigeons" on Rhiwleden, and Forrest assumes that these were really
rock-doves, though R. W. Jones suggested that they might have been
stock-doves, which continued to nest there within recent memory.
Owing to inter-mixture with feral racing pigeons, the true status of
the rock-dove is extremely difficult to ascertain in Wales and England
today, but there seems no reason to doubt that in Pennant's time there
were at least some genuine rock-doves on the Ormes. On the credit side
of the ornithological balance is the arrival of the fulmar in the course of
its great expansion southward and eastward along the coasts of Britain.
After it had prospected the cliffs for several years, its nesting was proved
in 1945, this being also the first Welsh record. Gannets have appeared, in
1908 and 1941, and occupied ledges, but have not been proved to nest.

SN.   U

The bays and estuary of the Conway attract a number of ducks, grebes and a few divers, as well as waders on the shore. For many years Dr. Alex. Hamilton contributed an annual report on these to the Chester Society of Natural Science; they are mentioned in R. W. Jones's paper, and recently by I. Whittaker, who also states that the black redstart is a regular visitor to the Creuddyn. This was suggested earlier by Jones, whose information on the land birds of the peninsula shows some interesting contrasts to the highland region, for example the presence of corn- and cirl-buntings and the absence of the pied flycatcher. Of rarities, he recorded the first Caernarvonshire Richard's pipit in 1921, and the nesting of the white wagtail in 1926.

The sandhills on either side of the mouth of the Conway have a representative flora of dune type, though it is not as spectacular is that of the limestone. Their chief claim to natural-history fame is in the identification on them by C. S. Gregson of the sand-lizard. But there are no recent records, and the reptile is now probably confined on this side of Britain to a similar habitat in Lancashire. Of Amphibians, Forrest gives occurrences of the great warty newt in this part of Caernarvonshire, which is also the westward limit of the natterjack toad.

PUFFIN ISLAND

From the coast at Conway one looks across to the low hump of the variously named Ynys Seiriol, Priestholm or Puffin Island. This small island has been trodden by the feet of many eminent naturalists, from Ray onwards, and at its tip is the ruin of a former Biological Station. As the flora and fauna of such islets tend to be unstable in composition, some remarks on a visit in May 1946, when a permit was granted by the Baron Hill Estate, may be of interest.

The island is about half a mile long and less than a quarter of a mile at its widest; it lies roughly from north-east to south-west; the south-eastern slope, facing Caernarvonshire, is abrupt: rocky terraces alternate with steep, slippery banks. The summit ridge is bumpy, but fairly level, and falls away gently to the north-west, terminating, however, in cliffs more considerable than any on the other long side; the north-east point is also rocky. All along the top is a dense vegetation cap in which clumps and single bushes of elder (*Sambucus nigra*) rise from a bed of alexanders (*Smyrnium olusatrum*), a yellow-flowered umbellifer. Associated with these dominant species are nettles, henbane (*Hyoscyamus niger*), that sinister weed of waste places, burdock (*Arctium* sp.), wild arum (*Arum maculatum*) and ferns, with wood-sage, scentless mayweed (*Matricaria inodora*) and ground ivy (*Glecoma hederacea*) in open spaces and along the edge of the cap, above the open north-west slope, covered mainly with thrift and patches of bluebells. On the south-east terraces grow tufts of thrift with rock cress (*Spergula rupestris*) and pellitory (*Parietaria diffusa*). The scarcity of any sort of grass is striking, though Woodhead recorded a meadow-grass (*Poa* sp.) in a list of twenty-six species of flowering plants made in 1927. Some of these plants suggest an ecology strongly influenced by man, and we know that the alexanders, at least, are of ancient establishment, since their abundance impressed both Ray and Pennant; Aspden says they were planted by the monks of "Priestholm." Plants seen by Ray included scurvy-grass (*Cochlearia anglica*), samphire (*Crithmum maritimum*), sea beet (*Beta maritima*) and sea storksbill (*Erodium maritimum*); Pennant adds the gladdons (*Iris foetidissima*), but neither mentions the elder-bushes which are so conspicuous today.

Several wood-pigeons flew out of the elders, though I found no nests, and a wren sang. It is no doubt from this zone that earlier records of the nesting of small land-birds come. The accounts of Forrest, Orton, Coward—in an extremely readable article, giving much general information about the island—and Aspden include observations of starlings (in the ruins), sky-larks (singing over the island), meadow-pipits, whitethroat, song-thrush (bred 1903), blackbird (two nests found by Aspden and seen by us in 1939), robin (probably bred 1902), and dunnock, while Forrest had records of golden plover and corncrake, presumably on passage. Associated with the burrows are jackdaws, wheatears, stock-doves and sheld-duck, while ravens, carrion-crows and peregrine falcons have all nested on the cliffs.

Apart from the ubiquitous herring-gulls, the sea-birds also keep to fairly well-defined zones. The lesser black-backed gulls were concentrated in the thick vegetation of alexanders, which on a wet day proved something of a disadvantage owing to the obstructing effect of the wet foliage; I was able to catch and ring one bird before it could rise from its nest, although it flew away perfectly from my hand.

The great black-backed gulls keep to the barest rock, either on the summit ridge or at the foot of the north-west slope, above the sea-cliffs. This colony seems to have been built up since 1926. A few pairs of all three big gulls nested together on the slope, the zone of the oyster-catchers and of the puffin colony which gives the island its

modern name, though they were there when Ray visited it and
Pennant said the island swarmed with them, that they dispossessed the
rabbits and that peregrines preyed on their young. About a century
later, however, they fell on hard times, being exterminated, so Forrest
says, by shipwrecked rats, and deserted the island completely for several
years in the 1880's. Coward disbelieved this story, as based on a visit
made out of season; in any case the puffins soon returned in strength,
but have been subject to violent fluctuations: in 1903 fifty pairs was
the estimated population; by way of "very numerous" in 1905, it
increased to about 2,000 pairs (?) in 1907, when the birds were said to be
farmed. This may have led to a new nadir of about 20 pairs in 1911,
since when there has been a considerable increase. I should have put
the figure at several hundred pairs in 1946, rather less than my impression in 1939.

Razorbills (Pl. XXIIa, p. 291) breed all round the island at the
lowest level of cliffs, but the guillemots, which were intensively studied
by Aspden, are found on the bigger faces opposite the headland of
Penmon in Anglesey; they allow an extremely close approach, and
the sites do not compare with the vertiginous heights of the Ormes.

Neither cormorants nor shags were nesting on the island in 1919;
the shag is very scarce today, but I estimated the cormorant colony at
about 150 pairs, all along the south-east terraces. As with many of the
gulls, the nests are built largely of the stiff hollow stems of alexanders;
the birds are persecuted by local fishermen, and eggs in all the accessible
nests had been destroyed just before our visit, although the birds
continued to sit and in some cases had laid again already. The few
shags nest, quite apart, at the eastern end of the island, and, with rock-
pipits, make up the normal breeding association. Although seen in the
surrounding waters, there is no proof that the Manx shearwater has
ever nested.

Ray's list of the birds was "two sorts of sea-gulls, cormorants,
puffins . . . razorbills, guillems, scrays two sorts, which are a kind of
gull"; Pennant only noted the puffins, but Forrest and Orton allude
to the nesting of the kittiwake. There was a "fair-sized colony" when
Coward wrote and Aspden records a few pairs still in 1926.

The rabbit is the mammal of Puffin Island, though we only found
remains on our visit, and the numbers no doubt fluctuate; one persistent story, which was told us locally as almost topical, is of a fox being
marooned on the island and destroying all the rabbits. This actually

PLATE XXI

Eric Hosking

a. PINE MARTEN in captivity

John Markham

b. PINE MARTEN habitat. North Wales, June

PLATE XXII

C. A. Gibson-Hill

a. Razorbills on the cliff-top. Puffin Island, Anglesey, May

Eric Hosking

b. Little Tern approaching its nest. Taken in Norfolk, June

BIRDS OF THE COASTAL "SANCTUARIES"

happened in 1928, and Aspden records a fearful carnage amongst the gulls. On this visit he also watched a party of ravens systematically attacking puffins as they came out of their burrows. The invertebrate fauna was formerly closely studied and some interesting species identified, including two coccid bugs in the roots of thrift, and representatives of eight genera of mollusca.

MENAI AND VAYNOL

As one proceeds westward from Puffin Island, past Beaumaris into the narrowing Menai Strait, the shores become wooded, and the Anglesey side, with a number of small rocky islets, is particularly attractive. Conditions are very favourable to plant growth and, at Rhianva, the Verney family have built up a remarkable collection of shrubs from all over the world. The tall Mediterranean heaths (*Erica* spp.), flowering in early spring, are perhaps the most notable element. Only in this part of the island is the woodland community of birds well established. The marine life of the Strait has been thoroughly investigated, and has been described recently by L. H. Jackson. Ornithologically the Menai is famous as the place where the only example of the American hooded merganser (*Mergus cucullatus*) in Britain—there have been three in Ireland—was satisfactorily identified in 1830-31, and Forrest gives evidence of a second bird there in 1911. Another very rare vagrant from across the Atlantic, the yellow-billed cuckoo (*Coccyzus a. americanus*) was also recorded in the vicinity in 1899—one of about fourteen that have occurred in the British Isles.

Below the bridges, on the Caernarvonshire side, is the great park of Vaynol, where, by permission of Sir Michael Duff, we were able to visit and photograph the herds of wild cattle and deer established by his family. The park has been the home of a variety of wild animals, while the tench and other coarse fish have been introduced into the pools.

Forrest gives the rather complicated derivation of the Vaynol cattle; their ancestors were purchased from Sir John Campbell-Orde of Kilmory in Argyll, whose herd was apparently three-quarters "Park Cattle"—from Cadzow in Lanarkshire—and one-quarter Highland, which accounts for the shagginess of their coats. They arrived about 1870, and in 1896 a Cadzow bull was brought in, but was a failure, for coloured calves were occasionally dropped afterwards. Forrest describes the cattle as nervous of strangers, drawing together "with calves in the centre and bulls in the forefront." They would gallop away from the intruder, then wheel and watch him; if persistently approached, they would eventually charge. Solitary bulls might be dangerous and the cows hid their calves, which were very pugnacious. As Pl. 26 (p. 287) suggests, these alarming tendencies are not evident today. On seeing the car, in which we had prudently thought fit to remain, the herd trotted forward and right up to it, and one or two of the beasts began rubbing themselves on the mudguard. The difficulty, in fact, was to get them sufficiently far off to allow a general picture of the herd.

Altogether we counted 26 animals; the young bulls showed the shaggy Highland strain, the cows appeared smoother. Their horns varied a great deal and were reminiscent of both Ayrshires and Shorthorns. The coat is white, though with a slightly "rusty" appearance on heads and necks; black is confined to the margin of the muzzle, to the rims of the eyes and the eyelashes, to the ears and to the hocks, though it may be absent from these or broken up with white spots. In spite of their docility, it was not unimpressive to be looking at probable descendants of the original *Bos primigenius*. With them in the park were a herd of about fifty red deer, and the same number of fallow-deer, each with about twelve adult males. Several of the stags were magnificent animals, far superior to those seen in the wild state in Scotland today. The three species moved about indifferently amongst each other, and took little notice of human beings, though the deer reacted to a collie-dog. Seeing them with the Snowdon range as a background, we could not help feeling that the deer, at least, would be an ornament to the National Park, provided that they were confined to enclosures of wild country and not allowed to repeat the depredations of which old writers accuse the original stock.

LLANDDWYN AND NEWBOROUGH

Along both shores at the south-western end of the Menai there are sandhills, but those on the Anglesey shore are much greater in area and more important biologically: they form the famous Newborough Warren, at the western tip of which is the rocky Llanddwyn Island, about the same size as Priestholm, and a sanctuary of the Royal Society for the Protection of Birds. The island and part of the Warren is now proposed as a National Nature Reserve.

Llanddwyn was visited by Thomas Johnson (see p. 164), by Ray and by Pennant; it is lower than Puffin Island, but more irregular in outline and has preserved a more apparently natural vegetation, mainly a cover of grass, studded, in spring with vernal squill and wild pansy. There is an area of the brilliant bloody cranesbill (*Geranium sanguineum*) on the sandy landward end, and in the sheltered hollows leading down to the little beaches of the south side there is a thick growth of bracken, bluebells and even clumps of brambles; on the rocks sea-campion, rock cress and Portland spurge (*Euphorbia portlandica*) are prominent, with the universal thrift. Ray, whose visit was also in May, noted the vernal squill and also samphire, golden-samphire (*Inula crithmoides*), now at any rate a scarce plant in Wales, sea-lavender (*Limonium vulgare*) and the fern, sea spleenwort (*Asplenium marinum*). Pennant has nothing to say of the botany.

Llanddwyn has been famous as a ternery, but apparently, as often happens with these volatile summer visitors, there has recently been a movement away, and large colonies have been forming on the mainland. Certainly none were nesting when we visited the island at the end of May 1946, though some common terns had arrived. The common species of the sanctuary appear to be rock-pipit, oyster-catcher, lapwing, ringed plover and herring-gull, while many cormorants nest on a stack separate from the main island.

Crossing the Warren to the island—the more usual route is by boat from Caernarvonshire—we noted the profusion of wild pansies and, on a second visit to the area in June, of centaury, here dwarfed in habit, two plants which impressed Johnson over 300 years ago. The Warren is dry and therefore has a less varied flora than the dunes of South Wales with their wet hollows. Marram-grass (*Ammophila arenaria*) is generally dominant over the hummocks and ridges, and Pennant remarked that the chief industry of Newborough was making mats and ropes out of "Sea Reed Grass" or *Rhosir morhesg*, which had been protected by Queen Elizabeth because of its sand-fixing qualities. Mr. Hyde informs me that ropes made as recently as 1934 are in the Botany Department of the National Museum of Wales. The dwarf willow (*Salix repens*) is locally dominant in dense patches, while the bottoms between the dunes are often pebbly and devoid of all vegetation. Here and there stand plants of hound's tongue (*Cynoglossum officinale*), viper's bugloss (*Echium vulgare*), groundsel (*Senecio sylvaticus*) and ragwort (*S. jacobaea*), the last assuring that the cinnabar moth (*Hypocrita jacobaeae*) will be abundant. On the landward side of the Warren there is more soil; heath and meadow plants begin to appear, and it was here that our eyes were caught at a distance by a close white circle of mountain everlasting (see p. 192).

As well as the cinnabar, the common blue butterfly was flying over the dunes in May. Rabbits were everywhere, and in one locality were a number of black individuals. The birds were those normally associated with the habitat: sky-lark, meadow-pipit, wheatear, sheld-duck, stock-dove, oyster-catcher and lapwing, but there were also several curlews and herring-gulls, both of which were obviously nesting: on the Abermenai Point, which is a tongue of the Warren jutting out towards Caernarvon, we found some herring-gulls' nests, consisting of depressions in the sand, surrounded by a frame of marram roots. Somewhere here Ray found the sea-cottonweed, now extinct in Wales, and the sea-stock (*Matthiola sinuata*). On the way to Abermenai the Warren becomes wetter near the shore, which means both a growth of rushes and the addition of the redshank to the birds; at the end of June we found a number of plants of the orchid *Epipactis dunensis* (formerly regarded as a variety of *E. leptochila*), which, in Wales, occurs only in Anglesey and Monmouthshire.

The tern colony in this neighbourhood was known to H. Ecroyd Smith in 1856 (see p. 168). In 1946 it was moderately flourishing: our estimate was 70 pairs of common terns and 40 of little terns (see Pl. XXIIIb, p. 298) with oyster-catchers and ringed plovers nesting amongst them. Coward's article "West of Llanfair P.G." also deals with the Newborough district.

YSTUMLLYN

The final locality in this peripheral tour of the National Park lies across the backbone of Llŷn. This great south-west-pointing peninsula comprises nearly a third of Caernarvonshire, and ends in Ynys Enlli (Bardsey Island), the natural history of whose few acres seems to have been more thoroughly investigated than that of any other part of the county, except the Creuddyn. The southern coast of Llŷn makes an angle with the coast of Merioneth at the mouth of the Glaslyn; two miles west of this, at the foot of the isolated Moel-y-gest, a landmark from many directions, lies the permanently flooded area called Llyn Ystumllyn or Ystumllyn Marsh, which is distinct in character from any habitat yet examined (Pl. 27b, p. 302). Our visits were made by kind permission of the owner, Colonel M. I. Williams-Ellis.

Superficially the marsh is composed of a triangle of reed-beds with two main pools of open water, divided by a low island. On closer inspection, several well-marked zones appear. At the lowest level are the pools, in which grow rafts of white water-lilies, bogbean, water bistort (*Polygonum amphibium*), and the tall, dark-green *Scirpus tabernaemontani*. The pools may be edged by the reed-beds, by mud and short grass or by wet sedge (*Carex rostrata*) patches, with clumps of yellow iris scattered throughout. In places the reeds thin out to wet areas with tussocks of moor-grass, sedge (*Carex curta*), plants of bog-myrtle, isolated sallow bushes, and clumps of brambles on the ridges formed by the excavations from old drains, which criss-cross the whole area. Elsewhere the reed-beds become fairly dry with a succession to groups and copses of sallow. Above the grass margins to the pools is the rush zone, while in places there are patches of pure sedge, quite dry underfoot. On the central island and the surrounding higher ground are dry zones, of rough grasses, of gorse and heather, or of gorse and bracken.

The nesting birds of Ystumllyn show varying adaptation to these divisions of the habitat. In the lacustrine zone is sited a large colony of black-headed gulls; the 1938 Survey (see p. 261) accorded this colony an indefinite status, as the nests were said to be regularly destroyed. But in May 1946, we estimated the strength at 400 to 800 pairs, practically all of whose nests were in bogbean or scirpus (Pl. 27a, p. 302), showing a very marked preference for this zone; only one or two nests were in rushes alongside an old drain. Coots are the other common species here, favouring the scirpus beds, as does the great-crested grebe in what seems to be its only breeding station in the county, and presumably the little grebe, though we failed to obtain current evidence of its nesting.

In the next zone, that of the pool margin, the coot is still the principal bird, found in the reed-beds, where they stand in water, and in the iris clumps, but this is also the zone of the moorhen and of the mute swan. Lapwings and oyster-catchers nest right to the edge in the open ground, while the wet sedges may attract reed-buntings and duck. At one remove from the pools, in the tussock and myrtle zone, are found the passerine birds: reed-buntings, sedge-warblers and the scarcer grasshopper-warbler; possibly duck and pheasants, and, since the sedge-warbler is its most numerous potential fosterer in the habitat, the cuckoo must be included here. In the pure reed-beds, as they progress from wet to dry, there is not much sign of birds actually in occupation of territory, though one would expect to find the water-rail if it does occur—its status in Caernarvonshire, according to Forrest, is that of a resident—while the fact that there is no evidence for the reed-warbler, in such a perfect locality for it, suggests that the district is really outside its range and that reports of its appearance elsewhere in the county should be carefully investigated.

The sallow clumps are the special zone of the lesser redpoll and may provide sites for birds not typically of the association, such as wrens and wood-pigeons, both of which were seen in them. The rushes are the principal zone for reed-buntings, mallard, teal and redshank, probably also of snipe, which are not very common in the nesting season, and of pheasants. The shoveler nests quite freely—Mr. Speake has found up to a dozen nests in a good season—and has an interesting preference for the short-grass zone, where the birds can be seen quite easily sitting on their nests; the redshank is found here also, while the other rush-zone birds will be found in the dry sedges.

Of the higher zones, the short grass, mainly fescue-bent, attracts sky-larks and meadow-pipits; the gorse and heather of the island, linnets and duck, which are also found in bracken and thick cover at some distance from the marsh; in fact, Speake considers that the mallard may nest in pockets a long way away, bringing their young down to Ystumllyn.

Such are the main relationships of plant cover and bird population briefly indicated as the result of one visit and the information supplied by Mr. Speake. Ystumllyn is an area which would repay detailed ecological study of other forms of life, of whose abundance, from dragonflies through sticklebacks to otters (of which we saw many traces), there is plenty of evidence. Apart from the dominant plants, there are many other species of interest, but none is more delightful than the marsh violet (*Viola palustris*, Pl. 25a, p. 286) which brings an early touch of delicate colour.

However, it is probably as the bird sanctuary that the marsh will be regarded, should it ever find itself scheduled as a Nature Reserve, though it is not amongst those proposed in the recent White Paper. We saw over 50 species on or over it in April and May, and M. C. Wainwright, who has watched it for a number of years, has informed me of many passage and winter visitors. It seems that whooper swans are now seen annually, while white-fronted geese are regular and Canada geese occasional. Garganey, pintail (both seen by us), and scaup, which were present in strength in January 1947, are the more interesting ducks; the possibility of the first two remaining to nest, and thus to swell Caernarvonshire's somewhat meagre total of breeding waterfowl, cannot be overlooked. Of individual rarities, A. W. Boyd and James Fisher saw a little gull in 1931, Wainwright has seen a bittern, Speake described to me what was evidently a marsh-harrier, perhaps one of those which nested in North Wales in 1945, and he once picked up a rose-coloured starling at Wern, though this is not strictly on the Marsh; it is interesting that another was recorded near Criccieth in 1945.

There was time to make a survey only of the birds in the area round Ystumllyn in 1946, but this resulted in direct proof of the breeding of 34 species and strong evidence for at least another 45; in fact it would not be too sanguine to suggest that over 80 different kinds nest regularly on some 3,000 acres, covering the marsh, and the woodlands, uplands and rocks of Moel-y-gest to the east, which combine to provide an ecological Eryri in miniature. Only the full moorland association (see pp. 259 and 262) of birds is absent, though individual members of it occur. If other forms of life show anything like the same concentration, then the claims of the area to preservation are strong indeed. For the present, however, having watched Mr. Speake at work, we feel that it is under adequate protection.

The whole area of Tremadoc Bay has yielded many interesting ornithological records since Britain's first sand-grouse (*Syrrhaptes paradoxus*) in July 1859. Caton-Haigh made copious observations during the years he lived in the neighbourhood, and some of the waders reported on the Glaslyn may actually have been over the boundary of the National Park region, for this is one end of the flight-line which he and other observers since have traced northward between the main Snowdon range and the Nant Conwy moorlands. But enough has been written to show the natural-history importance of the Caernarvonshire coast, and, though apparently so different from that of the region with which this section has been mainly concerned, the wild-life of both is closely related; gulls fly to the tops of the Snowdonian mountains, where are growing some of the same plants which flower by their nests on Puffin Island; the otters of Ystumllyn may penetrate to the highest tarns where fish are found, and, as we have seen, the foxes of the Moelwyns proverbially hunt to the extremity of Llŷn.

References for Chapter 12

Anon. (1909) (1915), Aspden (1928), Boyd and Fisher (1931), *British Birds* (1919-47), Campbell (1947), Colling and Brown (1946), Coward (1922),

Fisher and Waterston (1941), Fisher and Vevers (1943), Fisher and others (1946), Ford (1945), Forrest (1907) (1919), Gardner (1909), Gresley-Jones (1910), Griffith (1895), Hamilton (1920-30), Hyde and Wade (1934), Jackson (1940), Johnson (1641), Jones (1910) (1913) (1922) (1926) (1928), Lowe (1925), Orton (1913), Pennant (1784), Pyefinch (1937) (1943), Ray (1846), E. B. Roberts (1925) (1930), Roebuck (1884), Tomlin (1886), Whittaker (1942), Wild Life Conservation Committee (1947), Witherby and others (1938-41), Woodhead (1928).

Communications from E. Roberts (1946), Speake (1946), Wainwright (1947),

PLATE XXIII

Eric Hosking

a. Dipper: a characteristic position. Radnorshire, May

Eric Hosking

b. Grey Wagtail: female at nest. Radnorshire, May

BIRDS OF FAST-FLOWING WATER

PLATE XXIV

John Markham

a. IRON AGE FORTRESS: pointed stones used as a defence work below the walls of Pen-y-gaer, Nant Conwy

John Markham

b. BIRTHPLACE OF BISHOP MORGAN: Gwibernant. Morgan (born *c*. 1540) was the first to complete the translation of the Bible into Welsh

III
THE HISTORICAL BACKGROUND

By Richenda Scott

of the main Prehistoric Periods as represented in Wales

STONE AGE

PALEOLITHIC
Man first entered Wales perhaps between   15,000 and 10,000 B.C.

MESOLITHIC   *circa*   8,000–2,500 B.C.

NEOLITHIC   „   2,500–2,000 B.C.
Neolithic A culture (Windmill Hill)
Neolithic B culture (Peterborough)

BRONZE AGE

EARLY BRONZE AGE
Invasions of Beaker people and develop-
ment of Food Vessels   „   2,000–1,500 B.C.

MIDDLE BRONZE AGE
Development of "native" Bronze Age   „   1,500–1,000 B.C.

LATE BRONZE AGE
Invasions   „   1,000 B.C.

EARLY IRON AGE
IRON AGE A
(Hallstatt-La Tène I culture)
Iron Age Invasions   500 B.C.

IRON AGE B
(La Tène II)   „   300 B.C.

IRON AGE C
(La Tène III and the Belgae settlers)   „   50 B.C.

ROMAN PERIOD   43-*circa* 400 A.D.

Based on the Table given on p. xii of *The Guide to the Collection of the Prehistory of Wales* in the National Museum of Wales, Cardiff, written by W. F. Grimes, M.A., F.S.A., and published by the National Museum of Wales and by the Press Board of the University of Wales, 1939.

CHAPTER 13

INTRODUCTION TO
THE HISTORICAL BACKGROUND

THE following chapters attempt to trace in broadest outline the economic and social development of North-West Wales together with those political movements that had a decisive effect on the evolution of life and manners in the region. No one can understand that development, for instance, without some knowledge of the Anglo-Norman impact on the country, the Edwardian conquest and its sequel over two hundred and fifty years later in the Act of Union, or of the shattering effect of Glyndwr's revolt on the social life of the countryside. Restrictions of space have made a rigid selection of material necessary throughout, and no one is more conscious of the many sins of omission than the writer. This is but a brief introductory sketch, written in the hope that it may awaken in some readers at least an interest in the history of the Principality which they can pursue at leisure.

Reference will be found in the text and in the bibliography to the books and the manuscript sources consulted. I am particularly indebted to the invaluable work of Sir Cyril and Lady (Aileen) Fox in the archaeological chapters and also to Mr. Colin Gresham's detailed study of the area, and, in the medieval section, to Sir John Lloyd's two volumes on *The History of Wales to the Edwardian Conquest*, to Mr. T. P. Ellis's *Welsh Tribal Law and Custom in the Middle Ages* and to Dr. E. A. Lewis's books and articles. My attention was only drawn to the recent valuable work by Dr. T. Jones-Pierce, chiefly in the form of articles in the Caernarvonshire Historical Society's Transactions, after the fifth chapter was already in draft, and there was only time to insert the brief references on pp. 339 and 359 and slightly modify some of my remarks on the Welsh tribal system on p. 338 in the light of his researches.

Personal thanks and acknowledgments are due, however, to many individuals for their generous help and advice. The Librarian of the National Library of Wales, Sir William Ll. Davies, and his assistants gave ready access to much valuable manuscript material and allowed me to reproduce the map of the tribal divisions of the region as Map 6 on p. 344; Dr. Tom Richards, late librarian of the University College of North Wales, Bangor, allowed me to use the very fine collection of estate papers under his charge relating to the area; Muriel Hicks, assistant Librarian of Friends House, London, gave much patient help in tracing obscure volumes that I wished to consult and procuring them for me through the Central Library service. Mr. Bob Owen of Croesor poured out the wealth of his knowledge in an evening's delightful conversation, and allowed me to use some of his transcripts of sixteenth- and seventeenth-century wills; while Mr. Clough Williams-Ellis of Plas Brondanw generously lent me the personal account book of his ancestor William Williams and the MS. autobiography of Samuel Holland, on which I have drawn so freely in Chapter 22. Dr. Elfyn Hughes gave up a day of his time to show me some of the medieval and sixteenth-century sites in the lower Conway Valley and gave me permission to quote from his valuable paper in the Caernarvonshire Historical Society's transactions, 1940. My collaborator, Dr. F. J. North, provided much useful material on the history of the slate industry, read my chapters and made some helpful suggestions, while his colleague at the National Museum of Wales, Dr. Nash-Williams, very kindly read the early chapters on the archaeology of the region. My husband and Mr. Duncan Cameron of the Ministry of Agriculture and Fisheries gave much time to discussing the problems of rural Wales and made many helpful suggestions for the final chapter.

Last, but by no means least, my deepest thanks are due to two personal helpers without whose aid the work could never have been achieved in the time, and in the difficulties of a wet summer. My friend, Norah Williamson, drove me day after day, risking her car over the rough mountain roads, to enable the photographer, Mr. John Markham, and myself to cover the area in the time at our disposal, while her interest in the work was a never-failing source of encouragement. And when we returned, however wet we were from tramping over the hills after abandoning the car, Mrs. Thomas of Betws-y-coed was always there to welcome us with unfailing cheerfulness and attend to our needs, taking from us the burden of domestic work to leave us free for the venture of writing the book.

PLATE 27

C. A. Gibson-Hill

a. BLACK-HEADED GULLS on their nests in Ystumllyn Marsh. May

John Markham

b. YSTUMLLYN MARSH, a locality of great interest to the naturalist on the edge of the proposed National Park. April

PLATE 28

John Markham

a. The entrance to the tomb, Bryn Celli Ddu, Anglesey. June

John Markham

b. The tomb at Capel Garmon, showing the entrance passage, the central and eastern chambers and a corner of the great capstone still roofing the western chamber. July

MEGALITHIC TOMBS

CHAPTER 14

THE FIRST COLONIZERS
OF NORTH-WEST WALES AND
THE ROMAN INVASION

UNTIL man has learned to harness natural forces to his purpose, and by growth of knowledge and skill and the development of improved tools or machinery to control his environment, his choice of habitation is dominated by the physical features of any territory which he enters. That choice is limited by such factors as topography, climate and prevailing winds, soil-types with their differing covers of forest, moorland or marsh, land drainage and water supply. At the dawn of the Neolithic period the windswept coastlands and cliffs of Wales were probably fairly open ground, but the immediate hinterland and the hills rising from it were clad with an unbroken forest cover, reaching perhaps to a height of 1,500 feet in the inland valleys, though the prevailing westerly winds would possibly restrict tree growth to a lower level on the seaward slopes of Caernarvonshire. Sessile oak predominated, but alder was found on the wetter patches, and birch on the upper forest fringes. The areas sufficiently open to invite settlement would be very limited to a people whose most effective implements were a stone axe or an antler pick. Therefore, in this county, traces of the earliest colonizers are found on the coasts of Llŷn and Harlech Bay, or on the high flanks of the mountain valleys.

In this corner of Britain human habitation was comparatively late. There was little to attract Palaeolithic man, for the hills of Caernarvon offered no ready supplies of flint for his weapons; until the art of grinding and polishing stone tools arose in the Neolithic age men made little use of the hard igneous outcrops which do occur here. We must, however, remember that considerable subsidence has taken place along the North Wales coast and in Cardigan Bay, initiated probably not later than the third millenium B.C., though legends of this drowning of the land have lingered so persistently in connection with those areas, that the subsidence has often been attributed mistakenly to a date within historic times. It is possible that stray hunters, wandering into the region for a period, or later Aurignacian cave-dwellers, seeking a home in the cliffs of the submerged coast, may have left traces of their passing which are now lost beneath the sea. Also, the great "factory" of the New Stone Age, which extends for a mile or two round the mountain of Penmaen-mawr between the 500- and 1,000-foot contours, may have been worked by seasonal bands of craftsmen from earlier Neolithic villages in Britain before the arrival of the first definite settlers on the coastal fringe of North Wales. The pottery found in association with the tools and weapons fashioned here shows that two main streams of Neolithic culture, deriving respectively from a western and a north-eastern European source, met and mingled on this bleak hillside. Axes from this floor, made from the felsitic rock commonly termed Penmaenmawr granite, were traded widely in Wales, and specimens have been found as far afield as Wessex and the Midlands.

At the beginning of the Neolithic phase, the Welsh coast-line followed much the same course as at the present day, allowing for minor alterations in the succeeding centuries. The country as a whole formed a considerable part of the highland zone, as defined by Sir Cyril Fox, who distinguishes two main regions into which Britain divides south of the Forth-Clyde isthmus. The one is the western and northern part of the country, an area of hill and high moorland, the other, the southern and eastern lowland zone, with its wide river estuaries opening to the North Sea and the English Channel. The damp clay soil of the Midlands, bearing a triangular stretch of heavy oak forest, which reached from the mouth of the Severn to that of the Dee, was a further barrier between Wales and new influences spreading from the lowlands. Contact with the outer world for the earliest dwellers on the Caernarvon hills lay principally by sea; but there was some intercourse overland with the upland settlers of the Derbyshire hills and the Yorkshire wolds, and later a certain amount of infiltration along the flanks of the Severn and Dee valleys shows that a few intrepid explorers and traders dared the perils of the midland forest and broke in direct from the east.

The geographic position of Wales on the western fringe of Britain was of paramount importance for her cultural development at this time. The visitor who is fortunate enough to win to the crest of Snowdon on a clear day will realize at a glance that he stands here in a frontier land. At his feet lies the long sweep of the coast-line, visible from St. David's Head to Morecambe Bay, while the map will carry his vision beyond, southwards to the peninsulas and islands of the Atlantic seaboard, Cornwall, Brittany, the Morbihan, Spain, and northwards to the clustering islands, the broken, deeply indented coastline of Scotland, terminating in Caithness, the last landfall before striking across the open sea to Orkney and Scandinavia. Westward, the hills of Wicklow are misty on the horizon; north-west, beyond the flat expanse of Anglesey, the Isle of Man is a darker shadow on the waters. He is, in fact, surveying a large stretch of the western sea-route, which formed one of the most important lines of communication between the Mediterranean and the North in the Megalithic and early Bronze Ages, and again in the first centuries of the Christian revival after the Saxons had overrun lowland Britain. As he turns to look east and south-east, he is confronted, on the other hand, with range after range of hill and moorland crowding in upon him, cleft only by deep and narrow valleys. Time and again in the history of the country the mountain massif of Wales, and the Snowdon range in particular, have proved the final retreat of earlier settlers, the last stronghold of the island against the invader sweeping in from north and east across the midland plain and the Cheshire flats. For this reason, strands of earlier civilizations and traditions were preserved in the hill districts; by the time the new techniques, ideas and manner of life of the last intruder penetrated to these lonely regions, the native tradition had become strong enough to fuse with and absorb the new, and even at moments to re-assert itself in local arts and customs. At the present day, the hills of Wales preserve some of the last remnants of an indigenous peasant culture in these islands, and a language far older than the English tongue; we find here a people whose traditions, customs and way of thought, though enriched by contact with the foreigner from overseas or across the border, Roman or Norman, Irish or Anglo-Saxon, are yet essentially their own, the outcome of their long history, experience and isolation.

The first colonizers of North-West Wales, who rowed their narrow, dug-out boats into the creeks and inlets of her coast somewhere about the year 2,000 B.C., represent the Mediterranean and Megalithic phase of the New Stone Age culture. They arrived either direct from Brittany, Spain or Portugal, or as a secondary movement of population from earlier colonies founded in Ireland. Their great, chambered tombs are distributed along the western seaboard of Britain, particularly in the peninsulas of Cornwall and South and North Wales, and on the hill slopes of the immediate hinterland. These dark, sturdy people, with their long, narrow heads, who have left their physical imprint stamped indelibly on the modern population in many parts of Wales,[1] brought the Neolithic culture to its final heights. By her geographical position, Wales was swung into the mainstream of this advance, and was linked by a common tradition of burial customs and religious ritual with a civilization that spread from Sardinia and the Mediterranean lands to Denmark and Sweden. The chambered tomb, ancestor of the modern family vault, designed for communal burial of the dead over a long period, developed various forms and characteristics in different areas, which there is no room to trace here. Fifty still exist in Anglesey and twelve in Caernarvonshire, those on the mainland being mainly concentrated in Llŷn; but many of the graves have been swept away by later builders and road-makers, who found a quarry ready to hand in their great stone slabs. Within the region of the National Park, two are still to be found; one, a gaunt cromlech, stands at the height of nearly 1,000 feet on the ridge of hills rising behind Aber and Llanfair-fechan, through which the pass of Bwlch-y-ddeufaen opens to the moorlands above Ro-wen and the Conway valley below. The second lies on the east, or Denbighshire, side of the river at a height of 800 feet, built on a shelf of the Hiraethog moorlands where these begin to fall towards the Conway. Here, near the village of Capel Garmon above Betws-y-coed and Llanrwst, is a single tomb, believed to be the survivor of three on this site, while two and a half miles to the east across the moors is the long barrow at Nebo. A third group formerly existed in the neighbourhood at Cerrig-y-druidion on the Pentrevoelas uplands.

The tomb at Capel Garmon (Pl. 28b, p. 303) is a very fine example of a passage grave, the passage leading into a central chamber with transepts on either hand, built in the long side of an oval or oblong mound. It is a late neolithic structure of elaborate design. The covering mound of earth and stones can still be deciphered in part, though the entrance passage and two of the chambers lie open to the sky. The third, at the western end of the mound, has its massive capstone[2] in position. The dry stone rubble walling which filled the interstices between the great uprights, was partially restored when the tomb was excavated by the Office of Works in 1930, but the original can still be

[1] An anthropometric survey carried out by Dr. Elwyn Davies in 1939 showed that in the vale of Conway and the commotes of Arfon and Eifionydd the proportion of people bearing these physical characteristics was 36 per cent and 38 per cent respectively of the total population, while in Anglesey it was 41 per cent of the total.

[2] The Megalithic burial chamber was built of three or more great upright stones, on which rested another massive stone slab, forming the roof of the chamber, and known as the capstone.

traced here and there. A most interesting feature of the monument is the recessed or "horned" false entrance at the eastern end of the mound, sealed by stone slabs. It gives no access to the burial chambers, but the slabs are backed simply by the filling of the mound; the entrance passage, fifteen feet in length, is on the south. The purpose of the false door is uncertain, but Dr. Mortimer Wheeler suggests that it may have been devised to mislead marauders, either physical or spiritual. A false entrance has often been noted in the Egyptian *mastaba*, a rectangular brick or stone tomb, and three of the Cotswold long barrows have this curious feature. The Capel Garmon tomb had been opened and considerably despoiled many years before the scientific investigation of 1930; the western chamber was used as a stable in the eighteenth century. Only a few sherds of pottery were found, some of a late Neolithic date, and some fragments of bone, human and animal, the latter probably those of a cow and a sheep. At the base of the chamber walls a number of white quartz pebbles had been scattered; we find their counterparts occasionally on the graves of a modern cemetery in the country districts of Wales.

Of the powerful religious impulse prompting the great effort in labour and organization necessary to erect these massive burial chambers and the ideas that lay behind it, we know little or nothing. Some archaeologists have believed they may represent the enclosing darkness of the womb with the promise of a new life into which the dead would be reborn. Occasionally traces are left of burial rites of a spectacular and grim nature; in the great circular mound of Bryn Celli Ddu (Pl. 28a, p. 303), which stands in the parish of Llandaniel, Anglesey, and is one of the most impressive of the chambered tombs remaining in the British Isles, the marks of fire which were found all over the central area, and the large deposits of cremated and unburnt bones, suggested to the excavator, Mr. W. J. Hemp, the possibility of human sacrifice on a large scale rather than a series of successive burials, while there was evidence that the tomb had been finally sealed after the obsequies.

The Neolithic phase of our history, which probably endured only for five hundred years or so in Wales, was a time of revolutionary change in customs and manners. It was a period of intense intellectual vigour and activity as men learned for the first time to master the domestic arts of grain-growing, stock-rearing and pottery-making, and to build for themselves a fixed and abiding home. It was doomed to undergo great changes almost before it reached its full flowering, by the invasion of new explorers, the Beaker people, who arrived on the eastern and southern shores of Britain from the neighbourhood of the Rhine delta about 2,000 B.C. and quickly overran a large part of the British Isles. Nevertheless, our Neolithic ancestors were the pioneers of cultural advance, the founders of a way of life which, in the main, is still pursued today by the farmer and peasant of western Europe, despite the changes and modifications wrought by man's inventiveness in the intervening centuries.

The Beaker people, so called from the distinctive vessel which we find buried with their dead, were apparently not acquainted with the use of metals when they reached our shores. But many centuries before metal tools and weapons had been in use among the great riverine civilizations of Egypt and Mesopotamia, and at about the time of their arrival, traders from the Continent, where knowledge of metallurgy had gradually spread, were introducing flat daggers of copper and bronze into Southern Britain, which were purchased by the inhabitants. A native school of metallurgists was also growing up in Ireland around the copper deposits of Kerry; flat axe-heads of copper, and the decorative gold collar or *lunula*, wrought from the alluvial gold of Wicklow, were filtering into North Wales from this source. The new colonizers in the highland zone continued for some time to use stone weapons; only two metal daggers have been found in association with the Welsh beakers, one of these being in Anglesey, but they bought ornaments of Irish gold.

The Beaker people penetrated to North-West Wales by an overland route, probably across the Shropshire hills; all the examples of their characteristic pottery found here are late, with a debased form of ornamentation. In the Capel Garmon tomb red fragments of a beaker, dating to about 1500 B.C. were found, a clear indication that the new immigrants had by that time reached the Denbighshire moorlands and settled on a previous Megalithic site. They found it expedient, probably for political reasons as Sir Cyril Fox suggests, to adopt the burial rites of the displaced Megalithic chieftain, instead of resorting to their own custom of individual interment beneath a round barrow, an interesting example of the continuity of tradition in the Welsh uplands.

The Beaker folk were a dominant, restless people, largely pastoralists and hunters, and little inclined to agriculture. As the course of events at Capel Garmon shows, they subdued the earlier, Neolithic population, took over their grazing grounds, and assumed the rôle of leadership in the little community. Traces of them linger, perhaps, in the folklore of this region of Snowdon, in the fair-haired, handsome and light-complexioned fairies who hunted through the forests on grey horses, or sported on the hills above Betws-y-coed in the evening light, floating down into the abyss of the Fairy Glen when their dances were over to vanish among the rocks without harm.

During the next few centuries the Beaker and Neolithic populations of the highland zone were settling down together in a fusion of tradition and custom, erecting the great stone circles which are found here and there on the hills of the English countryside in honour of the new religion that looked to the open skies and the sunrise for its inspiration. In the ceramic arts the indigenous Neolithic culture reappears in the evolution of the Food Vessel, a somewhat clumsy native development of the Beaker forms. It is probable that the Food Vessel people were active leaders in the growing trade in metal goods; the most common type of this pottery found in Wales is of northern origin, the design probably handed on along the trade routes together with the exchange of tools and weapons. Save for the intrusion of a band of colonists in Wessex, brought hither by fresh upheavals and shifting of peoples on the Continent, the Early and Middle Bronze Ages in these islands were a time of comparative quiet, of a fusion and blending of the existing cultures introduced here, and of expanding trade with the Continent, uninterrupted by the disturbance of further large-scale immigrations. A change in religious ideas with, perhaps, a more spiritual conception of the after-life, is witnessed by the practice of cremating the dead, a custom which had become generally adopted throughout the country, even in our remote region of the north Welsh hills, by the Middle Bronze Age. The cinerary urn with its overhanging rim was probably developed in this country from the Food Vessel pottery forms, though in the present state of knowledge its place of origin is as yet unknown. On a farm situated on rising ground a quarter of a mile to the north of Brynkir station, ten cinerary urns were found in 1821, filled with bones and ashes, while one contained a piece of copper. A similar group of these clay sepulchral urns was disclosed on another farm three and a

Map 5.—The Historical Geography of Snowdonia

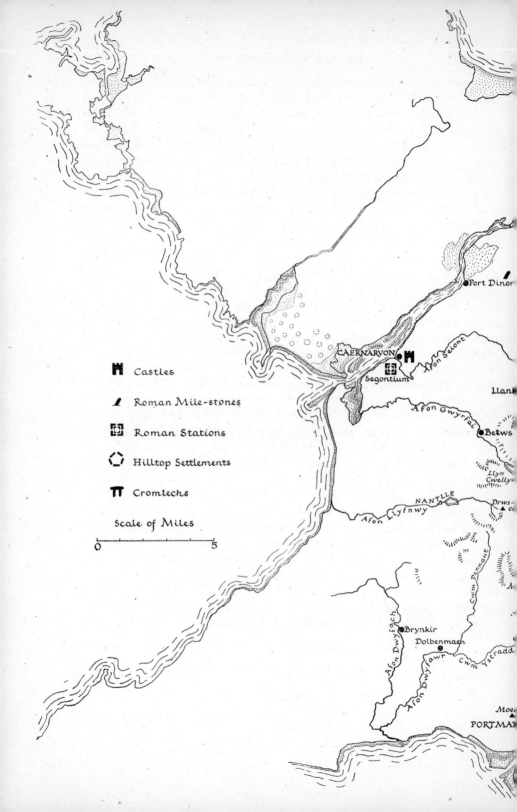

⊞	Castles
◢	Roman Mile-stones
⊞	Roman Stations
⬡	Hilltop Settlements
⊓	Cromlechs

Scale of Miles

0   5

Port Dinor

CAERNARVON

Afon Seiont

Segontium

Llan

Afon Gwyrfai

Betws

Llyn
Cwelly

NANTLLE

Drws-
co

Afon Llyfnwy

Cwm Pennant

M

Afon Dwyfach

Brynkir

Dolbenmaen

Cwm Ystradd

Afon Dwyfawr

Moe

PORTMA

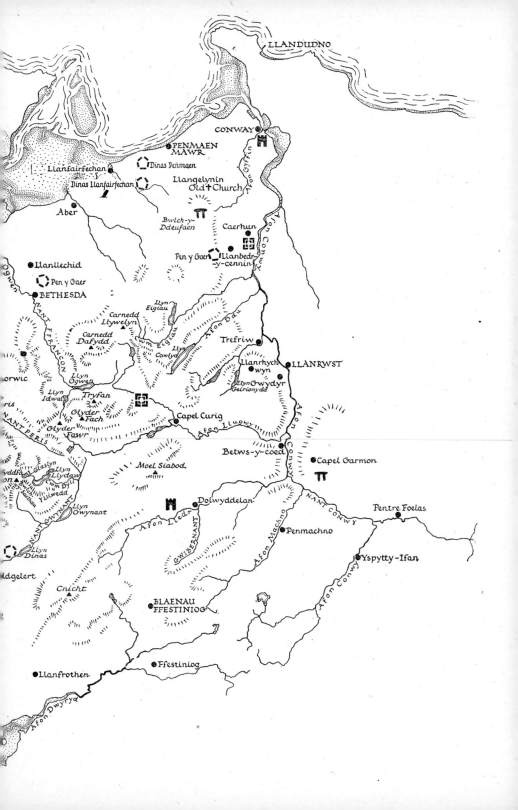

half miles to the south east of Brynkir station in 1850, a small bronze knife appearing among the ashes. Other cinerary urns within the National Park or on its borders have been discovered on the slopes of Penmaen-mawr, and on the Menai shore near Llanbeblig. These two urns were accompanied by pygmy or "incense" cups, which are sometimes found in association with such burials. They seldom exceed three inches in height and their use is unknown to us, but they obviously served some ritual purpose. An urn containing calcined bones and charcoal was also unearthed at the foot of a standing stone or maenhir in Glynllifon Park at Llandwrog, an indication that the maenhir sometimes, though by no means universally, marked the site of an important burial.

The British metallurgists meanwhile discovered better methods and new types for their implements, improvements that were furthered by the impact of foreign traders; the palstave, the looped spear-head and the rapier appeared in due sequence, replacing the flat axe and the dagger. The appearance in Caernarvonshire of an exceptional form of the palstave, the typical axe-head of the Middle Bronze Age, shows the intrusion of Spanish influence and the continuance of direct contact by sea with the Mediterranean even after the clearing of the great trans-continental land routes.

The dry, boreal period which prevailed during the greater part of the Bronze Age greatly denuded the forest growth of Snowdon, and made possible for the first time the penetration and settlement of the flanks of her inland valleys. The spade of the peat-cutter and the archaeologist, turning up their weapons and ornaments, has revealed the presence of our Bronze Age forerunners at the head of Llŷn, on the rocky knolls that were once islands in the Glaslyn estuary, at Penrhyn-deudraeth and on the lower slopes of Cnicht, and at several points in the neighbourhood of Brynkir and Caernarvon. Bronze Age remains at Beddgelert, Dolwyddelan, Capel Curig, on the slopes of Carnedd Llywelyn and at Trefriw and Conway witness how far they had thrust into the fastnesses of the inland hills. It has been tentatively suggested by Mr. Hemp that the immediate hinterland of the Glaslyn and Dwyryd estuaries was so important as a meeting-point of trade routes and a distributing centre that it may be considered as a sort of pre-historic Liverpool. Here converged the coastal seaways from the Mediterranean, Ireland and northern Europe, merchants transhipping their wares and portering them across the neck of Llŷn to save the

dangerous passage round the headland and Bardsey. From Traeth
Mawr, the sandy head of the estuary, a route ran by way of Nant
Gwynant and Nant Conwy to the North Wales coast, a possible
meeting-ground with traders from Yorkshire coming by way of the
Aire gap to the mouth of the Mersey and the Dee. Ornaments of amber
and jet found in Bronze Age graves in Anglesey indicate the luxury
goods of the Baltic and Yorkshire coasts exchanged for the bronze and
gold of Ireland. North-west Wales thus lay in the main path of trade
and cultural exchange through her position on the transit route of the
Irish gold trade, which drew merchant venturers from many parts of
England and Europe. The conservatism of the highland zone is to be
found again in the pottery of the late Bronze Age, derived from the old
food vessel, and apparently quite uninfluenced by new ceramic forms
introduced into the lowland zone by some of the new immigrants.
This highland pottery, the encrusted urn, lavishly decorated by strips
of clay applied to the vessel, spread from Scotland and north-east
England to the Isle of Man, Ireland, and Wales, a further indication
of the course followed by the trade routes.

The socketed axe, the riveted spear-head, and the leaf-shaped
sword which can both cut and thrust, probably first forged on the
plains of Hungary, appear also in the Caernarvonshire hills, but some
of these bronze implements found in the Welsh uplands reflect the
persistence of older forms, or the absorption of new Continental types
direct from the Atlantic trading highway, which are not found in the
lowland area. The relics of the late Bronze Age, the circular embossed
shields from Moel Siabod and Harlech, the gold horse peytrel from
Mold, the gold pennanular bracelet from Beaumaris, all suggest the
presence in North Wales at this period of an aristocratic military caste,
skilled in horsemanship, with an appreciation of the finer arts and
luxuries of life.

The closing years of the Bronze Age and the early centuries of the
Age of Iron were again a time of upheaval and shifting of peoples, due
in part to further climatic changes and pressure on land. Fresh waves
of immigrants and refugees came flocking into Britain, bringing with
them knowledge of the new material and the skill to fashion it into
weapons and tools; we hear an echo of those troubled years at the far
end of Europe ringing through the story of the Iliad. The wet, stormy
weather of this period drove the inhabitants of North Wales back to
the higher reaches of the hills, away from the fresh tangle of woods and

undergrowth springing up on the lower slopes and choking the valleys. It is possible that some of the stone hut-circles found at a height of 800 to 1,000 feet or over may belong to the late Bronze Age. They usually lie in groups of two or three, each dwelling separated by a few feet from its neighbour, and there is no encircling boundary wall around the settlement as in the case of the Iron Age groups described below. Mr. Colin Gresham, who has made a survey of them, states that they appear to occur in greatest numbers on the hills of the Middle Conway valley and of Nant Gwynant, on the mountains around Cwm Pennant and Cwm Ystradllyn and on those enclosing the Traeth Mawr, especially on the slopes leading up from the coast. The huts are sited wherever possible on a sheltered ledge with a south or south-west aspect, and on dry soils that will not become boggy with rain or hold stagnant water. Adjoining them are usually little paddocks, divided by low walls of loose stones, and varying in size from a few square yards to three or four acres; the larger fields retain traces of hoe cultivation. No evidence is forthcoming at present to throw any light on the age of most of these habitation sites; they may, as suggested, belong to some pre-Roman era of our history; they may be no earlier than the Dark Ages or even the medieval period. It may, however, be noted that Dr. G. Griffith, who examined a group of these hut circles in Nant Gwynant "near the spot where the outflow from Llyn Llydaw reaches the main valley," came on a quantity of stone implements— celts, flint arrow-heads and a stone gouge, while one hut-circle con- tained the slag refuse from the smelting of copper ore.

The centuries of the early Iron Age which immediately precede the Roman occupation are very obscure in North Wales. The bronze hanging bowl from Cerrig-y-druidion, which represents the earliest phase of the La Tène[1] culture, and a La Tène shield found in a ditch of the fortress of Moel Hiraddug in Flintshire, show that somewhere between 500 and 300 B.C. Celtic traders and settlers were pushing into the hill districts of the country even to the outskirts of Snowdon. By the time that the Romans crossed the Welsh borderland the whole country was occupied and settled by different tribal groups of these Celtic peoples, the Ordovices predominating in the north; they had so effectively subdued the earlier inhabitants that the Celtic tongue had ousted the existing speech and become the language of the country.

[1]The La Tène civilization is named from the centre on Lake Neuchatel where the most prolific remains of this culture were found. The term "Celt" is used throughout to designate a culture and language group, not a race.

It was these invaders who developed the rites and teaching known as Druidism as the official religion of the Celts of Gaul and Britain. According to Caesar, the latter country was the cradle of the faith, and it is probable that British Druidism embodied certain beliefs and customs of earlier inhabitants of the country. The priests or Druids who presided at the sacrifices were recognized as members of a permanent federation forming a church, comparable, as Professor Jullian suggests, to the bishops of the Catholic church. They were a confraternity of wise men, who gave oral instruction in the doctrines of their religion and in philosophy, practised the arts of divination, and were skilled in astronomy and medicinal lore. They also acted as arbiters and judges in civil and criminal cases. The instruction of the youth of the tribe was in their hands, and the youth of Gaul were sent to Britain, Cæsar tells us, for their education and for initiation into the mysteries of the fraternity. Mona or Anglesey was the great centre of this religion in Britain, in fact the only place named in the British Isles by the early authorities in connection with it.

As the instruction was for the most part oral and the pupils were expected to memorize the scientific or religious doctrines or the traditions of their race, we know very little that is authentic of their beliefs and practices, and imagination has had free reign in saddling the Druids with an enlightened wisdom or a barbaric custom, for neither of which can definite proof be adduced. The mistletoe growing on an oak tree appears to have been a symbol of particular significance, and the cutting of the mistletoe with a golden knife to have played an important part in their rites. They undoubtedly held a belief in the immortality of the soul, and possibly taught the doctrine of the transmigration of the soul. Confraternities of women were sometimes attached to some particularly sacred spot, and were probably themselves priestesses; it was a group of these who awed the troops of Suetonius Paulinus in his attack on Anglesey. It is possible that the tradition of human sacrifice which persists so strongly in connection with this religion has some foundation in fact but we know too little to speak with any assurance. It must also be remembered that below the Druid priesthood a number of other priests existed, serving the major Celtic deities or the little local gods of the wayside spring or stretch of bogland, whose customs might be attributed mistakenly to the Druids themselves by later writers.

The Druid religion represented a national faith that was bitterly opposed to the imperial policy of Rome; its destruction therefore was an essential part of the conquest. Suetonius Paulinus evidently regarded this Celtic religion as a powerful source of defiance and incipient rebellion. His first move, when turning to North Wales, was a raid across the country to Anglesey in 61 A.D. to slay the priests and hew down the sacred groves as a necessary preliminary to the subjugation of the country. The revolt of Boudicca recalled him before he could attempt the second part of his task, but the religious stronghold was destroyed before he turned his face again to the east.

The first human dwellings which can be dated with any assurance in North Wales were raised by the descendants of the early Celtic invaders during the second century A.D. when the pacification of the country by the Romans had been completed. Recent research suggests that some of these hill forts may date to an earlier phase of the Iron Age, and were altered or strengthened under successive re-occupations, possibly extending to medieval days. If this is confirmed, the suggestion of a programme of defensive works carried out during the Roman occupation would no longer be valid as an explanation of their origin. Thence we have two lines of native development, the great fortified hill camps overlooking the main passes and the coastal plain, and the little homesteads or hamlets, gathered within an enclosing wall of earth or stone, scattered over the lower, seaward slopes of the hills to the west of the Conway valley and on the Anglesey shore of the Menai Straits. The relation of the two remains as yet an unsolved problem; though some of the forts may have been used primarily as places of refuge for the farm dwellers around in times of disorder or threatened attack, others, such as Tre'r Ceiri on the easternmost peak of Yr Eifl or Braich-y-dinas on the summit of Penmaen-mawr, with their little streets of solid stone huts, suggest a more continuous occupation. This is borne out by the Roman coins and fragments of pottery unearthed from the floors of these dwellings, which include types running from the second to the fourth century. The existence of these fortresses, which were sometimes even rebuilt and strengthened during the Roman occupation, itself presents a difficulty. Dr. Mortimer Wheeler has suggested that the subjugation of the tribes of North Wales was so effectively achieved by the campaigns of A.D. 75–80 that the Romans found it possible to enlist the help of the hill people in maintaining order in this outpost of the military zone. Their aid would be sought particularly in the third and fourth centuries, when pirates and marauders from Ireland were continually harrying the Welsh coast, and eventually succeeded in overrunning the countryside and establishing little nests of colonists.

The fortresses vary greatly in size and altitude, but are usually situated on the crests of the lower hills, especially on the outliers of the higher ranges where these drop towards the coast or the main river valleys. The builders were very skilful in utilizing the natural defences offered by precipices or steep slopes of scree, adding their walls and ditches only to reinforce these at any point of weakness. Within the National Park some of the best known examples were on the hill above Llanfairfechan, 1,200 feet above the sea, though here no traces of the fortification remain above ground, Castell Caer Lleon on Conway mountain, Dinas Dinorwic, commanding the entrance to the Llanberis pass from the sea, and Dinas Emrys (Pl. 29a, p. 334), the great crag which towers over the road to Beddgelert near the foot of Llyn Dinas, joined to the range of hills behind only by a narrow strip of rock.

One of the most interesting is the fortress of Pen-y-gaer above Llanbedr-y-cennin near the entrance to the Conway valley. It is sited on a spur of hill 1,225 feet above sea level running down from the heights of Carnedd Llywelyn towards the river, and the defence works are of a most elaborate nature. The internal area of the fort covers four and three-quarters acres, and contains the foundations of a number of circular huts; fifteen of these, examined by Mr. Harold Hughes, averaged 19 feet 6 inches in diameter ; some were so built that the living rock of the hillside formed the back wall. Lumps of iron slag and traces of refuse from a blast furnace on one hut site show that the smelting of iron was carried out on the spot. The ground falls sheer to the north and east and no special defences were felt to be necessary, but on the south and west where there is a more gentle slope the position was defended by a rubble wall $14\frac{1}{2}$ feet thick, and faced with great blocks of stone: it still stands in places to a height of 4 or 5 feet. Below it lies a series of steep glacis which could be swept by sling stones from the walls above, while four ditches, now much silted up, with ramparts of earth and stone, acted as additional impediments to advance. In the second ditch on the south, and on the slope below the rampart, the position was further strengthened by studding the ground with numbers of sharp, pointed stones, set up on end, and protruding a foot or more above the soil, to serve as a trap for foot soldiers (Pl. XXIVa, p. 299). This *chevaux de frise* is a very unusual feature of hill fort defences; no other examples are known in

England or Wales, and only two have so far been discovered in
Scotland. The lower slopes were also covered with a loose scree, which
is now buried beneath the soil.

From the walls of this fortification the fourth-century defenders
must have watched with anxious eyes the little black coracles, which
had dared the perils of the voyage from Ireland, creeping into the
mouth of the Conway and crowding up the river like "a swarm of
insects roused from slumber," as Gildas described them.

The second group of Iron Age dwellings, the walled homesteads
and hamlets, give rise in turn to another series of problems. Mr. Colin
Gresham and Mr. W. J. Hemp, who have made a study of them, have
found that they exist in considerable numbers on the seaward slopes of
the mountains, running from the estuary of the Conway to that of the
Mawddach, where they are found chiefly at a height of 400 to 800 feet;
there are also several on the Menai coast of Anglesey and in Llŷn. In
these dwellings and villages the buildings are clustered round a central
courtyard touching one another, and the whole settlement is enclosed
within a wall of earth or stone; though generally circular in form, both
the boundary walls and the buildings within them are occasionally
rectilinear. The huts are usually constructed of great boulders set
upright to form the inner and outer face of the walls, with a filling
of smaller stones between. They often remain standing to a height of
three or four feet, and probably never exceeded this; a conical roof of
thatch or turves was supported on boughs running from the walls to a
central pole. If the hut were so large that additional support was
necessary, a further ring of posts was added. The fire was built in a
hollow lined with clay sometimes made in the centre of the hut, sometimes against one of the walls, the smoke escaping through a hole in the
roof and through the low door.

These enclosed homesteads are often associated with a system of
cultivation terraces; the stones cleared from the land were built into
retaining walls which might be five or six feet in height, holding the
level platforms of earth that were ploughed for grain-growing. The
slopes on which the farms are situated are usually gentle enough to
permit ploughing without any such artificial aid, nor are these terraces
found on foothills in other parts of the country where early settlements
were established. Mr. Hemp therefore suggests that they represent a
tradition brought by settlers whose place of origin lay in a steep and
barren countryside where such terracing would be a necessity.

The Roman conquest of North Wales was finally achieved in the vigorous campaigns of A.D. 71–78, conducted by Petilius Cerialis, Frontinus and Agricola, and the frontier forts of the north-west were established either during these operations or in the years immediately following the pacification. The earliest were Kanovium (Caerhûn) and Segontium, constructed about A.D. 75. The country as a whole formed part of the imperial frontier system of Britain, designed to consolidate the position of Rome among the wilder and less civilized tribes of the hill districts. The area covered by these lines of defence in Wales has been described by Dr. Mortimer Wheeler as a roughly rectangular tract based on the legionary fortresses of Chester and Caerleon-on-Usk, and the advance auxiliary forts of Caernarvon (Segontium) and Carmarthen. From the base at Chester, home of the XXth legion of regular troops, 6,000 strong, a number of smaller garrisons of auxiliaries were thrust forward into the heart of the country; each was composed of 500 to 1,000 men, and was linked by road and sea to the base. Most important of these, as the northern key-point of the whole system in Wales, was Segontium, built on the low hill of Llanbeblig above the present town of Caernarvon, and commanding the entrance to the Menai Straits and the approach to Britain from the west. The next auxiliary fort of corresponding size was situated on a spur of Mynydd Maentwrog some twenty miles distant, guarding the main road to the south, which passed over Trawsfynydd. Between these centres lay two smaller fortified posts: Caerhûn, near the entrance to the Conway valley from the sea, where the river passes into the hills, and Caer Llugwy, built in a curve of the river Llugwy between Capel Curig and Betws-y-coed, with the peak of Moel Siabod towering above it. The outlines of the small square or rectangular encampments can be traced, at least in part, in each case. Caer Llugwy, established probably in the last decade of the first century, appears to have been constructed of local stone at the outset, but at Kanovium and Segontium the first barracks were of wood and the defences were earthen banks, revetted with stone and bearing a timber stockade; these were replaced by stone walls and buildings early in the second century. The siting of these stations on the floors of the river valleys or on the coastal plain gave the initial impetus to the valleyward movement of the native population. Kanovium and Caer Llugwy were abandoned about the year A.D. 140, when the mobilization of troops on the Scottish border for the Antonine campaigns and the attempted conquest of Scotland stripped many of the Welsh strongholds of their garrisons. Segontium was likewise evacuated at this time but was re-occupied from A.D. 210 to 290. It was then again abandoned in some hurry, apparently in a time of upheaval and disorder; but the troops once more returned between 360 and 365 and remained till the Roman forces were finally withdrawn from Wales, probably between 380 and 390.

A system of roads connected the fortresses and linked them with the smaller outposts. The best-attested of these ran across the mountains from Deva (Chester) to Segontium, crossing the Conway at Tal-y-cafn and thence going by way of Kanovium over the Bwlch-y-ddeufaen to Aber and through Llanllechid and Deiniolen to Segontium. Three Roman milestones have been discovered marking this route in Caernarvonshire. The course of the other roads is more uncertain. One, the Sarn Helen, ran from Kanovium to Tomen-y-mur near Maentwrog, going south from Caer Llugwy by way of Bryn-y-geteiliau (the hill of the Smithies). The Romans had a small settlement of uncertain character near Tremadoc, and this was linked with Segontium by a road which probably followed the course of the Glaslyn river, through the famous pass, skirting the shores of Llyn Cwellyn. It would probably go by the present Betws Garmon and so to the Roman citadel (see Map 5, p. 310).

The auxiliary forces were recruited from the semi-barbaric frontier lands of the Empire overseas, whose standard of life was probably little, if any, more advanced than that of the Welsh tribes. But traders from as far afield as Greece or Syria followed in the wake of the armies, and a few may have reached even the outposts of the hills. A thin and narrow gold plate dug up near Segontium, designed to be worn as a talisman against the forces of evil, and inscribed in Greek characters with a Syrian Gnostic charm, is a witness to the mixture of peoples and faiths to be found within the walls of the Roman camp in the third and fourth centuries.

There must have been many contacts between occupying army and native farmer in the course of the two hundred years when the soldiers were passing in and out of the citadel at Segontium. Men who were far away from their own womenkind would seek a wife or achieve a hurried liaison with the women of the hills; their children, and the more adventurous sons of the local inhabitants, caught by the glamour of the marching cohorts, would steal down from their homes to volunteer for service under the Roman standards. The peasant, with an eye to profit, would bring his cattle and corn, or the skins of animals he had trapped, and trade them at the gate of the fortress; the coins he took home from his sales are dug up over a thousand years later from the floor of his little hut. Or he would purchase from the camp followers the strange grey or red pottery, so much smoother and better finished than his home-made ware, to take back a surprise for the wife from his marketing expedition; in time she would attempt to fashion a crude imitation of it. New words crept in to enrich the Welsh language, especially those connected with a higher material civilization; the terms in daily use for "window" and "couch," "book" and "bridge" are the gift of the legions.

Yet, despite a certain racial intermixture and the daily contacts of the market place, culturally native inhabitant and garrison soldier remained divided by a great gulf. The splendour of Roman civilization laid its spell on the tribesman of the Welsh hills, but it remained a mystery, half understood, inspiring awe and dread as well as admiration. We catch a memory of that dimly comprehended majesty and power in the Welsh medieval romance of Maxen Wledig's dream. The fortress at Caernarvon, with its tower-crowned walls and four great gates, whose most sumptuous building appears to have been the quartermaster's office with walls of painted plaster, is there transmuted into the legendary palace, roofed with gold, where Maxen came to seek his bride.

It is well known that the armies of the Republic and the early Empire were largely vegetarian in their diet; in Cæsar's Gallic campaigns, meat was used when corn was scarce, but it was regarded as an emergency ration. Meat-eating increased in the fourth century, the garrisons possibly maintaining cattle of their own on grazing-grounds bordering the fortresses, but the granary remained a feature of central importance within the British forts, built on a scale which would ensure on an average a year's reserve supply for the troops quartered there. The demand of the soldiers for corn must have acted as a spur to cereal cultivation on the more fertile lands in the neighbourhood and on the richer soils of Anglesey. Similarly, the growth of population which is likely to have been one result of the establishment of the *Pax Romana*, putting an end for the time being to the ravages of inter-tribal warfare, would tend to increase the area of land under cultivation and the number and size of the flocks and herds. Thus, directly and indirectly, one outcome of the Roman dominion in the Welsh uplands was perhaps to stimulate the attack on the waste lands in order to clear new areas for settlement, tillage and pasture-grounds.

References for Chapter 14

Wheeler (1925), Fox, C. (1938), Gresham (1941), Hemp and Gresham (1944), Wheeler (1923).

CHAPTER 15

HEROES OF LEGEND AND
THE RISE OF CELTIC CHRISTIANITY

I N the years that follow the withdrawal of the Roman troops we enter a world of shadows to encounter those heroric, half-mythical figures of popular legend, who yet had almost certainly an historical counterpart in flesh and blood. The Irish appear to have swept over Caernarvonshire when the Roman soldiers marched away, and for a short time possibly the whole of North Wales was in their hands. Yet there is little material evidence left of their presence; certain stories in the folklore of Snowdon preserve the memory of their invasion, a few memorial stones of the fifth to seventh centuries bear Ogham inscriptions, and the name commonly given to the clusters of hut-circles locally is "cyttiau'r Gwyddelod," the Irishmen's houses. About the year 400, Cunedda and his "sons" descended from the Scottish border to assist the Welsh in expelling the Irish settlers and to found the local ruling dynasty from which later kings were to trace their descent. The names of many of the modern counties of north- and mid-Wales are believed to derive from those of his "children" or tribesmen among whom the territory was partitioned. This story portrays, not the voluntary migration of a British tribe from one part of the Roman dominion of Britain to another, but a deliberate transference of population engineered, probably, by Stilicho when he arrived in the country to reorganize the shaken frontiers after the revolt of Maximus in 383, and to check the inflow of barbarians which followed from north, east and west. This policy was frequently adopted on the frontiers of the Empire to strengthen any point of particular weakness; as we have seen, the Roman garrisons had probably left Wales before the close of the fourth century, and the transplantation of a whole tribe, the Votadini, from the north-eastern frontier was adopted as the best means of reinforcing the threatened western shores.

Vortigern, who opened the door to the Saxon invasion by inviting the aid of marauding bands in his conflict with his local fellow princes and with the Picts, was of Welsh birth and maintained strongholds in North and South Wales. In the Welsh folk tales he is described as attempting to build a castle on the crag above Llyn Dinas, but was defeated by the local powers of magic, the foundations being removed each night. Myrddin Emrys, the Merlin of Arthurian legend, appeared as a youth to confound him, and when Vortigern had withdrawn Merlin dwelt for some time in the fortress of Dinas Emrys (Pl. 29a, p. 334) to which he gave his name. Here Aurelius Ambrosius came to seek him out and persuaded Merlin eventually to leave with him, presumably as his adviser and soothsayer, but before his departure the magician buried his treasure within the fortress, a story which has given rise to many an eager treasure hunt in later days.[1] Ambrosius emerges as a leader about the year 472, a man with Roman blood in his veins, striving to maintain some remnant of the Roman tradition against the disruptive forces of Celtic tribalism.

Arthur himself, who was probably the great general of Ambrosius, appears among the Snowdon hills. In so far as we can discern the historical figure through the mists of the medieval romances, he likewise stands as the representative of the imperial tradition, the acknowledged leader of the British people in both north and south. Sir John Rhŷs has argued that he probably held the office of *Dux Bellorum* with a mobile force at his disposal which could move swiftly to any point of danger. His work was two-fold: to revive some shadow of Roman order and discipline against the growing lawlessness and civil strife of the Celtic tribes, and to carry on an unceasing warfare against the Saxon invader. By his victory at Mount Badon Arthur halted the Saxon advance westwards for fifty years, while one modern writer has seen reflected in the fellowship of the Round Table his statesmanlike policy of forming a strong central executive against the disruptive localism of the age. According to Welsh tradition he met his death in a skirmish on Bwlch-y-saethau, the Pass of Arrows, which lies above the dark precipices of the horseshoe between Yr Wyddfa and Lliwydd near the summit of Snowdon. His knights stand resting on their shields asleep in a cave in the crags of Lliwedd above Llyn Llydaw (Pl. 30, p. 335), waiting the moment till Arthur shall come again to summon them by his bugle call to drive the Anglo-Saxon from the shores of Britain.

When the waters of Llyn Llydaw were lowered in 1856 to permit the building of a road along the shore, a primitive canoe was found embedded in the mud. Hollowed out of a solid oak trunk, it measured

[1]Twelve stud nails of bronze with traces of gold plating, probably used for riveting armour, have been found on the site of Dinas Emrys, together with some iron terrets coated with bronze, used in harnessing horses. Traces of a rectangular building were also found here, but may date to a later period in the Middle Ages.

some ten feet long by two and a half feet wide, the bow and stern being higher than the middle of the boat. Looking down from the heights into the dark waters of the lake, Sir John Rhŷs saw "with the eyes of Malory" the passing of Arthur enacted on its waters, the reluctant Sir Bedivere flinging Excalibur into the depths below, and the "barge" transformed into the prehistoric canoe, containing the three wondrously "fayr ladyes" who bore away the body of the mortally wounded king, stanching his wounds.

A further link with Arthurian legend in the topography of Snowdon is found in Mr. Derfel Hughes's volume on Llandegai and Llanllechid. He avers that a Carnedd Drystan or Tristram's cairn is situated on a spur of Carnedd Llywelyn lying to the east above Ffynnon Llyffant.

The sixth century has been described as a period of uneasy equilibrium. The new Saxon kingdoms were gradually taking shape in the east; Wales, and the whole western region of Britain to Strathclyde, was divided into a number of tribal cantons or petty kingdoms, ruled by native princes, whose authority was the source of such law as existed.[1] Between the two, in the area covered by the dense oak forest of the midlands, lay a no-man's-land, haunted by outlaws, or by such hardy venturers as dared to carve a home for themselves out of the tangled woodlands. Nevertheless, in the isolated region of North-west Wales, some form of civil government, which still held a faint echo of the Roman, lingered into the sixth century. In Penmachno church three of the earliest Christian tombstones to be found in the country are now preserved, all found in the immediate vicinity. One can be definitely dated for it was set up for the son of Avitorius in the time of Justinus the Consul, and we know that Justinus was consul in A.D. 540. A second is inscribed with the name of a citizen of Venedotia or Gwynedd, the first recorded mention of the northern kingdom by that name. During his lifetime he held the office of *magistratus*, the only existing record of a local inhabitant bearing this title in Britain in the post-Roman era. The inscription on the third stone runs: "Carausias hic iacit in hoc congeries lapidum"; the custom of building a cairn of stones over the dead was still maintained here in the days of early Christianity, a further witness to the long preservation of old habits in the lonely hill districts of the island.

---

[1]They were all Celtic peoples, who, in their struggle with the Saxons, became known as the Cymry, or fellow-countrymen. The first Saxon wedge was driven between them in the fateful years of the early seventh century, it is usually believed by the Saxon victory at the Battle of Chester in 613, though Professor Stenton, the great authority on Anglo-Saxon Britain, thinks that the Saxons may have reached the west coast twenty years earlier.

In this period the frontier lands of the Atlantic seaboard were again drawn into a living cultural unity under the impulse of Celtic Christianity. The source of the Christian movement in Roman Britain is unknown. One of the earliest recorded facts in the history of the western church, however, may be of significance, namely the persecution of the Christians dwelling in the Rhône valley at the end of the second century. This community in the neighbourhood of Vienne and Lyons was established as a colony from Asia Minor, and maintained close contact with the parent church. The colony of Provence was dispersed in the fierce persecution of A.D. 177, and it has been thought not unlikely that refugees fleeing across the Channel first carried the Christian message to Roman Britain. Some scholars have traced eastern influences in the liturgy and ritual of the Celtic church in these islands, and it is perhaps noteworthy that in the later conflict with Augustine, the Celts, Bede tells us, appealed to the authority of St. John as the Apostle whose tradition they followed. On the other hand, a view more recently advanced is that Christianity entered the country by way of the trade routes from the Continent, introduced by merchants and their servants who came to settle in the new cities of the island, and that the observances followed the Roman or western practices of the day. Be that is it may, Tertullian could claim, *circa* A.D. 208, that parts of Britain still untouched by Roman rule had been conquered by Christ, an indication that the new religion had penetrated to the highland zone and was not confined to the fully Romanized lowlands or the centres of civic life. But however far the message of Christ had won its way in this corner of Wales—a matter of great doubt—there would be many lapses into paganism among the converted with the disintegration of social standards and customs following the removal of Roman influence, and a growing indifference to the things of the spirit, while the bulk of the population had doubtless remained faithful to the old gods.

St. Martin of Tours (A.D. 316–397) was the pioneer of the ascetic and monastic movement which saved the life of the western church. When the barbarian hordes broke through the Roman lines and overran Gaul and western Europe, men, fired by his example, retreated to the islands lying off the coasts of France and Italy, and in the peace of their new-found seclusion kept alive the spark of Christian faith and culture. In these little cells was born the missionary fervour that drove men out in their frail craft along the old Atlantic trade routes to the shores of Ireland and of the mainland of Western Britain, to renew and strengthen the faith of those inhabitants who still clung to the Christian beliefs, and to launch the assault on the strongholds of paganism. The sixth century is pre-eminently the "age of the saints," of the founders of the Celtic monastic church. Welsh, Irish, Scottish, Cornishmen, stirred by the missionary impulse of the Continent, in turn took up the task of revivifying their Christian heritage and distributing its riches. There was much cultural interchange between Wales, Cornwall, Southern Ireland and Armorica or Brittany in the south, between North Ireland and Scotland in the north; long journeys were made on foot across the hills of the interior to carry the message of Christianity to the remote valleys and homesteads of North Wales. The Welsh saints were a remarkable group of men and women, a courageous, fiery and devoted band drawn for the most part from the upper ranks of society, the princely families, and often possessing great intellectual and spiritual ability, which in those days of restricted cultural pursuits could only find an outlet in the monastic life. We find the leaders of the missionary enterprise hastening from place to place throughout Wales, founding their little cells and churches, leaving a handful of zealous followers to carry on their work, and rushing off again on another journey which would culminate in a similar foundation, the rise of a fresh centre of religious and intellectual enterprise. In other cases, the loyal service of a local man and his friends would result perhaps in the growth of a single monastic venture near his home. The churches of Wales which bear the name of a now forgotten saint, the Llan or enclosure of Rhychwyn, or Peris or Padarn, where an early foundation is known to have existed, may be safely assumed as the personal dedication of that man or his immediate followers, according to Professor Bowen. They give a useful clue to the valleyward drift of the population in the Dark Ages; some we find situated at the head of a valley, others have crept some way down the more gently sloping hillsides, not a few penetrate to a clearing near the foot of a pass or in the valley bottom near a stream or river. The early churches were often built close by a well or spring,[1] whose magical and healing properties were still vouched for in the early nineteenth century, attracting numbers of stricken people; this choice of site is perhaps an indication that the founder had taken possession of some pagan seat of worship and turned the local god of the spring to the

[1] Llangelynin, Llanbedr-y-cennin, Dolwyddelan, Llanberis, for example.

service of his own Master. If the church stood at a nodal point of the trackways, a little hamlet might grow up about it; until the Reformation it would have a vital part to play in the life of the neighbourhood.

The early Celtic church was itself a largely tribal organization; whole families would be converted and flee the world together, and those gathered in the settlement, even if ties of blood were weak, would come to be regarded as a kinship group. The founder was also often related to the ruler of the district in which he made his permanent home. The church building was a small rectangular structure, of wood and wattle with a thatched roof, seldom more than 20 feet in length; the "monastery" a collection of little huts of wattle and clay gathered about it. Land was tilled and cattle were tended by members of the community, and schools were opened for the children of the prince's household and of the free tribesmen. It was part of the saint's duty to attend his royal patron in battle and freely curse his enemies; the curse of the holy man was a powerful and dangerous weapon, apt to be turned against the ruler and his family if he gave cause of offence, or even against a fellow monk for some unpardonable crime such as borrowing a book and not returning it. A bishop was usually allotted to the monastic foundation for purposes of ordination, but the early Welsh bishop had no territorial diocese, and might be under the actual jurisdiction of the monastic leader.

A rule of rigorous austerity was initiated by St. David in the sixth century; the monks of his community in Pembrokeshire harnessed themselves to the plough and employed no oxen or horses as beasts of burden. The pitiless discipline of his rule still survived at two centres in the late twelfth century, on the island of Priestholm off the north-east coast of Anglesey and at Beddgelert, which was declared by the Bishop of Bangor in 1283 to be the senior religious house in all Wales, except Bardsey. Here, in 1188, a little body of clergy were discovered by one traveller, Giraldus Cambrensis, practising a rigid chastity and abstinence though not attached to any monastic or canonical rule; their house was a common resort of the poor seeking charitable relief, and of English and Welsh travellers braving the grim mountain pass on the road from Ireland and the north-west to England. A priory of Austin Canons succeeded to the old Celtic foundation a little later; all that is left of their buildings is to be found in the nave and north transept of the parish church at Beddgelert; the two arches of the transept and the lancet windows of the east end are early thirteenth-century work, built before the fire of 1283 which destroyed both the house of the canons and their charters.

Schools of some fame arose within the Celtic church in Wales, particularly that of St. Illtyd in the south. Grammar, rhetoric, geometry and arithmetic were taught; the pupils of St. Cadoc had to get Virgil by heart, and that godly man wept every night because he could not bear to think of the great classical poet suffering the pains of Hell, till Virgil appeared to him in a dream urging him to continue his prayers for, the pagan poet declared, he would yet sing in Paradise. In the smaller communities of our mountainous region the standard may not have been so high as in the more famous centres of learning, but some remnant of the classical tradition was preserved even here. The Welsh Christian, however, despite the advantages of his geographical position, which brought him once again into the van of intellectual activity and development, refused to play any part in the effort to convert his Saxon neighbours. Furthermore, cut off by the pagan hosts of the eastern counties, of Gaul and of Spain, from direct contact with Rome, his church retained elements of its primitive ritual and custom which were frowned at by the new emissaries sent to England in 589 by Gregory the Great. The Welsh were antagonized by the haughty demeanour of Augustine and his somewhat tactless handling of them, and withdrew to the shelter of their hills, refusing to alter their practices and bring them into conformity with those of the official church. The Welsh church did not finally submit till the middle of the eighth century. So her people had no share in the great cultural revival of the seventh and eighth centuries following the growth of Christianity among the Saxons; as Europe was Christianized, the Atlantic sea-route ceased to be the channel of cultural exchange, and the position of Wales was shifted to the confines of the civilized world. Yet it is well to remember that it was the Christians of the western sea-board who preserved for us not a few of the arts of life and the values of the great classical tradition; who kept alive the Christian faith as an inheritance for future generations; and went to their task undaunted by the perils, darkness and adversity of the ages of invasion and the crumbling of the old world.

References for Chapter 15

Williams, H. (1912), Bede (Ecclesiastical History of the English Nation), Bowen (1944), Baring-Gould and Fisher (1907-13), Lloyd (1938).

CHAPTER 16

THE YEARS OF STRIFE

AS Wales emerges from the mists of the Dark Ages, we find the country divided into four petty kingdoms, each under its own ruler. The ancient kingdom of Gwynedd, in which Snowdon lay, comprised the territory to the west of the Conway, including Anglesey and the greater part of eastern Merionethshire; it was later extended to the east of the Conway to embrace the region covered by the modern counties of Flint and north Denbigh. The second, Powys, at its greatest extent stretched from Mold in Flintshire to the Wye, and the third, Deheubarth, at first extended over all South Wales, till the border counties of Monmouth and Glamorgan were distinguished as the territory of Morgannwg, with its two kingdoms, Gwent and Gwynllwyg. Maelgwn Gwynedd, ruler of that territory in the sixth century (he died *circa* 547) by his wit and ingenuity succeeded in establishing a loose ascendancy over the whole country, the other princes paying him yearly one hundred cows in acknowledgment of his overlordship.

In the life and personality of this man may be seen reflected the confusion and restlessness of the age, the strange admixture of a lawless paganism, an extreme asceticism and a love of beauty. Maelgwn was a freebooter, who did not shrink from the murder of his nephew to gain the woman he coveted, yet in the noonday of his power he cast from him wealth and position to seek a new peace in the backwaters of the monastic life. But after a few years the world reclaimed him and he returned to his throne and to his old ways, sinning again with the same wild extravagance, yet making his court a centre of the arts with the twenty-four bards he maintained there. Taliesin, one of the greatest of the early Welsh poets, who is believed to have lived for a time on the shores of Llyn Geirionydd in the hills above Trefriw, has left memory of his prowess in the legend of his mythical counterpart, the winner of a renowned victory over this school of court poets not merely by his superiority in measure and song, but by his greater skill in magic. Coming to Deganwy in search of his patron who had been imprisoned by Maelgwn, this legendary Taliesin left the court bards tongue-tied and spell-bound while he penetrated to the dungeon, where the thirteen locks opened before him and his master was free.

From the sixth to the thirteenth century the developments in economic and social life which are traced in the next chapter must be seen against a background of almost unceasing warfare and struggle. There are the fierce conflicts of inter-tribal and family strife, embittered by the tie of blood; there is the long struggle against the Saxon who was pressing in on the borders from the east and north-east from the early seventh century. By *c.* 784 Offa of Mercia was in a strong enough position on the Welsh border to throw up the great earthen dyke, which bears his name, as a visible limitation to the lands of the Welsh. The low, grass-covered barrier which ran from the vicinity of Prestatyn in the north to the Severn estuary in the south, stretching from sea to sea as Asser tells us, is still discernible and can be traced over the greater part of its course.

In the year 850 or 851 the first Norse raid on Anglesey is recorded; thereafter for the next two hundred years there is the new foe from the sea to encounter, pouring from the long ships in the early twilight to fire the little homestead and carry off the inhabitants to slavery. We, who in our day have seen homes and cities in our countryside gutted by the flames of a night's aerial bombardment, can realize something of the terror of those nights of bloodshed and plunder.

Finally, in the year 1070 the hosts of William the Conqueror first appeared on the borders of North Wales, in the year of his famous march from a devastated Yorkshire across the Pennines to Chester. William found a welcome outlet for the energies of the restless pioneers of his train by giving them permission to seize and hold by the sword such land as they could win in Wales and the Marches. There was a first swift onrush which threatened the whole territory of Gwynedd and Powys, carrying the Norman arms over the countryside to the east of the Conway and west of that river to Bangor and Anglesey. Then it was stayed by the rise of an able ruler of Gwynedd, Gruffydd ap Cynan who won his position of leadership about 1099; he gradually recaptured the lands even to the east of the Conway, destroying the Norman castles hastily built thereon. For the next hundred and fifty years the border-line swayed to and fro with the fortunes of war, but Gwynedd was blessed with a number of able princes in the twelfth and thirteenth centuries, who succeeded in holding back the advance. Owain Gwynedd, son of Gruffydd ap Cynan (d. 1170) and Llywelyn the Great (d. 1240) were both successful leaders of revolt against the rising Anglo-Norman power in the borderlands and the south of the country. Under Llywelyn the Great, "Prince of Aberffraw and Lord of Snowdon," Wales reached the apex of her power. Llywelyn led successful raiding parties again and again through the border counties and into mid- and South Wales, sweeping the invaders from their newly-won conquests; his prowess was such that all the other Welsh princes accepted his authority and overlordship. Though he struck hard where necessity arose against dissentient factions in his own kingdom, he succeeded eventually in moulding the country into a new unity by his skill and the force of his dominant personality. His aim was a land at peace within itself and thus strong enough to come to terms with the powerful neighbour established in the Marches, yet, despite the temptation to force the issue to the test of the battlefield, there are indications throughout his life of a deeper political wisdom, culminating in his act of homage to Henry III in his closing years. In this policy of Llywelyn lies the attempt to find a *modus vivendi* between the two peoples, once the growing power of the English within Wales had been checked and confined. It was doubtless with this end in view as well as to gain the English king's alliance against the Prince of Powys, that Llywelyn took to wife Joan, the natural daughter of King John, and welcomed inter-marriage between the ruling families of Wales and the great baronial houses of the Marches. His shrewd insight into the English political situation gave him many opportunities for skilful negotiation on behalf of Welsh interests, while in Wales itself he sought to establish a council of the Princes, with power to settle any dispute arising between them. In Llywelyn's council and his efforts towards the centralization of power, cutting across tribal boundaries and feuds, lay the germ of a national executive, able to free Wales from the turmoil and confusion of tribal quarrels, and leave her unhampered to develop her own unique gifts. The fact that within forty years of his death that purpose was ruined for ever, detracts in no way from the greatness of the man who had the vision to conceive such hopes, the courage to put them to the test of action. The stone coffin of Llywelyn rests now in the Gwydir chapel of the parish church of Llanrwst, the last tangible memorial of "that eagle of men who loved not to lie nor sleep," but so long as the Welsh tongue is spoken he lives again in the affection and the memory of his people.

Meanwhile, in the midst of this political strife and unrest, the social and economic life of Wales was taking shape. The broken, hilly nature of the country and the high rainfall were predisposing factors for the adoption of a largely pastoral economy. Recent archaeological research has proved that the Celtic hill-fort dwellers of North Wales were first and foremost stock-rearers. Professor Emrys Bowen has suggested that their cattle and sheep would be turned out to graze the hill slopes below the walls of the fortress, and in summer would be driven up to the bleak, exposed moorlands of the higher ranges above the camp sites, the beginning of the seasonal movement of cattle which continues, in a modified form, to the present day. Nevertheless, as we have seen, there is abundant evidence that tillage had an important place in the Dark Age programme of production, and continued to hold it throughout the medieval period.

There are indications that life in the hill-forts continued well into the Dark Ages, and they were possibly reoccupied later, from time to time, under threat of invasion. But in the sixth and seventh centuries the inhabitants were moving away from the shelter of their walls. Sometimes, as at Caerhûn and Segontium, we find traces of squatters among the ruins of the Roman stronghold, erecting their little huts in or near the old military centre, or adapting the existing buildings; at Caerhûn, especially, the coins and pottery found in the neighbourhood suggest a considerable Dark Age occupation. Others would venture on to a shoulder of hill below the fortress or at the head of a nearby valley; in a modern enclosure called Fridd Eithiniog, just below the fortress of Pen-y-gaer, Dr. Elfyn Hughes discovered a small settlement containing the ruins of several rectangular huts, accompanied by a series of cultivation terraces which bear the marks of a foot-plough agriculture.

A peculiar feature of many of the Dark Age and early medieval dwelling sites in Wales is the presence of a rectangular earthen platform, dug out of the hillside, on which the dwellings were erected, nestling into the shelter of the slope. There are usually two buildings, a house and a cattle shed, facing on to a yard enclosed by a low bank. Examples of such "platform" farmsteads were first discovered in Glamorgan by Sir Cyril and Lady (Aileen) Fox in 1934, but since their findings were published several instances of this technique have come to light in Caernarvonshire, chiefly through the researches of Mr. Hemp and Mr. Colin Gresham. The steadings are usually situated on the open moorland, at a height varying between 600 and 1,300 feet above sea level, and so far as present knowledge extends they appear to represent a form of construction confined to the Dark Age and medieval civilization of Wales.

The careful work of the archaeologists in laying bare the fragments of walling, or the post holes of the timber supports used in building, reveals that these houses were low, rectangular structures, their walls made of earth mixed with stones, or of wattle hurdles fixed to small, upright poles which were sunk in an earthen sill. The ridge pole of the roof was supported by two or three curved principals, or forks, rising from the floor near the centre of the room; the roof was a thatch of heather or rushes, or a covering of turves, supported on rods which ran from the ridge pole to the posts of the side walls. The floor was of beaten earth or pebbles; the hearth, a single stone slab, generally occupied a central position towards the back of the house, the smoke escaping through a hole in the roof. In the laws of Hywel Dda, a prince who died *circa* 950, and even in the medieval records of the early fourteenth century, we find documentary evidence of the employment of such building materials and of the general house plan. The cottage of the Welsh crofter or *tyddynwr* of the present day, built perhaps as recently as eighty to a hundred years ago in some cases, preserves the elements of this primitive design, for, as Sir Cyril Fox has pointed out, it is in essence a low, rectangular, single-roomed structure, open to the roof. The partitioning of the room into two, or the insertion of a loft over half the living space, dependent for light and air on the windows of the room below, are merely refinements of the early design.

Such primitive and ephemeral dwellings could be quickly raised, when required, by unskilled labour—a great advantage to the Welsh, aiding their mobility in time of stress. The favourite manœuvre of the inhabitants of Gwynedd under threat of invasion was to transfer themselves and their cattle with all speed to the fastness of the Snowdon mountains. Crops were ploughed in before they left, homes abandoned and new, temporary houses built in the shelter of Snowdon's slopes, where there was room "for all the herds of Wales" to graze through the summer months of a medieval campaign. Again and again in the course of history this retreat was successfully carried out. The light-armed, nimble-footed Welshman was a master in the art of guerilla warfare, swooping down suddenly from his precipitous strongholds to harry the flanks or advance guard of the invading host, then darting away into the hills where the heavily armoured Saxon or Norman could not, and dared not, follow. If the invader attempted to force a path by clearing a road through the wooded valleys, huge rocks would hurtle down upon the woodcutters, bringing instant death or mutilation.

PLATE 29

John Markham

a. DINAS EMRYS, in Welsh legend the home of Merlin. It is crowned with an ancient fortress. July

John Markham

b. LLYN PERIS with Dolbadarn Castle showing above the trees. The castle was a native stronghold built by the Princes of Gwynedd and often used as a prison
July

PLATE 30

John Markham

SNOWDON AND LLYN LLYDAW. In the foreground are the old buildings connected with the copper workings. Above lies the Bwlch Saethau and the cave where King Arthur sleeps. July

The winds and the rain of Snowdon were powerful allies of the Welsh; more than one army, settling out in the pride of great numbers, found itself soaked and floundering in quagmires, its supplies ruined and the country stripped of provisions, and was forced to retreat without giving battle. Seldom setting eyes on a Welshman, the soldiers were yet conscious all the time of the unseen foe, a shadow moving in the mist or through the undergrowth, ready at any moment to fall upon the unfortunate straggler, or from his hiding-place to launch a flight of arrows with an aim so unerring that it could pin the thigh of the rider to his horse.

William Rufus assembled a great armament in the autumn of 1095 for an attack on Gwynedd. The detachments, approaching North Wales by various routes, converged on Tomen-y-mur near Maentwrog, while battalions of woodcutters cleared the way before them. But the Welsh were hidden in the mists of Eryri ; the days grew shorter, the rain beat down upon the host, and the hearts of the men died within them as they came nearer to the grim and unknown hills. The Red King got no further than the vale of Ffestiniog, the mere outskirts of Snowdon, and was forced to retire discomfited.

Henry II, in 1165, summoned the largest army which had yet threatened Wales, and set out with proud and confident hopes for the northern hills. The Welsh princes, united for once in face of the common danger, assembled their forces at Corwen under the leadership of Owain Gwynedd, waiting and watching anxiously day by day for the vanguard of the great English muster. But it never came, for the storms of a wild and wet August broke the spirit of the invading troops. Supplies were soaked, food was pitifully scarce, and the camp a sea of mud; the morasses of the Berwyn hills sucked hungrily at their weary feet as they splashed knee- or waist-deep into the moorland sloughs. Though perpetually harried by the Welsh skirmishers, they turned for home without sighting the main army of the foe.

King John, breathing vengeance on his son-in-law, Llywelyn the Great, for his assaults on Marcher territory, brought his forces to Degannwy in 1211 to storm the gates of the Snowdon stronghold. But Llywelyn, says the *Brut y Tywysogion*, "moved . . . his property to the mountain of Eryri, and the forces of Mona with their property in the same manner." In Deganwy, the English army "was in such great want of provisions that an egg was sold for a penny halfpenny, and it was a delicious feast to get horseflesh, and on that account the king returned to England about Whitsuntide, with his errand imperfect, after disgracefully losing many of his men and much property."[1]

Only Earl Harold, the Saxon, mastered the tactics that could defeat the Welshman on his own ground. He sent a body of lightly armed troops into the fastnesses of the Snowdon range, supported by a fleet at sea to cut off supplies from Anglesey, and in the summer of 1053 hunted the ruler of Gwynedd from one hiding-place to another till, in the August of that year, he was finally betrayed and killed, and Wales was at last, for the moment, subjected to the Saxon host.

The second and final defeat of Wales occurred in the campaigns of Edward I in the years 1282-83. The grandson of Llywelyn the Great, Llywelyn ap Gruffyd, had also won ascendancy after long and bitter struggle over the other Welsh princes, and was acknowledged as their overlord; he was the first and last of the Welsh leaders to claim the title of "Prince of Wales." But if he shared his grandfather's vision of a strong and united kingdom, he failed in his dealings with the great English ruler; on two occasions he refused homage to the English king, and finally, driven by the discontents of his people, rose in rebellion. Edward I invaded Wales, establishing bases at Rhuddlan and Caernarvon, thus once again cutting off the Snowdon hills from Anglesey. The end came on a winter day of 1282 in an obscure skirmish in the upper Wye valley, to which Llywelyn the Last had withdrawn, hoping for promised reinforcements from the south. Here, in a meadow by the riverside, the champion of Welsh freedom was slain by the glancing blow of a soldier, who was not at first aware that the Prince of Wales lay dead at his feet, and that with him lay shattered not only the rebellion but the dream of an independent Wales.

References for Chapter 16

Williams, A. H. (1941), Lloyd (1938), Bowen (1941), Brut y Tywysogion (Rolls Series 1860), Annales Cambriae (Rolls Series 1860), Edwards, O. (1902), Bradley (1901), Hughes, R. E. (1940), Ancient Laws and Institutes of Wales (Record Commission 1841).

[1] It is true that John returned later in the year, and, aided by an exceptionally dry summer, harried and starved out Llywelyn in the fastness of Snowdonia, till the latter was forced to sue for peace on very onerous terms. It was the nadir of his power. But the set-back proved to be only temporary, and Gwynedd itself was neither overrun nor ceded.

CHAPTER 17

THE TRIBESMEN OF THE SNOWDON HILLS IN THE MIDDLE AGES

THE Laws of Hywel Dda give us our earliest picture of Welsh Society. This corpus of Welsh law is composed of three Codes relating to different parts of the country, and exists for us only in redactions of the twelfth to fourteenth centuries. But the kernel of the whole is doubtless based on the custom of earlier times, which was reduced to a systematic form by Hywel about 928. Through the accretions and alterations of the centuries, we can catch the reflection of an earlier order of society, however much it may be overlaid by the practice of a later day.

By the tenth century, the little kingdoms of Wales were partitioned into a number of districts called cantrefi (literally "a hundred townships"), each of which was in turn sub-divided into two or more cwmydau or commotes. The cantref in the Laws as we have them was already rather a shadowy entity, though it may have representedoriginally the land of a single tribe; the commote and the tref or town-ship had become the effective units of administration by the Middle Ages.

The free tribesmen of the commote were under obligation to attend the court at which all the judicial business of the region was transacted. This was not held at any fixed place; if a dispute had arisen as to rights over land, it was generally summoned to meet within the boundaries of the disputed territory. The commote was divided again into trefi, some occupied by free men of the tribe, some by bondmen or villeins. The tref was the unit on which were assessed the food rents demanded by the lord of the commote—the prince of the region, for the upkeep of his household. The tref or township was not a cluster of houses, grouped together, as the name would imply to an Englishman, but was simply a division of the countryside over which the farms straggled. Every homestead in the tref had attached to it a few acres of arable and meadowland, some four in all. The holding, together with the house, barn and outbuildings for cattle was termed a *tyddyn*. The lands of the tref were occupied and worked by large family groups, each claiming descent from a common ancestor, for the basis of Welsh society was tribal, and the laws reflect the adaptation of the primitive pastoral kinship groups to the settled life of cultivators of the soil, involving permanent habitation of a territory. The family of the Welsh laws, including members to the fourth degree of kinship, occupied land as a unit and acted as a joint family; it was known as the *gwely* (literally, a bed, or the offspring of one bed), and the holding was known as the gwely of so-and-so, named after the first occupier. Originally the right to occupation of these territories was conceived as vested in the living head of the family, not in the individual members composing it nor in the group as a whole, and the property could neither be sold nor alienated. Except for the rights over his tyddyn or homestead, which approach more nearly to the common understanding of ownership, the member of Welsh society in its early days had only a right to the use of a share in the property of his gwely to ensure him an adequate maintenance. But with the passage of time, particularly as individuals came to reclaim and occupy fresh lands, the sense of personal ownership grew, and one important result of the Edwardian conquest was to clarify this position, and give definitive form to the tendency of personal appropriation.

On the death of the founder of the gwely, the inheritance was divided among his sons in equal portions according to certain rules; first, a division of sites for the erection of homesteads, and then the remaining cultivated lands in the open fields of the tref. In addition each had a share in the wide pasture lands of the mountain-side and the waste, computed as his fractional share in the whole complex of tribal rights over the territory. The second and third generations of descendants, if they so desired, could engage in a further redistribution of the family property on the same terms, with the exception of the homesteads, but with the accession of the fourth generation there could be no further division of the family lands. The earlier writers on Welsh tribal society assumed that the division took place automatically within each generation, but Mr. T. P. Ellis, in his illuminating work on *Welsh Tribal Law and Custom in the Middle Ages*, pointed out how very unlikely this would be in actual fact. The older concept of the gwely was probably far too clear-cut and rigid to fit the more nebulous ordering of a tribal society and the changes which time and differing economic circumstances would introduce. Perhaps it may be safer, as he suggests, to regard the gwely as an association of men bound by some tie of blood —but not necessarily strictly limited to relatives within the fourth degree—who were joined together in a family group for purposes of

PLATE XXV

John Markham

DOLWYDDELAN CASTLE, part of which was built *c.* 1170. It was probably the early home of Llywelyn the Great

PLATE XXVI

John Markham

MASSIVE STONES USED FOR DOORWAY: the old house of Fedw Deg, Gwibernant

mutual protection and support and to share in the common property of their clan. The group would tend to change and sub-divide in the course of the years; pressure on land, through an extension of numbers, or exhaustion of soil by continuous cropping, might lead to the splitting-off of some members and the founding of a new gwely on unbroken land within a generation or two; on the other hand, where economic conditions were favourable, and there were untilled wastes close at hand to be cleared as the family grew, the gwely might remain undisturbed as the unit of land-holding in a region for many generations.

Closely allied to the gwely was a similar institution known as the *gafael* which means simply a "holding." Dr. Jones-Pierce, in his detailed study of the tribal society in the lower Conway valley, has suggested that the large number of gafaelion to be found in several townships there by the mid fifteenth century may represent the distribution of the old gwely lands after a second or third partition, while the situation of this property indicates pressure on the valley lowlands and extension of cultivation to the hill slopes.

In medieval Wales the position which a man held, the rights, duties and responsibilities devolving upon him, were determined by his birth and by virtue of the kinship which he thus acquired, not by the quantity of his possessions. The great social distinction was one of status not of wealth, and lay in the cleavage between the free man, member of the tribe, and the unfree who had no claim to the bond of blood. These less fortunate members of the community, the aillts or taegs, were probably descendants of the earlier inhabitants of the country when the Celts overran it, their numbers recruited by the dispossessed who, through some crime, had forfeited their position and kindred. In another category, but likewise outside the ranks of the free kindred, were strangers who had come to take up residence in the country.

The bondman could not rise into the position of a free man unless he were granted some office about the prince's court. These men of servile status fall into two main categories. In the one, the members were grouped into gweliau or gafaelion, holding and dividing their land on the principles of the free gwely; their property, however, was closely grouped about the township in which they dwelt, while the lands of the free gwely might be scattered in half a dozen townships, and there lie dispersed among the plots of other families. These bondmen were responsible for certain dues and services rendered at stated intervals to the lord of the commote, the ruler of the territory. In Dinorwic they made an annual payment for the support of their lord's otter-hounds, in lieu of the earlier custom of maintaining the dogs and their keeper for a stated number of days, in Eifionydd they paid towards the maintenance of his falconer whom they had formerly had to entertain for a period with his birds. At the feast of All Saints each commote had to furnish the prince of Gwynedd with a number of cows and oxen and a measure of oats for which he paid a fixed sum. Inhabitants of the commote in which the lord's court was situated were responsible for the maintenance of its structure; they also rendered porterage or carrying services to their lord, particularly when he was on tour from one part of his domain to another. In Eifionydd the bondmen had to bring stones and timber to repair the mill, in Dinorwic they were also charged with the maintenance of the weirs. Such renders, in money, kind or labour, were assessed on the gafael or, in the case of the more servile trefgevery tenure, on the township as a whole, so that if the numbers were depleted through pestilence or warfare, the surviving members were bound to fulfil the customary obligations. This was a powerful incentive to that wholesale flight from the land which occurred among the servile tenants after the ravages of the Black Death.

Secondly, near the court or Llys, the residence of the prince, the bondmen of the second category were grouped in nucleated villages or hamlets (the maerdref); their primary task was the support of the prince's household. The arable land of the village was cultivated in common by the serfs, part of the produce being allotted to them for their own maintenance, the rest going to the court. The land set aside for the use of the villagers was common to all the tenants; plots might be allocated to individuals for a season, but however long they and their sons were in occupation, these never became family lands. The same applied to the trefgevery townships; the land was the common property of the tenants and no individual or group could acquire personal rights over it.

The crop most widely grown in medieval Caernarvonshire was oats, but wheat, barley, rye and flax were also included in the produce of the Middle Ages. Wheat, especially, was raised in Anglesey on the fertile soils which made that island, with the peninsula of Llŷn, the granary of North Wales at this period. Probably at first only one ploughing of the land was customary, in March or April, but by the late thirteenth century two ploughings were the rule, in spring and autumn. A heavy wooden plough was used drawn by a team of oxen, four or eight in a team; one of the necessary qualifications of the ploughman was that he should be able to make his own plough and fix the iron share and coulter into place. The open fields of the tref were worked in common; regulations for their cultivation in the unfree gafaelion are laid down in Hywel Dda's laws. The cultivators contributed the oxen for the plough team and shared in the labour of ploughing, the quillets of land being apportioned among them annually. The cultivators of the arable in the free gwely must have had some similar arrangement; the dispersed nature of their strips in the common fields of several townships must have led to a number of such contracts with neighbouring occupiers for joint assistance at plough-time. In a clause laying down rules in case of a dispute arising between co-tillers over the clearing and ploughing of "rough, bushy land" we get a glimpse of the extensive system of agriculture, necessitated by the exhaustion of soils continuously cropped and inadequately manured, and by the growing numbers to be maintained in the tref. Some form of grain-drying was employed, essential for successful harvesting in the wet mountain climate; the Laws decree that if a man dry corn upon the kiln of another he is answerable for any damage that might occur through the outbreak of fire "unto the end of three nights and three days." The serfs in the maerdref had to build a kiln and dry the grain of their lord as part of their labour services.

The division of land incurred under the Welsh system of inheritance is one factor leading in the course of time to the small and scattered holdings and lonely farms which are such a characteristic feature of the Welsh landscape. The irregular shape of the fields surrounding the hill farms suggest their piecemeal incorporation from the waste as the years went by; the Welsh homestead was, as a general rule, largely self-sufficing till the mid nineteenth century, so the use to which the land was put was very varied. Grain crops, flax and hay were included in the tillage of each steading, together with paddocks of rough pasture; very rarely in north-west Wales there might be a small orchard, and from the late eighteenth century a potato patch was frequently added.

During the summer months the sheep and cattle were moved from the valley meadows or the lower grazing-grounds, the fridds of the foothills, to the high mountain pastures, the farmer and his household migrating with them to a temporary house called the *hafod* which was perched in a cwm of the higher hills. It must be remembered that ewes as well as goats and cows were milked in the Middle Ages; goats usually accompanied the cattle as a safeguard, for they could graze without harm the herbage on the shelf of a precipice or an overhanging crag which it would be perilous for a cow to attempt; they are used for the same purpose on the Alpine pastures of the present day. The family returned to the permanent or old homestead, the *hendref*, in the late summer in time for the harvesting, bringing with them the cheeses made during the time in the mountains. The months of May, June and July were usually spent in the hafod; harvesting took place in August or September, or even later if the season were wet, for there is remembrance in the Pentrevoelas uplands of reaping by the October moon.

For all its simplicity we get the impression of a vivid intense life, mirrored in the songs and the romances of the Middle Ages. It was lit with the drama of the blood feud, the cattle raid across the border or into a neighbour's territory, the call to arms against the advancing war bands of a rival prince or the Saxon or Norman enemy. The Welsh were ever renowed for their hospitality; Giraldus Cambrensis, son of a Norman baron and a Welsh mother in whose veins the blood of the princes flowed, has left us an account of his journey through the country in 1188, when he came with Archbishop Baldwin to recruit for the crusade against Saladin. The house of the free man was open to the wayfarer, who had merely to relinquish his arms on entering, and could then regard it as his own home during his stay. If he arrived in the morning, he would be entertained throughout the day by the conversation of the young women of the family, and by the playing of the harp, an art cherished above all others. Music and song, the recitation of the great deeds of the past or the prowess of a living leader by the household or travelling bard, the eloquence of set speeches, so beloved of the Welshman, these were the common forms of recreation when the day's work or hunting was over. The house of the small farmer "boasted neither tables, cloths nor napkins," Giraldus says, but the food was set on wooden platters among the rushes of the floor, and the company sat down in messes of three to partake of it. The fare was plain, unenlivened by spices or seasoning; broth and meat, cheese, fish from river or lake, and a thin oatcake, baked daily, comprised the meal. Milk was drunk in large quantities; when Llywelyn ap Gruffydd went up to London in 1277 to pay his homage to the English king, taking with him a considerable body of retainers, the resources of their hosts at Islington were greatly strained, because the Welshmen demanded milk and despised the London beer.

Thus, we catch a glimpse of the Welshman of the Middle Ages, alert, restless, warlike, yet with something strangely appealing about him, and about the life of his simple household, filled with music in the evening light. We suspect that even then he had an intense love of the beauty of his country, which was to find expression in some of Dafydd ap Gwilym's songs in the fourteenth century; we know how her history and mythology were woven into the stuff of his dreams. Above all, we sense his courage in the long and desperate struggle for independence, the hope that would never die.

Giraldus has left, scattered through his writings, a vivid little sketch of the Welsh he encountered nearly eight hundred years ago:

> "These people," he says, "being of a sharp and acute intellect, and gifted with a rich and powerful understanding, excel in whatever studies they pursue, and are more quick and cunning than the other inhabitants of a western clime . . .
>
> "In their rhymed songs and set speeches they are so subtle and ingenious, that they produce, in their native tongue, ornaments of wonderful and exquisite invention both in the words and sentences. . . . Nature hath given not only to the highest, but also to the inferior classes of people of this nation, a boldness and confidence in speaking and answering, even in the presence of their princes and chieftains . . .
>
> "Hermits and anchorites more strictly abstinent and more spiritual can nowhere be found; for this nation is earnest in all its pursuits, and neither worse men than the bad, nor better than the good, can be met with."

In another passage, speaking of their physique and training he tells us that they were:

> "light and active, hardy rather than strong, and entirely bred up to the use of arms; for not only the nobles, but all the people are trained to war, and when the trumpet sounds the alarm, the husbandman rushes as eagerly from his plough as the courtier from his court, . . . they esteem it a disgrace to die in bed."

So, in the long contest with the Norman, the blood of the Welsh was poured out in defence of a lost cause; the Saxon forces were broken in a day at Hastings, but it took the followers of William nearly two hundred years to conquer this difficult terrain, this proud and indomitable people.

References for Chapter 17

Ancient Laws and Institutes of Wales (Record Commission 1841), Bowen (1941), Ellis (1926), Record of Caernarvon (Record Commission 1838), Jones-Pierce (1939) (1942), Rhys and Brynmor Jones (1900), Lloyd (1938), Giraldus Cambrensis (1188).

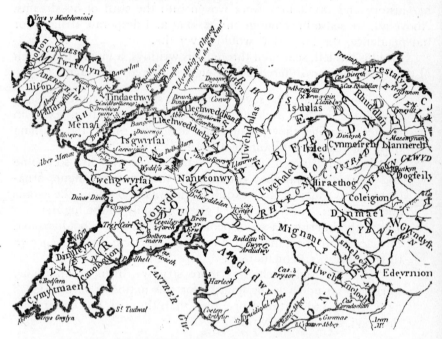

MAP 6.—A map of North Wales, according to the Ancient Divisions with their respective Cantreus subdivided into Cornots

By William Owen, 1788.   By courtesy of the National Library of Wales

CHAPTER 18

HOUSE AND CHURCH BUILDING
IN SNOWDONIA

THE vigorous culture of the Norman, itself enriched by contact with the higher civilization of the East in Spain and the Holy Land, gradually penetrated the indigenous culture of Wales to change and modify it. With the impetus of new ideas, impressions and craftsmanship came the flowering of a national renaissance, the rise of a school of poets to proclaim the valour and munificence of the Welsh leaders, and of writers to weave the romances of the Kings of Britain into a fabulous history, or to collect the folk tales and myths which fill the pages of the *Mabinogion* with glowing colour, recalling the memory of a world so ancient that men have forgotten the significance of much that they write.

The first attempt to build in stone on a scale comparable with the achievements of the invader were made in the twelfth century. Iorwerth of the Broken Nose, father of Llywelyn the Great, who apparently inherited Nant Conwy as his share of the kingdom of Gwynedd, built the castle of Dolwyddelan in 1170 (Pl. XXV, p. 338); the grim, rectangular keep stands on a great rock a mile beyond the village. It is possible that Llywelyn was born here, and he almost certainly passed the early years of his life within its walls, before he was taken to Powys for safety as a small child after the death of his father. Similarly, in the cantref of Arfon, a new royal fortress was built at Dolbadarn; the ruined shell of the stone tower stands on the shore of Llyn Padarn at the opening to the Llanberis pass (Pl. 29b, p. 334). According to Leland, the traveller and antiquary of the sixteenth century, Llywelyn ap Gruffydd imprisoned his older and recalcitrant brother Owain Goch (Owain the Red) in this gaunt fortress some say for over twenty years, and here Owain Glyndwr, in the first successful flood-tide of his rebellion, confined his implacable enemy, Lord Grey of Ruthin, after the battle of 1401 at some unidentified spot between Ruthin and Corwen. The servile tenants of the adjoining commote of Isgwyrfai were charged with the maintenance of the structure, bringing stone and timber for repairs when necessary, while the tenants of Nant Conwy were similarly made responsible for the upkeep of the fabric of Dolwyddelan.

As time passed the farmers themselves adopted the practice of strengthening the wattle walls of their dwellings with a clay daub, which in turn, perhaps, led to the construction of mud walls, a material still in common use for cottages in the eighteenth and early nineteenth centuries. Thus Penruddocke Wyndham, who made two journeys through Wales in 1774 and 1775, describes the houses of the lowland dwellers in Caernarvonshire:

> Their habitations are low, mud-built hovels, raised over the natural earth, which is as deficient in point of level within, as without. Notwithstanding the severity of the climate, the windows are frequently destitute of a single piece of glazing. If the inhabitants wish to enjoy the light, they must at the same time suffer the cold.

The inner and outer walls of the small farmhouse of Ffynnon Bedr, on the outskirts of Llanbedr-y-cennin, which Messrs. Hughes and North ascribe to the fourteenth century, are of mud, and are three and a half feet thick; the core between is filled with bran to keep out the damp. The roof was raised in the eighteenth century to insert an upper storey, but when built the one long living-room was open to the rafters. The magnificent oak beam of the ingle nook is doubtless part of the original structure, but the interior of the house has been radically altered in the course of the centuries.

On the uplands and in districts where loose fragments of rock or shale abounded the use of these materials was also adopted, "piled together without mortar or whitewash" as the Report of the Commissioners on Education in 1847 described them. At first, the masons retained the building methods employed in the wood and wattle houses; the great curved oak principals or crucks, holding the ridge-pole, still sprang from the floor as they had to do in the wattle dwelling where they carried the main thrust—the walls acting merely as a screen from the weather and lending no support to the roof. An interesting example can be seen at Hafod Yspytty in the parish of Ffestiniog. Hughes and North, writing in the early years of the twentieth century, found many traces of this method of construction in Caernarvonshire, which they assigned to the fourteenth and fifteenth centuries. Frequently two such principals were employed, "starting from the floor, against the side walls, and meeting at the ridge," but many examples were also discovered where only one pair of crucks was used, set up near the centre

PLATE XXVII

John Markham

a. Llangelynin: note small east window, thick sloping walls, and boarded roof of sanctuary

John Markham

b. Caerhun: this fourteenth-century church (built on the Roman encampment) presents an interesting contrast

C. A. Gibson-Hill

c. Dolwyddelan old church: early stone pillar of the transept arch, and rood screen

John Markham

d. Llanrhwychwyn: early font of unusual design, probably of the thirteenth century

CHURCH INTERIORS

PLATE XXVIII

John Markham

DOLWYDDELAN OLD CHURCH: with early roof of thick slates

of the building, the ridge-pole of the roof resting in the fork of these and on the stone gable-ends. It is believed that many of the old churches were built in this way, and that the close-couple roof was only introduced by the monks who followed the Normans and the English into Wales. The cruck construction is found throughout the highland zone of Britain, and Dr. Iorwerth Peate, in his interesting study of the Welsh house, adduces evidence to show that it represents a north-western European building tradition and was established throughout the greater part of Wales in the medieval period.

At first, large undressed boulders were used to form a projecting sill on which the wood and wattle wall rested, and these great boulders or slabs of living rock *in situ* are incorporated in the foundations of many of the early stone-built houses and barns. The walls rise from the projecting plinths with a slight inward slope or batter, which gives an impression of unshakable strength and solidity to the smallest cottage or cow-house. The stones selected gradually decrease in size with the height of the wall so that those in the upper courses are small enough for a man to handle easily, a gradation that is very pleasing to the eye. The great, undressed blocks were pegged into position with smaller stones; Hughes and North point out that in the early nine-teenth century, when the stones for the walls were hammer-trimmed, the chippings were still used for this purpose. In the coastal region and the lower Conway valley as far as Trefriw, granite predominates as a building material, and heavy oak beams form the lintels of doors and windows, while in the vicinity of Snowdon and in its valleys—the Llugwy, the Lledr and the Machno—slate rock prevails. Very typical of the Snowdon group are the massive slate door-posts crowned with a rude arch, of the older houses; an excellent example from the farm of Fedw Deg, which stands on the hillside near the entrance to the little Alpine valley of the Gwibernant is shown in Pl. XXVI, p. 339. In its rugged magnificence and crudity it suggests irresistibly the entrance to a Megalithic tomb.

The house originally had a great central chimney and another at one end, with a spiral stone staircase winding up behind it. In the old church at Betws-y-coed will be found the fourteenth-century effigy in armour of Gruffydd ap Dafydd Goch of Fedw Deg, grandson of Dafydd, the brother of Llywelyn the Last. Local tradition still preserves the memory of the difficulty which the bearers found in carrying the body of Gruffydd down the steep hillside to its last resting place, for he was a very heavy man. A path running up the hill from the farm of Tan-yr-allt in the Lledr valley below is still called the path of Gruffydd ap Dafydd Goch.

An early development in Welsh domestic architecture was the "long house," of which Dr. Iorwerth Peate has made a special study. It was designed to bring the farmer and his animals under one roof and thus to give him ready access to his cattle in all weathers. Dr. Peate states that houses of this type are widely distributed throughout Europe where primitive economic conditions still prevail; in Wales examples have been found, or memory of their existence noted, in nine out of the thirteen counties. The house was a long, single-storeyed, rectangular structure; the living quarters of the family occupied one end, usually the upper, the cow-house the other or lower end, set at a slightly lower level with a step down into it. At first no division appears to have existed between the two; a traveller in Caernarvonshire in 1797 notes that men and livestock "pig promiscuously together," implying that the living room in this outlying region was not generally partitioned off even at the dawn of the nineteenth century. In the examples that exist, however, there is a wall dividing the cow-house from the single living-room, with a door giving access to it, and frequently with a narrow passage running between the two and serving as a feeding walk. A door also opens into the passage from the exterior of the house and another leads from the living-room into the open air. The dwelling-room is generally paved, while the cow-shed has an earthen floor, and the fireplace of the living quarters is usually placed in the centre of the building against the dividing wall between house and cow-shed. In the examples which he examined Dr. Peate found that frequently the single living-room had been split up into two or more, to provide a parlour, dairy and bedroom, or the roof had been raised and an upper storey added in modern times, entirely altering the aspect of the house.

The fire was the centre of social and family life, regarded as almost sacred, and never allowed to die out. (The curious may find a lonely farm on the Pentrevoelas uplands today where the fire has not been out for a hundred years.) It was built on the floor against the *pentanfaen* or fire-back stone; in the king's house, the Welsh laws tell us that it was placed between the central pair of crucks, dividing the hall into two. Giraldus describes how at night-time, in the house of the freeman or *uchelwyr*, a bed of rushes was made up along the wall at the side of the room, covered with a coarse cloth or blanket of native manufacture, and the household lay down in common to sleep, the fire burning at their feet throughout the night. The grate and the closed oven are comparatively late importations, generally not found till the nineteenth century in the hill districts; all the cooking, including the baking of bread in a crock, was done on the open fire of wood or peat.

It is not so much, however, in domestic architecture as in the simplicity and strength of the little churches of the countryside, which have escaped the hands of the nineteenth-century "restorer," that we find the essence of the peasant culture which has been the great gift of Wales to the life of the British Isles. The Celtic church, in its primitive design, was a small, rectangular structure, seldom exceeding 20-40 feet in length. There was usually only one window, at the east end; this was square-headed, for the arch was avoided in the work of the early Welsh wherever possible. "Local Welsh work is an architecture of lintels, not of arches, and has descended thus from earliest times," says Mr. H. L. North. If it were found necessary to enlarge the building various devices were adopted; first, perhaps, a second church was added close by (there were originally two at Penmachno); secondly, a very common practice was to lengthen the nave; thirdly, a transept was thrown out to one side, built level with the chancel, as at Dolwydde-lan, Betws-y-coed old church, and Capel Curig; while fourthly, in Denbighshire and more rarely in Caernarvonshire, a second aisle was added, running the whole length of the building, as at Llanrhychwyn.

During the early years of the twelfth century, the Cistercians first made their way into Wales and spread rapidly in different parts of the country. The earlier monastic houses of the Benedictine Order, founded by the conquering Norman, were regarded with indifference or hostility by the Welsh, but these new Puritans of the Roman Church made an instant appeal to the religious sentiment of the native people. Men who still honoured the life of the hermit on his storm-battered rock or island or in his mountain retreat, could appreciate the impulse which drove the Cistercians into the most barren solitudes to found their religious houses and reclaim land for their flocks or for grain cultivation. In 1186 the monastery of Aberconway was founded by a colony sent out from the earlier house of Strata Florida in Cardiganshire. For a few years the new cell apparently found a home near Caernarvon, but it shortly moved to the mouth of the Conway river, where the great Abbey was built on land granted to the community by the royal house of Gwynedd. The chancel, nave and aisles of the existing parish church of Conway formed part of the original structure of the monks; the transept was added in the fourteenth century. Llywelyn the Great extended his special protection to the community, once he had established his supremacy in Gwynedd, granting to the Abbey a famous charter which confirmed and extended all previous gifts and privileges, and included territory in the hills of Nant Conwy and in Nant Gwynant in its bequests.

It was probably under the imaginative stimulus provided by the proud buildings of the new Abbey that Llywelyn turned his attention to the church of Llanrhychwyn, which local tradition associates so closely with his name. Climbing up into the hills from Trefriw we come upon it, set in the midst of fields and looking out over the rolling slopes that lead up to the peak of Carnedd Llywelyn. It is almost buried in the great yews which surround it, trees whose symbolism typifies alike death and resurrection, and which have been held in superstitious awe at least since Roman times (Pl. 31a). The early roof of thick slates remains on the south aisle, the eaves reaching to within eight feet or so of the ground, and the narrow doorway, less than three feet wide, is also typical of such early buildings (Pl. 31b). This south aisle, which was later extended (for the Church was originally a simple parallelogram), may contain a little twelfth century work in the thick, sloping walls of the south and west, but dates for the most part from the early thirteenth century, and was possibly restored by Llywelyn. The north aisle, with its sturdy, square pillars, was added in the sixteenth, probably by Meredydd ap Ieuan, the ancestor of the Wynns of Gwydir, who built Dolwyddelan church, for the addition bears certain structural resemblances to the latter. Great oak beams rest on these pillars, underpinning the roof throughout the length of the church; it is the only example in the locality of the roof of an added nave supported by a lintel in place of arches. There is a deep font of early Celtic design (Pl. XXVIId, p. 346), probably from the twelfth century, and fragments of medieval and sixteenth-century painted and stained glass, yellow and brown, are to be found in the east windows. About this little building in its bare simplicity lies a strange, primitive beauty; for a moment, as nowhere else in North Wales, we seem to touch the pulse of that earlier world when Llywelyn the Great came here to worship.

The church at Trefriw, suffering much from its restoration, is of interest because it lays claim to have been built by Llywelyn to save

PLATE 31

John Markham

a. The church and lychgate, almost buried in the surrounding trees. July

John Markham

b. The south aisle, the oldest portion of the building. Note the narrow doorway
July

LLANRHYCHWYN CHURCH

PLATE 32

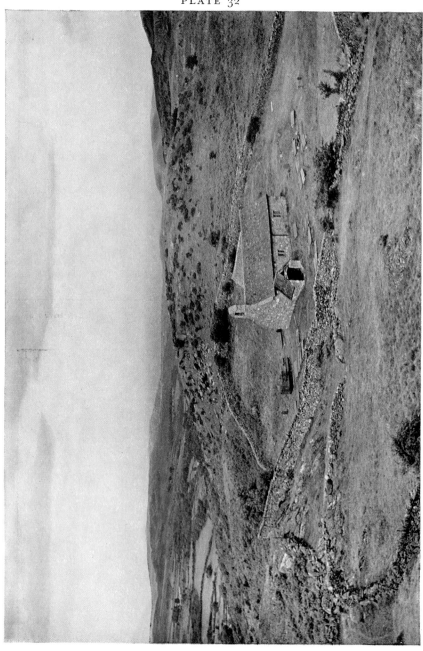

John Markham

LLANGELYNIN, the lonely windswept church, high above the Conway valley. For 500 years it has served the scattered inhabitants of these uplands. June.

his wife, Joan, the long walk up to Llanrhychwyn. Leland declares that Llywelyn and his wife had a castle at Trefriw, the ruined walls of which were pointed out to him on his visit here in 1536.

Llangelynin is another of the rare, unspoilt peasant churches, lost in the hills above the lower Conway. The nave, a portion of the original structure, is very early; the roof is constructed of three curved principals and may itself date from the opening years of the thirteenth century. The chancel is of late fourteenth-century work with a rather elaborate window inserted at the east end a hundred years later, and the roof of the sanctuary is boarded (Pl. XXVIIa, p. 346); the large north transept with its earthen floor and the porch are likewise from the fifteenth century. The most interesting feature of this church is the remnant of a solid oak screen of horizontal planks, which ran at one time across the whole building. Though traces of it are very rare nowadays, this screen was commonly found in the earliest Celtic churches, cutting off the chancel from the nave, as no structural division existed between the two in the simple design of these little buildings.

As we look down upon the grey, wind-battered walls of this little church in its wild and lonely setting, the great spaces of the Conway valley appearing over the shoulder of the hill beneath which it crouches, there comes to us a sense of the part it must have played as a centre of peace and consolation throughout the centuries to the dwellers of these uplands, battling for a livelihood on the untamed mountain slopes (Pl. 32).

Caerhûn, a church of the fertile valley, built at one end of the Roman camp on the banks of the Conway, presents an interesting contrast, representing the more prosperous and settled life of the lowland farmers. The west front, with its high façade and double bell-cot, adds much to the impression of dignity; within we find a very long and narrow building (69 feet by 17 feet), the appearance of great length heightened by the close-couple roof with its intermediate rafters (Pl. XXVIId, p. 346). The nave and the east window of three lights date from the thirteenth or early fourteenth century; the south transept was not added till 1591 but is built in the local, traditional style. Unfortunately, the interior fittings were entirely swept away in the restoration of the 1850's.

Dolwyddelan old church, built about 1512, reflects the still greater sophistication of the sixteenth century (Plate XXVIII, p. 347). The influence of Italian Renaissance architecture which Meredydd ap Ieuan had encountered on his travels, is very marked: witness the

z

broad, semi-classical east window. The transept was added in the early seventeenth century; the "rude Tuscan column" which supports the transept arch is believed to have been brought from the earlier building a quarter of a mile away (Pl. XXVIIc). The nave is almost square, and there is a fine oak rood screen of the late fifteenth century and some early family pews. The great treasure of the church is the small bronze bell, dug up nearby, typical of those used by the Celtic saints and which, with their magical properties, figure in the mythology of the early church. There is no means of dating it exactly, but it may belong to the sixth century of the Christian era.

Both the stone houses and churches were probably thatched in many cases; a visitor to Llanbedr-y-cennin in 1810 mentions that the church there had been thatched within living memory. But by the late fourteenth and the fifteenth century, straw and rushes were more and more commonly replaced by thick slates, varying from a half to three-quarters of an inch, but gradually reduced, in thickness. These roofs were apt to be both leaky and draughty, so in the Snowdon area they were laid on a bed of sphagnum moss, a "moss-man" coming round at intervals to push up fresh supplies beneath the slates with a rod bearing a flattened iron tip. A fine example of this "cerrig mwsog" (moss stone) roofing can be seen at Dolwyddelan old church, but it is now all too rare. The thin, uniform slate of the nineteenth century, which we know so well throughout the English countryside, has ousted the older roofing material, and many of the old buildings of North Wales have been repaired with them as necessity arose.

The monastic biographer of Gruffydd ap Cynan, who extended the control of Gwynedd over the counties of Flint and Denbigh between the years 1100 and 1114, extols the monarch for inducing the progress of the domestic arts in the long years of peace brought by his rule. The farmers of Gwynedd no longer built their homes and sowed their crops with an eye to the needs of a single year, dreading the descent of the raider to give house and field to the flames, but they dared to plan for the future. Land was drained and enclosed, orchards were planted, he says, and building in stone was undertaken, particularly of churches, which, dazzlingly white in the sunlight under a coat of limewash, flashed like the stars of heaven across the hills of North Wales. None of these buildings has survived for us, but the churches of Llanrhychwyn and Llangelynin arise from the inspiration of the same peasant culture a century or so later, to give us a glimpse of the struggling creative life of the Middle Ages in the hills of Snowdon, finding its own simple expression for the deepest impulses of worship.

References for Chapter 18

Lloyd (1938), Leland (1906 ed.), Wyndham (1781), Hughes and North (1908), Peate (1940), Giraldus Cambrensis (1930 ed.), North, H. L. (1906), Hughes, H. (1927), Buchedd Gruffydd ap Cynan (*Arch. Camb.* 1866), Hall (Bangor Manuscript 908).

CHAPTER 19

THE DEVELOPMENT OF
SOCIAL AND ECONOMIC LIFE IN THE
FOURTEENTH AND FIFTEENTH CENTURIES

BY the Statute of Wales, promulgated in 1284, Edward I annexed the territory of the last Prince of Gwynedd as a possession of the English Crown. Out of the Kingdom of Gwynedd and the old seigniory of Snowdon he carved the shires of Anglesey, Caernarvon, Merioneth and Flint; the towns and castles of Carmarthen and Cardigan, with the lands appurtenant to them, which Edward had inherited from his father, were first effectively reorganized as shire-ground, and placed under the Justiciar of West Wales. The whole territory, termed the Principality, was vested in his eldest son, born at Caernarvon, when the Prince came of age. Flint was made dependent upon the county Palatine of Chester, but the other three shires of North Wales were placed under the general control of a Justice of Snowdon, established in the new castle which Edward built at Caernarvon. A sheriff was appointed for life in each county to preside over the county court, and coroners to watch over the crown pleas. Welsh law was showing signs of decay before the overthrow of Llywelyn, and encroachments of English practice were to be observed even in North Wales, but Edward was anxious not to meddle unduly with established usages where these were of a reasonable character. He maintained the old cantrefi and commotes as subdivisions of the shire under their own Welsh officials, and though changes and modifications were introduced, the existing Welsh law was largely retained; the new counties were not brought under the sway of the English legal system. Neither did they return any members to Parliament; the Principality was a territory apart, like the Counties Palatine, and was not regarded as in any sense an integral portion of the realm of England.

The congeries of Marcher lordships remained untouched by the Statute of Wales. These districts of the border counties, and of Glamorgan and Pembroke, each amounted to a petty kingdom, the royal officers having no right of entry or of jurisdiction within them save in cases of escheat, i.e. if a lord Marcher died leaving no heirs. Each had its own *jura regalia* or royal rights, its chancery, courts and officers, the

PLATE 33

John Markham

CAERNARVON CASTLE, built under Edward I's instructions, after his defeat of the last independent Prince of Wales. The building began in 1285 and the castle was completed by 1322. It was much repaired in the mid nineteenth century

PLATE 34

John Markham

a. HAFOD YSPYTTY: the lonely farmhouse between Yspytty Ifan and Ffestiniog, a favourite meeting-place of bandits in the late 15th century. A part of the original house still remains. July

John Markham

b. WELSH BLACK CATTLE by the River Conway. June

courts exercising powers of judgment in both civil and criminal actions.
So long as this system continued there could be no unity of organization
within the country, and conditions of anarchy too often prevailed,
spreading from the lordships of the March into the shires.

The economic and social effects of the conquest were more far-
reaching; gradually, in the next two hundred years, the structure of
the tribal economy was undermined and a new system of relationships
grew up between man and man. The last two Llywelyns by their
centralizing policy had already set the movement in train. The com-
mutation to a monetary payment of renders in kind, or of hospitality
demanded on the royal progress of the prince or the chief officers of
his court, had advanced under their jurisdiction. It is interesting to
observe in this connection that in 1121 Maredudd ap Bleddyn of
Powys purchased peace from Henry I by the payment of a fine of
10,000 cattle, while Llywelyn the Great in 1228, at the close of Henry
III's unsuccessful campaign against Kerry, paid the sum of £2,000
for concessions granted to him by the King. The royal officials of
Edward, concerned primarily with raising revenue from the newly-won
lands to meet the expenses of administration and conquest, regarded
the commote as a fiscal unit rather than as an administrative division
supplying the local needs of the people and the household of the
overlord. The residue of gifts in kind and of labour services were
converted into cash sums, and a heavy financial burden was thus
suddenly imposed on the inhabitants of the North Wales shires. The
money rental from the husbandmen of Nant Conwy, for instance, was
thus increased from £7 to £20 annually, as the former dues of butter
and grain and the customary services were abolished.

The crown officials, faced with the problem of lands escheating to
their master, regarded the gwely in Caernarvonshire as a definite
territorial unit, composed of so many bovates or acres, of which they
conceived the members as holding fractional shares. Thus, by a stroke
of the pen of accountant or lawyer, the members of the gwely acquired
a legal recognition of the right to land instead of the old right to
maintenance. Escheats could arise in various ways, through lack of
heirs within the fourth degree, or through an act of felony or rebellion
on the part of the occupier, rendering his holding forfeit; the king was
anxious to lease the properties he thus acquired at an increased rental.
A new feature was thus introduced into Welsh life, for the lessee became
a tenant of the crown for a stated number of years, instead of a member

of a kinship group with an hereditary life share in the family property, encompassed about with duties and responsibilities to his kindred. This new concept of landlord and tenant arising in the tref or township would tend to weaken the relationships of the gwely as the years passed. The old inhibitions and hesitations regarding the alienation of family lands would gradually be broken down. Under pressure of financial need, the tribesman would find that he could transfer his allotment to a neighbour by a Welsh process akin to mortgage, known as *tir prid*; his successors, if they wished, could recover the land parted with on these terms by payment of the initial purchase price. More occasionally in the fourteenth century, the Welsh farmer might obtain the royal licence to sell his holding outright. Thus strangers and even bondmen would enter upon the lands of the free gwely, further weakening the family ties.

As the counterpart of such transactions, a man of ambition might add to his holding by taking up the lease of adjacent lands which had fallen into the King's hands, or which a neighbour wished to mortgage, and thus might lay the foundation of a modern farming unit. The old tribal bonds were thus severely strained; new ideas were abroad, fresh relationships were growing up based on the personal responsibility of tenant to landlord, new possibilities opened before the adventurous young farmer of advancing his economic position beyond the rough equality imposed by the tribal order.

Beneath the great castles which Edward built at Conway, Caernarvon (Pl. 33, p. 354), Harlech and Beaumaris, to hold his possessions in North Wales, he established a series of new boroughs, colonized by English citizens and traders. In some cases, notably at Caernarvon, these little towns received their charters of incorporation even before the castle was completed. The English burgesses provided a nucleus of loyal and stable citizens in the midst of a hostile population, and the Welsh, who occupied property in the vicinity of the chosen sites, were removed to other districts and compensated with land elsewhere. Over 5,000 acres were involved in this appropriation, of which more than 1,446 occur at Caernarvon and some 700 at Conway.

The land was taken from the royal demesnes of the native princes, including that of the neighbouring villein hamlets, to avoid interference with the family properties of the free gweliau. At Caernarvon, the town rose on the site of an old Welsh maenor or royal residence and

of the serf vill of Llanbeblig; at Conway, on the estate granted to the
Cistercian abbey by the Welsh princes from their demesne lands in the
commote of Creuddyn; at Criccieth the town was built on the demesne
of the royal maenor beneath the earlier castle which Edward re-
modelled, supplemented by the lands of an escheated gwely near
Ystumllyn. The monks of Aberconway were sent up the river to
build their new home at Maenan; holders of gwely lands in this area
were removed to make room for them, and were distributed in the
commote of Creuddyn and in Anglesey. Such transfers, and the
re-arrangement of lands involved, must have led to a further disintegration of tribal customs and relations. In some cases the bondman gained
his freedom in the course of these transactions, receiving the grant of a
free gafael in another district in return for his old holding.

The walled towns of Conway, Caernarvon and Beaumaris provide
excellent examples of the early fourteenth-century planning of colonial
settlements.

> "These towns," writes Dr. E. A. Lewis in his *Medieval Boroughs
> of Snowdonia*, "were built on a regular plan, the principal streets
> wide, open and straight, crossing each other at right angles, with
> a large market place invariably in the centre of the town . . .
>
> "The prevailing characteristic of these medieval municipalities
> was their rural appearance. . . . There was no close amalgamation
> of town houses, much less overcrowding of the urban populace.
> The well-arranged terraces of burgages were interspersed with
> green strips of land not appropriated by the dwelling-houses.
> Royal roads or streets leading to the forum, or market-place of the
> borough, intersected the terraces. These were daily traversed by
> the burgesses attending to their lands beyond the walls, and by
> the country folk on their coming to market for purposes of
> exchange."

The burgage of Caernarvon and Criccieth, the same writer notes, was
eighty feet long by sixty feet broad; a burgage signifies a dwelling
with the land immediately around it. The houses were built of wood
from the forests of Snowdon, or of stone left over from the materials of
the castle and walls, sold cheap to the burgesses. In 1295 a certain
Madoc Cragh with sixty-four co-workers was engaged in conveying
timber and slates by packhorse from Beddgelert for the royal granary
at Caernarvon; the citizens also had their barns and storehouses built

within the town walls to store the produce from their fields beyond.

The normal garrison maintained in the castles was a small one numbering about 16 men in each case, but immediately after the conquest and in times of stress, such as Glyndwr's revolt or the Wars of the Roses, Conway might have as many as 30 in the castle guard and Caernarvon 40, half of them being crossbowmen. Small town garrisons were also introduced at such times, under the control of a captain. The adjoining commotes were charged with the payment of an annual sum, the *staurum principis* or *castrorum*, for provisioning the castle. The commotes of Creuddyn, Ughaph, Isaph and Nant Conwy sent annual contributions of 11s. 8d., 16s. 8d. or 25s. to Conway, these sums representing the half value of varying numbers of cows and oxen. The commotes of Uwchgwyrfai, Isgwyrfai and Dinllaen were charged with similar amounts to provide for the garrison at Caernarvon. Castle and town thus became administrative as well as military centres; their influence on the surrounding countryside was heightened by the fact that Edward also made his new boroughs the centre of a market district. The Welsh were forbidden to trade save in the urban markets and fairs; hitherto such buying and selling as was necessary had taken the form of private transactions carried out between neighbours in the hills. Under the new economic policy the little Welsh farmer came fearfully to the strange walled town, driving his livestock before him or bearing his bundles of produce, armed cap-à-pie as though for battle, and in his ignorance transgressing all the market regulations. From the proceeds of his sale of cheese and butter, skins or wool, or a roll of coarse cloth, he could purchase such necessities as salt and iron, or perhaps a little wine for a luxury, and other small articles of merchandise. The trading monopoly of the English boroughs was only gradually broken by the rise of such Welsh centres of exchange as Aber, Llanrwst and Trefriw; the two latter in time succeeded in drawing to themselves all the commerce of Nant Conwy.

The burgesses were only part-time merchants or craftsmen, pursuing meanwhile their farming activities on the town lands which they rented outside the walls. The researches of Dr. Lewis have shown that their ranks included a miscellaneous collection of petty shopkeepers and artisans, skinners, glovers, brewers, tailors, bakers, smiths and cobblers.

Among their number were individuals who became active pioneers in the new land market. One, Bartholomew Bolde of Conway, had acquired through mortgage or purchase by 1463 a considerable estate of over 1,800 acres in the middle Conway valley, including in one block near Llwydfaen the whole territory of an earlier township or hamlet. Dr. Jones-Pierce has found that the boundary of a single farm of 200 acres on this site roughly coincides with that of the medieval vill. But if the townsman gave the impetus to estate building on a large scale in this area, as he suggests, Welsh families were by no means backward in the race for land. An inquisition *post mortem* held on the estate of William ap Gruffydd of Penrhyn in 1430–31 revealed that on his death he was in control of a territory of 1,015 acres, mostly situated in the neighbourhood of Corwyrion but including lands and messuages in Bangor and Nant Ffrancon, much of which he had obtained by gift, purchase or lease.

The distribution of certain fifteenth-century farmsteads in the Conway valley suggests that such concentration of land in the hands of fewer tenants and owners gave rise to a class of "displaced persons" in the late medieval period. The less successful farmers appear to have been pushed into the upland regions, shifting the margin of cultivation to a higher level. Dr. Elfyn Hughes, in his detailed and interesting study of the lower Conway, found a group of fifteenth-century farms, now in ruins, lying on or near the 1,000 foot contour just below Cwm Eigiau on slopes which must have been covered with oak and birch scrub when the new homeless arrived. He mentions the unerring insight with which they sought out the pockets of better soil on these bleak heights for clearance and tillage, and even succeeded in growing wheat here, if the field names which linger on are to be trusted.

While the Welsh people were slowly adapting themselves to the changed conditions following the conquest, the disaster of the pestilence known as the Black Death broke over the country in 1349. It took heavy toll of the population of Snowdon, particularly of the bond tenants. Some of the villein townships of the lower Conway valley and of the commote of Eifionydd were completely depopulated and in others it was found necessary to establish new tenements because the families of the former occupiers had died or fled. In the region of Dolgarrog, Dolwyddelan and Penmachno the villeins were swept away or vacated their lands and concealed themselves elsewhere, being unable, with their depleted numbers, to meet the burden of payments falling on their holdings. Nearly a hundred years later the tax payment substituted for the old renders of cattle for the royal herd, the *staurum domini*, could not be collected in those areas because no bondmen could be found dwelling there. Some of the vacated bond townships were leased, but men were chary of taking them lest their tenure involved loss of status; it was perhaps to overcome this difficulty and to deal with the problem of their depopulation, that Henry VII, in 1507, granted a charter emancipating all the villeins of the three shires of North Wales, and giving them the right in future to hold their lands by a free tenure. As a result, a number of squatters took up residence on the abandoned territories, whose descendants were to puzzle the Elizabethan lawyers with the claim that they were in possession of ancient freeholds.

Glyndwr's great revolt at the close of the fourteenth century, in a last desperate bid for Welsh freedom, brought further social disaster to the hills and valleys of Snowdon. It is one of the tragedies of history that this man, with his deep love for his country and his great gifts of leadership, whose political vision led him to embark on the experiment of the first Welsh parliament, and who dreamt of extending the boundaries of his country into the English midlands, and of establishing a university of Wales, with a college in both north and south, should, in the long run, have involved his people in years of suffering and wasted hopes, when the anarchy of the old tribalism once again reared its head.

Caernarvon and Conway were both besieged by the armies of the rebel leader, with resultant disorganization of trade; the cathedral at Bangor was burnt because the Bishop was loyal to the Crown, and the property of royalist sympathizers was ruthlessly destroyed. The mountains of Snowdon once again served as an impregnable retreat to the great Welsh patriot. On the hillsides above Cwm Ystradllyn, Glyndwr drilled his recruits and fashioned an army out of raw farm lads. Rhys Goch, the poet and his staunch friend, lived at Hafod Garegog on the banks of the Nantmor river; the hafod of the present day comprises the kitchens and servants' quarters of the old house. Here, says a local story, Glyndwr was surprised by the followers of a neighbouring, hostile squire; he fled with Rhys, both disguised as serving men, and while the latter turned towards Nantmor, Owain swam what was then the tidal estuary of the Glaslyn, and, skirting Llyn Oerddwr, struck out for Moel Hebog. His pursuers were close on his heels, and in desperation he attempted the precipitous chimney of Hebog which reaches nearly to the peak. None dared to follow him, so, having made the ascent in safety, he turned along the ridge of Diffwys to a cave just below the brow of the precipice in which that mountain terminates, and which is still called the Ogof Owain Glyndwr, where he is said to have lived in hiding for six months, the Prior of Beddgelert supplying him with food.

Nant Conwy suffered particularly in this struggle, Owain destroying everything in the fertile valley that might aid the armies of the crown, and the English in their turn burning and plundering as they passed through. So great was the desolation that Sir John Wynn of Gwydir, recounting the stories current in the latter sixteenth century, states that grass grew in the market place of Llanrwst and deer fed in the churchyard. When the revolt died away in failure, and Glyndwr had disappeared into the misty solitude of the hills, heavy disabilities were imposed on the insurgents. No man of Welsh birth was allowed to purchase land or houses in any town of Wales or the Marches, to bear arms or to own a fortified residence; no Welshman could hold office in his own land, or could convict an Englishman for a wrong suffered. The bards, those active propagandists of the national cause, were suppressed; if an English burgess married a Welshwoman he thereby lost his burgess rights. Doubtless these bitter measures fell into desuetude with the lapse of time; it is noteworthy for instance what a great part Welshmen played in the French wars of Henry V, but no attempt was made on a generous scale to improve matters or promote intercourse between the two peoples till the days of the Tudor monarchy.

In the middle of the fifteenth century, over forty years after the disappearance of Glyndwr, the outbreak of the Wars of the Roses again involved the inhabitants of Snowdon in fresh suffering and social disorder. Many of the great baronial families drawn into the contest were Marcher lords with bands of Welsh followers in their train, and a number of skirmishes took place on Welsh soil. At the beginning of the conflict, the Yorkist interests predominated in the Marches, the Lancastrian in the Principality, South Wales and Pembroke. It was at Twthill, just outside the town of Caernarvon, that Jasper Tudor and the Lancastrians of North Wales made a last stand on October 16th, 1461, eight months after the victory of Edward at Mortimer's Cross which opened the road to London and the crown. In the following years Jasper was constantly moving from hiding-place to hiding-place in the mountains of North Wales; it was to a Flintshire port that he came, hidden beneath a bundle of pease straw, to make his escape to Brittany. In 1466 three adherents of Edward IV in North Wales were commissioned to enquire into the report that the greater part of the revenues and rents from Caernarvonshire and Merioneth had not been paid during his reign owing to the refusal of the tenants to meet their obligations. Two years later Jasper Tudor returned to stir up rebellion; he succeeded in crossing the country from the Merioneth coast to Denbigh, the people flocking to join him. Lord Herbert was despatched by the king to intercept him, and encountered Jasper and his force somewhere between Denbigh and the Conway valley. In the ensuing fray Jasper was worsted and several of his party were taken prisoner. Herbert then pressed on up the Conway valley to Dol-wyddelan, leaving behind him a trail of desolation from the ravages of his troops. The whole district in the vicinity was laid waste; Sir John Wynn, writing nearly 150 years after that fateful march, could declare: "The imprint of the devestation is yet extant, the verie stones in manie habitations in and along my demaynes carrying yet the colour of fire."

The effect of these events on the social life of the area was disastrous. Since the days of Glyndwr lawlessness and unrest had been rife. Bands of outlaws infested the Snowdon hills, living upon cattle raids and the plunder of private warfare. In or about the year 1189 a Hospital of the Knights of St. John had been founded in the upper Conway valley, giving its name to the village of Yspytty Ifan (Pl. 38a, p. 387). Its purpose was to give shelter and succour to travellers across the bleak moorlands that surround the headwaters of the Conway, and various privileges and immunities were bestowed on this house by the rulers of Gwynedd. When the Knights of St. John had gone the right of immunity attaching to their lands remained, so that no royal officer could enter their boundaries to arrest malefactors fleeing thither. The old hospice became "a veritable wasps' nest" of evildoers, who held the country in terror for twenty miles around. The farm of Hafod Yspytty, a favourite gathering-place of these outlaws, can be found in a lonely dip of the hills between Yspytty Ifan and Ffestiniog; part of the fifteenth-century structure still stands (Pl. 34a, p. 355).

It was also the custom for the gentlemen of the countryside to receive the outcasts of society and maintain them as bands of private desperadoes, ready to wage war against any neighbour or relative who had given cause of offence, and to protect their patrons against counter-attack. They were concealed by day in the outbuildings or in the dwelling-house, and stole forth at night on their lawless errands. Bitter family feuds were waged to the death, and the situation was exacerbated by the common practice of sending the children from the households

PLATE 35

John Markham

GWYDIR CASTLE, the home of Sir John Wynn of Gwydir in the 16th century
The house was much altered and partially rebuilt in the early 19th century

PLATE 36

Photographed by permission of Mr. Clough Williams-Ellis   *John Markham*

PLAS BRONDANW, Llanfrothen, home of William Williams, one of the pioneers in reclaiming land from the estuary on which the town of Portmadoc now stands. July

of the well-to-do to foster-parents for their upbringing, so that they grew up estranged from their own brothers and sisters. Linked by ties of affection to the foster-family rather than to their own kin, they were apt to regard the latter with jealousy and mistrust. Meredydd ap Ieuan, ancestor of Sir John Wynn, who was involved in such family strife, left his patrimony near Traeth Mawr and came to Dolwyddelan in the late fifteenth century, although Nant Conwy was a favourite hunting ground of the outlaws, saying he preferred to fight with thieves and bandits rather than with his own kindred. He purchased the castle of Dolwyddelan and dwelt there for a time, later building a house near Penmachno, "being the principal best ground in Dolwyddelan." He also built the existing old church at Dolwyddelan, because the earlier structure was situated in a thicket a quarter of a mile or so from the present site, where he feared an ambush might shelter to attack him on his way to worship. Even so, he found it expedient to post a watcher on a rock within view of both the church and his house, who could raise the alarm if his residence were attacked in his absence.

Yet against these shadows of anarchy and lawlessness must be set the quiet, patient service of the little peasant farmer to his land and his beasts, which is, after all, the abiding strength of a countryside. Bewildered by the changes all about him, the strife of the rising class of Welsh squires, and later the claims of a new religion often taught in an alien tongue, he continued steadily in the path of an age-old routine. If there were no changes introduced to improve the customary methods of tillage or stock-rearing, there was yet the slow, painful endeavour throughout these centuries to clear and drain the waste places and reclaim them for man's use. And all the time there must have been countless homes in which the affections and responsibilities of family life were upheld, and perhaps even strengthened by the turmoil and uncertainty of the age.

References for Chapter 19

Rees, J. A. W. (1938), Williams, W. Ll. (1907-08), Lloyd (1938), Lewis (1902-03) (1903) (1912), Ministers Accounts (Public Record Office, fourteenth and fifteenth centuries), Jones-Pierce (1939), Bangor, Penrhyn MS. 16, Baron Hill MSS. *passim*, Charter of Henry VII (*Arch. Camb.* 1847), Bradley (1901), Jenkins (1899), Evans (1915), Wynn (1927 ed.).

CHAPTER 20

THE NEW SQUIREARCHY OF SNOWDON IN TUDOR AND STUART TIMES

WITH the victory of Henry Tudor at Bosworth in 1485, a new chapter opened in the history of Wales. The Tudor king was hailed by the bards as one who could claim descent from the royal tribes of their country; he was regarded by the Welsh as a man of their own blood, with whom they could share the pride of a common heritage. Henry's great-grandfather, as Sir Frederick Rees reminds us, had fought for Glyndwr and had been executed for his part in the revolt, while his uncle, Jasper Tudor, had held the allegiance of North Wales for many years, and numberless men of Gwynedd had laid down their lives in his cause. If it be true, as Sir Frederick maintains, that for fifty years after the Battle of Bosworth the Tudor policy as it concerns Wales was one of opportunism, nevertheless there was a radical change in attitude towards the country and its people. The disabilities under which the Welsh had laboured, at least in theory, since the days of the Glyndwr rebellion, were removed; Welshmen were welcomed at court, and the attempt of Henry VII to deal with the poverty resulting from the depopulation of the villein lands of the northern counties has already been mentioned. The Council set up in the Marches of Wales by Edward IV to administer the lands held by, or escheating to, the Crown, was revived by Henry VII, and apparently re-formed as the Council of the Prince of Wales, till the untimely death of Arthur, the heir to the throne, in 1502, brought the scheme to an end for the time being.

In the early years of Henry VIII's reign the idea of a Council of the Marches again took shape, this time in the form of a prerogative court as a means of enforcing law in the border counties, a court which would strengthen the hands of local officials and bring some measure of order into the chaos of Marcher jurisdictions. Within the shires, Welshmen of character, like Meredydd ap Ieuan in Nant Conwy, took courageous action to reduce the worst disorders of their countryside; the latter was successful in so thwarting the banditry that they were forced to seek a home elsewhere. The building of such mansions as Cochwillan near Llanllechid, or the first wing of Gwydir castle, at the end of the fifteenth century implies a more stable and ordered condition of affairs. Cochwillan belonged to a younger branch of the family of Gruffydd of Penrhyn, and is one of the finest examples of fifteenth-century work in the district. The house, or all that remains of it, is now used as a barn, but the heavy oak screens remain, dividing the great hall into three, and there is a fine hammer-beam roof with a delicate pierced cornice running below it.

The old house of Gwydir, largely rebuilt by Sir John Wynn, stands on the west bank of the Conway at the foot of Carreg-y-gwalch, the rock of the falcons, which formed the hiding place of Dafydd ap Shenkin, staunch supporter of the Lancastrian cause in the Wars of the Roses. It lies in the midst of the rich river meadows, the traditional site of a bloody battle fought by the poet prince of the Cymry, Llywarch Hen, in A.D. 610. Pennant tells us that the place-name is derived from Gwaed Dir, the Blood Land, though this is not accepted by modern philologists.

The gutted and roofless wing of Gwydir (Pl. 35, p. 362) may have formed part of the earlier building on the site, but the house was greatly extended in the latter part of the sixteenth century, and was built round a great quadrangle and a lesser court. Much of it was pulled down in the nineteenth century and some rebuilding was done, though part of the earlier structure was left and the interior was never modernized. A great fire in the years between the two world wars swept away its remaining splendours. Sir John Wynn declared that it was "the fairest house in all North Wales" and the most fit to entertain a royal guest on the journey to or from Ireland. It is claimed that Queen Elizabeth visited it in its fresh glory, and that Charles I came here for rest and shelter after his defeat near Chester. But today it is the forlorn ruin shown in Plate 35, though one wing is being painstakingly repaired by the present owner.

The introduction of new measures for enforcing the King's peace paved the way for an advance in the standards of living and for the great changes of the mid sixteenth century, which were to put an end to the remnants of tribal custom, to abolish the old religion, and to see the birth of a society based upon wealth rather than upon the status conferred by birth. In 1536 the Act of Union, which annexed Wales to the realm of England, was passed. By this Act the territories covered by the great Marcher lordships were brought within the English county system, and the public law of England was substituted for the private law of the barons' demesnes and the Welsh custom governing the shires and the outlying regions. A Court of Great Sessions was established, independent of the Court of Westminster, and the country was divided into four circuits, each with its own Judge, thereby introducing a measure of local government in judicial matters. The Court of Great Sessions was retained till 1830; in that year, with its abolition, Wales was brought finally within the jurisdiction of the English circuits. Primogeniture was introduced as the rule of inheritance, and was generally adopted within a generation or so, thus halting the subdivision of land, though in some districts the old Welsh system of dividing the inheritance among the heirs lingers to the present day. The Welsh counties and boroughs were given representation in Parliament; henceforth the Welshman was a member of the Kingdom of Britain and no longer a foreigner once he crossed the border.

The greater security to life and property entailed by the establishment of a single legal system throughout the country resulted in a great improvement in the general orderliness. This gave encouragement to the accumulation of riches, which there was thus some reasonable assurance of handing on to an heir. The contacts with the central government and the court opened hitherto unknown possibilities of advancement; the Welshman might now hope to gain access to some lucrative office under the Tudor administration, or to make his way in one of the professions, such as law or the church. The dissolution of the monasteries gave the Welsh gentry fresh opportunities of enlarging their estates, while trade and commerce grew apace with the added stability of social conditions. Thus there arose a new type of Welsh landowner and country gentleman, divorced from the peasantry and the old ways of subsistence farming, acquiring riches, building fine houses, sending his sons to the new grammar schools and the English universities for their education, and himself speaking the English tongue, an essential qualification for tenure of office both within and without Wales.

The old houses of the countryside each has its family history, linking the life of the outlying regions of Snowdon with national movements and events, and with the great personalities of the sixteenth and seventeenth centuries. The young gallants of Elizabeth's reign, seeking their fortune on the high seas, followed Drake in his harrying of the Spaniards, and laid the foundation of their riches in plunder. Piers Gruffydd, for instance, of the house of Gruffydd of Penrhyn, according to the statements of both Pennant and William Williams of Llandegai, played a part in the rout of the Spanish Armada, though he was only a minor when the fleet swept up the Channel. Some doubt has been cast on these stories, but it is certain, nevertheless, that he acquired some of his wealth by the capture of Spanish prizes, for in 1600 the Lord High Admiral issued a commission to six persons to appraise and apportion the cargo of the Spanish ship, *Speranza*, brought to the mouth of the Cegin river in Caernarvonshire by Piers.

Other families sought wealth through the legitimate channels of trade, such as Hugh Gruffydd, son to John Gruffydd of Cefn Amwlch in Llŷn, or Maurice, a son of Sir John Wynn of Gwydir. Both entered the fellowship of the Merchant Adventurers in London and served as factors abroad; Hugh Gruffyd was at one time trading with £1,200 on his own credit. John Williams of Hafod Llwyfog in Nant Gwynant set off for London as a young man to seek his fortune; by 1612 he was acting as goldsmith to James I and had become a very wealthy man. He won some fame as a collector and antiquary, and became the friend of Michael Drayton, the poet, supplying the latter with much material concerning Wales for his *Polyolbion*. The hafod, his birthplace, is described by Hughes and North as one of the most interesting specimens of local seventeenth-century work in Caernarvonshire, with its post and panel partition between kitchen and parlour, its rich mouldings and heavy oak beams.

One of the best-known examples of the new type of country gentry in the area is Sir John Wynn of Gwydir, a restless, energetic, choleric landowner of the latter sixteenth century, constantly involved in litigation with his neighbours or tenants, amassing extensive properties in the Conway valley and the surrounding district, and grasping at every available office for himself or his children. He was a man of fertile brain and imagination, full of schemes to enhance his own welfare and to profit the countryside by a fuller exploitation of its natural resources. He was an eager prospector for minerals in the locality, and successfully worked the lead veins found on his own estate. He was interested in agricultural improvements and in stock-rearing, and it was he who first conceived the possibility of reclaiming the Glaslyn estuary by damming the tidal waters at the head of Traeth Mawr by a great embankment. In his enthusiasm he wrote off to Sir Hugh Myddleton, the engineer of London's new water supply, but Myddleton was chary of embarking on such a costly venture and the matter was eventually dropped. At one time Sir John proposed to introduce Irish weavers into the Conway valley and set up a factory system of cloth production, but this scheme likewise proved abortive.

One of his sons, Richard, was sent off to London to attend at court; he served as Groom of the Bedchamber to the young prince who afterwards became Charles I. When the Prince stole out of England secretly, travelling with Buckingham under the name of Smith, to ride across Europe and woo the Infanta of Spain, Richard Wynn accompanied the two adventurers. He took but a poor view of the Spanish landscape, however, after the beauties of his native land.

"We may think ourselves lucky to have everything in Wales," he wrote in a letter home, "for both of the kingdoms of Castile and Aragon are not worth one of our worst counties."

It was this Sir Richard, who, when he had succeeded to the estate and title, added to the parish church of Llanrwst the Gwydir Chapel, "from a design of Inigo Jones," says Philip Yorke, without citing his authority for this statement. The bridge across the river, with its three elliptical arches, is also sometimes attributed to his munificence. But Richard Fenton, in his account of his tours through Wales between 1805 and 1813, states that there was in the possession of his friend, Paul Panton, a record for the Quarter Sessions of Denbighshire, with a mandate from the Privy Council directing the rebuilding of the existing bridge which had become ruinous, at an estimated cost of £1,000 to be shared equally between the counties of Caernarvon and Denbigh. The bridge was built in 1636 (Pl. 38b, p. 387), and is usually cited also as the work of Inigo Jones, though there is no definite evidence to substantiate this claim. In support of it, Fenton asserts that the order from the Privy Council was issued in the ninth year of Charles I's reign, when Inigo Jones was Surveyor of the Board of Works.

The nephew and successor of the first Sir Richard Wynn, the second baronet of that name, likewise served for a time as a courtier, and was Chamberlain to Catherine, wife of Charles II. He is said on one occasion to have presented her with a pearl from a Conway mussel —noted at that time for their pearl-bearing properties—which she wore as a conspicuous jewel in her crown.

Two families who achieved some fame in the legal world were the Prices of Plas Iolyn and Gilar. The former was the home of Dr. Ellis Price, or "Dr. Coch" as he was nicknamed, a notorious lawyer of Tudor days. His father, Sir Robert ap Rhys ap Meredydd, served as chaplain and cross-bearer to Cardinal Wolsey; the alabaster effigy of Sir Robert and that of Dr. Coch's mother, Lowry, and of his grandfather, Rhys, are to be found in the church of Yspytty Ifan. Dr. Coch was a friend and follower of Dudley, Earl of Leicester, and through his master's offices obtained large grants of ecclesiastical land at the Dissolution, including the manor of Yspytty. He was much feared and hated as an oppressor of the people; rumour asserts that he combined his official duties as sheriff of Denbigh or Merioneth, and as a member of the Council of the Marches, with illegal practices more befitting the rôle of highwayman. He built a tower, three storeys high, the ruined base of which can be seen on the modern farm of Plas Iolyn, which commanded a wide sweep of the surrounding country and the old road running across the moors from the Dee to the Conway. The story goes that from his watch tower Dr. Coch would spy out travellers at a long distance over the lonely moorland; as they approached his followers would rush out to seize and rob them, imprisoning those who protested, and seemed likely to prove troublesome, in the dungeon at the foot of the building.

The family at Gilar won fame in a very different manner. The most noted member, Baron Price, was a famous lawyer in the reigns of Charles II and James II, and won immortality over the stand which he made after the revolution of 1688, when William III wished to transfer the lordships of Bromfield and Yale to his favourite, William Bentinck. "The submitting of 1,500 freeholders to the will of a Dutch lord is putting them in a worse position than their former estate under William the Conqueror and the Norman lords," thundered Price, and so moved the House of Commons by his speech that they supported his motion for an address to the Crown opposing the grant. William found it wise to withdraw his suggestion, but realizing the integrity and worth of his antagonist, he presently made him a judge of the Brecknock circuit, while on her accession Anne immediately constituted him a Baron of the Exchequer.

Gilar, the birthplace of Baron Price, is situated about half a mile distant from Plas Iolyn in a sheltered corner beneath Garn Brys. The house stands at one end of a great walled quadrangle, which is approached through the archway of a gatehouse with a room above, bearing the date 1623 (Pl. 37, p. 363). The present dwelling-house is believed to have been built by Thomas Pryce Wynn, who was High Sheriff of Denbigh in 1624; it is a very fine example of late sixteenth- or early seventeenth-century work in this part of the world, with its stout, sloping stone walls, and entrance porch. The parlour within is panelled in oak, and divided from the entrance passage by a partition of thick oak planks, ornamented with beading.

A rising standard of comfort, a demand for new luxuries in the furnishing of the home and for greater privacy, is reflected in these domestic buildings of the sixteenth and seventeenth centuries, with their additional rooms and rich oak furnishings. We find these changes in the smaller mansions and the solid farmhouses, as well as in the tarnished magnificence of Gwydir, Gilar or Cochwillan; in the little, early seventeenth-century manor of Plas Brondanw at Llanfrothen, for instance (Pl. 36, p. 363), set in its walled garden above the lands reclaimed from the estuary by one of its most noted inhabitants, William Williams; or in the grey farmhouse and great barns of Ty Lasar in the Machno valley, perhaps built on the site of an old lazar house, and once the home of a Lord Chief Justice of North Wales (Pl. XXIXa).

The fault of the Tudor administration, therefore, lay not in any lack of effort to advance the material prosperity of the country, nor in a wilful attempt to suppress the native traditions and customs of Wales, but in a blind ignorance of all that Welsh culture had to give to the life of the nation as a whole. The Tudor statesman made the tacit assumption that the task of the Welshman was to assimilate English thought and manners, to become to all intents and purposes an Englishman. His aim, therefore, was to ignore the differences between the two peoples, to allow the Welsh language to deteriorate and sink into oblivion by introducing English speech as the language of polite society, to turn men's thoughts from the past and its traditional responsibilities and lead them instead to the exciting opportunities of a future built on individual enterprise.

References for Chapter 20

Rees, J. F. (1947), Wynn (1927 ed.), Pennant (1810 ed.), Rees, W. (1938), Williams, W. Ll. (1907-08), Bowen, E. G. (1941), Edwards, O. (1902), Bangor Penrhyn MS. 88, Jenkins (1899), Hughes and North (1908), Calendar of Wynn Papers (1926), Yorke (1887 ed.), Fenton (1917 ed.), Bezant-Lowe (1912-27).

PLATE XXIX

John Markham

a. Ty Lasar, Penmachno: a solid, stone farmhouse probably built on the site of an old Lazar house in the eighteenth century

John Markham

b. Bishop Morgan's house: note the rocks incorporated in the foundations; see also Pl. XXIVb

DOMESTIC ARCHITECTURE

PLATE XXX

John Markham

EARLY BRIDGE, Machno Valley, often called the "Roman Bridge". July

CHAPTER 21

THE CHANGING COUNTRYSIDE

THE face of the countryside was gradually changing in the course of the centuries, for the activities both of men and of animals were constantly making inroads on the forest cover of the Snowdon hills. One natural agent of destruction, the beaver, appears to have made its home in the rivers of Snowdon as late as the Dark Ages, when its damming operations caused serious flooding of the Conway, according to a well-known folk tale. It was, however, becoming rare by the tenth century, for in the laws of Hywel Dda its skin is valued at six score pence, fifteen times the value of an ox skin. The browsing of domesticated livestock, particularly of goats and sheep, would seriously retard the young tree growth, and it is possible that rabbits should be added to this list, for among the losses entailed in Glyndwr's attack on Conway in 1401 were 2,400 rabbit skins stored in a bark-house or tannery in the suburbs. Some of these doubtless came from the great Newborough warren in Anglesey, but it is likely that a number were the product of the mainland, for in his *Topographical Dictionary of Wales* Lewis mentions extensive warrens near the coast.

The human inhabitants were constantly breaking into the woodlands for building materials and for fuel, both to supply heat for their houses and for use in the smelting of iron. Royal forges were established at Penmachno and Dolbenmaen, for there is a note of their being leased in the Minister's accounts of the reign of Richard II. Wood was used for many domestic utensils such as platters and bowls, for the plough and other farm implements, for the shafts of arrows and spears, and bark was a requisite of the tanning industry carried on in the outskirts of the Edwardian boroughs and of the little Welsh towns of Nant Conwy and the coast. Both the Roman and Anglo-Norman invaders drove their roads through the forests, clearing a wide tract of brushwood on either hand to reduce the dangers of an ambush, and these highways were maintained between Edward's boroughs. Many great oaks from the forest of Snowdon were being floated down the Conway from Trefriw in Elizabeth's reign, while in the eighteenth and early nineteenth centuries a boat-building industry grew up in many of the little ports of the North Wales coast, providing another important market for timber. Such depredations, carried on over long periods, with no attempt at fresh planting, would in themselves considerably reduce the tree growth, without any wholesale programme of felling, such as the older historians attributed to Edward I.

Nevertheless, the oaks of Snowdon were still abundant when Leland came riding through the district in the years between 1536 and 1539. All Craig Eryri, the heights of the main range, he says, was forest but the best wood was to be found in the vales of the Lledr and the Llugwy, especially by Capel Curig, and at Llanberis. "Meately good woods" were also to be seen about the abbey at Maenan, in the Machno valley and around Coetmor and Coed-y-parc near Bethesda. Little corn was grown in the hills away from the fertile coastal strip; he found only small quantities of oats and barley and "scantly rye" on the hill farms, and suggests that the destruction of the grain by the deer was a chief cause of this scarcity. Deer were not extirpated in the area till about the year 1626.

The settled condition of the borderlands after the Act of Union made available a growing trade in Welsh cattle and cloth for the English markets. By the middle of the sixteenth century the attack on the alder woods and the reed beds fringing the lowland streams had begun in the valleys of the Conway and the Gyffin to reclaim the potentially rich meadowlands of the area and so increase the supply of hay for winter feeding. Even on the wetter soils above the rim of the valley it was found worth while, with the growing demand for store cattle, to clear the oak and birch scrub for summer grazing. Dr. Elfyn Hughes has found evidence of extensive clearing and fencing of land in the year 1545 in the neighbourhood of the little medieval holdings below Cwm Eigiau, embracing a ten-year programme of improvement. Above, in the cwm itself, which had long been used as a summer pasture ground, four substantial houses were built as permanent residences in 1554, and one hundred cattle were maintained there.

In the region of Penmachno and Dolwyddelan, the Wynn family were leasing tenements in the latter half of the sixteenth century on condition that the occupiers cleared the land of alders and drained it, presumably to increase the area under hay. Ten medieval hafodau in this district, which could maintain 552 head of cattle annually in the fourteenth century, by 1568 could support 1,280 to 1,340, a growth which indicates extensive clearance of land for pasture in the intervening two hundred years. Serviceable and balanced little dairy herds were built up on some of these farms, comprising both cows in milk and the requisite number of followers; the tenants were dependent on the sale of their surplus butter, cheese and milk or their bull calves to provide the money for their annual rents. To take a few examples, the hafod of Bertheos, whose name survives in a farm on the road between Dol-wyddelan and Ffestiniog, which had 60 cattle on its pastures in 1355, was stocked with 78 cattle in 1569, of which 21 cows were in milk, and was also running 92 sheep and 55 goats; Coetmor, in the same township of Dolwyddelan, which again had only 60 cattle on its pasture in the middle of the fourteenth century, could boast 176 head, including 25 calves and 26 cows in milk, in 1569. In the same year the farm of Gwastad Annas at the head of Llyn Gwynant was supporting 106 cattle, with 15 cows in milk, and also 78 sheep; Hafod Llwyfog in the same valley in 1697 had a herd of 63.

The main incentive to the reclamation of hay meadows and pasture lands, however, was the cattle trade and its rapid growth in the sixteenth and seventeenth centuries. In some instances the hafod at this time was used throughout the year by a tenant or a bailiff of a large landowner, the young stock moving down to the shelter of the lowland pastures for the winter; but the old practice of transhumance, the farmer moving up with his beasts to the summer grazing grounds, still continued in many places, lingering on into the early nineteenth century. So valuable an asset had the cattle trade become that, on the outbreak of the Civil War in 1642, a petition was sent up to Charles I by the gentlemen of North Wales, asking for the free passage and safe conduct of cattle, cloth and wool through the Royalist lines. This trade, they declared, was the support of many thousands of families in the mountainous regions, who sowed little or no corn, but depended for their livelihood on the sale of their cattle, wool and cloth.

The trade grew in volume and importance with the expansion of London and some of the midland towns in the eighteenth century to feed the rapidly increasing urban populations of the English capital and the new industrial centres. Pennant, on his visit to Caernarvon-shire in 1778, suggests that 3,000 head were sold from Llŷn alone each year, and a clergyman, reporting on the agricultural condition of North Wales in the first decade of the nineteenth century, estimated that 6,000 were exported annually from Anglesey, these beasts swim-ming the Straits at the start of their long journey.

Occasionally English graziers came to the markets of the border towns to buy the animals and drive them to the pastures of Kent and Essex for fattening before sale. More usually, Welsh drovers gathered up the cattle from the farms or from some centre near at hand to which they had been driven, and took them up to the great fairs of Barnet or St. Bartholomew's in London, or to the midland towns. Here they were purchased by English graziers for fattening before re-sale to the urban butchers. The animals were shod for the journey; forges which supplied shoes for cattle as well as horses were to be found near the Ogwen falls, at Dyffryn Mymbr, Llanrwst, Betws-y-coed and Yspytty Ifan. The drovers, avoiding where possible the main roads with their traffic and, later, their toll gates, struck across country, sometimes following an old, grass-grown British track, and put up for the night at some handy inn with large paddocks adjoining in which to turn the animals. They raised a strange cry as they approached any farm or village, to give warning of their advance, so that the farmers had time to shut up their own cattle and prevent them getting mixed with the travelling herd. There would be from 500 to 600 beasts in a drove, those from the northern counties were mostly small, black animals; the Welsh black of the present day is a larger type of the same strain (Pl. 34b, p. 355). Sheep, and sometimes the sturdy mountain ponies, called merlins, were also taken to the English markets and fairs along with the kine.

The drovers came to play a very important part in the economic life of the country. As they were the only people making regular and frequent journeys to the capital, they were often entrusted with responsible commissions: the proceeds of the famous Ship Money Tax from Denbighshire, for instance, were transmitted to London by them in the seventeenth century. Sometimes a country gentleman with a debt to meet in the capital would request these men to discharge it from the proceeds of their cattle sales, and would so avoid the dangers of transferring cash over long distances on roads infested with footpads. Through their aid in such transactions the drovers became eventually the first bankers of Wales; in 1799 the best-known of these early banks was opened at Llandovery by one of their number, the notes issued bearing the insignia of a black ox-head. Others followed at Aberystwyth and Carmarthen in the early nineteenth century.

The drovers were the bearers of the news, rumour and gossip of the city and the highway to the isolated Welsh hamlet, bringing into the village inn a breath of the larger world that lay beyond the hills.

Those who had to make the tedious and perilous journey to London often chose to travel in the company of their caravans for protection. William Morgan, for instance, the translator of the Bible into Welsh, rode with them in 1587, when bearing his precious manuscript to the capital for publication. Statutes issued in the reigns of Edward VI and Elizabeth ordained that the drovers must be at least thirty years of age, married men and householders, not mere vagrants and vagabonds, and that they must be licensed annually by Quarter Sessions. Some degenerated into rogues and sharp dealers, who give the drover his bad reputation in popular Welsh ballads; others became men of substance, who might even, by the seventeenth century, aspire to the post of Sheriff of the county.

The second staple commodity of Welsh trade was cloth, the product of the cottage spinning-wheel and loom. Welsh wool was of a somewhat coarse texture in the early days, and ranked low in the great wool marts of the Middle Ages, though some found its way overseas to the Flemish market. But the quality was gradually improved, and it is noteworthy that after the loss of the English possessions in France and Normandy in 1450, many Welshmen taken prisoner in the French wars, sent for wool from their farms to pay their ransoms. Spinning and weaving had formed an essential part of the domestic economy of the household as far back, probably, as the days of the Neolithic colonists, and all the processes of dyeing, spinning, carding and weaving were carried on in many farmhouses till the early years of the nineteenth century. But some division of labour was common by the early medieval period, for it was ordained in the Laws of Hywel Dda that "weaving women" who "took webs or other balls under their care" were to pay their value if they should be damaged by fire. Though many homes in the Middle Ages and the later centuries might have a loom, some favourably situated households would often take the yarn of their neighbours to weave it into cloth, employing a few extra hands for the purpose.

The introduction of the fulling mill in the fourteenth century gave a great impetus to cloth production; a surplus began to be produced in many homes at this period, and was sold in the Welsh fairs of Llanerchymedd in Anglesey or at Ruthin, while some found its way to the border towns of Chester and Oswestry. The russets and friezes were heavy and rough materials, more suitable for distribution to the poor on Ash Wednesday than for the gown of baron or courtier. Nevertheless, by the end of the fifteenth century, cloth had become one of the principal commodities of Welsh trade, finding its way overseas to France, Spain, Portugal, and even to Iceland. It is interesting to note that the pioneers of the Hudson's Bay Company, over two hundred years later, were clad in Welsh frieze. Though the Welsh clothier might occasionally find his way to the cloth fair at St. Bartholomew's, for the most part the English merchants came to the Welsh cloth markets, centred at Oswestry in the sixteenth century, at Shrewsbury in the seventeenth, to purchase the wares brought in by the farmer on his rough mountain pony, and carry them up to Blackwell Hall. From the reign of Henry VIII, North Wales began to draw to itself the industry of the southern counties, Pembroke, Carmarthen and Cardigan, which had hitherto been among the most flourishing centres of the trade. It was still carried on as a scattered domestic industry of farmhouse and cottage, combined with farming and cattle-rearing. Sometimes, as we have suggested, on the larger farms a few additional hands would be hired as part-time weavers, and looms set up in the outbuildings, but there was nothing approaching a factory system of production till the early years of the nineteenth century. A variety of cloth known as "Welsh cottons" formed the typical product of the industry in the seventeenth century, and some bales of this were included in the cargo of the *Mayflower*. Flannel was also first heard of in this and the preceding century, though its manufacture was concentrated in the counties of Merioneth and Montgomery, the other Welsh counties sending their yarn thence to be woven.

In 1802 William Williams of Llandegai wrote that the mountain people of North Wales still employed their time, besides tending their cattle, in carding and spinning wool and in weaving cloth for their own use and for sale in the neighbouring markets. "Vast quantities of this and excellent woollen stockings are carried to Llanrwst, Caernarvon and other markets far and near," he says, including a striped linsey-woolsey material called "stuff" which was used for women's gowns. Any surplus wool was also sold; the principal mart was held at Llanrwst Fair on July 21st, to which the English buyers came. The price realized here was the standard price of wool for the year. Coarse linen was spun from home-grown flax, but the greater part was sold, Williams states, as the Welsh usually slept between blankets and the men wore flannel shirts.

The first wool mill to be opened in Caernarvonshire was probably that at Tremadoc about the year 1800, a venture of the builder of the embankment across the estuary to provide employment in his new town. Water-driven machinery was installed in addition to handlooms, and the mill was leased to two partners who, if rumour is to be credited, engaged not only in the manufacture of webs for the expanding Merioneth industry, but in making cloth to smuggle overseas for the uniforms of Napoleon's troops. By 1815 other mills, including similar water-driven machinery for carding, were established near Penmachno, at Llanrug, Llanwnda, Y Tryfan and Dolgarrog; the latter had acquired a spinning jenny by 1818 and was carrying out all the processes of manufacture on the spot. As late as the inter-war years, between 1918 and 1930, it was still a common practice for the hill farmer to take his raw wool to the nearest mill and have it spun and woven into cloth for his own use.

The growing importance of the woollen industry led to a growth of sheep-farming at the expense of cattle, a change which was noticeable by the seventeenth century. Thus at Hafod Ruffyd near Beddgelert we find, in 1698, 141 sheep as against 61 cattle, while in 1745 the same farm was supporting a flock of 500 sheep and had only 59 cows and steers. Hafod-y-llyn in the same parish had 13 cattle, 38 sheep and 24 goats in 1675; in 1772 the sheep-flock numbered one hundred. The 106 cattle reared at Gwastad Annas in 1569 had shrunk to 39 by 1787, while the sheep had risen from 78 to 357.

The water-driven mill, which concentrated the scattered industry of the cottage fireside within the factory walls, and brought a sudden rapidly expanding demand for wool, was, however, perhaps the most important agent in turning the Welshman from dairy- to sheep-farming on a large scale. Gwastad Annas today can boast a flock of over 2,000 and one of the largest sheep-runs on the flanks of Snowdon; Hafod-y-llyn has over 1,000 sheep in place of the hundred of 1772 and a run to the crest of that mountain. From the early years of the nineteenth century, cattle were confined to the lower slopes of the hills; the long stone walls so often to be seen running horizontally across the face of the mountains were built to retain them within these lower pastures, while the sheep were turned on to the great upper sweeps of grazing land. With the decline in the milking herds and the concentration on store cattle and sheep, the practice of transhumance died away in the first half of the nineteenth century, and the hafodau now lie in ruins. The yearly movement is confined to the animals, for young sheep are brought down from the mountainside in winter to graze in the sheltered

meadowlands of the Conway valley and of Eifionydd, which still
continue to play an important part in the farming economy of the
area.

There is less evidence for the progress of arable farming in the
sixteenth and seventeenth centuries. The wording of the petition to
Charles I cited on p. 373 suggests that much of the tilled land on the
hill farms of the north-west region had been thrown into pasture and
that these people must already have been buying such grain as they
needed. During the later Middle Ages it was often found necessary to
import corn into Caernarvon and Conway and supplies were sought
in Chester, Anglesey and Ireland rather than in the valleys near at
hand, though one traveller at the end of the eighteenth century noted
that Conway was then exporting corn from that fertile vale. Agriculture
must have suffered greatly in the disorders of the fifteenth and early
sixteenth centuries, but it is difficult to estimate how far the decline
had gone and to what extent subsistence farming had already lapsed.
The testimony of the visitors of the eighteenth and early nineteenth
centuries suggests that it was still widespread in those days, but the
change to cash farming was undoubtedly evident in some mountainous
districts of North Wales by the middle of the seventeenth century.

The freer land market of the latter Middle Ages and the sixteenth
century would encourage the more enterprising farmer to concentrate
his land into compact holdings by selling or exchanging outlying strips
for others adjoining his main plot, and this consolidation of the farming
unit was almost invariably accompanied by the enclosure of the arable
fields and of the meadows. The open-strips of the commote lands
rarely or never survived the closing years of the medieval period. The
enclosure movement of the early nineteenth century in North Wales
was concerned with the great stretches of common on the hillsides; the
territory of different landowners, who had established their claim over
the waste, were then frequently demarcated by walls running vertically
down the slopes. Little or no attempt was made to improve agricultural
methods or to increase the output per acre till the late eighteenth
century, when the revolutionary improvements carried out in the
English lowlands a generation earlier gradually filtered through to
this isolated countryside.

The great cultural gift of the early modern period was William
Morgan's translation of the Bible, which had a profound effect on the
Welsh language and literature. Morgan was the son of a family of

PLATE XXXI

Painting by Warwick Smith

LLANBERIS COPPER MINES and ore-handling equipment, 1792

PLATE XXXII

By courtesy of H.M. Stationery Office. Crown copyright reserved   *Engraving by Ordnance Survey*

a. ORDNANCE SURVEY MAP, 1840: showing Snowdon's cwms and the sharp ridges that separate them

By courtesy of the National Museum of Wales   *Painting attributed to William Williams*

b. SHIP-BUILDING NEAR LLANFROTHEN: the Glaslyn Estuary before it was reclaimed in 1812 by the building of the embankment by W. Madocks

hereditary bondmen of the Wynns of Gwydir, and was born at Ty
Mawr, a farmhouse at the head of Gwibernant, *circa* 1540 (Pls. XXIVb
p. 299, and XXIXb).   His intelligence as a boy was noticed, and he
was brought to Gwydir to be educated with the sons of the house.
Later, he went to St. John's College, Cambridge, where he became
a proficient scholar in Greek and Hebrew, and where he was encouraged by his tutor to enter on his life's task of turning the Hebrew
Scriptures into his own tongue.   As Welsh was the language of
his childhood's home, he was fitted to produce a living translation,
free from the scholarly archaisms of the earlier attempt of William
Salesbury, who, as the son of a country gentleman, was reared in
a household where English was the common speech.   On leaving
Cambridge, after his ordination, Morgan went first to the vicarage of
Welshpool, and then in 1578 to the quiet country parish of Llanrhaiadr,
where he could continue his work of scholarship undisturbed.   But
various factions were stirred up against him; his parishioners complained of his neglect of his parochial duties, and some of the country
gentry declared that he was unfitted and ill equipped for the great task
he had entered upon.   Finally, Whitgift, the Archbishop of Canterbury,
summoned him to Lambeth to answer the charges, and he must have
ridden to London with an anxious heart, carrying with him the
completed books of the Pentateuch as his vindication.   Whitgift was so
impressed with Morgan and his work that he sent him back to the
country to finish it, and himself aided its publication.   The translation was published in 1588, the year of the Spanish Armada, and
had a revolutionary effect upon both spoken and written Welsh.
The use of English, which had become the daily speech of the educated
both in the home and in business in the years following the Act of
Union, had a disastrous effect upon the vernacular: neglected and
despised as the tongue of the lower classes, it rapidly deteriorated. "It
may be said," writes Mr. Nevins in his book on Wales during the Tudor
period, "that Morgan found the Welsh vernacular a congeries of
dialects and spellings, some of them deserving only of death, and he left
it a language that has held its place with increasing estimation during
a period of three hundred years." Morgan's work was recognized in
his lifetime, for he became first Bishop of Llandaff and then of St. Asaph,
while his influence radiated throughout the succeeding centuries,
particularly when the Charity and Circulating School movement of
the eighteenth century opened the riches of his translation as revised by

Parry, to the people of Wales. As the modern historian of this movement has said:

"The steady concentration upon piety as the aim and end of all instruction changed a gay and simple people, indifferent in religion and lacking in political consciousness, into a people whose dominant interests were religious and political. The Bible had become the Welshman's manual. Its language was his language, its teaching dominated his social and political life."[1]

Note

I am indebted to Mr. Bob Owen of Croesor for the sixteenth- and seventeenth-century figures of livestock maintained on the farms. He kindly allowed me to make a selection from his transcripts of wills of the period.

References for Chapter 21

Ancient Laws and Institutes of Wales (Record Commission 1841), Public Record Office Exchequer Q.R. A/cs. (sixteenth century). Ministers' Accounts (fourteenth century), Leland (1906 ed.), Hughes, R. E. (1940), Calendar of Wynn Papers (1926), Record of Caernarvon (Record Commission 1838), Transcripts of sixteenth- and seventeenth-century wills supplied by Mr. Bob Owen, Phillips (1874), Skeel (1922) (1926), Pennant (1810 ed.), Davies (1810), Hughes (1943), Williams, W. (1802), Dodd (1933).

[1] C. M. G. Jones. *The Charity School Movement* (1938), p. 321.

CHAPTER 22

THE CENTURY OF INVENTION
AND ITS IMPACT ON LIFE IN
THE SNOWDON HILLS

IN the canvases of Richard Wilson we see the Snowdon peaks and valleys almost for the last time unscarred by the thoughtless hands of the pioneers of the new industrial age in their eager search for the wealth which the stone and minerals of the hills could yield. It is fitting that he chose at times to paint his landscapes lit with the glow of early evening, for a whole era was drawing to its close. From the middle years of the eighteenth century Wales was a land teeming with new industrial ventures; the raw gash of the great slate quarries appeared in the passes of Llanberis and Nant Ffrancon, cutting across the face of the mountains; the slopes of Yr Wyddfa on Snowdon herself were disfigured with the shafts of copper mines. The untidy ruins of barracks in which the miners were housed and of buildings connected with the workings are strewn along the shore of Llyn Llydaw and Glaslyn. New fashions in building arose, the square, finely proportioned, slate-roofed manor houses, with their rows of sash windows and columned porticoes. New roads were driven over the precipices of Penmaen-mawr or through Nant Ffrancon to Capel Curig, opening the beauties of Snowdon to a stream of visitors, who were cut off from their Continental haunts by the wars with France in the closing decade of the century.

It was a period of mental and spiritual awakening and of intense intellectual activity. The ballads and dramatic interludes of the unlettered Twm o'r Nant, who hailed from the region of Pentrevoelas, reflected the hopes and despairs of the common people, succeeding the miracle plays of earlier centuries, and giving a new expression to the living folk culture. The poetry of Wales was enriched by the classic metres of Lewis Morris of Anglesey and the strange beauty of Goronwy Owen's song. The researches and translations of the antiquaries, the Morris brothers of Anglesey, Evan Evans of Cardiganshire, brought new inspiration to the poets of the romantic revival in England, for, as Mr. Hughes has reminded us in his discussion of Welsh influences in English literature, the antiquary is often the forerunner of the poet, preparing his way. Thomas Gray, John Dyer, William Cowper and Walter Scott,

SNOWDONIA

382

together with a host of lesser writers, found fresh subject-matter in the legends and traditions of the ancient British race to fire their imagination. Evan Evans and the Morrises were in touch with many of the leaders of English literary circles: Gray, Bishop Percy (of *The Reliques of English Poetry*) and Thomas Carte the historian were among their correspondents in the latter eighteenth century, says Mr. Hughes, and Carte apparently used much material supplied to him by Morris in his history of England, but without acknowledgment, as the Welshman bitterly complains. James Thompson wrote of the majesty of Penmaenmawr in his *Seasons*; Wordsworth, who came to explore the district round Beddgelert in 1791, has left us a description of a moonlight night on Snowdon in the final book of *The Prelude*.

Above all, this was a century of religious and emotional fervour, swept by the rising tide of Methodism and the power of the great Welsh preachers and hymn writers, Hywel Harris, Williams "Pantycelyn," Thomas Charles of Bala, who called men out of their lethargy to a sense of their great and awful destiny.

In the scattered hill farms the old ways of life were followed with little change. The Rev. N. Owen, writing a handbook to Caernarvonshire in 1792, remarked that the produce of the soil, though not very abundant, was more than sufficient with good husbandry to supply the needs of the inhabitants. The land would produce good corn where it was thoroughly manured, but he found the farmers in general very backward in their methods, lacking any desire to experiment, and loth to lay out money in improvement unless they were the owners of the land. "Prejudiced to the old mode of husbandry, they toil in the beaten track, and are not dissatisfied with their fortune if they can but barely pay the rent, and maintain a homely subsistence." They still depended on the sale of their cattle for the wherewithal to meet their rents, and this interest detracted from the attention given to corn-growing. A certain amount of dairy-farming was carried on, but the milch cows were not selected with any care, so that the yields were low. The butter made on the farms, however, was of excellent quality, though as the milk and cream were churned together there was no skim milk to feed the pigs, and the bacon and pork were consequently very lean. The sheep, grazing on the upland pastures, produced a sweet and tender mutton; the average weight of these animals was ten pounds a quarter when they were killed. The bulk of the mountain pastures were unenclosed till the opening years of the nineteenth century, the farmers enjoying customary rights of grazing therein for their animals, frequently without stint.

The size of the farms was very small; in 1939 the average cultivated holding in Caernarvonshire was only 26.4 acres, and one landowner of the county giving evidence before the Land Commission of 1896 said that on his estates the average size of the total farm was 60 acres, and that they ran from three acres upwards. These holdings were worked by family labour, with perhaps the aid of one or two additional men who were odged in the outhouses or in a loft over the stable, and took their meals in the kitchen with the farmer and his household.

Life in the hills was a hard and busy one with little in the way of amusement to alleviate its harshness. Any time that could be snatched from tending the fields and stock was, as we have seen, employed in spinning and carding wool, even the very small children assisting as they could in such tasks. The principal fare at the end of the eighteenth century was oat-bread, butter, cheese, milk and potatoes, with occasionally a little dried and smoked mutton or beef from the herd in the winter. Fresh meat was a rarity. The furnishing of the home was simple: it consisted of beds filled with soft hay, a few wooden chairs and stools, a long table, and usually a high-backed settle, and a *cwpwdd deuddarn* or *tridarn*, the two- or three-piece cupboard found today in many a farm kitchen. This was often fashioned on the spot for the bride's home from an oak cut down on the farm. The woollen, home-spun clothing was coloured with vegetable dyes, made from lichens collected off the rocks. In the winter evenings members of the scattered households would gather in one of the larger farmhouses, the community centre of the district, and would spend their time round the fire knitting, carding wool, or peeling rushes for the lights, joining together in song and discussion, or perhaps enlivened by the music of some wandering harper who held the place of honour at the fireside.

Agricultural methods were still very primitive. Farmers generally were most extravagant with their seed corn, sowing it in such quantities that much of it perished, and very small yields resulted. The people of Dolwyddelan as late as 1810 maintained that the produce of their oat harvest was only three and a half bushels to every one sown, a yield so low that the enquirer felt scarcely able to accept it. In the village of Penmachno in the adjoining valley, where open patches of corn were grown between the valley bottom and the walls of the fridds, the return was six to one. Under pressure of wartime needs the margin of cultivation was thrust back into the bleaker heights. One traveller found wheat being produced in small quantities in the neighbourhood of Llangelynin church, 927 feet above sea level, in the year 1810; while at Llanrhychwyn (700 feet) oats were successfully cultivated at this time. They were laid in small sheaves on the slate roofs of the houses to dry, "where the heat of the sun acts with redoubled power."

Squatters in some numbers were settling on the great wastes during the eighteenth century, and thereby reclaiming some of the poorer land for tillage. At Llanfairfechan, a very fertile tract noted for its early crops of grain, an enclosure was to be seen on the stretches of hillside above the fridds, bearing plentifully both potatoes and barley and planted by one of these intruders. A little hamlet of these people had grown up on the common at Garn Dolbenmaen, who proved a wild and lawless crowd, and were dubbed by one observer as fitted only to swell the ranks of the recruiting sergeant of the militia. Seventeen new houses arose at Penmachno in the first ten years of the nineteenth century, chiefly the homes of these encroachers on the waste lands. There was an old tradition that if a man could get his house up in a night and have smoke issuing from the chimney stack by daybreak, he could lay claim to the building and the adjacent plot and could not be turned out. In the slate regions squatters also abounded, forming little companies to dig the slates in shallow pits, but regarding their quarrying as a part-time occupation while they maintained their smallholdings and a few head of stock along with their industrial enterprise. When the series of Acts for the enclosure of the commons came into force (ten were passed for Caernarvonshire between the years 1790 and 1815), many of these men had a rude awakening, for they could produce no title-deeds and in many cases their term of residence was insufficient to establish "squatter's rights."

The hay grown by the hill farmers appears to have been of a poor quality at this time, though some clover was being sown in north-west Wales by 1774. Penruddocke Wyndham, writing in that year of the meadows along the Dwyryd near Maentwrog says that the grass was not as high as his shoes, though, but for the rain, it would have fallen to the scythe many days before. As winter provision for the cattle was the chief concern of the husbandman, he saw a meadow mown in the neighbourhood of Traethfynydd between Penmaen and Tan-y-bwlch, which was "as short as a park lawn," and he affirmed that 20 acres of it would not have produced a ton of hay. On the other hand Pennant, in his various expeditions to the peaks of Snowdon in 1778, came upon a remarkably soft hay in the lower meadows on that mountain "consisting in a great part of the fine bent grass, *Agrostis capillaris.*"

Improvements, initiated by the large landowners, were gradually made, though for the most part not till the opening years of the nineteenth century. On these estates, pioneers such as Richard Pennant, afterwards the first Baron Penrhyn, introduced new crops and a scientific rotation; better farmhouses were built for the tenants, and plantations were established on waste ground. In 1807 the Agricultural Society of Caernarvonshire was formed, whose purpose was to improve agricultural methods by organizing ploughing matches, distributing seeds, demonstrating new implements and practices, and arranging gatherings of the larger owners to discuss the possibilities of experiment. An agricultural meeting of this nature was held at Gwydir, and much rough ground was broken-in here, while in the county generally "afforestation of the waste lands became the pastime of the well-to-do." Edmund Hyde Hall, a visitor to Caernarvonshire about 1810 who has left a most interesting manuscript survey of the county, parish by parish, states that George Smith Esq. of Pendyffrin in the parish of Dwygyfylchi had introduced a turnip crop and reclaimed much land, and that the inhabitants were greatly indebted to him for generally improving rural conditions. At Llanfair Isgair a tenant of Lord Uxbridge in the same year was earning the scorn of his neighbours by first draining the land of his farm of about 200 acres, which was "a mere bed of stones mixed into a bed of bog," when he took it over, and then utilizing the stones he had removed to line and cover the ditches with which he irrigated his crops. The whole proceeding seemed to his fellow farmers sheer madness, first freeing the land of water and then bringing it back in newly-dug drains, but as a result "on a spot where a young calf was actually smothered there is now a solidity of ground sufficient to support the weight of a cathedral," Hall declares, and the farmer was enabled to employ 36 persons where formerly one family could support life with difficulty. At the head of Llyn Dinas another landowner, Daniel Vawdrey, had not only planted several acres of the higher ground with trees, but was successfully cultivating the damp meadow-lands near the lake and encouraging his neighbours by offering prizes to those who excelled in various branches of husbandry. (Plas Gwynant, the home of Vawdrey, was occupied for a few years from 1850, by the historian, James Anthony Froude, and here he wrote some of the best of his *Short Studies on Great Subjects* and entertained many of his friends and colleagues, among them Charles Kingsley.)

The personal account book of William Williams of Plas Brondanw, ancestor of Mr. Rupert and Mr. Clough Williams-Ellis, throws an interesting sidelight on the daily life and concerns of a country gentleman of the latter half of the eighteenth century. It runs from 1767 to the year of his death in 1778, and contains a few entries by his successor. We see Williams, the small squire busied about the affairs of his estate and household, checking his livestock and corn yields, his household linen and his personal wardrobe, and dreaming of the ways in which he can add to the prosperity and attractiveness of his demesne. A walled garden is added to the house in 1774, the two masons employed claiming a wage of 1s. each a day, but the labourers hired in January to work on the garden itself proved anything but satisfactory, and absented themselves every other day. A careful account is kept of the cattle sent up to two or three different hafodau each May, and of the surplus stock sold annually at Holyrood Fair. In 1776, 15 runts and 3 heifers realized £67. On the 24th May 1774 Williams had in all 92 head of cattle and 74 sheep; the herd comprised 13 cows and a bull, 19 calves, and 39 heifers varying in age from one to three years. Wheat and barley raised on his fields were sold in small quantities to neighbours and friends at Wern, Coyty and Careg in addition to supplying his own needs, though occasionally Williams himself had perforce to buy a few measures of oats and the dairy could not always meet the demand of the house for butter, for this commodity was bought in some quantities in February and March 1777. A side of mutton was also occasionally sought off the farm in addition to such luxuries as brandy, rum or "Bohea tea."

Coarse, homespun cloth and a material of finer weave were sent away from the house for bleaching, and a certain Sarha (sic) Jones was engaged to come to Brondanw in the month of June to spin the home-grown wool at a wage of 1s. 3d. per week. "Richard ye cowman" was hired on November 11, 1774, for £6 6s. a year and "a pare of showse for ye year beginning at All Saints." Evan Griffith, the second farm servant, received only £5 15s. and "he is to have lether under his shouse in ye bargain." The serving maid, Catherine, was to have £2 7s. if she stayed the full twelvemonth, but only £1 if she left after the winter. "Owen the husbandman" agreed on June 5th, 1776, to

PLATE 37

John Markham

GILAR, the 17th-century gatehouse: this small mansion was the birthplace of the noted lawyer, Baron Price, who resisted William III's attempt to transfer Welsh land to one of his Dutch favourites

PLATE 38

John Markham

a. Yspytty Ifan, on the Upper Conway. The bridge probably dates from the 18th century

John Markham

b. The bridge, which bears the date 1636, crossing the River Conway at Llanrwst

OLD STONE BRIDGES

work for Mr. Williams till All Saints day at a wage of 9d. per day; the mowers of the hay, who were scything for 32 days, received 9½d., but the reapers of the corn only got 8d. a day for the first 23 days' work and 6d. for a further 25 days, though ale and two calves were provided for the harvest home festivities. The threshers and haymakers appear to have been a constant source of worry by their irregular attendance. The former disappeared on a Friday afternoon in October and did not return till eleven o'clock on the Monday, as Mr. Williams indignantly notes; Sally Jones, a second woman hired at the rate of 6d. a day to make hay, turned up on July 2, 1774, but "went of" till four o'clock on the evening of July 6th; the exasperation of the careful farmer, her employer, burns in these pages across the gulf of nearly two centuries. "Jack, my little lad, who came to his plase," on May 20, 1774, to embark on the adventure of life as a farm hand, received £2 2s. a year, but "a peice of cloath" provided for him by Mrs. Williams was valued at 5s. and this sum was carefully deducted from his wages. Nevertheless, there is a certain tenderness whenever Williams speaks of the boy which warms the reader to that gentleman; he refers to him always as "my little lad" or "my little servant," notes with pride his quickness on one occasion at adding a sum, and gives him 3s. of his wages before he goes home on holiday for his sister's wedding.

The biggest experiments in land reclamation were made in the region of Traeth Mawr, near which Plas Brondanw is situated. As his tomb in Llanfrothen church attests, William Williams was the first to embark on the venture of stemming the tidal waters by the construction of earth banks. Traces of the embankments he erected can be seen from the terrace of his house. Other neighbouring landowners followed suit; between 1770 and 1800, areas varying between 50 and 100 acres were enclosed by these earth barriers so that altogether some 1,500 acres were recovered from the sands on the margin of the estuary. In 1798, Mr. Madocks purchased the estate of Tan-yr-allt near Penmorfa marsh and shortly after settling there projected his scheme for a much larger undertaking. First, he enclosed a large stretch of sand on the west of the estuary, on which he built the town of Tremadoc. This is a very interesting example of eighteenth-century town planning, with its wide streets, unbroken rows of simply proportioned stone houses and dignified market hall; there is a generosity about the whole design in pleasing contrast to the mean squalor of much town building in the early decades of the next century. In 1807, Madocks obtained per-

mission by Act of Parliament for further experiment in reclaiming the
rest of the Traeth. Work started soon afterwards on the great embankment, a mile in length and carrying a road along its crest, which runs
from the Merioneth shore of the estuary to the town of Portmadoc built
on the Caernarvonshire side. This was completed in 1811; amid great
rejoicings an ox was roasted whole in the middle of the embankment,
and Madocks was hailed as one of the great benefactors of the country
and of the age. But the joy was short-lived for early in the following
year, the sea, in a great storm, made a breach in the enclosure and
came pouring through, and the work was to do all over again. With the
volunteer aid of many hundreds of local farmers in carting materials,
and with the enthusiastic support of the poet, Shelley, who had leased
Tan-yr-allt, the task of rebuilding began. Shelley spent many weeks in
trying to raise subscriptions for the work among his friends in London,
or travelling the country in the same pursuit; when at home he was to
be found poring over plans in the dusty files of Mr. Madocks's office.
His wife, Harriet, did not share his enthusiasm, and was one of the first
to complain that the view from their house was spoilt now that the tide
no longer came up to fill the estuary. By the end of September 1814,
the reconstruction was finished; 1,500 acres of what was to prove rather
poor grazing land was won back from the sea, and a safe passage was
provided across the dangerous quicksands, where many a traveller had
ridden to his death, trapped in the treacherous shiftings or caught by
the sudden inrushing tide.

Save for the roads which the Romans had driven across the county,
communications within Caernarvonshire were of the rudest, consisting
for the most part of miry tracks and paths, passable only on foot or
horseback and perilous even to such travellers after heavy rain. An
early bridge in a setting of great beauty (Pl. XXX, p. 371) can be found
in the valley of the Machno, the so-called "Roman bridge," which is
at the earliest a late medieval structure. On the hillside above, where
the later Panorama Drive was constructed for pleasure parties of the
nineteenth century to admire the view, an old track apparently led
across the slopes to the valley of the Lledr and to Gwibernant. The
farm of Coed-y-ffynnon on this route was built on the site of a medieval
chapel or chantry; a fragment of the ecclesiastical building is incorporated in the thick-walled entrance porch. The road peters out into
a rough moorland path a little distance beyond the farm, indicating
the nature of the medieval trackway.

Pennant tells us that in 1778 the road through the Llanberis pass was a "succession of rude and stony stairs" cut out of the rocks high above the lakes, and the track through the vale of Ogwen and Nant Ffrancon, also worked into rough, shallow steps over the greater part of its course, was "the most dreadful horse-path in Wales." Mr. Frank Ward, who examined part of this trackway in 1939, found that it diverged at the lake, with branches running on the north and south sides of Llyn Ogwen, the latter leading through the vale to Capel Curig. Many paths coming down from the mountains met this route, from Cwm Idwal, Bwlch-y-tir-marchog, Cwm Cowlyd and elsewhere, while at the Ogwen falls the main trackway again branched, leading through Nant Ffrancon on the east and west sides of the pass. This must have been one of the most important routes through the mountains from medieval times at least, a gathering-point for raiders and for skirmishing parties setting out to attack the straggler from the Norman hosts advancing on Bangor and Anglesey.

Improvement began about the year 1750, under pressure from the great estate owners, who could not reap the profit from the mineral resources or stone of their lands till there was some method of transport to the coast. They were seconded by the larger farmers, eager for better access to port or market. At first the attempts at improvement were made piecemeal by the local parishes, with no large-scale plan in mind for the development of through routes; then the big landlords entered the field, seeking to co-ordinate parochial developments and building through highways by their personal enterprise. In 1768 the first Turnpike Act for Caernarvonshire was passed, and a road was opened from Tal-y-cafn ferry to Conway and Bangor, and continued to Caernarvon and Pwlhelli; in 1776 it was extended up the Conway valley to Llanrwst. In 1770-72, the construction of a coach-road through the Sychnant pass and over the precipices of Penmaen-mawr was put in hand under the direction of Lord Bulkeley. The scheme was financed with with the aid of public subscription, in which many of the inhabitants of Ireland shared, as the road was to form part of the main route to Ireland by way of Chester and Holyhead. An older road had run higher up on the face of the mountain; Dr. Johnson, who traversed this route in 1774 accompanied by Mrs. Thrale on the way to visit her old home at Bodvel in Llŷn, approached the Penmaen-mawr section with many misgivings. However, he says,

"we found a way lately made, very easy and very safe. It was cut
smooth, and enclosed between parallel walls, the outer of which
secures the passenger from the precipice, which is deep and
dreadful," while the inner wall. "preserves the road from loose
stones, which the shattered steep above it would pour down . . .
The old road was higher, and must have been very formidable.
The sea beats at the bottom of the way."

Richard Pennant, Lord Penryhn, who succeeded to his estate in
1765, was a pioneer among private landowners; he built a road capable
of bearing wheeled traffic from his quarries at the foot of Nant Ffrancon
to Bangor, eventually extending it eastwards through the pass and
along the shore of Llyn Ogwen to Capel Curig (Pl. 39, p. 394). Mr.
Assheton Smith followed suit within the next twenty years, laying down
a road from his quarries near Llandeiniolen to Port Dinorwic. By 1802
the highway from Caernarvon to Pont Aberglaslyn, which runs through
Betws Garmon and by the side of Llyn Cwellyn, had been reconstructed
by public subscription, and was so carefully sited that "a horse could trot
or gallop it all the way." Mr. Madocks followed up his land-draining
enterprise by constructing roads in the reclaimed area, including one
from Pont Aberglaslyn through Tremadoc to Nevin. In 1810 the first
parliamentary committee was appointed to consider the rebuilding of
the highway from London to Holyhead, and a year later Thomas
Telford was commissioned to survey the route. He had completed his
famous road and the bridges over the Menai Straits and the mouth of
the Conway by about 1830, a masterpiece of engineering skill throughout; the Menai Bridge is among the first constructions of the industrial
age to reveal the possibilities of a functional beauty even in that
difficult and most unprepossessing of materials, iron.

There is a strong local tradition, unsupported by historical evidence,
that copper had been worked in Caernarvonshire in Roman times,
notably at Drws-y-coed, a region much frequented by the fairies in
Welsh story. In 1899 old people were still living in Nant Colwyn, which
runs from Beddgelert to Rhyd-ddu, who claimed to have seen them
dancing on the hillsides every moonlit night, while the air was filled
with their music. The land which they most frequented in this vale,
says Mr. D. E. Jenkins[1], stretched from Cwm Hafod Ruffyd, across the
slope of the mountain of Drws-y-coed to Llyn-y-dywarchen, the lake

[1] *Beddgelert* by D. E. Jenkins (Portmadoc, 1899).

on which Giraldus was told a floating sod or island was often to be seen. The narrow pass beyond the lake, leading to Drws-y-Coed proper, was an area of prehistoric settlement; several cairns were once to be found in the locality, and about the year 1832 five stone cists containing ashes and human bones were disclosed by a man digging. The copper mine lies some distance down the road beyond the pass; the vein has puzzled many prospectors by its irregular windings. By 1761 a group of Cornish miners had come to seek the ore here, and despite the lack of success which met these early attempts the work was revived again before 1815. The decline of the Parys mine in Anglesey in the 1830's brought many of the men and women of the island to seek employment at Drws-y-Coed. The opening of the railway to the slate quarry at Nantlle in 1824-25 was of great benefit to the miners, giving easy access to Caernarvon for the ore, from which it was shipped to Swansea, and Drws-y-coed proved a lucrative concern for many years.

Before the middle of the sixteenth century, copper was being raised at Aberglaslyn, Bryn-y-felin, and Sygun in the parish of Beddgelert, and later other mines flourished for a time at several places in this parish. The workings on the north-east face of Yr Wyddfa were started about the middle of the eighteenth century; the ore was carried on the backs of the miners to the lip of cwm Glaslyn, and thence dragged by sledge down the hillside to the track skirting Llyn Cwellyn, where it was transferred to packhorses or carts for the rest of the journey to Caernarvon. When the new highway was opened through the pass of Llanberis, early in the nineteenth century, a rough road was made from Gorphwysfa to the lakes, boats being used to carry the ore across Llyn Llydaw until by lowering the level of the lake it proved possible to continue the track along its shores. Many of the miners here came from Beddgelert, tramping over the Bwlch-y-saethau to their homes for the week-end, and spending the week in the cottage barracks now lying roofless in Cwm Dyli.

A company which had previously leased the Parys mine transferred to the hills of the Llanberis pass in the latter half of the eighteenth century, building their stamping mill at the edge of Llyn Peris, and starting on extensive mining operations for the ore, which was said here to yield 20 per cent pure copper (Pl. XXXI, p. 378). A traveller in the district in 1798 noted that some hundred men and boys were then employed here, their womenfolk maintaining smallholdings for grazing stock on the hills nearby.

The opening of new roads and the re-making of existing ones through the passes of Snowdon and along the coast made possible for the first time a large-scale expansion of the slate trade as the major industrial concern of the county of Caernarvon. "Slate quarrying," says Professor Dodd, "is in a sense the most Welsh of all Welsh industries. In the quarries themselves English is a foreign tongue, and those shapeless, monotonous villages which flank them, grey and drab, but clean . . . are the homes of a vigorous national culture." Purple slate from the Bethesda-Nantlle area was used by the Romans both for roofing and flooring at Segontium, and Conway was renowned for its slate-roofed houses in the fourteenth century, while we have already noted the supplies brought down the river from the Beddgelert-Nantlle region, in the year following the conquest, for Edward's new borough at Caernarvon. An export trade with Ireland in this commodity is indicated in the latter half of the sixteenth century for as many as 100,000 slates were shipped from Caernarvon between February and September 1587. But quarrying remained a small-scale operation, undertaken haphazardly by groups of tenants who paid a nominal rent of a few pence a year to the landowner, or gave him a proportion of the value of the slates produced. The desire to gain control of these sporadic workings gave an additional impetus to the movement for enclosing the common lands on which they occurred. In the middle of the eighteenth century the Penrhyn quarries employed about 80 workmen, who were also part-time farmers, and the export of slates was some 1,000 tons per annum. Lord Penrhyn eventually bought out these quarrymen or maintained their leases in his own hands as they fell in, gained control of the adjoining land, and began the systematic exploitation of the quarries. When war broke out with France in 1793 the annual export had risen to nearly 15,000 tons and about 600 workmen were employed, a number of whom were housed in the model village (from which any ale-house was excluded), built by Penrhyn in the valley of the Ogwen near the quarry. The war brought a period of depression to the industry; building activities, as usual in war-time, were curtailed, and a duty of 20 per cent *ad valorem* was imposed on slates carried in the coastal trade. Lord Penrhyn was obliged to dismiss many of his quarrymen, but his Lordship, as Walter Davies tells us,

"in order to find them employment for a season, set them about enclosing, draining, and otherwise improving a large tract of very poor turbary soil which, after a certain rotation of crops, was to be laid down in grass and let as a ley to feed the cows of the cottagers."

This process was adopted and continued in many areas fringing the quarries, resulting in little settlements of *tyddynau* (crofts) at a height of some 750 feet, such as those around Dinorwic or the example illustrated in Plate 40 (p. 395) near Nazareth and Nebo some two miles south of Pen-y-groes, while scattered individual holdings occur on such improved land up to 1,000 feet above sea level. Secondly, the energetic quarry-owner used the slack period to construct a narrow-gauge railroad for the passage of horse-drawn trams from the quarry to the wharf, replacing the broad-wheeled waggons which had conveyed the slates hitherto. By 1801 the railroad, six miles in length, was finished ; after the Peace of Amiens, when trade revived, over 100 tons of slates travelled along it daily, and on the death of Lord Penrhyn in 1808 the profits of the quarry were some £7,000 a year.

Mr. Assheton Smith, lord of the manor of Dinorwic, likewise found a number of small quarrymen working on his lands on the declivity of the hill above Llyn Padarn; their houses formed the nucleus of the more concentrated settlement so noticeable on this hillside. After trying a policy of leasing the larger workings that he managed to acquire to two chief tenants, Mr. Assheton Smith himself took them over in 1809; previously to this he had been engaged in wresting their common rights and their little pits from his own tenants and from neighbouring squatters on the waste lands. Bitter stories are still told in the village of Dinorwic of these transactions. In 1806 and 1808 he obtained Acts for the enclosure of the parish of Llandeiniolen, which stretches from the shores of the Menai to Llyn Padarn and the northern slopes of the mountain of Elidir Fawr. Riots of the quarrymen squatters broke out, but availed nothing in halting these measures. New and larger workings were started, and the industry expanded rapidly under the more efficient methods, though Smith was faced with greater difficulties of transport than Penrhyn. The slates were dragged down to the lake in horse-drawn sledges, an extra horse harnessed behind to act as a brake; they were then rowed across by boat and loaded on to carts for the journey by road to Felin Heli (later Port Dinorwic). A narrow-gauge tram-road was also built here in 1824-25 to overcome the difficulties and perils of the earlier mode of transport.

In the Nantlle valley, the bulk of the land has remained in the hands of the Crown. There has been no other large landowner to exploit the slate of the region; the Crown has adopted the policy of granting a number of leases to companies of quarrymen or to individuals, and has not attempted to consolidate the workings into one or two large concerns. There is no single enterprise on the scale of the Penrhyn or Llanberis quarries. The economic blast of the 1930's, when the slate industry was battling with new difficulties and the competition of alternative roofing materials, was felt keenly in this valley, and the depressed state of the Nantlle industry is one of the most pressing problems of the Snowdon region at the present day.

The romantic story of the development of the first large quarry at Ffestiniog about 1800 has been told in some detail by Professor Dodd in his *Industrial Revolution in North Wales*. Here again there was no single large landowner to undertake the exploitation of the rock ; from early times slate had been taken as required for local use by little groups of quarrymen, digging for it in small, shallow pits. The geological structure of this area is such that when a more systematic exploitation was embarked upon it was found that the slate had to be mined rather than quarried, a process which, of itself, tended to the development of independent concerns, whose consolidation was a matter of greater difficulty than in the case of the great surface cuttings on the mountain face in the Bethesda and Llanberis regions.

The three Lancashire men, William Turner and the brothers Casson, who undertook the first large venture at Ffestiniog, were themselves comparatively poor, without any capital, and risked all they had in the venture. But their fortunes prospered after the first difficult days, and the great Diffwys quarry was the outcome of their labours. In 1811 Samuel Holland, who had been engaged in copper- and lead-mining operations in North Wales, and had assisted Lord Penrhyn by undertaking the sale of all his slates, himself started a slate quarry at Rhiwbryfdir in the parish of Ffestiniog. His son, a second Samuel Holland, was put in charge of the undertaking in the year 1821 at the age of eighteen; his autobiography gives a vivid impression of the stern stuff of which the pioneers of the industrial age were made and of their abounding energy and enterprise. Summoned at a moment's notice by his father to replace a drunken foreman, the youth left Liverpool by boat for "Bagillt," and then, after a short coach journey to Holywell,

PLATE 39

John Markham

LLYN OGWEN from the London to Holyhead road, which skirts its shores. April

PLATE 40

John Markham

FIELD PATTERN of the tyddynod on the hillside near Nazareth, Caernarvonshire. The settlers here farm these little holdings and work part-time in the quarries near by. July set off on foot, carrying his carpet bag, to walk to Ffestiniog via St. Asaph, Llanrwst and Dolwyddelan. He took two nights and a day on the journey, getting only a few hours sleep at St. Asaph and Llanrwst on the way. On arrival, (being "somewhat tired" he had got a man to carry the carpet bag from Llanrwst), he was ordered by a message to walk a further couple of miles from the village to the quarry, where his father greeted him with the remark that he had expected him the preceding night.

The boy shouldered his task straight away, and in 1825 was able to sell the quarry to the newly-formed Welsh Slate and Copper Mining Company, of which Lord Palmerston was chairman, for £25,000, together with a farm and its stock on the lands adjoining, which brought the total up to £28,000. Samuel Holland, senior, meanwhile reserved his rights on the upper part of the mountain, where a second quarry was opened and worked by the son, who borrowed from an uncle and a cousin the necessary capital to start the new enterprise; he was joined in a few years by his brother Charles. The Holland brothers continued to work this quarry till the lease ran out in 1877. Meanwhile, they brought many improvements to the area; Samuel Holland, the younger, tells us that while engaged in managing the first venture at Rhiwbryfdir, he got the quarry roads improved and persuaded some of the farmers, hired to transport the slates, to use waggons instead of carts to carry them from the quarry to the wharf at Pentwyn-y-garnedd. From here they were taken by boat to vessels lying afloat in the river, for there were no quays built at Portmadoc then. In 1829, Holland was discussing with an Irish barrister and adventurer, Mr. Henry Archer, whom he had encountered in the inn at Pen-y-groes on his journeys from Ffestiniog to Caernarvon, the possibility of constructing a railway from the Ffestiniog quarries to Portmadoc. "He said it must be a single line, about two feet wide, that it would cost much less, and less to pay for the land taken." The help of the engineer, Charles Spooner, was enlisted, and that of Thomas Pritchard, "one of Stevenson's headmen." After setbacks and delays encountered in getting a Bill through Parliament to enable the work to be undertaken, the railway was started in February 1833 and opened on the 20th April 1836. "We had a grand opening day," writes Samuel Holland. "I had a short train and waggons loaded with slates and a great number of carriages laden with people, workmen and others. . . . All went up to the inclines in carriages drawn by horses, but we all came down

without horses, the inclination being sufficient to enable us to do so."
The horses were carried in a box at the rear of the train "feeding all
the way"; the incline was sufficient to carry slates and passengers
to the middle of the Portmadoc embankment, when the horses were
removed from the boxes and harnessed to the train, dragging it the rest
of the way to the wharves, which were built at Portmadoc in 1824.
They also drew the empty trucks back up the hillside to the quarry.
Eventually, ten slate quarries were opened in the neighbourhood of
Ffestiniog, all bringing down their slates to Portmadoc by the light
railway, till the work increased so much that horse traction was no
longer sufficient.

The plans of the line sent out to various locomotive-builders,
asking them for suggestions for a suitable design of steam engine,
provoked a discouraging response; it was declared that no engine
could be built to work so narrow a gauge round such short curves.
Holland's nephew, who was staying with him at the time, nevertheless
believed it to be possible. Eventually this young man planned an
engine himself, and two were constructed to his design. "Both engines
worked admirably from the first go off," says the delighted uncle,
although the Ffestiniog-Portmadoc line was the first to use steam
traction. It was presently employed in carrying passengers as well as
slates, enlarging and enriching the life of the industrial villages by bringing them into contact with other areas and interests. The Ffestiniog
railway and locomotives became the pattern for narrow-gauge mountain railway systems in other continents in the course of the nineteenth
century, notably in India and the United States, while the whole
system of narrow-gauge quarry railroads played an important part in
opening up communications between some of the most isolated valleys
of Snowdon and the outside world. It will be found that the branch
railway lines of this region all run to or through the quarry areas.

Secondly, the needs of the slate industry gave a spur to the ship-
building activities of the estuary: many a small farmer, shopkeeper or
doctor welcomed the opportunity to invest his little savings in a boat
for the slate trade and so come to feel that he had a share in the great
industrial enterprise of the new age. In Plate XXXIIb (p. 379) we
show an illustration from a contemporary painting of boat-building
near Llanfrothen in the early years of the nineteenth century, before
the Portmadoc embankment was built and the upper region of the
estuary drained of its waters.

The quarry villages represent the new development of Welsh culture in the industrial age; as their names—Bethesda, Nazareth, Bethania—imply, that culture was the product not merely of the thriving industry but of the great religious revival of Methodist Wales. In the zeal of a living faith, gripping the people as nothing had done since the days of the early Celtic church and its heroic missionaries, life was transformed and filled with a new significance, with the grim or radiant destiny of Calvin's strange creed. The colourful past, living again in the songs of the harper and poet, the old stories of the fairies and their dealings with mankind, handed on from generation to generation, the strange, half-pagan mythology, were eclipsed by the new absorbing interest in personal salvation. It was in the passionate sincerity of the preacher, swaying the congregation by the fervour of his spirit, in the jubilance of hymn singing, or the solemn funeral rites over the dead, that the Celtic love of drama now found its outlet. The new religion penetrated but slowly to the mountain hamlet and farm; Owen in 1792 deplored the superstition of the country people, their habit of resorting to witches and wizards, and the prevalence of Popish customs whose significance was long forgotten. In the uplands, the *twlwyth teg*, the beautiful people of the fairy world, still entranced the eyes of the fortunate mortal, or tempted him in pursuit of the fairy gold that later turned to a handful of leaves. But in the industrial villages and towns, raw and ugly in the wild beauty of the hills, the new faith swept into men's lives like a tempest, purging, uprooting, tearing at mind and spirit.

Into this land of arresting contrasts the tourists came flocking in increasing numbers over the new roads, during the last decades of the eighteenth century. They included men and women of very varied types and interests: the poet, finding in the hills a strange beauty and peace, the archaeologist and botanist, and later the geologist, pursuing his researches, the lady of fashion seeking the fillip of a new adventure to stir her jaded appetite for sensation. By the time that they discovered Snowdon, the hills were stripped of their forest growth, for the descriptions left by these wayfarers all tell of the barren slopes, the naked rocks and perilous screes which dominate the landscape today in the neighbourhood of the higher peaks. An engraving published in 1780 to illustrate Penruddocke Wyndham's *Tours through Wales and Monmouthshire in 1775*, depicts the pass of Aberglaslyn with bare hillsides where the twentieth-century visitor finds it a tree-lined chasm. Wyndham could not believe the tradition that "these uncouth and savage mountains formerly abounded with woods," so devoid of timber were the slopes he looked upon. The increase in the number of sheep maintained by the farmers from the latter seventeenth century, with their close grazing of the herbage, was probably one of the most potent causes in preventing the upspringing of new woodland growth to repair the gaps made by man, and by the great flocks of goats which ranged almost wild over the hills and would be a major factor accounting for the decline in the two centuries since Leland's visit. The goat population of Snowdon, however, was decreasing rapidly by the end of the eighteenth century; the only flock of any size which one traveller encountered in the early years of the next decade, was on the hills near Dolbadarn Castle. Pennant attributes their disappearance to a change in fashion, and the discarding of the wig, which was commonly made of goat's hair, but Wyndham states that they were being systematically destroyed in many districts because of their destructiveness to the new plantations.

The mountains broke upon the vision of the travellers with a splendour for which they seem to have been totally unprepared. Henry Eyre, driving with a friend from Corwen to Llanrwst in 1796, has recorded his first impressions: three miles short of the inn in the latter town, he says:

> "a scene the most grand and awfull burst at once on our sight, mountain piled on mountain, Alpine in their shape, magnificent in colour and character, exceeding everything of the sort we had witnessed."

The more strenuous could not rest till they had found a guide to lead them to the summits, particularly to the crest of Snowdon herself. The Snowdon ranger track is probably the oldest, according to Mr. Alan Monkhouse, but the P.-y-g. track, running from Pen-y-gwryd to Crib Goch, and the Llanberis path were also familiar to the walker two hundred years ago.

It was customary to hire guides not only for the ascent of Snowdon or other peaks, but in moving from one valley or district of the county to another, so difficult and unknown were the paths. Wyndham made two expeditions in 1774 and 1775 seeking the Glyders, which one would have thought sufficiently obvious landmarks, but utterly failed to find them or to discover anyone who could point them out; he decided the name had been changed and that they were really to be identified with the peaks of Yr Eifl. Even a few miles from their own immediate locality, the guides appear to have been anything but trustworthy. It was no uncommon occurrence for these pathfinders to lose first themselves and the visitors and then their heads, becoming more terrified than the unfortunate people whom they were attempting to lead. The eighteenth-century wayfarers must have been a stout and intrepid crew; we find in the notes of one that for 13 days he saw neither coach nor chaise, but "had traversed the mountainous country for the space of 167 miles upon Welsh hackneys hired from place to place." The small ponies were so strong that they could travel 40 miles a day with a heavy burden, but their backs were "as sharp as a wedge" and "their flesh lay like furrows along their ribs."

The less adventurous drove to the famous beauty spots, particularly the waterfalls, the Conway, the Machno, the Rhaidol, which if they were not equal to that of Niagara, as the writer of one guidebook, boosting the claims of his country, has sadly to confess, yet never failed to overawe the English spectator. Or they drove along the road "smooth as a bowling green" to Pont Aberglaslyn to watch the salmon moving upstream at the leap above the bridge, or took a little gentle exercise in the evenings wandering through the new plantations which the landowners kindly opened to them, and admired their fine country houses, especially the battlemented towers of Penrhyn Castle. First and foremost of the sights, however, was the great slate quarry at Penrhyn; here the tourists congregated to marvel at the achievement of their age with no thought of the desecration of the natural beauty involved. "In the snug summer box built in the eastern style of architecture," which Lord Penrhyn had erected among the rocks, pleasure parties "could recruit themselves with refreshment" which his lordship had thoughtfully provided, though the handbook advises them to bring their own wine or other beverages, as no inn or ale-house was to be found in the district, and the inhabitants had nothing but milk to offer. Similarly, when visiting Beddgelert or the Aberglaslyn pass the same mentor urges them to take their own refreshments—ham or cold chicken, for the inn at Beddgelert could only provide such humble food as butter, cheese and eggs. Naturally, the tourists grumbled at the poor accommodation of the inns (when have they not?) but if their journey took them to the town of Conway they were pleasantly surprised by the peaches, nectarines and plums provided by the gardens of the borough, which they found equal in flavour to that of any fruit tasted in more civilized quarters of the globe. The river was full of shipping and was navigable nearly to Llanrwst; the sheltered harbour of Conway was much frequented by coasting vessels, taking on board cargoes of timber, oak-bark and grain, the chief exports of the valley.

One of the first and most enduring impressions of all the visitors was that of the poverty of the country people, though they were over-whelmed by the open-handed hospitality of these peasants, who would share their coarse food with the utmost generosity, refusing any pay-ment. Even in the lowlands of Caernarvonshire, Wyndham found the state of the common people miserable "beyond the idea of an English-man to conceive," and remarks especially on the hard lot of the women, on whom fell most of the laborious drudgery. In the mountains he encountered an even worse poverty, but the hill farmers, nevertheless, appeared happy and contented in contrast to the lowlanders; robust and healthy, they lived to a ripe old age, though he asserts that there were parishes in which "a grain of wheat" or such simple luxuries as "garden greens" and leeks were never seen.

Another visitor in 1815 procured a guide near Aber who was the clerk of the parish. "He appeared to be a man of consequence, and lived in a cottage built of loose stones with one window in it. No feet to his stockings, a silk handkerchief once black but now rusty, and a well-patched jacket," is the description of this important personage, who would rank distinctly higher in the social scale than the peasant farmer. The corn was so scarce in the neighbourhood of Aber that year "that it was necessary to thrash out the grain as soon as housed."

With the influx of tourists, whether pursuing their scientific interests or purely bent on pleasure, came the forging of new links between Eng-land and Wales and the growth of a deeper understanding. The building of the Chester-Holyhead railway, which was opened in 1849, greatly increased the volume of holiday traffic, and the sprawling seaside towns of the North Wales coast grew up to accommodate the fresh influx from the midland and northern towns of England. The good railway accommodation, and the cheaper travel facilities provided, not only brought more and more Englishmen of the shopkeeper and artisan classes to the seaside and the hills of Snowdon, but, on the return journey, carried more and more Welshmen out of the country. The younger men, fired with a greater ambition than their fathers, sought an escape from the poverty of the upland life in the great commercial centres of Liverpool and London, where little colonies of Welsh settlers grew up, or overseas in the new worlds of the United States and the British dominions. Sometimes a whole band of young men would leave a village or the lonely homesteads of a valley together, to risk the dangers of a fresh start in the new countries, such as the group who emigrated from Capel Garmon in the early years of the twentieth century. The drift from the land of the stronger and more enterprising, which is still one of the main problems of rural Wales, began more than a hundred years ago, and was accelerated by the expanding industrial developments of the mid nineteenth century, and by the great emigration movements of its latter half. The growth of industrialism, with the concomitant rise of a new set of values, caused the final breakdown of the earlier communal forms of life.

The tourist of the twentieth century, treading in the footsteps of those earlier explorers of the beauties and mysteries of Snowdon, will find in many respects a changed countryside. The physical features, unchanged in the heart of the mountains, are themselves grotesquely distorted in the stone- and slate-quarrying regions, particularly noticeable in the great headland of Penmaen-mawr or above the lakes of the Llanberis pass. The industrial villages themselves are still clouded with the miasma of the trade depression of the 1930's. New trends in design in the inter-war years, the tendency in modern architecture to adopt the flat-roofed house or factory, combined with changes in taste which brought a demand for tiles and roofing shingles in place of slates even for the house with a pitched roof, were already having their effect on the industry, when the curtailment of building in the years of economic crisis struck a deadly blow to the life of the quarry districts. With the decline in the slate trade the boat-building industry of Portmadoc and other little harbours died away or lingered on in the construction of a few pleasure yachts annually; the life of the former busy little ports declined with the fall in the products formerly despatched from them.

The nineteenth century also saw changes in the utilization of land. We have already touched on the redistribution of population which took place, when whole families might leave for the coalfields and iron works of North and South Wales or to seek a new home on the far side of the world, leaving many of the upland farms derelict. But even in the richer valleys less and less attention was given to arable crops as the century progressed. Before the repeal of the Corn Laws, some tillage, however slight, had been maintained on the majority of farms as essential to the life of the inhabitants. But with the development of the great prairie lands of the world after the middle of the century, and the importation of grain duty-free, the tendency was for more and more of the arable land of Wales, particularly in the broken country of the north, to revert to hay and rough grazing. The importation of frozen meat and of wool from the Argentine and Australia in the closing decades of the century was a blow, in turn, to the stock-farmer, and was cited by some witnesses before the Land Commission of 1896 as one of the chief causes of the agricultural depression in Caernarvonshire. This changing economy, whereby men sought to make sufficient profit from the sale of their stock and wool to purchase the necessities of life—in other words the change from subsistence to cash farming—was a revolution as fundamental, if less spectacular, as the revolution in industry. We have seen cause to believe that some beginning of it may be found as far back as the seventeenth century, but the change was not completed, as the eye-witnesses of the Napoleonic era attest, for two hundred years.

References for Chapter 22

Hughes, W. J. (1924), Owen (1792), Royal Commission on Land in Wales and Monmouthshire (1896), Dodd (1933), Hall (Bangor MS. 908), Wyndham, H. P. (1781), Bowen, E. G. (1941), Pennant (1810 ed.), Williams W. (1802), Richards (1942-44), Davies, W. (1813), Holland (National Library of Wales MS. 4983), Monkhouse (1934), Eyre (Sir John Williams MS. 6364, N.L.W.), Cradock (1770), Fenton (1804-13), Evans (1804), Johnson (1816), Bingley (1814).

CHAPTER 23

CAN RURAL WALES SURVIVE?

Some Problems of the Welsh Hill Farmer
of the Present Day

RURAL Wales is still a land of small, dispersed family farms, their scattered distribution dictated partly by the physical nature of the hilly country, threaded by narrow valleys, partly by the historical fact of a system of divided inheritance. The aid of an extra man or two may be enlisted to supplement the labour of the household in working these little holdings, but in 1939, of all those who found in agriculture their full-time occupation, 60 per cent were farmers and their relatives. The sons and daughters employed usually receive only a few shillings a week pocket-money; the hope of economic advancement exists only for the eldest son on the day when he succeeds to the farm. Even so, the income which the land yields him is precariously small. In 1939 the cultivated area, including both managed pasture and tillage crops, of 67.7 per cent of all the holdings in Wales was under 50 acres, as compared with 72.3 acres for England. In Caernarvonshire, where this average was lowest, we have already mentioned that it amounted to only 26.4 acres. These figures do not include the rough mountain grazings which play an important part in the sheep- and stock-farming of the uplands, and which may run into several hundred acres. But they do represent the worked, productive area, and under modern conditions such holdings cannot be regarded as in any sense economic farming units. They are totally unfitted for the introduction of mechanization, even if the capital were forthcoming to supply the necessary equipment. Such concentration as has taken place in recent years has been of a haphazard nature, and not in any sense a policy of planned redistribution and alteration of farm boundaries. The standard of living, therefore, remains very low; Professor Ashby has estimated that there are some six thousand independent tenant farmers or owner-occupiers in Wales, whose annual income is less than that of the farm worker on the minimum wage, whom they may be forced by circumstances to employ.

Cottages are few, save on the large estates, and it is still the common practice for the farm labourer to board with his employer, which means, of course, the indefinite postponement of marriage, very primitive sleeping accommodation, and little in the way of comfort. It is not surprising, therefore, that with the expanding industrial development of the country in the middle years of the last century, Wales lost a fifth of her rural workers, the exodus being particularly marked among the younger members of the farming families and among the farm labourers. The slight revival which occurred in the early years of the present century, with more stable agricultural conditions, was again followed by a great drift from the land, particularly of the labourers, in the inter-war years. As a result, those remaining in the countryside tend to be men and women of late middle age, or boys and girls fresh from school before the opportunity has arisen to escape to the towns, which can offer social amenities from which the isolated homestead is almost entirely cut off.

The improvement of housing and living conditions for the small farmer raises a number of peculiar problems, as the Hobhouse Report on Rural Housing points out. Many of the outwardly attractive sturdily built farmhouses are totally lacking in sanitation, a piped water supply, or artificial lighting, other than lamps and candles, and a number are liable to be condemned, by any reasonable, modern standards, as unfit for human habitation. Before the war of 1939, these homes did not fall into the category of "Houses for the Working Classes," but under the new Housing Acts they will be thus classified. If the farmer is the owner of his house, his income, as we have seen, is not sufficient to allow any suggestion of rebuilding or of embarking on the substantial alterations so often necessary to bring it up to the requirements of modern standards of health. In the large number of instances where he is a tenant, the rent for house and holding perhaps averages £30 to £40 per annum, a total which does not make it feasible for the land-owner to contemplate such schemes. The usual remedy, under the Housing Acts, is for the local authority to carry out the necessary repairs and alterations, hoping to recover the sum expended from the owner, or to demolish the house and include the building of a new one in the next Council Housing Scheme. Neither course is practicable in the case of the small Welsh farms, and the problem of improvement remains unsolved, but it raises immediately the question of the possibility of consolidating the smaller units into holdings of an economic size, with all the attendant social difficulties and hardships for the displaced people.

In the case of the large sheep-runs, the collapse of prices and the loss of skilled labour and capital in the 1930's resulted in a failure to keep up the standard of land-management required for the successful breeding of ewes and lambs. The high returns which have been obtainable recently, by selling three- and four-year-old wethers for mutton, have also militated against the production of the hardy mountain ewes necessary for the maintenance of the hill flock. It has been suggested that it is difficult to make a reasonable living out of sheep-farming at the present time with a flock of less than a thousand head, and one rough estimate given to the writer was that there were probably only some hundred flocks of this size in the whole of Wales.

A further change in the rural economy of Wales took place in the thirties, and particularly during the years of the second world war, as more and more farmers swung over from the raising of store cattle to liquid milk production. Once, however, the supply of milk has been sufficiently increased to meet the rise in consumption of the past decades, the public will almost certainly begin to press for a higher-quality product, in other words, for clean milk. The existing buildings and the water-supply of the majority of Welsh farms are quite inadequate for this purpose. Also, the high cost of collecting small quantities of milk from isolated homesteads, with their rough and poor approach roads, is another factor likely to affect the Welsh hill farmer adversely, when the drive for cheap milk, which is bound to arise with a more plentiful supply, becomes operative.

On the other hand, the work initiated by Sir George Stapledon and the Plant Breeding Station at Aberystwyth, in the improvement of hill pastures, has provided the possibility of carrying an enlarged and improved head of stock on the uplands of Wales, could the difficulties we have raised be overcome. Both modern dairy- and sheep-farming call for men of skill and initiative—men who will inevitably demand for themselves and for their children a higher standard of living and of educational and social opportunities than the conditions of the country-side yet afford. Their problems and desires present some of the most thorny questions to the planners of the future, but the very life of rural Wales hangs upon their solution.

References for Chapter 23

Ashby and Evans (1944), Hill Sheep Farming in Wales, Cmd. 6498 (1944).

A LIST OF PLANTS AND ANIMALS

by Bruce Campbell

THE general purpose of this Appendix was explained at the end of Chapter 5; it attempts to give a picture, mainly in list form, of the wild-life of the Caernarvonshire section of the future North Wales National Park. As the boundary of this area is ecologically rather arbitrary, and in any case does not even have legal existence or exact definition at the time of writing, the decision to include many species, particularly of plants, rests only on the probability of their occurrence. This very ambiguity will, it is hoped, stimulate interest, once the Park is a fact, in the compilation of authoritative lists.

THE VASCULAR PLANTS

The scientific nomenclature of the Vascular Plant list is that of Clapham (1946); the English names follow Hyde and Wade (1934), the Welsh, Griffith (1895), but see page 176. Species marked with an asterisk are known to occur in the rock-faces of the semi-alpine zone. (See pages 189–96.)

RANUNCULACEAE

Clematis vitalba L.	Traveller's Joy	Cydd-y-coed, Dringiedydd
* *Thalictrum alpinum* L.	Alpine Meadow Rue	Arianllys-y-mynydd
* *T. minus* agg.	Small Meadow Rue	
(4 segregates recorded.)		
T. flavum L.	Common Meadow Rue	Arianllys cyffredin, Troed-y-barcud
* *Anemone nemorosa* L.	Wood Anemone	Blodeuyn-y-gwynt
Ranunculus circinatus Sibth.	Rigid-leaved Water-Crowfoot	
R. trichophyllus Chaix	Water-Crowfoot	
R. heterophyllus Weber		
R. peltatus Schrank		
R. pseudofluitans Baker & Foggitt		
R. lenormandi F. Schultz		
R. hederaceus L.	Ivy-leaved Water-Crowfoot	
R. sceleratus L.	Celery-leaved Crowfoot	Crafanc-yr-Eryr
R. flammula L.	Lesser Spearwort	Poethfflam
R. lingua L.	Greater Spearwort	Blaen-y-gwaew mwyaf
R. auricomus L.	Wood Crowfoot	Peneuraid
* *R. acris* L.	Meadow Buttercup	
R. repens L.	Creeping Buttercup	Crafanc-y-fran ymlusgaidd

R. bulbosus L.	Bulbous Buttercup	Chwys mair, Blodau-y-menyn
R. ficaria L.	Lesser Celandine	Llygad Ebrill
Caltha palustris L.	Marsh Marigold	Troed-yr-ebol
C. radicans T. F. Forst.		
* *Trollius europaeus* L.	Globe Flower	Cronell

NYMPHACEAE
Nuphar lutea (L.) Sm.	Yellow Water Lily	Bwltis, tili melyn y dwr
Nymphaea alba L.	White Water Lily	Magwyr wen

PAPAVERACEAE
Papaver somniferum L.	Opium Poppy	
P. rhoeas L.	Common Red Poppy	Pabi Crwn-ben-llyfn, Llygad-y-cythraul
P. dubium L.	Red Poppy	
P. argemone L.		
P. hybridum L.		
* *Meconopsis cambrica* (L.) Vig.	Welsh Poppy	Pabi Cymreig
Chelidonium majus L.	Greater Celandine	Dilwydd felen, Llym-y-llygad

FUMARIACEAE
Corydalis claviculata (L.) DC.	Climbing Fumitory	Mwg-y-ddaear
Fumaria capreolata L.	Ramping Fumitory	
F. bastardii Bor.		
F. officinalis L.	Common Fumitory	
F. confusa Jord.		

CRUCIFERAE
Nasturtium officinale R. Br.	Watercress	Berwr-y-dwr
Barbarea vulgaris R. Br.	Winter Cress	Berwr-y-gaeaf
* *Arabis petraea* (L.) Lam.	Northern Rock Cress	
A. hirsuta (L.) Scop.	Hairy Rock Cress	Twr-ged-blewog
* *Cardamine amara* L.	Large Bitter Cress	Hydyf-y-waun, Blodeuyn-y-gog
Cardamine pratensis L.	Lady's Smock	
C. hirsuta L.	Hairy Bitter Cress	Hydyf blewog
* *C. flexuosa* With.	Hairy Bitter Cress	Hydyf chwerw
C. impatiens L.	Impatient Bitter Cress	
* *Draba incana* L.	Hoary Whitlow-Grass	
Erophila verna (L.) Chevall.	Spring Whitlow-Grass	Llys-y-bystwn
* *Cochlearia alpina* Wats.	Alpine Scurvy-Grass	
Hesperis matronalis L.		
Arabidopsis thaliana (L.) Heynh.	Thale-Cress	
Sisymbrium officinale (L.) Scop.	Hedge-Mustard	Arfog meddygol
Alliaria petiolata (Bieb.) Cavara & Grande	Jack-by-the-hedge	Garllegog, Troed-yr-asen

Erysimum cheiranthoides L.	Treacle-Mustard	
Subularia aquatica L.	Water Awlwort	Mynawydlys dyfrdig
Brassica napus L.	Rape	Bresych-yr-yd
B. campestris L.	Wild Turnip	Meipen, Erfinen
Sinapis arvensis L.	Charlock	Cedu gwyllt
Capsella bursa-pastoris (L.) Medik.	Shepherd's Purse	Llys Tryfal, Pwrs-y-bugail
Lepidium smithii Hook.	Smooth Field Pepper-wort	Pybyrllys
Thlaspi alpestre L.	Penny Cress	
Raphanus raphanistrum L.	Wild Radish	Rhyddygl gwyllt

RESEDACEAE
Reseda luteola L.   Weld

VIOLACEAE		
Viola odorata L.	Sweet Violet	Millyn glas, Crinllys
V. hirta L.	Hairy Violet	Gwiolydd flewog
V. palustris L.	Marsh Violet	Gwiolydd-y-gors
V. riviniana Rchb.	Wood Violet	
* *V. rupestris* Schmidt.	Rock Violet	
Viola canina L.	Dog Violet	Pen-y-neidr
V. arvensis agg.	Corn Pansy	Trilliw-yr-âr
Viola tricolor agg.	Wild Pansy	Fioled dau-wynebog, Llys-y-drindod trilliw
V. lutea Huds.	Yellow Pansy	Fioled felyn

POLYGALACEAE		
Polygala vulgaris L.	Common Milkwort	Llys Crist, Amlaethai
* *P. serpyllifolia* Hose.	Heath Milkwort	

CARYOPHYLLACEAE		
Silene cucubalus Wibel	Bladder Campion	Glydlys codrwth, Menyg-y-gog
* *S. maritima* (Hornem.) With.	Sea Campion	Glydlys arfor, Glwydd-y-geifr
S. anglica L.	English Catchfly	
* *S. acaulis* (L.) Jacq.	Moss Campion	Glydlys mwsogl
Melandrium album (Mill.) Garcke	White Campion	Lluglys gwyn, Lluglys hwyrol
* *M. dioicum* (L.) Coss. & Germ.	Red Campion	Lluglys-yr-ychain
Lychnis flos-cuculi L.	Ragged Robin	Blodeuyn-y-fran
Cerastium viscosum L.	Mouse-ear Chickweed	Corn-wlyddyn
* *C. vulgatum* L.		
* *C. alpinum* L.	Alpine Chickweed	
* *C. edmondstonii* (Edmondst.) Murb. & Ostenf.	Arctic Chickweed	
C. arvense L.	Mouse-ear Chickweed	
Moenchia erecta (L.) Gaertn., Mey. & Scherb.	Upright Chickweed	Corn-wlyddyn syth

Myosoton aquaticum (L.)   Water Chickweed
   Moench.
Stellaria media (L.) Vill.   Common Chickweed   Gwlydd-y-cywion, Brechlys
   S. holostea L.   Greater Stitchwort   Tafod-yr-edn mwyaf
   S. graminea L.   Lesser Stitchwort   Tafod-yr-edn lleiaf
   S. alsine Grimm   Bog Stitchwort   Tafod-yr-edn y gors
* *Arenaria verna* L.   Vernal Sandwort   Tywodwlydd gwanwynol
   A. trinervia L.   Three-nerved Sandwort   Tywodwlydd
   A. serpyllifolia L.   Thyme-leaved Sandwort   Tywodwlydd
   A. leptoclados (Rchb.) Guss.
Sagina apetala Ard.   Annual Pearlwort
   S. procumbens L.   Procumbent Pearlwort   Corwlydd gorweddol
   S. subulata (Sw.) C. Presl.   Heath Pearlwort
   S. nodosa (L.) Fenzl   Knotted Pearlwort   Corwlydd clymog
Spergula arvensis L.   Corn Spurrey   Troellig-yr-yd, Llindro
   S. sativa Boenn.   Smooth-seeded Spurrey
Spergularia rubra (L.)   Red Sand-spurrey   Tywodylydd glasrudd
   J. & C. Presl.

PORTULACEAE
Montia verna Neck.   Water Blinks   Dyfr-wlyddyn-y-ffynnon
   M. fontana L.

ELATINACEAE
Elatine hexandra   Six-stamened Waterwort
   (Lapierre) DC.

HYPERICACEAE
Hypericum androsaemum L.   Tutsan   Creulys bendigaid, Llys
         perfigedd, Dail-y-twrch,
         Gwaed-y-gwyr
   H. perforatum L.   Perforated St. John's   Eurinllys trydwll
       Wort
   H. quadrangulum L.   Square stalked St. John's   Eurinllys pedrongl
       Wort
   H. undulatum Willd.   Imperforate St. John's
       Wort
   H. humifusum L.   Trailing St. John's Wort   Eurinllys man ymdaenol
* *H. pulchrum* L.   Upright St. John's Wort   Eurinllys man syth
   H. hirsutum L.   Hairy St. John's Wort
   H. elodes L.   Bog St. John's Wort   Eurinllys-y-gors

MALVACEAE
Malva moschata L.   Musk Mallow   Hoccys-mws, Llys Simwnt
   M. sylvestris L.   Common Mallow   Hoccys cyffredin

TILIACEAE
Tilia cordata Mill.   Small-leaved Lime
   (4 segregates recorded.) Introduced

LINACEAE
Linum catharticum L.   Purging Flax   Llin y tylwyth teg

GERANIACEAE

Geranium sanguineum L.	Bloody Cranesbill	Pig-yr-aran rhyddgoch
G. pratense L.	Wood Cranesbill	Pig-yr-aran weirglawdd
G. molle L.	Dove's foot Cranesbill	Troed-y-golomen
G. pusillum L.	Small-flowered Cranesbill	
G. dissectum L.	Cut-leaved Cranesbill	Pig-yr-aran llarpiog
G. columbinum L.	Long-stalked Cranesbill	Pig-yr-aran hir goesog
G. lucidum L.	Shining Cranesbill	Pig-yr-aran disglaer
* *G. robertianum* L.	Herb Robert	Coes goch, Llys-y-llwynog

OXALIDACEAE

* *Oxalis acetosella* L.	Wood-sorrel	Suran-y-coed, Suran-y-gog

BALSAMINACEAE

Impatiens glandulifera Royle	Indian Balsam

AQUIFOLIACEAE

* *Ilex aquifolium* L.	Holly	Celynen

CELASTRACEAE

Euonymus europaeus L.	Spindle-Tree	Piswydden

RHAMNACEAE

Rhamnus cathartica L.	Common Buckthorn	Rhafnwydden
Frangula alnus Mill.	Alder Buckthorn	

ACERACEAE

Acer pseudo-platanus L.	Sycamore	Masarnwydd

LEGUMINOSAE

Genista anglica L.	Petty-Whin	Cracheithin, Eithinen-yr-iar
Ulex europaeus L.	Common Gorse	Eithinen Ffreinig
Ulex gallii Planch.	Western Gorse	Eithin
U. minor Roth	Small Gorse	Eithin man
Sarothamnus scoparius (L.) Koch.	Broom	Banadlen
Ononis repens L.	Creeping Restharrow	Cas gan Arddwr
O. spinosa L.	Spiny Restharrow	
Medicago sativa L.	Lucerne	Maglys rhyddlas
M. lupulina L.	Black Medick	Maglys gwinenddu
Trifolium pratense L.	Red Clover	March-feillionen, Meillionen goch
T. medium L.	Zigzag Clover	Meillionen wyrgam
T. hybridum L.	Alsike Clover	
T. repens L.	White Clover	Meillionen wen
T. campestre Schreb.	Hop Trefoil	Meillionen hopysaidd
T. dubium Sibth.	Suckling Clover	Meillionen felen fechan
Anthyllis vulneraria L.	Kidney Vetch	Meillionen felen
Lotus corniculatus L.	Birdsfoot Trefoil	Pysen y Ceirw
L. uliginosus Schkuhr.		
Ornithopus perpusillus L.	Birdsfoot	Troed yr Aderyn

Vicia hirsuta (L.) S. F. Gray.	Hairy Vetch	Corbysen flewog
Vicia cracca L.	Tufted Vetch	Tagwyg bysen
Vicia orobus DC.	Bitter Vetch	
V. sylvatica L.	Wood Vetch	Ffygbysen-y-wig
V. sepium L.	Bush Vetch	Ffygbysen-y-cloddiau
V. angustifolia L.	Narrow-leaved Vetch	Ffygbysen maethol
Lathyrus pratensis L.	Meadow Vetchling	Ydbysen-y-waun
* *L. montanus* Bernh.	Tuberous Bitter Vetch	Pysen-y-coed

ROSACEAE		
Prunus spinosa L.	Blackthorn	Draenen ddu, Eirin-berth
P. avium L.	Gean	Ceiriosen, Sirianen
P. cerasus L.	Wild Cherry	
* *P. padus* L.	Bird Cherry	Ceiriosen-yr-aderyn
Spiraea salicifolia L.	Bridewort	Erwain helyg-ddail
Filipendula ulmaria (L.) Maxim.	Meadowsweet	Erwaint, Chwys Arthur, Meddlys
* *Rubus saxatilis* L.	Stone-Bramble	
R. chamaemorus L.	Cloudberry	
R. idaeus L.	Raspberry	Afanllwyn, Mafonen, Mafon-llwyn
R. caesius L.	Dewberry	
Rubus spp.	Bramble	Miaren, Mwyaren
53 micro-species listed by Griffith, excluding hybrids and varieties.		
* *Dryas octopetala* L.	Mountain Avens	Derig
Geum urbanum L.	Herb Bennet	Mabgoll, Bendigaidlys
* *G. rivale* L.	Water Avens	Mabgoll glan-y-dwr
Fragaria vesca L.	Wild Strawberry	Mefysen-y-goedwig
Potentilla sterilis (L.) Garcke	Barren Strawberry	Coeg-fefysen
* *P. crantzii* (Crantz) Beck	Alpine Cinquefoil	
P. erecta (L.) Räusch	Tormentil	Tresgl-y-moch, Tresgl-yr-eithin
P. procumbens Sibth.	Trailing Tormentil	Pumnalen ymlusgaidd
P. reptans L.	Creeping Cinquefoil	Pumnalen gyffredin
P. anserina L.	Silverweed	Tinllwyd
Comarum palustre L.	Marsh Cinquefoil	Llygad ysgyfarnog
Alchemilla arvensis (L.) Scop.	Parsley Piert	Troed-y-dryw
* *A. vulgaris* (L.) agg.	Lady's Mantle	Mantell Fair
Agrimonia eupatoria L.	Agrimony	Tryw, Caliwlyn-y-mel
Rosa arvensis Huds.	Field Rose	Ciros gwyn
R. spinosissima L.	Burnet Rose	Mwccog
R. canina L. agg.	Dog Rose	Ciros, Egroeswydd
R. afzeliana Fr. agg.	Dog Rose	
R. villosa L. agg.		
R. tomentosa Sm. agg.	Downy Dog Rose	Rhosyn lledwlanog
R. micrantha Sm. agg.	Small-flowered Sweet Briar	Rhosyn per
* *Sorbus aucuparia* L.	Rowan	Criafolen, Cerddinen
S. aria agg.	White Beam	

Malus pumila Mill.	Crab-Apple	Afallen
Crataegus monogyna Jacq.	Hawthorn	Draenen-wen, Yspyddaden

SAXIFRAGACEAE
* *Saxifraga oppositifolia* L. — Purple Mountain Saxifrage
* *S. nivalis* L. — Alpine Saxifrage
* *S. stellaris* L. — Starry Saxifrage
* *S. aizoides* L. — Yellow Mountain Saxifrage
Occurrence not accepted by Farmer and others.
  S. tridactylites L. — Rue-leaved Saxifrage
* *S. cespitosa* agg. — Mossy Saxifrage
  S. cespitosa L.
  S. rosacea Moench.
  S. sponhemica C. C. Gmel.
  S. platypetala Sm.
* *S. hypnoides* agg. — Mossy Saxifrage
  S. hypnoides L.
  S. leptophylla D. Don
* *Chrysosplenium oppositifolium* L. — Opposite-leaved Golden Saxifrage — Eglyn cyferbynddail

PARNASSIACEAE
Parnassia palustris L. — Grass of Parnassus — Briall-y-gors

CROSSULARIACEAE
Ribes uva-crispa L. — Gooseberry — Grwyswydden, Eirin Mair
R. alpinum L. — Alpine Currant — Rhyfwydden mynyddol
Introduced.

CRASSULACEAE
Umbilicus pendulinus DC. — Wall Pennywort — Crondoddaidd, Bogail-y-forwyn
* *Sedum rosea* (L.) Scop. — Roseroot — Pren-y-ddanodd
  S. telephium L. — Orpine — Berw Taliesin
  S. anglicum Huds. — English Stonecrop — Briweg y cerrig, Gwenith y brain
  S. album L. — White Stonecrop
  S. acre L. — Biting Stonecrop — Bywydog boeth, Pupur y fagwyr
* *S. rupestre* L. — Rock Stonecrop
  S. forsteriana Sm. — Welsh Stonecrop
  S. reflexum L. — Reflexed Stonecrop — Bywydog, Glys
  Sempervivum tectorum L. — Houseleek

DROSERACEAE
Drosera rotundifolia L. — Round-leaved Sundew — Toddaidd rudd, Tawddrudd
D. anglica Huds. — Great Sundew — Tawddrudd mawr
D. longifolia L. — Long-leaved Sundew

HALORAGACEAE
Hippuris vulgaris L. — Marestail — Rhawn-y-gaseg
Myriophyllum spicatum L. — Spiked Water-Milfoil
M. alterniflorum DC. — Alternate-flowered Water-Milfoil

CALLITRICHACEAE
Callitriche palustris L. — Vernal Water-Starwort — Brigwlydd gwanwynol
C. intermedia Hoffm.

LYTHRACEAE
Peplis portula L. — Water Purslane — Troed-y-gywen
Lythrum salicaria L. — Purple Loosestrife — Gwyarllys, Llys y Milwr

ONAGRACEAE
* *Chamaenerion angustifolium* (L.) Scop. — Rosebay Willowherb — Helyglys hardd
Epilobium hirsutum L. — Great Hairy Willowherb — Helyglys per
E. parviflorum Schreb. — Small-flowered Willow-herb — Helyglys man-flodeuog
E. montanum L. — Broad-leaved Willowherb — Helyglys llydanddail
E. obscurum Schreb. — Willowherb
E. palustre L. — Narrow-leaved Willow-herb — Helyglys culddail
* *E. alsinifolium* Vill. — Chickweed-leaved Willowherb — Helyglys gwlyddynddail
E. pedunculare A. Cunn.
Circaea lutetiana L. — Enchanter's Nightshade — Swynddlys, Llys Stephan
C. intermedia Ehrh.
C. alpina L.

CUCURBITACEAE
Bryonia dioica Jacq. — White Bryony

UMBELLIFERAE
Hydrocotyle vulgaris L. — Marsh Pennywort — Ceiniog-y-gors
Sanicula europaea L. — Wood Sanicle — Golchwraidd, Clyst-yr-Arth
Conium maculatum L. — Hemlock — Cegiden
Smyrnium olusatrum L. — Alexanders — Dulys
Apium nodiflorum (L.) Lag. — Marshwort — Dyfr-foronen syp-flodeuog
A. inundatum (L.) Rchb. f. — Lesser Marshwort
Carum verticillatum (L.) Koch. — Whorled Caraway — Carwas troellog
* *Pimpinella saxifraga* L. — Burnet Saxifrage — Gwraiddiriog
Conopodium majus (Gouan) Lor. & Barr. — Pignut — Bywi, Clor, Cneuen-y-ddaear
Myrrhis odorata (L.) Scop. — Sweet Cicely — Creithig, Sisly ber
Chaerophyllom temulum L. — Rough Chervil — Gorthyfail garw
Anthriscus scandicina (Weber) Mansf. — Common Chervil — Gorthyfail
A. sylvestris (L.) Hoffm. — Smooth Chervil — Gorthyfail llyfn
Oenanthe fistulosa L. — Water Dropwort — Dibynlor

O. lachenalii C. C. Gmel.	Parsley Water-Dropwort	Dibynlor
O. crocata L.	Hemlock Water-Dropwort	Dibynlor, Gypslys
O. aquatica (L.) Poir.	Fine-leaved Water Dropwort	
O. fluviatilis (Bab.) Coleman		
Aethusa cynapium L.	Fool's Parsley	Geuberllys
* *Angelica sylvestris* L.	Wild Angelica	Llys-yr-Angel y goedwig
* *Heracleum sphondylium* L.	Hogweed	Efwr cyffredin
Daucus carota L.	Wild Carrot	Moronen-y-meusydd
Torilis anthriscus (L.) C. C. Gmel.	Hedge Parsley	Eulunberllys
T. nodosa (L.) Gaertn.	Knotted Hedge Parsley	Tored-y-cyw clymog

ARALIACEAE
Hedera helix L.	Ivy	Eiddew, Iorwg

ADOXACEAE
* *Adoxa moschatellina* L.	Moschatel	Anfri, Mwglys

CAPRIFOLIACEAE
Sambucus nigra L.	Elder	Ysgawlwyn, Ysgawen
S. ebulus L.	Danewort	
Viburnum opulus L.	Guelder Rose	Corswigen
Lonicera periclymenum L.	Honeysuckle	Gwyddfid, Llaeth-y-geifr

RUBIACEAE
* *Galium boreale* L.	Northern Bedstraw	
G. verum L.	Lady's Bedstraw	Briwydd felen
G. mollugo L.	Hedge Bedstraw	
* *G. saxatile* L.	Heath Bedstraw	Briwydd wen
G. palustre L.	Marsh Bedstraw	Gwenwlydd-y-Gors
G. uliginosum L.	Bog Bedstraw	Gwendon arw y migyn
G. aparine L.	Goosegrass	Gwlydd-y-perthi
Asperula odorata L.	Sweet Woodruff	Llys-yr-eryr perarogl
Sherardia arvensis L.	Field Madder	Corwreiddrydd

VALERIANACEAE
Valeriana officinalis L.	Great Valerian	Llysiau Cadwgan
V. pyrenaica L.	Heart-leaved Valerian	

DIPSACEAE
Knautia arvensis (L.) Coult.	Field Scabious	Clafrllys, Penlas
Succisa pratensis Moench.	Devil's Bit Scabious	Clafrllys gwreidd-don

COMPOSITAE
Eupatorium cannabinum L.	Hemp Agrimony	Byddon chwerw, Cywarch gwyllt
* *Solidago virgaurea* L.	Golden-rod	Eurwialen Melyneuraid
* *S. cambrica* Huds.	Welsh Golden-rod	
Bellis perennis L.	Daisy	Llygad-y-dydd
Aster tripolium L.	Sea-Aster	

Filago germanica L.	Upright Cudweed	Edafeddog lwyd
F. minima (Sm.) Pers.	Small Cudweed	Edafeddog leiaf, Digoll lwyd
* *Antennaria dioica* (L.) Gaertn.	Mountain Everlasting	Edafeddog fynyddig
Gnaphalium uliginosum L.	Marsh Cudweed	Edafeddog benddu
Inula helenium L.	Elecampane	Marchalan, Llwyglys
Achillea millefolium L.	Yarrow	Gwilffrai, Milddail
A. ptarmica L.	Sneezewort	Ystrewlys, Tafod yr wydd
Anthemis cotula L.	Stinking Mayweed	Milwydd, Camri-y-cwn
Chrysanthemum segetum L.	Corn Marigold	Gold-yr-yd
* *C. leucanthemum* L.	Oxeye Daisy	Aspygan, Llygad-y-dydd mawr
C. parthenium (L.) Bernh.	Feverfew	Tartgryd, Wermod wen
Matricaria inodora L.	Scentless Mayweed	Ffenigl-y-cwn
M. chamomilla L.	Wild Chamomile	Amraenwen
M. matricarioides (Less.) Porter	Rayless Chamomile	
Tanacetum vulgare L.	Tansy	Tanclys, Gystlys cyffredin
Artemisia absinthium L.	Wormwood	Cherwyn, Wermod lwyd
A. vulgaris L.	Mugwort	Bydiog lwyd, Llwydlys
Tussilago farfara L.	Coltsfoot	Alan bychan, Pesychlys, Carn yr ebol
Petasites hybridus (L.) Gaertn., Mey. & Scherb.	Butterbur	Alan mawr, Dail y tryfan
Senecio vulgaris L.	Groundsel	Greulys, Penfelen
S. sylvaticus L.	Heath Groundsel	Greulys, Penfelen mynyddol
S. squalidus L.	Oxford Ragwort	
S. jacobaea L.	Common Ragwort	Carnedd felen wryw, Llys-y-gingroen
S. aquaticus Hill	Marsh Ragwort	Penfelen-y-gors
Carlina vulgaris L.	Carline Thistle	Ellast
Arctium lappa L.	Greater Burdock	Cedowrach mwyaf, Cacamwci
A. vulgare (Hill) A. H. Evans	Intermediate Burdock	
A. minus (Hill) Bernh.	Lesser Burdock	Cedowrach Ueiaf
Cirsium vulgare (Savi) Ten.	Spear Thistle	March ysgallen
C. palustre (L.) Scop.	Marsh Thistle	Ysgallen-y-gors
C. heterophyllum (L.) Hill	Melancholy Thistle	Ysgallen fwyth
C. arvense (L.) Scop.	Field Thistle	Ysgallen gyffredin yr âr
* *Saussurea alpina* (L.) DC.	Alpine Saw-Wort	Dant y pysgodyn mynyddig
Serratula tinctoria L.	Saw-Wort	Dant y pysgodyn, Llif-lys
Centaurea nigra L.	Black Knapweed	Penglaed-y-benddu
C. cyanus L.	Cornflower	Cramenog-yr-yd, Penlas-yr-yd
Cichorium intybus L.	Chicory	Ysgallen-y-meirch
Lapsana communis L.	Nipplewort	Cartheig
Picris hieracioides L.	Hawkweed Ox-tongue	
Crepis capillaris (L.) Wallr.	Smooth Hawkbeard	Gwalchlys llyfn

SN.

C. paludosa (L.) Moench.   Marsh Hawksbeard   Heboglys-y-gors
* *Hieracium* spp.   Hawkweed
31 micro-species listed by Griffith.
Hypochaeris radicata L.   Long-rooted Cat's-ear   Melynydd gorwreiddiog
Leontodon leysseri (Wallr.)   Hairy-headed Hawkbit   Peradyl blewog
   Beck
L. autumnalis L.   Autumnal Hawkbit   Peradyl
Taraxacum officinale Weber   Dandelion   Dant-y-llew
T. palustre (Lyons) DC.   Marsh Dandelion
Lactuca muralis (L.) Fresen.   Wall-Lettuce   Gwylaeth-y-fagwyr
Sonchus oleraceus L.   Smooth Sow-Thistle   Ysgallen y moch,
   Llaeth ysgallen
S. asper (L.) Hill   Rough Sow-Thistle   Llaeth ysgallen arw
S. arvensis L.   Corn Sow-Thistle   Llaeth ysgallen yr yd

CAMPANULACEAE
Lobelia dortmanna L.   Water-Lobelia   Bidawglys dyfrdig
Jasione montana L.   Sheep's Bit Scabious   Clefryn
Wahlenbergia hederacea (L.)   Ivy-leaved Bellflower   Clychlys, Eiddew-ddail
   Rchb.
Campanula trachelium L.   Nettle-leaved Bellflower   Clychlys dynad-ddail
* *C. rotundifolia* L.   Harebell   Clychlys amryddail

VACCINIACEAE
* *Vaccinium vitis-idaea* L.   Cowberry
* *V. myrtillus* L.   Bilberry   Llusen
Oxycoccus quadripetalus   Marsh Cranberry   Llygaeron, Ceiros y waun
   Gilib.

ERICACEAE
Andromeda polifolia L.   Moorwort
* *Calluna vulgaris* (L.) Hull   Heather   Grug cyffredin
Erica tetralix L.   Cross-leaved Heath   Grug croes-ddeiliog
E. cinerea L.   Bell Heather   Grug lledlwyd
Pyrola minor L.   Lesser Wintergreen   Glesyn-y-gaeaf

PLUMBAGINACEAE
* *Armeria maritima* Willd.   Thrift   Archmain, Clustog Fair

PRIMULACEAE
* *Primula vulgaris* Huds.   Primrose   Briallen
P. veris L.   Cowslip   Briallen Mair sawrys,
   Dagrau Mair
Lysimachia vulgaris L.   Yellow Loosestrife   Trewynyn
L. nummularia L.   Moneywort   Canclwyf
L. nemorum L.   Wood-Pimpernel   Trewynyn-y-goedwig
Anagallis tenella (L.) Murr.   Bog Pimpernel   Gwlydd Mair y gors
A. arvensis L.   Scarlet Pimpernel   Brathlys gwryw,
   Gwlydd Mair

OLEACEAE
Fraxinus excelsior L.   Ash   Onnen

APOCYANACEAE
Vinca major L.	Greater Periwinkle	Llowrig, Perfagl mwyaf
V minor L.	Lesser Periwinkle	Erllysg leiaf

GENTIANACEAE
Centaurium umbellatum Gilib.	Centaury	Canrhi goch, Ysgol Fair
Gentiana pneumonanthe L.	Marsh Gentian	Crwynllys
G. campestris agg.	Field Gentian	Crwynllys-y-maes

MENYANTHACEAE
Menyanthes trifoliata L.	Bogbean	Ffaen-y-gors

BORAGINACEAE
Symphytum officinale L.	Comfrey	
S. tuberosum L.	Tuberous Comfrey	
Myosotis caespitosa K. F. Schultz.	Tufted Forgetmenot	
M. scorpioides L.	Marsh Forgetmenot	Ysgorpionllys-y-gors
M. arvensis (L.) Hill	Field Forgetmenot	Ysgorpionllys-y-meusydd
M. collina Hoffm.	Early Scorpion-Grass	
M. versicolor Sm.	Parti-coloured Scorpion-Grass	Ysgorpionllys amrywliw
Lithospermum arvense L.	Corn Gromwell	Maenhad yr âr, Grawn y Llew

CONVOLVULACEAE
Calystegia sepium (L.) R. Br.	Greater Bindweed	Cloffrwyn y cythraul, Cloffrwyn y mwci
Convolvulus arvensis L.	Small Bindweed	Cynghafog fechan

SOLANACEAE
Solanum dulcamara L.	Woody Nightshade	Elinog

SCROPHULARIACEAE
Verbascum thapsus L.	Great Mullein	Tewbannog, Sircyn-y-melinydd
V. blattaria L.	Moth Mullein	
Linaria cymbalaria (L.) Mill.	Ivy-leaved Toad-flax	
L. elatine (L.) Mill.	Sharp-leaved Fluellen	
L. vulgaris Mill.	Yellow Toadflax	Llin-y-llyfaint
Antirrhinum orontium L.	Weasel-Snout	Trwyn-y-llo bychan
Scrophularia aquatica L.	Water Figwort	Gornerth-y-dwr
S. nodosa L.	Knotted Figwort	Deilen ddu dda, Gornerth
Mimulus guttatus DC.	Monkey-flower	
* *Digitalis purpurea* L.	Foxglove	Ffion-y-ffridd, Bysedd cochion
Veronica hederifolia L.	Ivy-leaved Speedwell	Rhwyddlwyn eiddew-ddail
V. polita Fr.	Grey Speedwell	
V. agrestis L.	Field Speedwell	Rhwyddlwyn gorweddol
V. arvensis L.	Water Speedwell	Mur-rwyddlwyn
V. serpyllifolia L.	Thyme-leaved Speedwell	Rhwyddlwyn gwrywddail

* *V. humifusa* Dicks.	Speedwell	
V. officinalis L.	Common Speedwell	Rhwyddlwyn meddygol
V. chamaedrys L.	Germander Speedwell	Rhwyddlwyn blewynnog
V. montana L.	Mountain Speedwell	Rhwyddlwyn mynyddol
V. scutellata L.	Marsh Speedwell	
V. beccabunga L.	Brooklime	Llychlyn-y-dwr
* *Euphrasia officinalis* agg.	Eyebright	Torfagl, Llysiau llygad

13 segregates recorded for Caernarvonshire.

Odontites rubra Gilib.	Red Bartsia	Gorudd, Gwaedlys bychan
Pedicularis palustris L.	Marsh Lousewort	Melog-y-waun
P. sylvatica L.	Heath Lousewort	Mel-y-cwn
* *Rhinanthus minor* agg.	Yellow Rattle	Cribell melyn, Arian-y-gweirwyr
Melampyrum pratense L.	Common Cow-wheat	Gliniogai melyn

OROBANCHACEAE
Orobanche apiculata Wallr.	Broomrape	Gorfange

Parasitic on hazel.

LENTIBULARIACEAE
Pinguicula vulgaris L.	Butterwort	Toddaidd melyn

VERBENACEAE
Verbena officinalis L.	Vervain	Cas-gan-gythraul, Llys-yr-hudol

LABIATAE
Mentha rotundifolia (L.) Huds.	Round-leaved Mint	Mintys lledgrynddail
M. longifolia (L.) Huds.	Horse Mint	
M. piperita L.	Peppermint	
M. aquatica L.	Water Mint	
M. verticillata L.	Whorled Mint	Mintys troellaidd
M. gentilis L.	Fringed Mint	
M. arvensis L.	Field Mint	Mintys yr âr
Lycopus europaeus L.	Gipsywort	Llys y sipsiwn
Origanum vulgare L.	Marjoram	Mesuriad
Thymus serpyllum agg.	Wild Thyme	Gruwlys gwyllt

5 segregates recorded for Caernarvonshire.

Clinopodium vulgare L.	Wild Basil	Breninllys gwyllt
Glecoma hederacea L.	Ground Ivy	Llysiau'r-esgyn
Scutellaria galericulata L.	Skullcap	Cycyllog mwyaf
S. minor Huds.	Lesser Skullcap	Cycyllog lleiaf
Prunella vulgaris L.	Selfheal	Meddyges las, Craith unnos
Stachys officinalis (L.) Trev.	Wood Betony	Cribau St. Fraid, Llys dwyfog
S. palustris L.	Marsh Woundwort	Briwlys-y-gors
S. sylvatica L.	Hedge Woundwort	Briwlys-y-goedwig
S. arvensis L.	Corn Woundwort	Briwlys-yr-ar
Galeopsis ladanum L.	Red Hempnettle	
G. speciosa Mill.	Large-flowered Hempnettle	

G. tetrahit L.	Common Hempnettle	Penboeth cyffredin
Leonurus cardiaca L.	Motherwort	Mamlys, Llys-y-fammog
Lamium amplexicaule L.	Henbit	Marddanadlen goch, Cylchddail
L. purpureum L.	Red Deadnettle	Marddanadlen goch
L. album L.	White Deadnettle	Marddanadlen wen
Galeobdolon luteum Huds.	Yellow Archangel	Eurddanadlen
Ballota nigra L.	Black Horehound	Marddanadlen ddu
Teucrium scorodonia L.	Woodsage	Triagl-y-Cymro, Chwerwlys yr eithin
Ajuga reptans L.	Bugle	Golchenid, Glesyn-y-coed

PLANTAGINACEAE

* *Plantago maritima* L.	Sea Plantain	Bara can y defaid, Llyriad-y-mor
P. lanceolata L.	Ribwort Plantain	Llyriad llwynhidydd, Llwyn-y-neidr
P. media L.	Hoary Plantain	
P. major L.	Greater Plantain	Llyriad mwyaf
* *Littorella uniflora* (L.) Aschers.	Shoreweed	Beisdonell merllyn

ILLECEBRACEAE

Scleranthus annuus L.	Annual Knawel	Dinodd blynyddol

CHENOPODIACEAE

Chenopodium album L.	White Goosefoot	Troed-y-gwydd
C. bonus-henricus L.	Good King Henry	Sawdl-y-Crydd, Llys y gwr da
Atriplex patula L.	Orache	Llygwyn tryfal
A. hastata L.		

POLYGONACEAE

Polygonum convolvulus L.	Black Bindweed	Taglys-yr-yd, Perthlys
P. dumetorum L.	Copse Buckwheat	
P. aviculare agg.	Common Knot-Grass	Canclwm, Berwr yr iar
P. hydropiper L.	Water Pepper	Tinboeth
P. persicaria L.	Common Persicaria	Elinog goch
P. lapathifolium L.	Pale Persicaria	Costog-y-dom
P. nodosum Pers.	Large Persicaria	
P. amphibium L.	Water Bistort	Canwraidd goch
P. bistorta L.	Bistort	Llys neidr
* *P. viviparum* L.	Alpine Bistort	
P. cuspidatum L.	Japanese Fleeceweed	
* *Oxyria digyna* (L.) Hill.	Mountain Sorrel	Suran-y-mynydd
Rumex conglomeratus Murr.	Sharp Dock	Tafolen
R. sanguineus L.	Green-veined Dock	
R. obtusifolius L.	Broad-leaved Dock	Tafolen cyffredin
R. crispus L.	Curled Dock	Tafolen grych
R. acetosa L.	Sorrel	Suran-y-waun, Suran-y-cwn

R. *acetosella* L.   Sheep's Sorrel   Dringol, Suran-yr-yd

LORANTHACEAE
Viscum album L.   Mistletoe   Uchelog, Prenawyr

EUPHORBIACEAE
Euphorbia peplus L.   Petty Spurge   Llaeth-y-cythraul
E. helioscopia L.   Sun Spurge   Llaeth ysgyfarnog
E. amygdaloides L.   Wood Spurge
* *Mercurialis perennis* L.   Dog's Mercury   Clais-yr-hydd, Bresych-y-cwn

ULMACEAE
Ulmus glabra Huds.   Wych Elm   Llwyfanen lydanddail
U. procera Salisb.   English Elm   Llwyfanen gyffredin

CANNABINACEAE
Humulus lupulus L.   Hop   Llewig y blaidd, Pensoeg

URTICACEAE
* *Urtica dioica* L.   Stinging Nettle   Danadlen fwyaf
U. urens L.   Small Stinging Nettle   Dunadlen leiaf

MYRICACEAE
Myrica gale L.   Bog Myrtle   Madwydd, Helygen Mair

BETULACEAE
Betula pendula Roth.   White Birch   Bedwen
B. pubescens Ehrh.   Common Birch   Bedwen
Alnus glutionsa (L.)   Alder   Gwernen

CORYLACEAE
Corylus avellana L.   Hazel   Coll-lwyn, Collen

FAGACEAE
Quercus robur L.   Oak   Derwen
Q. petraea (Mattuschka) Liebl.   Sessile Oak
Fagus sylvatica L.   Beech   Ffawydden

SALICACEAE
Salix triandra L.   Almond Willow   Helygen deirgwryw
S. fragilis L.   Crack Willow   Helygen frau
S. purpurea L.   Purple Willow
S. viminalis L.   Osier   Helygen afonol
S. caprea L.   Sallow   Helygen grynddail
S. aurita L.   Auricled Sallow   Helygen grynglustiawg
S. atrocinerea Brot.   Grey Sallow
* *S. herbacea* L.   Least Willow   Helygen leiaf
Populus alba L.   White Poplar
P. canescens (Ait.) Sm.   Grey Poplar
P. tremula L.   Aspen   Aethnen, Crydaethnen

EMPETRACEAE
* *Empetrum nigrum* L.   Crowberry   Creiglys
  E. hermaphroditum (Lange)
    Hagerup

HYDROCHARIDACEAE
Elodea canadensis Michx.   Canadian Waterweed

ORCHIDACEAE
Hammarbya paludosa (L.)   Bog Orchis
  O. Kuntze
Neottia nidus-avis (L.)   Bird's Nest Orchis
  L. C. Rich.
Listera cordata (L.) R.Br.   Small Twayblade
L. ovata (L.) R.Br.   Twayblade   Caineirian Gefellbys
Spiranthes spiralis (L.)   Ladies' Tresses   Teircaill
  Chevall.
Cephalanthera longifolia   Narrow-leaved
  (L.) Fritsch   Helleborine
Epipactis purpurata Sm.   Clustered Helleborine
Orchis morio L.   Green-winged Orchis   Tegeirian-y-waun
* *O. mascula* (L.) L.   Early Purple Orchis   Hosanau'r-gog
O. latifolia L. sec. Pugsl.   Marsh Orchis   Tegeirian-y-gors
O. praetermissa Druce
O. pardalina Pugsl.
O. ericetorum (E. F. Linton)   Early Spotted Orchis
  E. S. Marshall
O. fuchsii Druce   Spotted Orchis
Ophrys apifera Huds.   Bee Orchis
Gymnadenia conopsea (L.)   Fragrant Orchis   Tegeirian peraroglaidd
  R.Br.
Leucorchis albida (L.) Schur.   White Frog Orchis
Coeloglossum viride (L.)   Green Frog Orchis   Baldar blodeuwyrdd
  Hartm.
Platanthera bifolia (L.)   Lesser Butterfly Orchis   Tegeirian ddwyddalenog
  L. C. Rich.
P. chlorantha (Cust). Rcbh.   Greater Butterfly Orchis

IRIDACEAE
Iris pseudacorus L.   Yellow Iris   Cammined-y-dwr,
      Gellhesgen

AMARYLLIDACEAE
Narcissus pseudo-narcissus L.   Daffodil   Gylfinog, Cenhinen Pedr
Allium ursinum L.   Ramsons   Craf-y-geifr

DIOSCOREACEAE
Tamus communis L.   Black Bryony   Gwinwydden ddu,
      Rhwymym-y-coed,
      Afal Adda, Meipen Fair

LILIACEAE
Scilla non-scripta (L.)   Bluebell   Bwtias-y-gog,
   Hoffmgg. & Link   Cenhinen-y-brain
* *Lloydia serotina* (L.) Rchb.   Mountain Spiderwort   Brwynddail-y-mynydd
Narthecium ossifragum (L.)   Bog Asphodel   Llafn y bladur
   Huds.

JUNCACEAE
Genus *Juncus* L.   Rushes
15 species recorded for Caernarvonshire, of which at least 9 occur in the Park area,
and 2 on rock faces.
* Genus *Luzula* DC.   Woodrushes
4 species occur in Caernarvonshire and in the Park, 2 on rock faces.

TYPHACEAE
Genus *Typha* L.   Reed-Maces
2 species occur in Caernarvonshire.

SPARGANIACEAE
Genus *Sparganium* L.   Bur-Reeds
4 species occur in Caernarvonshire, and in the Park.

ARACEAE
Arum maculatum L.   Cuckoo-pint

LEMNACEAE
Genus *Lemna* L.   Duckweeds
3 species in Caernarvonshire, one certainly in the Park.

ALISMATACEAE
Alisma plantago-aquatica L.   Greater Water-Plantain   Dyfr-lyriad mwyaf
Baldellia ranunculoides (L.)   Lesser Water-Plantain   Dyfr-lyriad bychan
   Parl.
Luronium natans (L.) Raf.   Floating Water-Plantain   Dyfr-lyriad nofiadwy

JUNCAGINACEA?
Triglochin maritima L.   Sea Arrow-Grass   Saethbenig-y-morfa

POTAMOGETONACEAE
Genus *Potamogeton* L.   .   Pondweeds   Dyfr-llys, Tafod-y-ci
14 species in Caernarvonshire, of which at least 4 occur in the Park.
Genus *Ruppia* L.   Tassel Pondweeds
2 species in Caernarvonshire.

ZANNICHELLIACEAE
Zannichellia palustris L.   Horned Pondweed   Llyn-wlyddyn

CYPERACEAE
Genus *Eleocharis* R.Br.   Clubrushes   Clwp-frwynen
2 species occur in Park out of 5 in Caernarvonshire.
* Genus *Scirpus* L.   Clubrushes
At least 4 species in Park out of 9 in Caernarvonshire ; 1 on rock faces.

* Genus *Eriophorum* L.   Cotton-Grass   Sidan-y-waun,
    Plu gweunydd
2 species in Park and Caernarvonshire ; 1 on rock faces.
Rhynchospora alba L.   White Beakrush
* Genus *Carex* L.   Sedges   Hesgen
At least 20 species occur in Park out of about 44 in Caernarvonshire ; 8 on rock faces.

GRAMINEAE

Phalaris arundinacea L.   Ribbon-Grass   Gwyran, Corswellt
    amryliw

Anthoxanthum odoratum L.   Sweet Vernal Grass   Melynwellt-y-gwanwyn
Genus *Alopecurus* L.   Fox-tail   Rhonwellt-y-cadno
2 species at least occur in the Park.
Phleum pratense L.   Timothy Grass   Rhonwellt-y-gath
Genus *Agrostis* L.   Bent-grass   Maeswellt
2 species at least occur in the Park.
Aira praecox L.   Early Hair-Grass   Brigwellt-y-gwanwyn
* *Deschampsia caespitosa* (L)   Tufted Hair-Grass   Brigwellt monog
    Beauv.
* *D. alpina* (L.) Roem. &   Alpine Hair-Grass
    Schult.
* *D. flexuosa* (L.) Trin.   Heath Hair-Grass   Brigwellt gwyrgam
    mynyddol
* Genus *Holcus* L.   Soft-Grass   Maeswellt
2 species in the Park.
Arrhenatherum elatius (L.)   False Oat-Grass   Maeswellt ceirchaidd
    J. & C. Presl.
Sieglingia decumbens (L.)   Heath-Grass   Gwaunwellt
    Bernh.
Phragmites communis Trin.   Common Reed   Corsen
Cynosurus cristatus L.   Crested Dog's-tail   Rhonwellt-y-ci
Molinia caerulea (L.)   Moor-Grass
    Moench.
Dactylis glomerata (L.)   Cock's-foot   Byswellt, Troed-y-ceiliog
Briza media L.   Quaking-Grass   Eigryn, Gwenith
    ysgyfarnog
* Genus *Poa* L.   Meadow-Grasses   Gweunwellt
6 species occur in the Park ; 3 of them on rock faces.
Glyceria fluitans (L.)   Floating Meadow-Grass   Gweunwellt nof
Vulpia bromoides (L.)   Squirrel-tail Fescue   Peisgwellt
    S. F. Gray
* Genus *Festuca* L.   Fescues   Peisgwellt
2 species occur in the Park ; 1 on rock faces.
Genus *Bromus* L.   Brome Grasses   Pawr-wellt
At least 4 species occur in the Park.
Lolium perenne L.   Perennial Rye-Grass   Efryn parhaus
L. temulentum L.   Darnel   Afryn coliog
* *Nardus stricta* L.   Mat-Grass   Cawnen ddu,
    Cas-gan-bladurwr
Genus *Hordeum* L.   Barleys   Haidd-wellt
1 species occurs in the Park.

CUPRESSACEAE
Juniperus communis L.   Common Juniper   Merywen cyffredin
* *J. sibirica* Burgsd.   Dwarf Juniper   Merywen goraidd fynyddig

TAXACEAE
Taxus baccata L.   Yew   Ywen

PINACEAE
Pinus sylvestris L.   Scots Pine   Pinwydd
It must be remembered that this is an introduced species into the modern flora of Wales
(see pages 228, 268) and it is included on the strength of its ability to reseed naturally
in some places ; on this basis several other coniferous species may eventually claim
admission.

FERNS AND FERN ALLIES
Botrychium lunaria (L.) Sw.   Moonwort
Ophioglossum vulgatum L.   Adder's Tongue
Osmunda regalis L.   Royal Fern   Rhedyn cyfrdwy
Pilularia globulifera L.   Pillwort
* *Hymenophyllum tunbrigense*   Tonbridge Filmy Fern
     (L.) Sm.
* *H. peltatum* (Poir.) Desv.   Wilson's Filmy Fern
* *Trichomanes speciosum*   Killarney or Bristle Fern
     Willd.
Pteridium aquilinum (L.)   Bracken   March-redynen
     Kuhn.
* *Cryptogramma crispa* (L.)   Parsley Fern
     Hook. & Bauer.
* *Blechnum spicant* (L.) Roth   Hard Fern
Phyllitis scolopendrium (L.)   Hart's Tongue   Tafod-yr-hydd
     Newm.
Asplenium trichomanes L.   Maidenhair Spleenwort
* *A. viride* Huds.   Green Spleenwort
A. obovatum Viv.   Lanceolate Spleenwort
A. adiantum-nigrum L.   Black Spleenwort
A. septentrionale (L.) Hoffm. Forked Spleenwort
A. ruta-muraria L.   Wall-rue
Ceterach officinarum DC.   Ceterach
* *Athyrium filix-femina* (L.)   Lady Fern
     Roth
* *Cystopteris fragilis* (L.)   Brittle Bladder Fern
     Bernh.
* *Woodsia ilvensis* (L.) R.Br.   Oblong Woodsia
* *W. alpina* (Bolton)   Alpine Woodsia
     S. F. Gray.
* *Dryopteris filix-mas* agg.   Male Fern
* *D. villarsii* (Bell) Woynar   Rigid Buckler Fern
* *D. dilatata* (Hoffm.) A. Gray Broad Buckler Fern

* *D. aemula* (Ait.) O. Kuntze   Hay-scented Buckler Fern
* *Polystichum lonchitis* (L.)   Holly Fern
   Roth
  P. setiferum (Forsk.)   Soft Shield Fern
   Woynar
* *P. aculeatum* (L.) Roth   Hard Shield Fern
  Thelypteris palustris Schott Marsh Fern
  T. oreopteris (Ehrh.) C.Chr. Mountain Fern
* *T. phegopteris* (L.) Slosson   Beech Fern
* *Gymnocarpium dryopteris*   Oak Fern
   (L.) Newm.
  G. robertianum (Hoffm.)   Limestone Polypody
   Newm.
  Polypodium vulgare L.   Common Polypody   Rhedyn-y-derw
  Equisetum spp. L.   Horse-tails
  4 occur in Park.
* *Lycopodium selago* L.   Fir Club-Moss
* *L. clavatum* L.   Common Club-Moss
* *L. alpinum* L.   Alpine Club-Moss
  Selaginella selaginoides (L.)
   Link
  Isoetes lacustris L.   Quillwort
  I. echinospora Durieu

THE LOWER PLANTS

There is no more recent work collected than Griffith's on these Groups, although no doubt much unpublished data exist.

CHARACEAE

Griffith considered this family with the Fern-Allies. He identified one species of *Chara* (*C. fragilis* Desv.) and two species of *Nitella* (*N. flexilis* Agardh., and *N. opaca* Agardh.) in Caernarvonshire.

LICHENS

Griffith recorded just over 350 species in Caernarvonshire, with many varieties and forms.

MOSSES

Griffith recorded 250 species in Caernarvonshire.

LIVERWORTS

Griffith recorded 42 species in Caernarvonshire.

FUNGI

See Knight, Lister and Anon. in *Transactions of the British Mycological Society* (all 1924).

SUMMARY OF THE INVERTEBRATE FAUNA

The other sections are based on one or more published lists of species ; for the invertebrate phyla of the region only a few lists of isolated groups exist, and if it were not for the card index compiled by Mr. Colin Matheson in the Zoology Department of the National Museum of Wales, it would have been impossible to make even the brief summary which follows. This index includes references both in standard works and in periodicals to all animals occurring in Wales, and is invaluable to anyone making a survey of the fauna of the country ; I am very grateful to Mr. Matheson for permission to use the index, which has taken several years to compile. The nomenclature of the insects is that of Kloet and Hincks (1945).

THE PRIMITIVE PHYLA

These groups have not been the subject of special study in the Park region, except from the agricultural aspect ; references occur in the many papers of Walton (1922, etc.) to organisms carrying disease to stock (see also pages 213 and 243). Rotifers are dealt with by Williams (1942). Marine forms have been studied in the Menai Strait by Jackson (1940) and, outside the area with which this book has been concerned, by Pyefinch (1937 and 1943) on Bardsey Island.

WORMS

The work on Annelids by Friend (1926–28), has been mentioned on page 271. Twenty-one parasitic genera are reported from Caernarvonshire by Walton (1927).

CRUSTACEANS

Six terrestrial species, from four genera, are noted by Collinge (1942) in Caernarvonshire ; a total of about eight genera seem to have been recorded in the county as a whole.

MYRIAPODS

Two genera of agricultural importance in Caernarvonshire are mentioned by Walton (1927).

MOLLUSCS

About 45 terrestrial and freshwater genera have been recorded in Caernarvonshire, particularly by Nicholls (1884) ; a number of subsequent references occur in the *Journal of Conchology* and the Journal of the *Malacological Society*; see also pages 188 and 286. Economically important species are mentioned by Walton (1927), and the molluscs of the Creuddyn were studied by Roebuck (1844) and Tomlin (1886).

ARACHNIDS

About 84 genera have been recorded in Caernarvonshire, and those of agricultural interest are mentioned by Walton (1927). Two alpine species are mentioned on pages 187 and 196. Other references occur in Bristowe (1939–41) and Savory (1935).

INSECTS

This huge class has been very poorly worked in the region of the Park. No doubt the large areas of similar habitat make for a population numerous in individuals but limited in species, all the same it is hard to believe that the total of less than 700 genera revealed by the literature, out of 4,714 in the British Isles (Kloet and Hincks), is anything near the real proportion.

Order *THYSANURA* Bristle-tails
At least 1 genus, *Lepisma*, in Caernarvonshire.

Orders *DIPLURA* and *PROTURA*
No references.

Order *COLLEMBOLA* Springtails
9 genera and 30 species noted for North Wales by Davies (1934); see also pages 187 and 196.

Order *ORTHOPTERA* Grasshoppers, Cockroaches, Crickets
Owing to the small number identified, and the fact that they are among the larger insects, a full list is given.
Blatta orientalis L. Common Cockroach
Omocestus viridulus L.
O. ventralis (Zetterstedt)
Myrmeleotettix maculatus (Thunberg)
Chorthippus bicolor (Charpentier)
C. parallelus (Zetterstedt)
C. albomarginatus (Degeer)
Leptophyes punctatissima (Bosc.)
Gryllulus domesticus L. Cricket

Order *DERMAPTERA*
Earwigs do not seem to have received any attention in the area ; only *Labia minor* L. is mentioned.

Order *PLECOPTERA* Stoneflies
5 species of 4 genera recorded for Caernarvonshire, mainly in *Entomologists' Monthly Magazine*.

Order *PSOCOPTERA*
Booklice have been studied in Merioneth, but not apparently in Caernarvonshire.

Order *ANOPLURA* Biting and Sucking Lice
No references.

Order *EPHEMEROPTERA* Mayflies
4 species from 3 genera as follows :—
Leptophlebia marginata L.
Recorded from Llynyparc.
Baetis pumilus (Burmeister)
Afon Llugwy.
Rhithrogena semicolorata (Curtis)
Afon Llugwy.
R. haarupi (Esben-Petersen)
Betws-y-coed.

Order *ODONATA* Dragonflies
15 species from 12 genera probably occur in the Park area (Longfield 1937 and Journals, especially *The Entomologist*).
Pyrrhosoma nymphula (Sulzer)

Ischnura elegans (van der Linden)
Enallagma cyathigerum (Charpentier)
Coenagrion puellum L.
Ceriagrion tenellum (de Villers)
Agrion virgo L.
Gomphus vulgatissimus L.
Cordulegaster boltonii (Donovan)
Aeshna juncea L.
A. cyanea (Mueller)
A. mixta Latreille
Orthetrum coerulescens (Fabricius)
Libellula quadrimaculata L.
L. depressa L.
Sympetrum striolatum (Charpentier)

Order *THYSANOPTERA*   Thrips
1 or 2 genera of agricultural importance in North Wales are mentioned by Walton (1927) ; no work done in the Park region on the order.

Order *HEMIPTERA*   Bugs
About 150 out of 473 British genera seem to have occurred in Caernarvonshire, according to Butler (1923), Saunders (1892), Theobald and Walton (1921-22), and the Journals. At least 2 very rare species have occurred in Creuddyn. Other species of particular interest in the Park region are :—
Cixius cambricus China
See page 198.
Cryptostemma alienum (Henrich Schaeffer)
Betws-y-coed.
Elasmucha ferrugata (Fabricius)
See page 250.
Trilobaphis caricis Theobald
First identified in this area.

Order *MEGALOPTERA*   Alder and Snake flies
Only *Sialis lutaria* L. appears to have been recorded from this small order.

Order *NEUROPTERA*   Lacewings
5 out of 18 British genera have been recorded, by Walton (1922), and in the Journals.

Order *MECOPTERA*   Scorpion flies
No references.

Order *TRICHOPTERA*   Caddis flies
About 12 genera have been recorded in Caernarvonshire, out of 70 known to Britain. Much more work has been done on this order in Merioneth. Species of local interest are :—
Hydropsyche instabilis (Curtis)
Rhyncophila dorsalis (Curtis)
Afon Llugwy.
R. munda McLachlan
Afon Lledr.
Sericostoma personatum (Spence)
Snowdon.

Order *LEPIDOPTERA*   Moths and Butterflies
This order, the most popular amongst collectors, shows a rather higher proportion of genera recorded in the region than any other : about 170 out of 657 in the *Check List*. In view of their general interest, a full list of the butterflies (*Papilionoidea*) is given. I am very

grateful to Mr. F. C. Best for checking this, and indicating the status of each species in the region. 34—just half those accepted by the *Check List* for the whole of Britain—occur, representing 26 genera. 3 others are of doubtful occurrence.

The nomenclature of this particular list follows Ford (1945), and not the *Check List* of Kloet and Hincks (1945).

Pararge aegeria L. Resident woodland zone.	Speckled Wood
P. megera L. Resident lowland zone.	Wall Butterfly
Eumenis semele L. subsp. *thyone* Thompson Local resident lowlands. Confined to Creuddyn.	Grayling
Maniola jurtina L. Common resident, except alpine zone.	Meadow Brown
Coenonympha pamphilus L. Common resident, all zones.	Small Heath
C. tullia tullia Mueller Very local resident, Nant Conwy.	Large Heath
Aphantopus hyperanthus L. Resident lowland zone.	Ringlet
Argynnis selene Schiff. Resident lowland zone.	Small Pearl-bordered Fritillary
A. euphrosyne L. Resident lowland zone.	Pearl-bordered Fritillary
A. aglaia L. Resident all zones, except alpine.	Dark Green Fritillary
A. cydippe L. Resident lowland zones.	High Brown Fritillary
A. paphia L. Resident woodland zone.	Silver-washed Fritillary
Euphydryas aurinia Rott. Very local resident.	Marsh Fritillary
Vanessa atalanta L. Variable migrant, all zones.	Red Admiral
V. cardui L. Rare migrant, all zones.	Painted Lady
Aglais urticae L. Resident, mainly lowlands.	Small Tortoiseshell
Nymphalis io L. Resident, mainly lowlands.	Peacock
Polygonia c-album L. Resident, mainly lowlands.	Comma
Plebejus argus L. Local resident on edge of region. subsp. *caernensis* Thompson Confined to limestone.	Silver-studded Blue
Aricia agestis Schiff. Local resident on edge of region.	Brown Argus
Polyommatus icarus Rott. Resident, all zones.	Common Blue
Celastrina argiolus L. Resident, woodland zones.	Holly Blue

Lycaena phlaeas L.	Small Copper.
Resident, all zones except alpine.	
Callophrys rubi L.	Green Hairstreak
Resident, grassland and lowland, possible alpine.	
[*Thecla betulae* L.	Brown Hairstreak]
Very doubtful, lowlands.	
T. quercus L.	Purple Hairstreak
Resident, woodland zone.	
[*Strymonidia w-album* Knoch.	White-letter Hairstreak]
Very doubtful, lowlands.	
Pieris brassicae L.	Large White
Resident, lowland zone.	
P. rapae L.	Small White
Resident, lowland zone.	
P. napi L.	Green-veined White
Resident, lowland zone.	
Anthocharis cardamines L.	Orange-Tip
Resident, all zones except alpine.	
Colias croceus Fourcroy	Clouded Yellow
Migrant, common 1947.	
Gonepteryx rhamni L.	Brimstone
Local resident, lowlands.	
Erynnis tages L.	Dingy Skipper
Resident, all zones except alpine.	
Pyrgus malvae L.	Grizzled Skipper
Resident, lowland zone.	
[*Thymelicus sylvestris* Poda	Small Skipper]
Doubtful occurrence.	
Ochlodes venata Bremer & Grey	Large Skipper
Resident, all zones except alpine.	

The Hawk-moths (*Sphingidae*) are represented by eight species from eight genera.

Hemaris tityus (L.)	Narrow-bordered Bee Hawk
Macroglossa stellatarum (L.)	Hummingbird Kawk
Deilephila porcellus (L.)	Small Elephant Hawk
Acherontia atropos (L.)	Death's Head Hawk
Smerinthus ocellatus (L.)	Eyed Hawk
Celerio galii (von Rottenburg)	Bedstraw Hawk
Herse convolvuli (L.)	Convolvulus Hawk
Laothoe populi (L.)	Poplar Hawk

No list of Welsh moths appear to exist[1], and records are mainly derived from reports of collecting trips given in the Journals. A list for Creuddyn was published by Gresley-Jones (1910). Two species of considerable local interest are:—

Sterrha eburnata Wocke   "Weaver's Wave"
First found at Bettws-y-coed in 1855, and confined to the northern part of the region (South, 1939).

Venusia cambrica Curtis   "Welsh Wave"
First identified in Cardiganshire in 1839, and since found in several localities, one of which is Merioneth (South, 1939).

[1]In 1948 the Chester Society of Natural Science published *The Butterflies and Moths found in the Counties of Cheshire, Flintshire, Denbighshire, Caernarvonshire and Merionethshire*, compiled by S. Gordon Smith—Eds.

Order COLEOPTERA   Beetles

About 180 genera are recorded out of 947 in Britain. A good deal of collecting has taken place in the region, and the water-beetles, as a result of Balfour Browne's work (1942), are probably the best known group o insects. A recent paper by Kaufmann (1946) shows that 7 spec es of longicorn beetles occur in Caernarvonshire, 5 of them in the Park region ; apart from these studies, information is fragmentary, though there are numerous references to Wales in Fowler (1887–91, 1913). Creuddyn beetles were studied by E. B. Roberts (1925) (1930).

Order STREPSIPTERA

No references.

Order HYMENOPTERA   Ants, Bees, Wasps, etc.

Only about 55 genera of this order, the most strongly represented in point of species in Britain, appear to be recorded in the region ; the *Check List* total is 1,071 genera. This position is due rather to neglect by entomologists than to a real weakness in the fauna, for Walton (1922) identified in North Wales 13 out of the 25 British species of *Bombus*, and 5 of the 7 species of *Vespa* have been recorded. 2 species of particular local interest are :—

Coelichneumon cyaniventis (Wesmael)
Gelis distincta (Foerster)
Associated with Trefriw.

Order DIPTERA   Flies

The position here, as regards information on the area, is probably worse even than in the case of the *Hymenoptera*, since less than 60 out of 1,132 " possible " genera seem to be recorded. The craneflies (*Tipulidae*) have been studied by Barnes (1924), and Davies (1930) worked on warble-flies from the agricultural point of view.

Order SIPHONAPTERA   Fleas

No references from Caernarvonshire, though some work has been done on this order in Merioneth.

THE VERTEBRATE FAUNA

The nomenclature of the bird list is that of Witherby (1941) ; for the other groups the British Museum (Natural History) *List of British Vertebrates* (1935) has been followed. Species which occur only on the coast, outside the future Park, but which have been mentioned in Chapter Twelve, are given in square brackets.

BIRDS

Abbreviations :

R.—Resident	V.—Vagrant (very rare visitor)
S.—Summer visitor	B.—Breeds
W.—Winter visitor	HB.—Has bred.
P.—Visitor on passage	F.—Formerly
O.—Occasional visitor	D.—Status doubtful

Precedence of status in the order given, i.e., a species that is both Resident and Winter Visitor, is only recorded as " R ".

Corvus corax corax L.	Raven	Cigfran	RB.
Corvus cornix cornix L.	Hooded Crow	Bran Iwerddon	OW. HB.
Corvus corone corone L.	Carrion Crow	Milfran	RB.
Corvus f. frugilegus L.	Rook	Ydfran	RB.
Corvus monedula spermologus Vieill.	Jackdaw	Coegfran	RB.
Pica p. pica. (L.)	Magpie	Pioden	RB.
Garrulus glandarius rufitergum Hart.	Jay	Ysgrech-y-coed	RB.
Pyrrhocorax p. pyrrhocorax (L.)	Chough	Bran big goch	RB.
Sturnus v. vulgaris L.	Starling	Drudwy	RB.
Pastor roseus (L.)	Rose-coloured Starling		V.
Oriolus o. oriolus (L.)	Golden Oriole		V.
Coccothraustes c. coccothraustes (L.)	Hawfinch	Gylfinbraff	D.
Chloris ch. chloris (L.)	Greenfinch	Llinos werdd	RB.
Carduelis carduelis britannica (Hart.)	Goldfinch	Teiliwr Llundain	RB.
Carduelis spinus (L.)	Siskin	Dreiniog	W. HB.
Carduelis flammea cabarei (P. L. S. Müll.)	Lesser Redpoll	Llinos bengoch	RB.
Carduelis flavirostris pipilans (Lath.)	Twite	Llinos-y-mynydd	P.
Carduelis cannabina cannabina (L.)	Linnet	Llinos	RB.
Pyrrhula pyrrhula nesa Math. & Ired.	Bullfinch	Coch-y-berllan	RB.
Loxia c. curvirostra L.	Crossbill	Gylfingroes	W. HB.
Fringilla coelebs gengleri Kleinsch.	Chaffinch	Asgell fraith	RB.
Fringilla montifringilla L.	Brambling	Bronrhuddyn-y-mynydd	W.
Emberiza calandra L.	Corn-Bunting	Bras-yr-yd	D.
Emberiza citrinella citrinella L.	Yellow Bunting	Llinos felen	RB.
Emberiza cirlus cirlus L.	Cirl Bunting		D.
Emberiza sch. schoeniclus (L.)	Reed-Bunting	Golfan-y-gors	RB.
Plectrophenax n. nivalis L.	Snow-Bunting	Bras-yr-eira	OW.
Passer d. domesticus L.	House-Sparrow	Golfan	R.
Passer m. montanus L.	Tree-Sparrow	Golfan-y-mynydd	D.

Lullula a. arborea L.	Woodlark		D.
Alauda a. arvensis L.	Skylark	Ehedydd	RB.
Anthus t. trivialis L.	Tree-Pipit	Pibydd-y-coed	SB.
Anthus pratensis L.	Meadow-Pipit	Gwas-y-gog	RB.
Anthus spinoletta subspp.	Water- and Rock-Pipits	Pibydd-y-graig	P.
Motacilla flava flava L.	Blue-headed Wagtail		P.
Motacilla flava flavissima (Blyth)	Yellow Wagtail	Tinsigl felen	SB.
Motacilla c. cinerea Tunst.	Grey Wagtail	Tinsigl lwyd	RB.
Motacilla alba yarrellii Gould	Pied Wagtail	Brith-y-fuches	RB.
Motacilla a. alba L.	White Wagtail		P.
Certhia familiaris britannica Ridgw.	Tree-Creeper	Cropiedydd	RB.
Sitta europaea affinis Blyth	Nuthatch	Cnocell	RB.
Parus major newtoni Prazak	Great Tit	Penloyn	RB.
Parus caeruleus obscurus Prazak	Blue Tit	Glas-y-pared	RB.
Parus ater britannicus Sharpe & Dress.	Coal-Tit	Yswidw benddu	RB.
Parus palustris dresseri Stejn.	Marsh-Tit	Yswidw lwyd	RB.
Parus atricapillus kleinschmidti Hellm.	Willow-Tit		RB.
Aegithalos caudatus rosaceus Mathews	Long-tailed Tit	Yswidw gynffon-hir	RB.
Lanius e. excubitor L.	Great Grey Shrike		V.
Lanius c. collurio L.	Red-backed Shrike	Cigydd cefngoch	SB.
Bombycilla g. garrulus L.	Waxwing	Adain gwyr	OW.
Muscicapa s. striata (Pall.)	Spotted Flycatcher	Gwybedog	SB.
Muscicapa h. hypoleuca (Pall.)	Pied Flycatcher	Gwybedog brith	SB.
Regulus regulus anglorum Hart.	Goldcrest	Dryw'r-eurben	RB.
Phylloscopus c. collybita (Vieill.)	Chiffchaff	Siffsaff	SB.
Phylloscopus t. trochilus L.	Willow Warbler	Dryw'r helyg	SB.
Phylloscopus sibilatrix Bechst.	Wood-Warbler	Dryw'r coed	SB.
Locustella n. naevia Bodd.	Grasshopper-Warbler	Troellwr bach	SB.
Acro ephalus schoenobaenus L.	Sedge-Warbler	Telor-yr-hesg	SB.
Acrocephalus scirpaceus scirpaceus Herm.	Reed-Warbler		D. HB.
Sylvia borin Bodd.	Garden-Warbler	Telor-yr-ardd	SB.
Sylvia a. atricapilla L.	Black-cap	Penddu	SB.
Sylvia communis communis Lath.	Whitethroat	Llwydfron	SB.
Sylvia curruca curruca L.	Lesser Whitethroat	Llwydfron fach	SB.
Sylvia undata dartfordiensis Lath.	Dartford Warbler		V.
Turdus pilaris L.	Fieldfare	Socan	W.
Turdus v. viscivorus L.	Mistle-Thrush	Tresglen	RB.
Turdus e. ericetorum Turton	Song-Thrush	Bronfraith	RB.
Turdus musicus musicus L.	Redwing	Adain-goch	W.
Turdus t. torquatus L.	Ring-Ousel	Mwyalchen-y-graig	SB.
Turdus merula merula L.	Blackbird	Aderyn du, Mwyalchen	RB.
Oenanthe oe. oenanthe. L.	Wheatear	Cynffonwen	SB.
Oenanthe oenanthe leucorrhoa (Gm.)	Greenland Wheatear		P.
Saxicola rubetra L.	Whinchat	Clap-yr-eithin	SB.
Saxicola torquata hibernans Hart.	Stonechat	Clochdar-y-cerrig	RB.

Phoenicurus ph. phoenicurus. L.	Redstart	Tinboeth	SB.
Erithacus rubecula melophilus Hart.	Robin	Bronrudd	RB.
Prunella c. collaris (Scop.)	Alpine Accentor		V.
Prunella modularis occidentalis Hart.	Hedge-Sparrow	Llwyd-y-berth	RB.
Troglodytes t. troglodytes L.	Wren	Dryw	RB.
Cinclus cinclus gularis Lath.	Dipper	Tresglen-y-dwr	RB.
Hirundo r. rustica L.	Swallow	Gwennol	SB.
Delichon u. urbica L.	House-Martin	Gwennol-y-mur	SB.
Riparia r. riparia L.	Sand-Martin	Gwennol-y-glennydd	SB.
Apus a. apus. L.	Swift	Gwennol gwblddu	SB.
Caprimulgus e. europaeus L.	Nightjar	Troellwr	SB.
Upupa e. epops L.	Hoopoe		O.
Alcedo atthis ispida L.	Kingfisher	Glas-y-dorlan	RB.
Picus viridis pluvius Hart.	Green Woodpecker	Caseg wanwyn	RB.
Dryobates major anglicus Hart.	Great Spotted Woodpecker	Delor fraith fwyaf	RB.
Dryobates minor comminutus Hart.	Lesser Spotted Woodpecker	Delor fraith leiaf	D.
Cuculus canorus canorus L.	Cuckoo	Cog	SB.
Athene noctua vidalii A. E. Brehm	Little Owl	Dylluan fach	RB.
Asio o. otus L.	Long-eared Owl	Dylluan gorniog	D.
Asio f. flammeus Pontopp.	Short-eared Owl	Dylluan glustiog	W.
Strix aluco sylvatica Shaw.	Tawny Owl	Dylluan felynddu	RB.
Tyto a. alba Scop.	Barn-Owl	Dylluan wen	RB.
Falco p. peregrinus Tunst.	Peregrine Falcon	Hebog tramor	RB.
Falco s. subbuteo L.	Hobby	Hebog-yr-ehedydd	OP.
Falco columbarius aesalon Tunst.	Merlin	Gwalch bach	RB.
Falco t. tinnunculus L.	Kestrel	Cudyll-y-gwynt	RB.
Aquila chr. chrysaetus L. Bred anciently.	Golden Eagle	Eryr euraidd	V.
Buteo l. lagopus Pontopp	Rough-legged Buzzard	Boda garwgoes	OW.
Buteo b. buteo L.	Common Buzzard	Boncath (= Boda Cath)	RB.
Circus ae. aeruginosus L.	Marsh-Harrier	Bod-y-wern	O. FB.
Circus c. cyaneus L.	Hen-Harrier	Bod tinwyn	O. ?FB.
Circus pygargus L.	Montagu's Harrier		P. FB.
Accipiter n. nisus L.	Sparrow-Hawk	Gwipia	RB.
Milvus m. milvus L. No recent records.	Kite	Barcud	FB.
Haliaetus albicilla L.	White-tailed Eagle	Eryr cynffonwen	V.
Pernis a. apivorus L.	Honey Buzzard	Bod-y-mel	?P. FB.
Pandion h. haliaëtus L.	Osprey	Moreryr	V.
Ardea c. cinerea L.	Heron	Creyr glas	RB.
Botaurus s. stellari L.	Bittern	Aderyn-y-bwn	OW.
Cygnus cygnus L.	Whooper Swan	Alarch gwyllt	W.
Cygnus b. bewickii Yarr.	Bewick's Swan		OW.
Cygnus olor Gm.	Mute Swan	Alarch dof	RB.
Anser albifrons albifrons Scop.	White-fronted Goose	Gwydd dalcen gwyn	D.

Anser arvensis subspp.	Bean and Pink-footed Geese		D.
Tadorna tadorna L.	Sheld Duck	Hwyaden-yr-eithin	RB.
Anas p. platyrhyncha L.	Mallard	Hwyaden wyllt	RB.
Anas c. crecca L.	Teal	Corhwyaden	RB.
Anas penelope L. WV. HB. Merioneth.	Wigeon	Chiwell	
Anas acuta acuta L.	Pintail	Hwyaden lostfain	WV.
Spatula clypeata L. WV. B. Llŷn.	Shoveler	Hwyaden lydan-big	
Aythya ferina L. WV. B. Anglesey.	Pochard	Hwyaden bengoch	
Aythya n. nyroca Guld.	Ferruginous Duck		V.
Aythya fuligula L.	Tufted Duck	Hwyad gopog	WV. HB.
Aythya m. marila L.	Scaup	Hwyaden lygad-arian	OW.
Bucephala c. clangula L.	Goldeneye	Hwyaden lygad-aur	WV.
Mergus merganser merganser L.	Goosander	Hwyaden ddan-heddog	W.
Mergus serrator L.	Red-breasted Merganser	Hwyaden fronrudd	W.
Phalacrocorax c. carbo L. RB. Coast ; regular visitor inland.	Cormorant	Mulfran	
Phalacrocorax a. aristotelis L. O. RB. Coast.	Shag	Mulfran gopog	
Sula bassana L.	Gannet	Hucan	V.
[*Puffinus p. puffinus* Brunn. RB. Coast.	Manx Shearwater	Pâl Manaw]	
[*Fulmarus g. glacialis* L. D. H B. Creuddyn.	Fulmar Petrel	]	
Podiceps c. cristatus L.	Great Crested Grebe	Gwyach gorniog	
Podiceps r. ruficollis Pall.	Little Grebe	Gwyach fach	RB.
Columba p. palumbus L.	Wood-Pigeon	Ysguthan	RB.
Columba oenas L.	Stock-Dove	Colomen ddof	RB.
[*Columba l. livia* Gm.	Rock-Dove		D.]
Streptopelia t. turtur L.	Turtle-Dove	Colomen Fair	D.
Numenius a. arquata L.	Curlew	Gylfinir	RB.
Numenius ph. phaeopus L.	Whimbrel	Coeg-gylfinir	P.
Scolopax rusticola L.	Woodcock	Cyfflog	RB.
Capella media Lath.	Great Snipe	Giach fawr	V.
Capella g. gallinago L.	Common Snipe	Giach	RB.
Lymnocryptes minimus Brunn.	Jack Snipe	Giach leiaf	W.
Calidris alpina schinzii Brehm	Dunlin	Pibydd rhudd-goch	SB.
Actitis hypoleucos L.	Common Sandpiper	Pibydd-y-dorlan	SB.
Tringa ochropus L.	Green Sandpiper	Pibydd gwyrdd	DP.
Tringa totanus britannica Mathews D. RB. Coast.	Redshank	Coesgoch	
[*Charadrius h. hiaticula* L. RB. Coast.	Ringed Plover	]	

Pluvialis a. apricaria L. SB. W. Coast.	Golden Plover	Cornicyll-y-mynydd	
Eudromias morinellus L.	Dotterel	Hutan	OP.
Vanellus vanellus L.	Lapwing	Cornicyll	RB.
Haematopus o. ostralegus Neum. R. Estuaries ; B. Coast.	Oystercatcher	Pioden-y-mor	
Chlidonias n. niger L.	Black Tern	Morwennol ddu	V.
Sterna h. hirundo L. SB. Coast.	Common Tern	Gwennol-y-mor	
[*Sterna a. albifrons* Pall. SB. Coast.	Little Tern		]
Larus r. ridibundus L.	Black-headed Gull	Gwylan benddu	RB.
Larus c. canus L.	Common Gull	Gwylan lwyd	W.
Larus a. argentatus Pont. RB. Coast, regular visitor inland	Herring-Gull	Gwylan-y-penweig	
Larus fuscus graellsii Brehm. SB. Coast : visitor inland	Lesser Black-backed Gull	Gwylan gefnddu leiaf	
Larus marinus L. RB. Coast ; O. Inland where HB.	Great Black-backed Gull	Gwylan gefnddu fwyaf	
[*Rissa t. tridactyla* L. RB. Coast.	Kittiwake		]
[*Alca torda britannica* Ticehurst RB. Coast.	Razorbill	Llurs	]
[*Uria aalge albionis* With. RB. Coast.	Guillemot	Heligog	]
Alle a. alle L.	Little Auk	Carfil bach	V.
[*Fratercula arctica grabae* Brehm. RB. Coast.	Puffin	Pàl	]
Crex crex L.	Corncrake	Rhegen-yr-yd	SB.
Rallus a. aquaticus L.	Water-Rail	Rhegen-y-dwr	D.
Gallinula ch. chloropus L.	Moorhen	Iar ddwr	RB.
Fulica a. atra L.	Coot	Cwtiar	RB.
Lyrurus tetrix britannicus With. & Lonn. Probably introduced.	Black Grouse	Grugiar ddu	RB.
Lagopus s. scoticus Lath.	Red Grouse	Grugiar	RB.
Phasianus colchicus L. Introduced.	Pheasant	Ffesant	RB.
Coturnix c. coturnix L.	Quail	Sofliar	OS. HB.
Perdix p. perdix L.	Partridge	Petrisen	RB.

FRESHWATER AND ESTUARINE FISH

Perca fluviatilis L. Introduced, Vaynol, 1882.	Perch	Draenog, Perc
Cottus gobio L. " Common round Bangor " (Forrest).	Miller's Thumb	Pentarw
Gasterosteus aculeatus L. Local.	Three-spined Stickleback	Crothell
Pleuronectes flesus L. River Conway as far as Trefriw.	Flounder	Lleden ddu

Salmo salar L. Larger rivers and lakes.	Salmon	Gleisiad, Eog
Salmo trutta L.	Trout (Brown Trout) (Sea-Trout or Sewin)	Brithyll Brithyll-y-mor

Common; both sedentary and migratory forms.

Salvelinus alpinus perisii Gunther	Welsh Char	Torgoch

Now apparently confined to Llanberis lakes in this area.

Osmerus eperlanus L. Rivers Conway and Ogwen.	Smelt	Brwyniad
Esox lucius L. Introduced locally many years ago.	Pike	Penhwyad
Clupea alosa L. Estuaries.	Allis Shad	Herlyn
Clupea finta Cuv. River Ogwen.	Twaite Shad	
Anguilla vulgaris Turt. Common up to 1,000 feet above sea.	Eel	Llysywen
Tinca vulgaris Cuv. Introduced Vaynol.	Tench	Gwrachen
Phoxinus laevis Agass. Common, lakes and rivers.	Minnow	Crothell-y-dom
Leuciscus rutilus L. Introduced to lowland pools.	Roach	Rhufell
Scardinius erythrophthalmus L. Local, in pools.	Rudd	Rhuddgoch
Acipenser sturio L. Conway estuary.	Sturgeon	Ystwrsion

AMPHIBIANS

Rana temporaria L. Common to good elevations.	Common Frog	Broga
Bufo calamita Laurent.	Natterjack Toad	Llyffnant gwineuddu

Reaches north-eastern edge of area in Conway Valley.

Bufo vulgaris Laurent. Common everywhere.	Common Toad	Llyffnant
Molge cristata L.	Crested Newt	

Doubtful in Park area, recorded Creuddyn.

Molge palmata Dum. & Bibr. Local, Llanberis, Capel Curig.	Palmate Newt	
Molge vulgaris L. Doubtful status in area.	Common Newt	Madfall

REPTILES

[*Lacerta agilis* L.	Sand Lizard	]

Formerly occurred at mouth of Conway.

Lacerta vivipara Wagl. Common.	Common Lizard	Genau goeg
Anguis fragilis L. Common.	Slow-Worm	Rhuddradr, Dallneidr

Tropidonotus natrix L.	Grass-Snake	Neidr fraith
Generally distributed.		
Vipera berus L.	Adder	Neidr ddu
Reputedly common.		

MAMMALS

Talpa europaea L.	Mole	Twrch daear, Gwadd
Common to moderate elevations.		
Sorex araneus castaneus Jenyns	Common Shrew	Llyg, Llygoden goch
Common.		
Sorex minutus L.	Lesser Shrew	
"Not very uncommon in west" (Forrest).		
Neomys fodiens bicolor Shaw	Water-Shrew	Llyg-y-dwr
Generally distributed in lowlands.		
Erinaceus europaeus L.	Hedgehog	Draenog, Mochyn-y-coed, Sarth
Common everywhere.		
Rhinolophus ferrum-equinum insulanus Barret Hamilton	Great Horseshoe Bat	
Recorded Bala.		
Rhinolophus hipposideros minutus (Montagu)	Lesser Horseshoe Bat	
Local.		
Myotis nattereri (Kuhl)	Natterer's Bat	
Doubtful status.		
Myotis daubentonii (Kuhl)	Daubenton's Bat	
Probably quite common.		
Myotis mystacinus (Kukl)	Whiskered Bat	
Common in south of area.		
Pipistrellus pipistrellus (Schreber)	Pipistrelle	Ystlum
Probably common.		
Nyctalus noctula (Schreber)	Noctule	Ystlum fawr
Occurs wooded lowlands.		
Plecotus auritus (L.)	Long-eared-Bat	Ystlum glustiog
Generally distributed.		
Vulpes vulpes crucigera (Bechstein)	Fox	Llwynog, Madyn Cadno
Common.		
Meles m. meles (L.)	Badger	Prif lwyd, Mochyn Daear
Probably scarce, and local.		
Lutra lutra (L.)	Otter	Dwrgi
"More or less common" (Forrest).		
Martes m. martes (L.)	Pine-Marten	Bele
Rare.		
Mustela erminea stabilis Barrett-Hamilton	Stoat	Carlwm
Common.		
Mustela n. nivalis L.	Weasel	Wenci
Common.		
Mustela p. putorius L.	Polecat	Ffwlbart, Gwichydd
Very local.		
Felis sylvestris	Wild Cat	Cath wyllt
Extinct.		

Oryctolagus cuniculus (L.)	Rabbit	Cwningen

Originally introduced, common.

Lepus europaeus occidentalis De Winton	Brown Hare	Ysgyfarnog

Generally distributed, but not common.

Lepus timidus scoticus Hilzheimer   Mountain-Hare
Introduced. very local.

Muscardinus avellanarius (L.)	Dormouse	Pathew, Bathor

Generally distributed in lowlands, rare in west.

Clethrionomys glareolus britannicus   Bank-Vole
(Miller)
Common.

Microtus agrestis hirtus (Bell.)	Field-Vole	Llygoden gynffon byr

Common.

Arvicola amphibius amphibius (L.)	Water-Vole	Llygoden-y-dwr

" Common, even up to moderate elevations " (Forrest).

Apodemus s. sylvaticus (L.)	Wood-Mouse	Llygoden-y-maes

Common.

Micromys minutus soricinus   Harvest-Mouse
(Hermann)
Some evidence from Conway Valley.

Rattus rattus (L.)	Black Rat	Llygoden ffrengig

Extinct.

Rattus norvegicus (Erxleben)	Brown Rat	Llygoden fawr

Common round habitations.

Mus musculus L.	House-Mouse	Llygoden fach

Very common.

Sciurus vulgaris leucourus Kerr	Red Squirrel	Gwiwer

Occurs in 23 of the 53 parishes in Caernarvonshire.

Cervus elaphus ?subsp.	Red Deer	Cyllaig, Carw (stag)

Extinct, except for semi-domesticated stock.

Dama dama (L.)	Fallow Deer	Gafr-ddanus

Semi-domesticated stock only.

Capreolus capreolus thotti   Roe Deer   Iwrch
Lönnberg
Extinct.

These lists include only works that are mentioned in the references at the ends of the appropriate chapters.

I. GEOLOGY AND THE PHYSICAL BACKGROUND

A full bibliography of books and papers relating to the geology of North Wales will be found in F. J. North's *The Slates of Wales (1946)*.

1. *General principles, maps, and place names*

HOLMES, A. (1937). The Age of the Earth. London
    (1944). Principles of Physical Geology. London, Nelson
NORTH, F. J. (1928). Geological Maps, ...with special reference to Wales. Cardiff
    (1935). The Map of Wales (before 1600 A.D.). Cardiff
READ, H. H. (1943-4). Meditations on Granite. *Proc. Geol. Assn.* 54: 64–85, 55: 45–93
STAMP, L. D. (1946). Britain's Structure and Scenery. London
WILLIAMS, IFOR (1945). Enwau Lleoedd. Liverpool

2. *Geological structures, glacial features and geological history of Snowdonia*

DAKYNS, J. R. (1900). First-fruits of a geological examination of Snowdon. *Geol. Mag.* Decade IV, Vol. 7: 267–73.
DAVIES, D. A. BRYN (1936). The Ordovician rocks of the Trefriw District (North Wales). *Quart. J. Geol. Soc. 92*: 62–90
DAVIS, W. M. (1909). Glacial Erosion in North Wales. *Quart. J. Geol. Soc.* 65: 281–350
FEARNSIDES, W. G. (1905). On the Geology of Arenig Fawr and Moel Llyfnant. *Quart. J. Geol. Soc. 61*: 608–40
FEARNSIDES, W. G., and DAVIES, W. (1943). The Geology of Deudraeth... Merioneth. *Quart. J. Geol. Soc.*, 99: 247–76.
GREENLY, E. (1905). On the probable Peléan origin of the Felsitic Slates of Snowdon, Pt. II. *Geol. Mag.*, Decade V, Vol. 2: 543–49
    (1919). The Geology of Anglesey. London
    (1938). The Age of the Mountains of Snowdonia. *Quart. J. Geol. Soc. 94*: 117–24
    (1942). The Glacial Phenomena of Arvon. *Quart. J. Geol. Soc. 97*: 163–78
    (1948). The Geology of Snowdonia in "The Mountains of Snowdonia," ed. H. R. C. Carr and G. A. Lister. London, 2nd ed.: 131–136
HARKER, A. (1889). The Bala Volcanic Series of Caernarvonshire and associated rocks. Cambridge

HOWELL, E. J. (1946). The Report of the Land Utilisation Survey of Britain. Parts 41-43, North Wales. London

JEHU, T. J. (1902). Bathymetrical Survey of the Lakes of Snowdonia. *Trans. Roy. Soc. Edin. 40*: 419-67

LAKE, P. (1934). The Rivers of Wales and their connection with the Thames. *Science Progress 113*: 25-40

MORRIS, T. O., and FEARNSIDES, W. G. (1926). The Stratigraphy and Structure of the Cambrian Slate-belt of Nantlle. *Quart. J. Geol. Soc. 82*: 250-303

NORTH, F. J. (1940). The Legend of Llys Helig; [its origin and its significance]. Suppl. to *Proc. Llandudno Field Cl.*

RAMSAY, A. C. (1866). The Geology of North Wales. London, *Memoirs Geol. Survey*, Vol. 3 [also 2nd edition, 1881]

SEDGWICK, A. (1843). Outline of the Geological Structure of North Wales. *Proc. Geol. Soc., 4*: 212

SHARPE, D. (1847-49). On Slaty Cleavage. *Quart. J. Geol. Soc. 3*: 74-105; *5*: 111-29

SMITH, B., and GEORGE, T. N. (1935). British Regional Geology, North Wales. London

TRIMMER, J. (1832). On the diluvial deposits of Caernarvonshire. *Proc. Geol. Soc. 1*: 331

WILLIAMS, D. (1930). The Geology of the Country between Nant Peris and Nant Ffrancon (Snowdonia). *Quart. J. Geol. Soc. 86*: 191-233

WILLIAMS, H. (1927). The Geology of Snowdon (North Wales). *Quart. J. Geol. Soc. 83*: 346-431

WILLIAMS, H., and BULMAN, O. M. B. (1930). The Geology of the Dolwyddelan Syncline. *Quart. J. Geol. Soc. 87*: 435-58

3. *Mining and Quarrying*

DEWEY, H., and others (1922). Lead and Zinc ores in the Pre-carboniferous Rocks of...North Wales. London

DEWEY, H., and others (1925). The Copper ores of the Midlands, Wales, the Lake District and the Isle of Man. London

NORTH, F. J. (1946). The Slates of Wales, 3rd ed. Cardiff

PULFREY, W. (1933). The iron-ore oolites and pisolites of North Wales. *Quart J. Geol. Soc. 89*: 401-30

SHERLOCK, R. W. (1917). The geology of the Trefriw pyrites deposits. *Quart. J. Geol. Soc. 74*: 106

STRAHAN, A., and others (1920). Pre-carboniferous and Carboniferous bedded ores of England and Wales. London

4. *The history of geological and topographical investigations in Snowdonia*

AIKIN, A. (1797). Journal of a Tour through North Wales...with observations in Mineralogy. London

BINGLEY, W. (1804). North Wales...delineated from two excursions...
    during the summers of 1798 and 1801. London, Longman and Rees
BORROW, G. (1862). Wild Wales. Everyman's Library Edition (1920).
    London: 172
BROWNE, C. A. (1871). Letters...of J. Beete Jukes. London
BYNG, HON. JOHN (1784). A Tour to North Wales (The Torrington Diaries,
    Vol. I, 1934, ed. C. B. Andrews). London, Eyre & Spottiswoode
CLARK, J. W., and HUGHES, T. McK. (1890). The Life and letters of the
    Reverend Adam Sedgwick. Cambridge
EVANS, J. (1800). A Tour through parts of North Wales in the year 1798.
    London
GIRALDUS CAMBRENSIS (1188). The Itinerary through Wales (trans. R. Colt
    Hoare). London: 127 (Everyman's Library, 1944)
GREENLY, E. (1938). A hand through time. London: 525-33
LHOYD [LLWYD], HUMFREY (1584). "A description of Cambria, now called
    Wales; Drawne first by Sir John Prise Knight, and afterwards aug-
    mented and made perfect by Humphrey Lhoyd", in "The Historie of
    Cambria now called Wales...corrected augmented and continued...
    by David Powell".
NORTH, F. J (1943). The centenary of the glacial theory. *Proc. Geol. Assoc.*
    54: 1-28
PENNANT, T. (1784). A Tour in Wales. London
    (1810). Tours in Wales. London
ROSCOE, T. (1836). Wanderings and Excursions in North Wales. London
WILLIAMS, WILLIAM (1802). Observations on the Snowdon Mountains.
    London

II. NATURAL HISTORY

ALEXANDER, W. B. (1945–47). *Ibis, 87*: 512–50; *88*: 1–24, 159–79, 271–86, 427–44; *89*: 1–28

ANON. (1909). *Proc. Llandudno Field Cl. 2*: 16–19, 24-25, 29–33; (1915). ibid. *7*: 15–20; (1924). *Trans. Brit. Mycol. Soc. 10*: 233–39; (1945). Geirfa Natur. Cardiff

ASPDEN, W. (1928). *Brit. Birds, 22*: 50–56, 103

BALFOUR-BROWNE, J. (1942). *Ent. Mon. Mag. 78*: 273–80

BARBER, D. C. (1943). *Brit. Birds 37*: 134

BARNES, H. F. (1923). *Ent. Mon. Mag. 59*: 261; (1924). ibid. *60*: 225–27; (1942). ibid. *78*: 240; (1943). ibid. *79*: 47

BARRAUD, P. J. (1899). *Entomologist, 32*: 30

BINGLEY, W. (1800). A Tour round North Wales. London

BLAGG, E. W. H. (1896). *Entomologist 29*: 298–91

BLAND, F. W. (1897). *Entomologist 30*: 19–20; (1899). ibid. *32*: 187

BOWES, A. J. L. (1942). *Ent. Rec.* 54: 49–50

BOYD, A. W., and FISHER, J. (1931). *Brit. Birds 25*: 130

BRAMBELL, F. W. R. (1942). *Proc. Roy. Soc. Lond. B130*: 462–79; (1944). *Proc. Zool. Soc. Lond. 114*: 1–45

BRAZIL, ANGELA (1925). *Proc. Llandudno Field Cl. 10*: 59–63

BRISTOWE, W. S. (1939-41). A Comity of Spiders. London

BRITISH MUSEUM (N.H.) (1935). List of British Vertebrates. London

BROWN, J. M. (1925). *Ent. Mon. Mag. 61*: 62–63

BURR, M. (1936). British Grasshoppers and their Allies. London

BUTLER, E. A. (1923). A Biology of the British Hemiptera-Heteroptera. London

CAMDEN, WILLIAM (1733). Britannia. 2nd edition, trans. and ed. E. Gibson. London

CAMPBELL, Bruce (1947). *Brit. Birds 40*: 21

CARR, H. R. C., and LISTER, G. A. (1925). The Mountains of Snowdonia. London

CHINA, W. E. (1935). *Ent. Mon. Mag. 71*: 39–40

CLAPHAM, A. R. (1946). *J. Ecol. 33*: 308–47

COLLING, A. W., and BROWN, E. B. (1946). *Brit. Birds 39*: 233–43

COLLINGE, W. E. (1943). *Northw. Nat. 18*: 5–20, 138–48, 262–70

COWARD, T. A. (1920). The Birds of the British Isles and their Eggs. London

(1922). Bird Haunts and Nature Memories. London

DAVIES, HUGH (1813). Welsh Botanology. London

DAVIES, WALTER (1797). The Agriculture and Domestic Economy of North Wales. London

DAVIES, WILLIAM (1936). In Stapledon (q.v.)

DAVIES, W. MALDWYN (1929). *Nature 124*: 55; (1930). *J. Ministr. Agric.* for December; (1934). *Northw. Nat. 9*: 115–24; (1934). *Ent. Mon. Mag. 70*: 90–94

DEFOE, DANIEL (1724–27). A Tour through England and Wales. London
DONISTHORPE, H. (1906). *Ent. Rec. 18*: 241
DRUCE, G. C. (1932). The Comital Flora of the British Isles. Arbroath
EDWARDS, F. W. (1920). *Ent. Mon. Mag. 56*: 204—; ibid. *77*: 21–32
ELLIMAN, E. G. (1898). *Ent. Mon. Mag. 34*: 257–58
ELLIS, A. E. (1940). *Proc. Malacol. Soc. 24*: 44–88
ELLIS, J. C. S. (1945). *Brit. Birds, 38*: 319
ELWES, H. J., and HENRY, A. (1906–13). The Trees of Great Britain and Ireland. Edinburgh
EYTON, T. C. (1838-40). *Mag. Zool. Bot. 2*: 537–42; *Ann. Nat. Hist. 1*: 285–93; *2*: 52-56; *3*: 24–29; *4*: 396–99
FARMER, J. B. (1925). In Carr and Lister (q.v.)
FISHER, J., and WATERSTON, G. (1941). *J. Anim. Ecol. 10*: 204–72
FISHER, J., and VEVERS, H. G. (1943). *J. Anim. Ecol. 12*: 173–213; *13*: 49–62
FISHER, J., and others (1946). *Brit. Birds 39*: 28–29
FITTER, R. S. R. (1945). London's Natural History. London.
FORD, E. B. (1945). Butterflies. London
FORREST, H. E. (1907). The Vertebrate Fauna of North Wales. London; (1919). Handbook of the Vertebrate Fauna of North Wales. London
FOWLER, W. W. (1887–91; suppl. 1913). The *Coleoptera* of the British Isles. London
FRIEND, HILDERIC (1926–28) *Northw. Nat. 1*: 201; *2*: 7–10; *3*: 14-18
GARDNER, WILLOUGHBY (1909). *Proc. Llandudno Field Cl. 2*: 5-11
GAY, J. (1863). *Bull. Soc. Bot. Fr. 10*: 270–78, 319–29, 382–92, 409–14, 420-31, 462-68, 485-92
GILMOUR, J. (1944). British Botanists. London
GLADSTONE, H. S. (1924). *Brit. Birds 18*: 66–68
GRESLEY-JONES, R. J. (1910). *Proc. Llandudno Field Cl. 3*: 67–88
GRIFFITH, J. E. (1895). Flora of Anglesey and Caernarvonshire. Bangor
HALL, E H. (1809-11). Bangor MS 908
HAMILTON, ALEX. (1920–30). Annually in *Proc. Chester Soc. Nat. Sci. 1920-30*.
HOLLOM, P. A. D. (1940). *Brit. Birds 33*: 202–21, 230-44
HUGHES, R. ELFYN (1940) *Trans. Caerns. Hist. Soc. 1940*: 1–25
HYDE, H. A. (1930). Suppl. to *Rep. Bot. Soc. Exch. Cl. 1930*; (1935). Welsh Timber Trees. Cardiff
HYDE, H. A., and WADE, A. E. (1934). Welsh Flowering Plants. Cardiff; (1940). Welsh Ferns. Cardiff
INGRAM, G. C. S., and SALMON, H. M. (1936). In Glamorgan County History, Vol. 1. Cardiff
JACKSON, L. H. (1940). *Trans. Anglesey Antiq. Soc. Field Cl. 1940*: 100-10
JOHNSON, T. (1641). Opuscula omnia Thomae Johnsoni (ed. W. Pamplin, 1847). London
JONES, R. W. (1910). *Proc. Llandudno Field Cl. 3*: 49-53; (1913) *Proc. Caradoc Severn Valley Field Cl. 6*: 23-36; (1920). *Brit. Birds 14*: 135; (1922). ibid. *15*: 207; (1926). ibid. *21*: 56; (1928). *Proc. Llandudno Field Cl. 14*: 17-18

KAUFMANN, R. R. U. (1946). *Ent. Rec. 58*: 106

KIMMINS, D. E. (1933). *Ent. Mon. Mag. 69*: 156–60; (1934). ibid. *70*: 61–66

KLOET, G. S., and HINCKS, W. O. (1945). A Check List of British Insects. Stockport

KNIGHT, H. H. (1924). *Trans. Brit. Mycol. Soc. 10*: 242–44

LELAND, JOHN (1536–39). The Itinerary in Wales of John Leland in or about 1536–39 (arranged and ed. L. Toulmin Smith, 1906). London

LEWIS, S. (1849). A Topographical Dictionary of Wales (4th ed.). London, 2 vols.

LISTER, A. (1925). A Monograph of the Mycetozoa (3rd ed. revised G. Lister). London

LISTER, G. (1924). *Trans. Brit. Mycol. Soc. 10*: 240–42

LLWYD, HUMPHREY (1584). A description of Cambria. . . .

LONGFIELD, CYNTHIA (1937). Dragonflies of the British Isles. London

LOWE, W. BEZANT (1925). *Proc. Llandudno Field Cl. 10*: 120–54

MATHESON, COLIN (1932). Changes in the Fauna of Wales in Historic Times. Cardiff

MITCHELL, M. (1939). *Proc. Llandudno Field Cl. 19*: 86–87

MONTAGUE, C. E. (1923). Fiery Particles. London

MORE, A. G. (1881). *Zoologist, ser. 3, 5*: 44–47

MORTON, K. J. (1901). *Ent. Mon. Mag. 38*: 134–36

NATIONAL PARKS COMMITTEE (England and Wales) (1947). Report. HMSO cmd. 7121. London

NEWBERY, E. A. (1889). *Ent. Mon. Mag. 35*: 159; (1903). *Ent. Rec. 15*: 286

NICHOLLS, A. W. (1884). *J. Conch. 4*: 174–84

OLDHAM, C. (1929). *Nature 124*: 229

ORTON, K. J. P. (1913). *Proc. Llandudno Field Cl. 5*: 40–45; (1925). In Carr and Lister (q.v.); (1930). *Proc. Llandudno Field Cl. 15*: 35–37

PEARSON, D. H. (1890). *Entomologist 23*: 319

PEATE, IORWERTH (1934). *Antiquity 8*: 73–80

PENNANT, THOMAS (1784). A Tour in Wales. London

POUNDS, H. E. (1942). *Brit. Birds 36*: 94

PRICE, J. (N.D.). Llandudno and how to enjoy it. Llandudno

PRICE-EVANS, E. (1932). *J. Ecol. 20*: 1–52

PYEFINCH, K. A. (1937). *J. Anim. Ecol. 6*: 115–37; (1943). ibid. *12*: 86–108

RAY, JOHN (1696). Synopsis Methodica (2nd. ed.). London; (1724). ibid. (3rd ed.). London; (1846). Memorials (ed. E. Lankester). London

REGAN, C. TATE (1911). The Fresh-water Fishes of the British Isles. London

RITCHIE, JAMES (1920). Influence of Man on Animal Life in Scotland. Cambridge

ROBERTS, E. B. (1925). *Proc. Llandudno Field Cl. 10*: 105–19; (1930). ibid. *15*: 91–93

ROEBUCK, W. D. (1884). *J. Conch. 4*: 216–24

SAUNDERS, E. (1892). The Hemiptera-Heteroptera of the British Isles. London.

SAVORY, T. H. (1935). Spiders and Allied Orders of the British Isles. London
SHARP, W. E. (1899). *Ent. Mon. Mag. 35*: 43-44; (1900). ibid. *36*: 131-32; (1907). ibid. *43*: 252
SHORTEN, MONICA (1946). *J. Anim. Ecol. 15*: 82-92
SOPP, E. J. B. (1899). *Ent. Rec. 11*: 22-23
SOUTH, R. (1939). The Moths of the British Isles. London
STAPLEDON, R. G. (1936). A Survey of the Agricultural and Waste Lands of Wales. London
TANSLEY, A. G. (1939). The British Isles and their Vegetation. Cambridge
THEOBALD, F. V., and WALTON, C. L. (1921-22). *Proc. Lancs. Cheshire Ent. Soc. 45-46*: 52-64
THOMPSON, J. A. (1940). *Entomologist 73*: 253
TOMLIN, J. R. B. (1886). *J. Conch. 5*: 28-29
TWEED, R. D., and WOODHEAD, N. (1945). *J. Ecol. 33*: 210-13
WALTON, C. L. (1922). *Ent. Mon. Mag. 58*: 271-75; (1925). *Proc. Llandudno Field Cl. 10*: 78-91; (1927). The Agricultural Zoology of North Wales. Bangor; (1928). *Northw. Nat. 3*: 77-80, 124-27
WATSON, H. C. (1825). Topographical Botany. London
WHITTAKER, I. (1942). *Brit. Birds, 36*: 36
WILD LIFE CONSERVATION SPECIAL COMMITTEE (England and Wales) (1947). Report. HMSO cmd. 7122. London
WILLIAMS, E. G. (1942). *Northw. Nat. 17*: 36-38
WILLIAMS, JOHN (1830). Faunula Grustensis, being an account of the Natural Contents of the Parish of Llanrwst. Llanrwst
WILLIAMS, R. (1895). History and Antiquities of the Town of Aberconway. Denbigh
WILLIAMS, W. (1802). Observations on the Snowdon Mountains. London
WILLUGHBY, F. (1676). Ornithologiae Libri Tres (ed. J. Ray). London
WILSON, A. (1928). *Proc. Llandudno Field Cl. 14*: 82-98; (1930). ibid. *15*: 11-12, 39-40; (1946-47). *Northw. Nat. 21*: 202-23
WITHERBY, H. F., and others (1938-41). The Handbook of British Birds. London.
WITHERBY, H. F. (1941). A Check-list of British Birds. London
WOOD, THEODORE (1901). *Ent. Mon. Mag. 37*: 22
WOODHEAD, N. (1926). *Northw. Nat. 1*: 126-29; (1928). *Proc. Llandudno Field Cl. 14*: 15-17, 27-29, 46-48; (1929). *Northw. Nat. 4*: 59-61; (1933). *Bull. Alpine Garden Soc. 2*: 12-21, 45-51
ZUCKERMAN, S. (1935). *J. Anim. Ecol. 4*: 146
The following people have kindly communicated unpublished information:-
ALEXANDER, W. B. (heronries, 1947), BEST, F. C. (Lepidoptera, 1946-47), DAVIES, J. L. (starlings, 1947), DONCASTER. C. C. (Bangor birds, 1947), FISHER, J. (birds, 1947), HAMPSON, J. R. (Gwydir, 1946), LEARMONTH, S. LIVINGSTONE (Tremadoc, 1946), MADDERS, M. A. (camping, 1946), ROBERTS, BRYMER (char, 1946), ROBERTS, EVAN (flora, 1946), SMITH, R. H. (Beddgelert and Gwydir, 1946), SPEAKE, M. (Ystumllyn, 1946), TEMPERLEY, G. W. (Alpines, 1933), WAINWRIGHT, M. C. (Traeth Mawr, 1947).

III. THE HISTORICAL BACKGROUND

Publications of Historical and Antiquarian Societies

The results of the most recent archaeological and historical research relating to North Wales will be found in the following : *Archaelogia Cambrensis*, the *Transactions of the Honourable Society of Cymmrodorion* and *Y Cymmrodor*, and the *Bulletin of the Board of Celtic Studies*. For the history of Caernarvonshire in particular, the *Transactions of the Caernarvonshire Historical Society* which began publication in 1939, contain material of great interest. Important articles relating to Wales are also to be sought in such journals as *Antiquity*, *Archaelogia* and the *Transactions of the Royal Historical Society*.

Among a number of manuscript sources consulted in writing the historical chapters of this book were Ministers' Accounts of the fourteenth and fifteenth centuries, preserved in the Public Record Office, comprising the annual returns of the local officials of the newly created Shire of Caernarvon, the Baron Hill and Penrhyn MSS in the library of the University College of North Wales, Bangor, including rentals and surveys of the fifteenth century, and a Manuscript Survey of the Parishes of Caernarvonshire (Bangor MS. 908) written by Edmund Hyde Hall about 1810, as a result of his visit to this region.

In the National Library of Wales at Aberystwyth the manuscript journals of several of the eighteenth and early nineteenth century visitors to Snowdonia were read, and various documents from the great collection of Wynn of Gwydir papers consulted. *The Calendar of the Wynn of Gwydir Papers* published by the National Library of Wales (London, 1926) is in itself a mine of information on seventeenth-century life and conditions in North Wales.

Prehistoric and Roman Times

Fox, Cyril (1938). The Personality of Britain. Cardiff, National Museum of Wales and University of Wales Press Board, 3rd ed., (gives a most readable introduction to the history of the intrusion of successive cultures into Britain from Neolithic to early historic times, emphasizing the geographical factors determining the distribution of early populations)

Grimes, W. F. (1939). Guide to the Collection Illustrating the Prehistory of Wales in the National Museum of Wales. Cardiff, National Museum of Wales and the University of Wales Press Board, (will be found a valuable book of reference)

Wheeler, R. F. M. (1925). Prehistoric and Roman Wales. Oxford, University Press.
(1923). Segontium, *Y Cymmrodor*, *33* (two standard works on these early periods)

Dark Ages and Early Medieval Period

WILLIAMS, A. H. (1941). An Introduction to the History of Wales. Cardiff, University of Wales Press Board, (a survey of the general position from Paleolithic times to 1063 A.D.)

WILLIAMS, H. (1912). Christianity in Early Britain. Oxford, University Press, (an account of the Celtic Church and some of its leading figures)

Medieval Period

Two essential books for student and general reader alike are :

ELLIS, T. P. (1926). Welsh Tribal Law and Custom in the Middle Ages. Oxford, University Press (2 vols.)

LLOYD, J. E. (1938). A History of Wales from the Earliest Times to the Edwardian Conquest. London, Longmans, Green & Co., 2nd ed., (2 vols.)

CAMBRENSIS, GIRALDUS (1188). The Itinerary through Wales *and* the Description of Wales. London, 1920, J. M. Dent & Sons, Ltd., Everyman's Library, (contain an eye witness account of life and customs at the end of the twelfth century)

LLOYD, J. E. (1931). Owen Glendower. Oxford, University Press

BRADLEY, A. C. (1901). Owen Glyndwr. London, G. P. Putnam's Sons, (these are invaluable for the later medieval period)

LEWIS, E. A. (1902). The Decay of Tribalism in North Wales. *Trans. Hon. Soc. Cymmrodor., 1902–03* : 1–75

(1903). The Development of Industry and Commerce in Wales during the Middle Ages. *Trans. Roy. Hist. Soc.* n. ser., *17* : 121–73

(1912). The Medieval Boroughs of Snowdonia, London, H. Sotheran & Co., (gives a detailed account of the Edwardian garrison towns)

(1913). A Contribution to the Commercial History of Wales, 1301–1547. *Y Cymmrodor, 24* : 86–188, (these three articles trace the social and economic development of these centuries)

JONES-PIERCE, T. (1939). Some Tendencies in the Agrarian History of Caernarvonshire during the later Middle Ages. *Caern. Hist. Soc. Trans. 1939* : 18–36

(1942). The Gafael in Bangor Manuscript No. 1939. *Trans. Hon. Soc. Cymmrodor., 1942* : 158–88

The Sixteenth and Seventeenth Centuries

WYNN, J. (1927). History of the Gwydir Family. Cardiff, University of Wales Press Board, 5th ed., (a book relating specifically to social conditions in North Wales for this period is this famous history of his own family by Sir John Wynn of Gwydir)

LELAND, JOHN (1536–1539). The Itinerary in Wales of John Leland in or about 1536–39. Arranged and edited by L. Toulmin Smith. London, 1906, George Bell & Son, (has several references to Snowdonia)

REES, W. (1938). The Union of England and Wales. Cardiff, University of Wales Press Board, (explains in concise form the meaning and significance of the Act of Union of 1536)

SKEEL, A. C. (1926). The Cattle Trade between England and Wales from the fifteenth–nineteenth centuries. *Trans. Roy. Hist. Soc.* ser. 4, **9** : 135–158.

(1922). The Welsh Woollen Industry in the Sixteenth and Seventeenth Centuries. *Arch. Camb.* **77** : 220–57, (portrays the growth of Welsh commerce and industry)

WILLIAMS, W. LL. (1919). The Making of Modern Wales. London, Macmillan & Co., (deals particularly with developments in the sixteenth and seventeenth centuries)

Those desiring a general account of the Civil War and its effect on Wales should consult :

PHILLIPS, J. R. (1874). Memoirs of the Civil War in Wales and the Marches. London, Longmans, Green & Co., 2 vols., (2nd ed. 1878 : the book needs revising, but the student will still find it useful)

The Eighteenth and Nineteenth Centuries

ASHBY, A. W., and EVANS, L. L. (1944). The Agriculture of Wales and Monmouthshire. Cardiff, Joint Publication of the Hon. Soc. of Cymmrodorion, and the University of Wales Press Board

DAVIES, T. TWISTON, and EDWARDS, A. (1939). Welsh Life in the Eighteenth Century. London, Country Life, (a general picture of Welsh life and progress in the eighteenth century)

DODD, A. H. (1933). The Industrial Revolution in North Wales. Cardiff, University of Wales Press Board, (an essential book for consultation by student and general reader)

The travellers of the late eighteenth and early nineteenth centuries left many accounts of their experiences in exploring the mountains of Snowdonia. Some of the best known of these travellers and their stories are :

BINGLEY, W. (1814). North Wales delineated from Two Excursions (1798–1801). London, 2nd ed.

CRADOCK, W. (1770). Letters from Snowdonia. London

FENTON, R. (1804). Letters written during a Tour through North Wales in the year 1798 and at other times. London.

JOHNSON, SAMUEL (1816). Diary of a Journey into North Wales in the year 1774. London, ed. R. Duffa

PENNANT, T. (1726–78). A Tour in Wales. London, 3rd ed. 1810, 3 vols.

WILLIAMS, W. (1802). Observations on the Snowdon Mountains. London

WYNDHAM, H. P. (1781). A Tour through Wales and Monmouthshire during the months of June and July 1774, and June, July and August 1775. London, 2nd ed.

General Studies of Welsh History and Culture

BOWEN, E. G. (1941). Wales, a Study in Geography and History. Cardiff, University of Wales Press Board.

REES, F. (1947). Studies in Welsh History. Cardiff, University of Wales Press Board.

HUGHES, V. J. (1924). Wales and the Welsh in English Literature. Wrexham and London, Hughes & Son

PEATE, I. C. (1940). The Welsh House : a Study of Folk Culture. *Y Cymmrodor*, 47

EDWARDS, O. (1902). Wales. London, T. Fisher Unwin, 2nd ed.

RHYS, J., and JONES, D. BRYNMOR (1900). The Welsh People, London, T. Fisher Unwin

EDWARDS, A. F. (1913). Landmarks in the History of the Welsh Church. London, John Murray

JENKINS, R. T., and REES, WILLIAM (1931). A Bibliography of the History of Wales. Cardiff, University of Wales Press Board, (is indispensable for the student)

Guide Books which will be found useful are:

LOWE, W. BEZANT (1912–1927). The Heart of North Wales. Published privately, 2 vols.

HUGHES, H., and NORTH, L. (1908). Old Cottages of Snowdonia. Bangor

JENKINS, D. J. (1899). Beddgelert. Portmadoc

MONKHOUSE, P. (1943). On Foot in North Wales. London

NORTH, L. (1906). The Old Churches of Arllechwedd. Bangor

PALMER, W. T. (undated). Odd Corners in North Wales. London, Skeffington & Son Ltd.

(undated). More Odd Corners in North Wales. London, Skeffington & Son Ltd.

INDEX

Figures in heavy type refer to pages opposite which illustrations will be found.

Dahl 394

352 N.3 Autumn 65.